PRINCIPLES OF COMPUTER COMMUNICATION NETWORK DESIGN

ELLIS HORWOOD SERIES IN ELECTRICAL AND ELECTRONIC ENGINEERING

Series Editors: **P. Brandon,** Professor of Electrical and Electronic Engineering, University of Cambridge, and **P. R. Adby,** Department of Electronic and Electrical Engineering, University of London King's College

APPLIED CIRCUIT THEORY: Matrix and Computer Methods
P. R. ADBY, University of London King's College

BOND GRAPHS FOR MODELLING ENGINEERING SYSTEMS
ALAN BLUNDELL, Coventry (Lanchester) Polytechnic

NOISE IN ELECTRONIC DEVICES AND SYSTEMS
M. J. BUCKINGHAM, Royal Aircraft Establishment, Farnborough, Hampshire

DIGITAL AND MICROPROCESSOR ENGINEERING
S. J. CAHILL, Ulster Polytechnic

DIFFRACTION THEORY AND ANTENNAS
R. H. CLARKE and JOHN BROWN, College of Science and Technology, University of London

MICROCOMPUTER ENGINEERING
Edited by D. A. FRASER, Chelsea College, University of London

COMPUTER-AIDED DESIGN IN ELECTRO-MAGNETICS
E. M. FREEMAN and D. A. LOWTHER, University of London, and P. P. SYLVESTER, McGill University, Montreal

NON-LINEAR AND PARAMETRIC CIRCUITS: Principles, Theory and Applications
F. KOURIL, University of Brno, Czechoslovakia

ELEMENTARY ELECTRIC POWER AND MACHINES
P. G. McCLAREN, University Engineering Department, Cambridge

INTEGRATED CIRCUIT TECHNOLOGY OF COMMUNICATION-BASED COMPUTERS
C. MOIR, Royal Signals and Radar Establishment

MICROWAVE PHASE MODULATORS
T. MORAWSKI and J. MODELSKI, Warsaw Technical University

CONTROL SYSTEMS WITH TIME DELAYS
A. W. OLBROT, University of Warsaw

POST-DIGITAL ELECTRONICS
F. R. PETTIT, Computing Teaching Centre, Oxford

HANDBOOK OF ELECTRONIC CIRCUITS
G. J. SCOLES, formerly English Electric Value Company, Chelmsford, Essex

HANDBOOK OF RECTIFIER CIRCUITS
G. J. SCOLES, formerly English Electric Value Company, Chelmsford, Essex

QUANTITATIVE ELECTRON-PROBE MICROANALYSIS
V. D. SCOTT and G. LOVE, University of Bath

PRINCIPLES OF COMPUTER COMMUNICATION NETWORK DESIGN
J. SEIDLER, Technical University of Gdansk, Poland

PRINCIPLES OF COMPUTER COMMUNICATION NETWORK DESIGN

J. SEIDLER
Institute of Fundamentals of Informatics
Polish Academy of Sciences, Poland

Translation Editor:
R. J. DEASINGTON
University of Strathclyde

ELLIS HORWOOD LIMITED
Publishers · Chichester

Halsted Press: a division of
JOHN WILEY & SONS
New York · Brisbane · Chichester · Toronto

English Edition first published in 1983
Reprinted 1984

ELLIS HORWOOD LIMITED

Market Cross House, Cooper Street, Chichester, West Sussex, England PO19 1EB

and

PAŃSTWOWE WYDAWNICTWO NAUKOWE

Warsaw, Poland

The publisher's colophon is reproduced from James Gillison's drawing of the ancient Market Cross, Chichester.

Distributors:

Australia, New Zealand, South-east Asia:
Jacaranda-Wiley Ltd., Jacaranda Press,
JOHN WILEY & SONS INC.,
G.P.O. Box 859, Brisbane, Queensland 40001, Australia

Canada:
JOHN WILEY & SONS CANADA LIMITED
22 Worcester Road, Rexdale, Ontario, Canada.

Europe, Africa:
JOHN WILEY & SONS LIMITED
Baffins Lane, Chichester, West Sussex, England.

North and South America and the rest of the world:
Halsted Press: a division of
JOHN WILEY & SONS
605 Third Avenue, New York, N.Y. 10016, U.S.A.

Translated by Peter Senn from the Polish
Analiza i synteza sieci łączności dla systemów teleinformatyczynch
Published by Panstwowe Wydawnictwo Naukowe

British Library Cataloguing in Publication Data
Seidler, Jerzy
Principles of computer communication network design.
1. Data transmission systems 2. Computer networks
I. Title II. Analiza i synteza seci lacnosci dla systemow teleinformatyczynch. *English*
001.64'404 TK5105.5

Library of Congress Card No. 82-23248

ISBN 0-85312-241-5 (Ellis Horwood Limited, Publishers – Library Edn.)
ISBN 0-85312-104-4 (Ellis Horwood Limited, Publishers – Student Edn.)
ISBN 0-470-27405-0 (Halsted Press – Library Edn.)
ISBN 0-470-27385-2 (Halsted Press – Student Edn.)

Typeset in Press Roman by Ellis Horwood Ltd.
Printed in Great Britain by R. J. Acford, Chichester.

Table of Contents

CHAPTER 2 – OPEN SYSTEMS WITH A COMMON CHANNEL

CHAPTER 3 – FEEDBACK SYSTEMS WITH A COMMON CHANNEL

CHAPTER 4 – COMMON CHANNEL SYSTEMS WITH COORDINATED NODE OPERATION

CHAPTER 7 – CONGESTION AND METHODS OF COUNTERACTING IT

CHAPTER 8 – OPTIMISATION OF CHANNEL CAPACITIES AND NETWORK TOPOLOGIES

APPENDICES

Author's Preface

Technological progress in the field of digital electronics has led to the construction of very powerful computers. At the same time, the number of computer users is rising rapidly. In this situation it was reasonable to develop multiaccess systems in which one or more computers would be used by many people located in different places.

If an organisation has a number of computers their memory resources and computing power can be used more efficiently if we interconnect the computers to make up one large computing system. The components of such a system might include specialised sets of programmes, data-bases or specialised equipment, like hybrid computers. Users can enter the system through one of the constituent computers or by special interfaces. Both systems affording remote access for several users, and those arising as a result of interconnecting a number of distant computers come under the heading of distributed computer systems.

The development of distributed computer systems is justified not only for economic reasons. Of great importance to society are the network systems for the transportation of goods and energy; there exists a tendency to computerise their control. To do this, we have to superimpose the secondary distributed computer system on to the primary network. The rapid growth of such distributed computer systems is proof enough of the advantages they offer. Although hardly a decade has passed since the first distributed computer systems started to operate, we have today quite a number of large systems, some covering whole continents, as well as hundreds of smaller systems. Moreover, we are witnessing a steady growth in their number (much data about current networks and discussions on their future can be found in the special issue of *IEE*, September 1978).

In most of today's distributed computer systems, the functions of information processing and transportation are separated. It therefore makes sense to consider the subsystem whose task it is to transfer computer information from one place to another as an autonomous system. The problems of the analysis and design of such a system are the subject of this book.

The low cost and great flexibility of communications computers permit quite complicated operations to be performed on the signals carrying computer information. We therefore have a fair degree of freedom when choosing the operating rules of a computer communication system, and the problem of the best choice of these rules becomes important. In this book we shall describe, classify and evaluate the quality and we shalll consider the optimisation of the rules of computer communication system operation.

It is obvious that if the communication resources of a network such as channel capacities or node storage capacities are fixed, the more we know about the state of the network the better we can use them. The analysis of the methods to improve the quality of the network operating rules, which is possible as a result of supplying and using network identification information, is the leading theme of this book.

The material in this book is organised in a way such that we try to introduce new concepts using the simplest possible examples. According to that principle, after the first introductory chapter in which we give an overall review of computer communications networks, we analyse in the second, third and fourth chapters systems in which several users transmit their computer information through a single common channel. It is possible to explain the majority of optimisation problems of using communications resources on the basis of these systems with simple topology. In the following three chapters, we investigate the problem of guiding a packet through a network in which the choice of path, i.e. the routing, is foremost.

The design of computer networks is one of the most complex problems of contempory technology. In this book we have decided to take a balanced approach to this question. We emphasise neither the queue-theoretical aspects, as, for example, in Kleinrock's excellent monograph, nor the strictly technical ones. In particular, we do not reproduce here detailed descriptions of existing networks; such descriptions can be found in a number of other publications. We explain here the essential factors determining the properties of a computer communications system, in particular the role of its status information subsystem. We try to give simplified derivations, sometimes we introduce heuristical elements; we do point out all the assumptions made, so that the limitations of our reasoning will be evident; more precise treatment is also suggested.

We assume that the reader is familiar with the principles of probability, the theory of stochastic processes, and the principles of operational research. To spare the reader searching references, at the end of the book we include appendices in which we discuss less well-known topics from queueing theory, especially queueing networks. The longer formal derivations of some formulae will also be found in the appendices.

The book is addressed to specialists in computer network design, and to graduate and post graduate students specialising in computer sciences. Although it does not contain typical students' problems, it does include a number of concrete examples of the application of the general aspects discussed. The book may also be useful to people interested in the general principles of information sciences. The book is based on an earlier one written by this author. Several changes have been introduced. Many of them came to mind as a result of experience gained from using the earlier book as a students' textbook, others resulted from discussions at postgraduate and specialist seminars held at the Institute of Fundamentals of Informatics of the Polish Academy of Sciences.

Notation

GENERAL PRINCIPLES

Script characters, e.g. $\mathcal{A}$, $\mathcal{K}$, denote sets, events.

Bold characters, e.g. **F**, denote sets of numbers, vectors matrices.

Upright characters, e.g. L, denote random variables, random processes; combined with bold, e.g. **F**, denotes random vector.

A symbol with ^, e.g. $\hat{L}$, denotes a predetermined value.

A symbol with bar, e.g. $\bar{L}$, denotes an average.

$P(\mathcal{A})$ denotes the probability of event $\mathcal{A}$.

(w_1, w_2) denotes the direct channel going from node w_1 to node w_2.

$\mathcal{P}(w_1, w_2, \ldots, w_K)$ denotes the path formed by the channels $(w_1, w_2), (w_2, w_3), \ldots, (w_{K-1}, w_K)$.

OP $Q, x | \mathcal{C}$ is the shorthand notation for 'optimisation problem with respect to variable x, with $Q(x)$ as criterion under the set of constraints $\mathcal{C}$'.

Abbreviations of names are frequently used in subscripts, e.g. ξ_{ch} denotes the information about the state (general notation ξ) of the common channel. Such subscripts are always explained in the text.

In a system with several similar components a parameter characterising a single component has an index indicating components number, but the corresponding parameter characterising the set of this components is denoted by the same symbol, but without an index, e.g. λ_m is the intensity of packets delivered by mth sources, while $\lambda = \Sigma_m \lambda_m$ is the intensity of packets delivered by all sources.

LIST OF MOST FREQUENTLY USED SYMBOLS

$a(\mathcal{P}_{sr}; w, v)$	– incidence coefficient: path $\mathcal{P}_{sr}$ channel (w, v)
A	– Lagrange multiplier
$A(\cdot)$	– admission rule
$\mathcal{A}(\mathbf{X})$	– flow continuity constraints
B	– batch size

$\mathcal{B}(C)$	– capacity constraints
cr	– as subscript means 'critical'
C	– general: capacity
C	– of common channel
C_k	– of kth subchannel
$C(k), C(w,v)$	– of kth (w,v) channel
$C(\mathcal{CV})$	– of the cut $\mathcal{CV}$
$\mathbf{C} = \{C(k), k = 1, 2, \ldots, K\}$	– set of capacities
$\mathcal{C}$	– constraint or set of constraints
$\mathcal{CV}$	– cut determined by set $\mathcal{V}$
d	– general: channel, path length
$d(k), d(w,v)$	– of kth, (w,v) channel
$d^*(k), d(w,v)$	– estimate of kth, (w,v) channel length
$d(\mathcal{P}_{uv})$	– of path $\mathcal{P}_{uv}$
$\mathcal{D}(v)$	– destination set
f	– general: normalised average flow intensity
$f_{sr}(u,v)$	– of flow from s to r passing through channel (u,v)
$f^-(u,v)$	– of flow lost in channel (u,v)
F	– general: average flow intensity
$F_i(u,v), F_{sr}(u,v)$	– intensity of flows of class i, (s,r) passing through channel (u,v)
$F_i(u,v;t)$	– of instantaneous (time dependent) flow
$F(u,v), F(u,v;t)$	– of total flow passing through channel (u,v)
$\mathbf{F} = \{F(u,v), (u,v) \in \mathcal{K}\}$	– set of average flow intensities in all channels
$\mathcal{F}^+$	– positivity constraints for flows in all channels
G	– general: average intensity along path
$G_{sr}(j)$	– jth, passing from s to r
$\mathbf{G} = \{G_{sr}(j), j = 1, 2, \ldots, J_{sr}; (s,r) \in (\mathcal{S}, \mathcal{R})\}$	– set of average flow intensities along paths
$\bar{H}_m, \bar{H}$	– average number of retransmissions or hops
$H(\mathcal{P}_{sr})$	– number of hops along path $\mathcal{P}_{sr}$
$H(L,F,A,A;t)$	– Hamilton function
i	– number of class, number of slot
I	– number of all classes
J, J_{sr}	– number of paths, from s to r
k	– number of channel, number of subchannel
K	– number of all channels
$\mathcal{K}$	– set of all channels
l	– general: number of packets
$l, l(t)$	– at all B–Tr units (at instant t)
$l_i(k), l_i(k,t)$	– at kth B–Tr unit of class i (at instant t)
$l_m(t_i)$	– at mth node at instant t_i
$\mathbf{l}$	– set of all $l_i(k)$

L	– general: average number of packets; indexing as for l
$\hat{L}, \hat{L}_i$	– bounds on packets number
$L(\mathcal{A})$	– number of elements of set $\mathcal{A}$
m	– number of source
M	– number of all sources or source–destination pairs
N	– number of bits (of signal) or of nodes (in mesh network)
N_{df}	– number of degrees of freedom of a set of signals
N_{p}	– number of bits a packet consists of
$\mathcal{N}_{\text{in}}(w)$	– set of channels going into node w
$\mathcal{N}_{\text{out}}(w)$	– set of channels going out of node w
p	– as index means 'packet'
P	– general: probability
$P(\mathcal{A})$	– of event A
P_{at}	– of retransmission attempt
P_{e}	– of error in information recovery
P_{ex}	– of error caused by external noise
$P_{\mathcal{D}}$	– of reaching destination (set)
$P_m(i)$	– of delivering packet of class i by source m
P^-, P_m^-	– of non-activity, (of mth source) non-acceptance, transmission failure
$P_{\text{c}}^+, P_{\text{pr}}^+$	– of successful transmission of a copy (primary packet)
$\mathcal{P}$	– general: path
$\mathcal{P}(w_0, w_1, \ldots, w_I)$	– consisting of nodes $w_0, w_1, \ldots, w_I$
$\mathcal{P}_{sr}$	– going from s to r
q	– general: rate of change of quality
$q(k, \mathbf{F})$	– of kth channel
$q(\mathcal{P}_{sr}, \mathbf{F})$	– of path $\mathcal{P}_{sr}$
Q	– general: quality
$Q(k), Q(w, v)$	– of transmission through kth (w, v) channel
$Q(\mathcal{P}_{sr})$	– of transmission over path $\mathcal{P}_{sr}$
$Q[\mathcal{R}(\cdot)]$	– of routing rule $R(\cdot)$
r	– receiving node (destination), in mesh networks
$\mathcal{R}$	– set of all receiving nodes
$\mathcal{R}(\cdot)$	– general: routing rule
$\mathcal{R}_{sr}(\cdot)$	– from s to r
$\mathbf{R} = \{\mathcal{R}_{sr}(\cdot), (s, r) \in (S, R)\}$	– set of all routing rules
s	– source node (in mesh networks), but also signal
$s[x(m), m, t]$	– delivered by mth node
$s_{\text{int}}(t)$	– of interference
$S_m(\cdot)$	– rule of remote access
$\mathbf{S} = \{S_m(\cdot), m = 1, 2, \ldots, M\}$	– set of all source nodes
t	– actual time

tr – as index: 'transmitter'

$\langle t_a, t_b \rangle$ – observation interval

T – general: time spent on some operation, delay or signal duration

- T_{ac} – anticollision time
- T_{as} – packet assembly time
- T_{ch} – delay of channel state information
- T_{c-t} – time taken to bring the copy from copy storage to transmitter
- T_{cy} – cycle duration
- T_{eh} – time spent in the entrance buffer
- T_f – time spent in the feedback channel
- T_{out} – out time
- T_{pr} – propagation time
- T_{pol} – transport time of polling information
- T_{qu} – queueing time
- T_r – round trip time
- T_{ref} – reference time
- T_{s-t} – time taken to bring the packet from source to the transmitter
- T_0, T_1, T_2 – slot duration

U – dependence removing operation

w – as index 'working'

W – general: power of

- W_{sm} – signals emitted by mth node
- W_z – of noise

var A – variance of random variable A

V – as index means 'vigilance'

$x, x(m)$ – information delivered by mth source

X – general: intensity (in bits/sec) of information flow delivered by a source (external information)

- X – delivered by all sources
- X_m – delivered by mth source
- X_{sr} – delivered by source s destined for r

$y(t), y_n$ – received signal

$z(t)$ – noise

Z – randomisation index

$\alpha, \alpha_k, \alpha(i)$ – weighting coefficient

α^+, α^- – acceptance (non-acceptance) decision

δ – parameter, jointly with another symbol – increment

$\delta(w, r | v)$ – shortest path from w to r over v

Δ – neighbourhood order, increment

Δf – frequency bandwidth

ϑ, ϑ_m	– specific instants
κ	– cost function
λ	– in general: intensity of starting instants
$\lambda(i)$	– of all packets of class i (in most cases $i = 0 \equiv$ directly delivered by a source, $i = 1 \equiv$ going successfully through)
$\lambda_m(i)$	– of packets of class i delivered by source in (Chapters 2–4)
$\lambda_i(k)$	– of packets of class i put into kth channel (Chapters 5–8)
Λ	– general: intensity of starting instants of packets delivered by a source during a time interval
$\Lambda_m(t', t'')$	– by mth source during the interval $\langle t', t'' \rangle$
$\Lambda_m(i)$	– by mth source during ith slot
$\Lambda_m(T_{cy})$	– by mth source during the cycle T_{cy}
$\mu, \mu(k)$	– intensity of completing packet transmission
ν	– general: normalised intensity, channel utilisation for working information transmission, duty ratio
ν_i	– internal duty ratio of pulsed signals
$\nu(i)$	– normalised intensity of packets of class i delivered by all sources into a common channel
$\nu(i \mid l)$	– defined as $\nu(i)$ but with constraint that the system is in state σ_l
$\nu_m(i)$	– normalised intensity of packets delivered by mth source during ith slot
ν_{tr}	– duty ratio of signals transmitted by a transmitter
ρ, ρ_m, ρ_{em}	– signal/noise ratio (power, energy)
$\varphi_k = d\kappa / dC$	– rate of change of kth channel cost
σ, Σ	– general: system state
$\sigma_{bu}, \sigma_{nbu}$	– busy, non-busy states
σ_v, σ_w	– vigilant, working states
$\Sigma(t_i)$	– state of the system at instant t_i
τ	– general: average delay
τ'	– normalised
τ_{ba}	– of a batch of packets
τ_ξ	– of n.s.i. (or s.s.i.)
ζ	– general: efficiency
ζ_{ad}	– of addressing
ζ_c	– of channel capacity utilisation
ζ_s	– of using signal for working information transmission
ξ	– general: information about systems (networks) state
ξ_{bu}, ξ_{nbu}	– about channels (nodes) activity (busy, non-busy)

ξ_f, ξ_r	– about type of systems operation (feedback, reservation)
ξ_{ch}	– state of the common channel
ξ_{pol}	– state of the polling system
ξ_f	– obtained by the feedback channel
ξ^+, ξ^-	– about the status of received signal–accepted, non-accepted)

ABBREVIATIONS USED IN FIGURES AND IN THE TEXT

A(S)AF	– asynchronous (synchronous) access system, with feedback
ACD	– anticollision delay (unit introducing it)
A(S)CH	– asynchronous (synchronous) system with access controlled by channel state
B–Tr	– buffer–transmitter unit
CCU	– central control unit
Eb	– entrance buffer
FEECH	– feedback channel
FIFO	– first in, first out service discipline
ID	– information destination
IS	– information source
LOCH	– local channel
LTr	– local transmitter
n.s.i.	– network state information
N_m	– mth node
NCU	– node control unit
Rec	– receiver
RUC	– reservation upon collision system
s.s.i.	– system state information
St	– storage (copy storage)
Tr	– transmitter

1

Fundamental concepts and problems of computer communication network design

We begin this chapter by discussing the basic types of communication network used in distributed computer systems. Next, we deal with the parameters characterising such networks, and finally we formulate the problems of network optimisation.

1.1 BASIC TYPES OF SPATIALLY DISTRIBUTED COMPUTER SYSTEMS

Modern computer systems typically serve many users, and consist of a number of remote subsystems for information processing and storage.† A system in which information coming from many information sources is to be brought to one destination is called an **inflow system**. A system in which information from one source is to be sent to many destinations is called an **outflow system**. Usually we have systems in which the inflow and outflow systems overlap; such systems are termed **inflow--outflow** information systems. A typical example of such a system is a centralised data base which accumulates data coming in from users, and sends data to them on request.

The user feeds information into, and receives information from the communication subsystem by means of a **terminal**. These inflow–outflow systems are also called **terminal-orientated** systems.

Generally, in inflow–outflow systems, the information sources representing the users have different properties from the information source representing the central computer system. In this sense, these systems are fundamentally inhomogeneous. Another kind of computer system is the spatially distributed multicomputer system where there are many physically separate processors and stores

† There is a vast literature describing the operating of computer communication networks. A general description of the best-known can be found in Abramson Kuo [1.1], Schwartz [1.2], Davies, Barber [1.3]. Current information can be found in such journals as *IEE Transactions on Communications* and *IEE Transactions on Computers and Computer Networks*, and in proceedings of regular conferences, such as the International Conference on Computer Communication (or Comnet).

which cooperate to realise the computational tasks. The cooperation of computer subsystems has many obvious advantages. It enables the individual subsystems to become specialised, it facilitates a more even distribution of load and, frequently the most important, it increases the potential operational realiability of the system. We shall call this type of system a **remote multicomputer system**. An example of this type of system is the ARPA network. Both kinds of system can be combined to form an inflow–outflow system (see Fig. 1.1) in which information is processed by a remote multicomputer system.

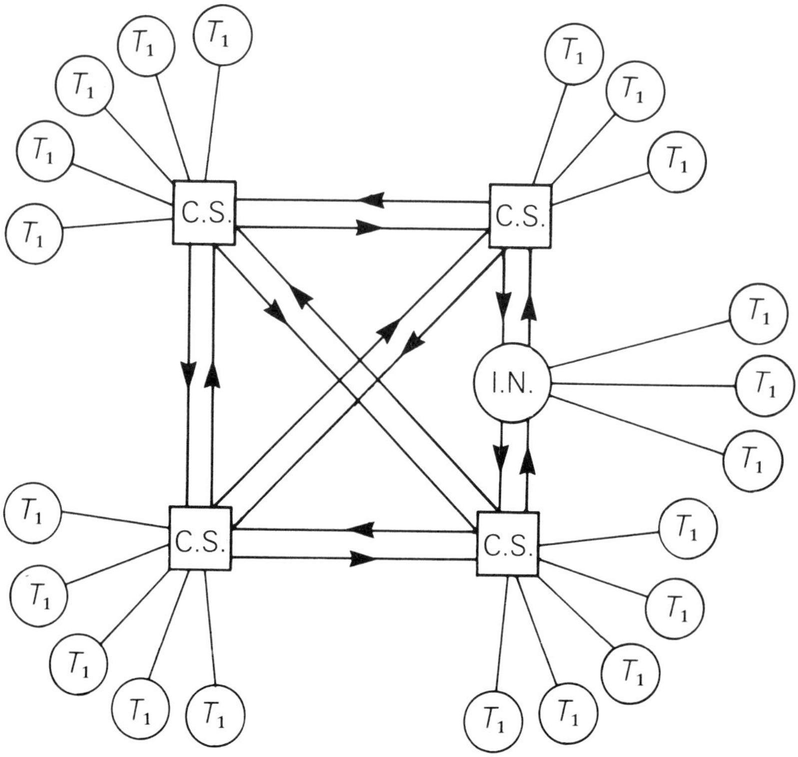

Fig. 1.1 – Multicomputer distributed system serving many terminals.
T. = terminal; C.S. = computer system; I.N. = interface node.

1.1.1 Time structure of computer information

The information fed into a system, be it by a terminal or a computer, possesses a specific time structure. We shall first deal with information sent by a terminal.

Three basic types of terminal are currently in use.† The first type comprises terminals, operated directly by a person, such as teleprinters and graphics terminals. Terminals of this type send information at rates varying from a few hundred bit/s to 100 kbits/s. The second type of terminal comprises those into which information is fed after preliminary processing such as punched card and paper-tape readers, discs and 'intelligent' terminals. The third kind of terminal comprises those into which results of measurements are automatically fed, e.g. in complex automation systems. The maximum rate of information transmission by these terminals varies from several hundred to many thousand bit/s, but are typically: 1.2; 2.4; 4.8; 9.6 kbit/s.

Often a cluster of terminals will be situated at some distance from the computer system. In this case it is convenient to send the information coming from the individual terminals by a common medium. Then, the equipment, usually a communication computer, combining information coming from the individual terminals, becomes a secondary terminal; we shall call it a **collective terminal**. The rate of information flow through collective terminals varies within the range of a few to a hundred kbit/s.

It can be seen from this short review of terminal types that they can differ quite considerably. One might therefore also expect the information passing through them to be very varied. It does seem to be characteristic of most terminals that information is sent in blocks which appear relatively rarely. In the first two types of terminal these blocks usually appear sporadically. This is because terminals frequently operate on a 'conversational' basis.

Figure 1.2 shows a typical example of the structure of information coming from a terminal of the first or second kind, or from a collective terminal. This consists of a sequence of blocks separated by intervals and starting in a sporadic way. In turn, a block consists of a sequence of smaller sub-blocks separated by smaller intervals etc. Typically the smallest block is a bit. Sequences of several bits (usually eight) correspond to alphanumeric symbols (letters of the Latin alphabet, numbers) in some code. Words are compiled from 10–20 alphanumeric symbols and so on. Groups of words form segments which make up the task set the computer by the terminal. The highest level units are sessions which correspond to time intervals during which the terminal is in contact with the computer.

Information sent by the computer to a terminal is, in principle, of a similar nature, except that the durations of particular blocks are usually different from those sent by a terminal.

From the above description of information structure, it is evident that various elements can be considered as blocks and their sub-blocks. For instance, if we treat a task as a block, the segments then become sub-blocks. If we assume

† A general description of terminals can be found in Hobbs [1.4]; while the current information is to be found in journals and conference proceedings mentioned in the footnote on p. 21.

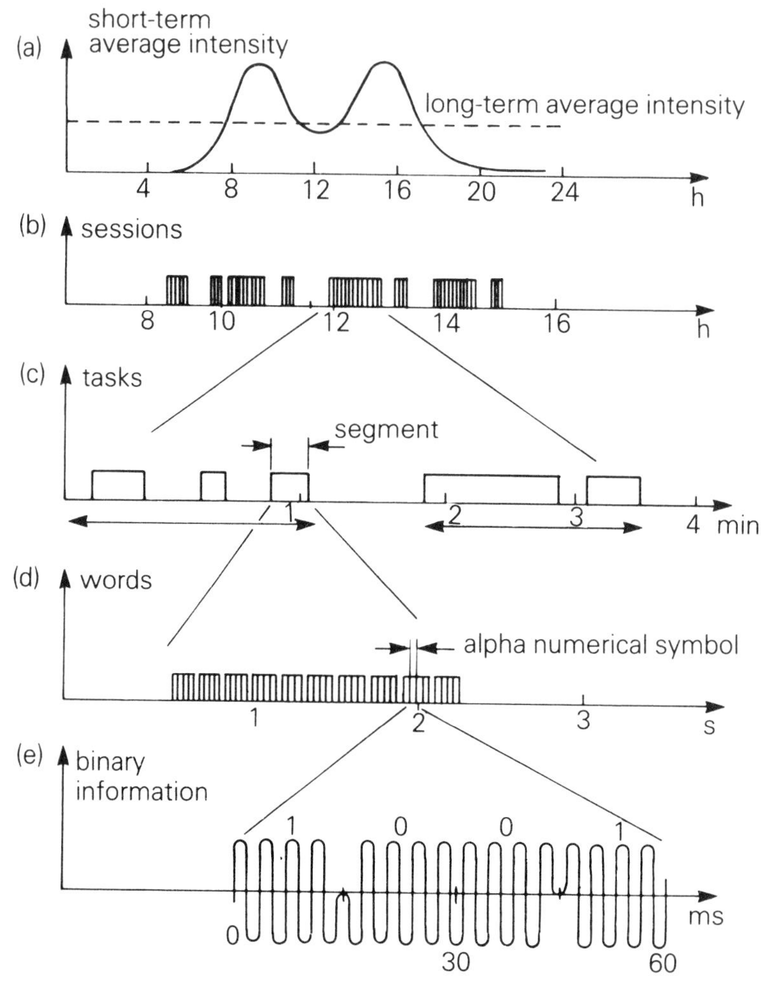

Fig. 1.2 – Model of information delivered by a terminal.

that, at one level, we do not consider the block structure and thus treat it as 'full', we can introduce the concept of the duty ratio of the sequence at the chosen level:

$$\gamma = \frac{\text{summed duration of blocks}}{\text{summed duration of blocks and idle intervals}}$$

where we sum over a sufficiently long interval. Statistical investigations have shown (see e.g. Fuchs, Jackson [1.5], Dudick *et al.* [1.6]) that for typical type one terminals, the duty ratio at the highest level (the largest blocks) is of the order of 10^{-3}, whereas the duty ratio taking into account all levels is of the order of 10^{-5}. We can therefore state that primary information is characterised by a very small duty ratio, and in addition, the blocks of which the information consists appear sporadically.

On the other hand, most communication channels operate best if signals are fed in rhythmically and, without idle intervals, with a duty ratio close to unity. Thus primary sources of computer information are fundamentally unmatched to telecommunication channels. One method of counteracting this mismatch is to attempt to convert the primary information sequence into one which is as rhythmic as possible, i.e. with a duty ratio close to unity. This process is called **concentration.** There are two mechanisms for concentration: **buffering** and **batch-processing.** They are illustrated in Fig. 1.3.

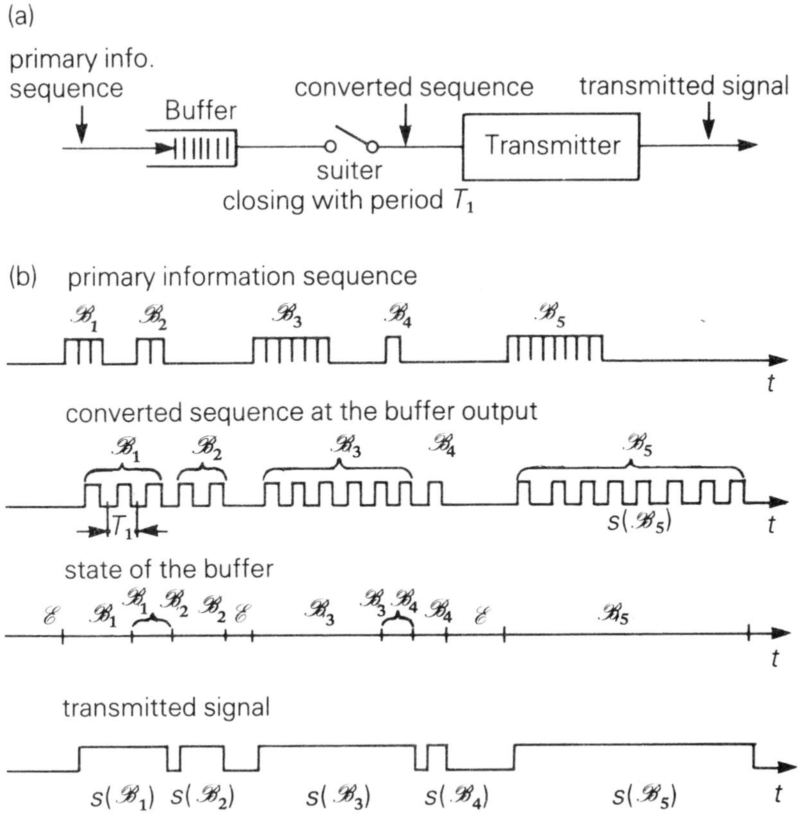

(c) → over

Fig. 1.3 – Illustration of buffering: (a) block diagram; (b) signals, $\mathscr{B}_n$-*n*th block of information; $s(\mathscr{B}_n)$-transmitted signal carrying the block; $\mathscr{E}$-the buffer is empty; and (c) batch processing, *T*-period for assembling into batches.

(C)

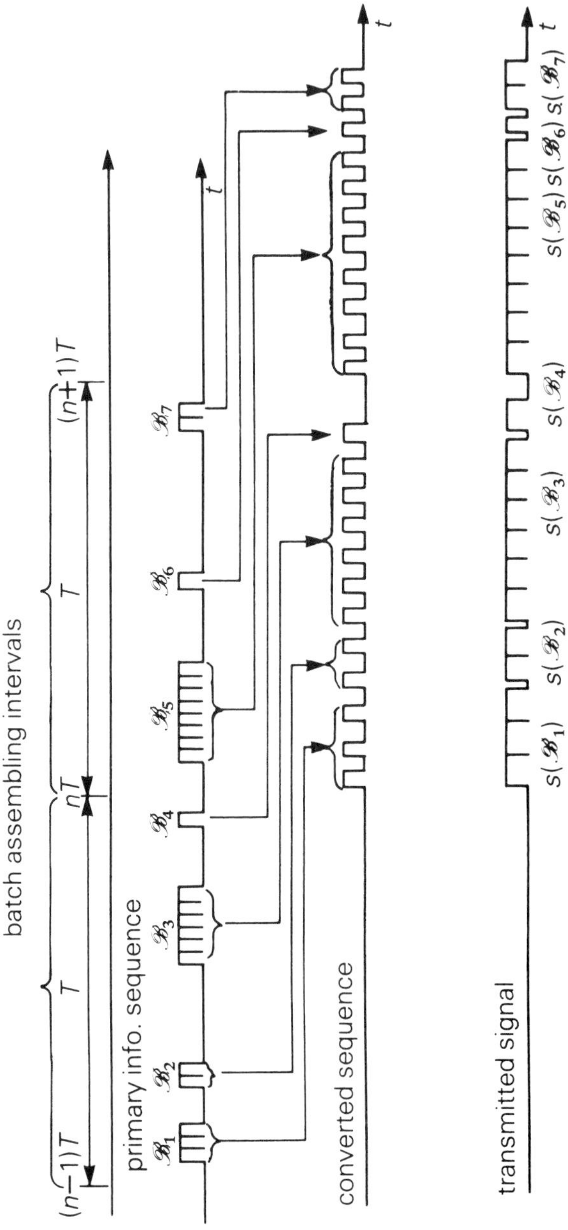
batch assembling intervals
(n−1)T
T
nT
T
(n+1)T
primary info. sequence
converted sequence
transmitted signal
t
t
t
S(𝓑₁)
S(𝓑₂)
S(𝓑₃)
S(𝓑₄)
S(𝓑₅) S(𝓑₆) S(𝓑₇)

An alternative method of matching information sources to communication channels is to use a common channel to send the information from many sources. This method will be discussed in the next two sections, and in more detail in Chapters 2, 3 and 4.

1.2 TRANSMISSION OF INFORMATION THROUGH A COMMON CHANNEL – CENTRALISED SIGNAL FORMATION

In this and the next section we consider in more detail systems with one common channel as shown in Fig. 1.4. In these systems, both the local transmitter and the common transmitter at the common channel input may affect the signal fed into the common channel. In this section we discuss systems where the common transmitter plays the deciding part. In the next section we discuss systems with **centralised signal formation** with **decentralised signal formation** in which the signal fed into the common channel is largely determined by the local transmitters. These cases are extreme ones. Usually the signal fed into the common channel is affected by both the local transmitters and the transmitter at the common channel input.

We are devoting so much attention to this type of system for two reasons. Firstly, such systems often occur in practice, either as autonomous systems, e.g. the ALOHA system (see [1.1], [1.2]), or as subsystems of more complex mesh structured systems. Secondly we can use this type of system to introduce the fundamental aspects of sharing communications resources between many users without introducing problems of routing which occur in mesh structured networks.

1.2.1 Fundamental concepts

In many cases we are dealing with a group of sources, e.g. terminals, clustered in a given area at some distance from the destinations, which are clustered in another area. We often implement such systems using a common channel as it is generally cheaper to build one channel having a large capacity than to construct many small-capacity channels. An additional argument for sending information from any sources through a common channel is that it is possible, without essentially altering the transmission quality of the information, to organise the joint use of the channel by many sources so that the duty ratio of the common channel signals will be far greater than if each source has only 'its own' channel at its disposal. Typically the common channel is a wire, or radio transmission. In the latter category we have both classical radio systems in which the transmitting and receiving antennas are located on the earth, and systems in which one of the antennas is on a satellite.

The information source is usually situated a short distance away from the common channel input and the local channels bring information from the source to the common transmitter. We call these remote access systems. These systems can be classified according the parts played by local transmitters and the common

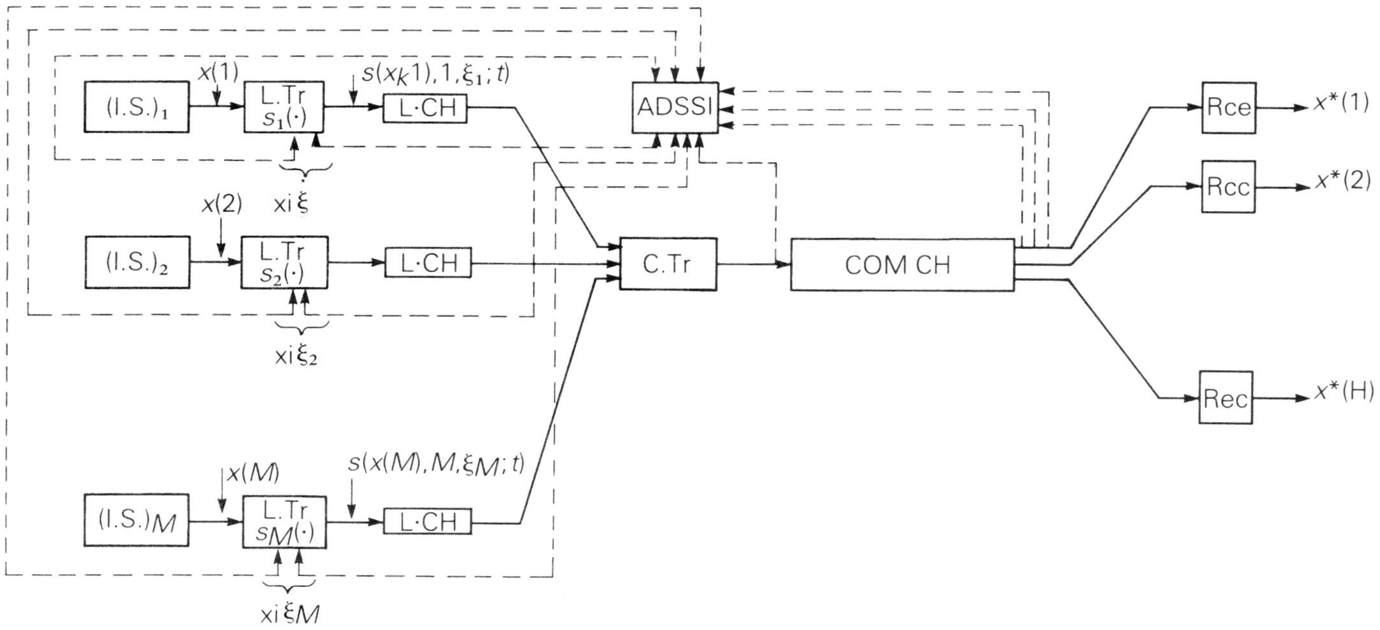

Fig. 1.4 – System with remote access to a common channel. $(\text{I.S.})_m$ = information source; L.Tr. = local transmitter; C.Tr. = common transmitter; L.CH. = local channel; COM.CH. = common channel; ADSSI = centre for acquisition and delivery of system state information; Rec. = receiver.

transmitter. At one extreme are systems in which signals are formed completely by the common transmitter. We call these systems with centralised signal formation. We will consider in this section the two most important types of such systems, namely systems using the common channel as a whole and systems in which the common channel is split into subchannels. In the next section we consider the other extreme case: where the dominant role in forming the signals put into the common channel is played by the local transmitters.

1.2.2 Systems with centralised signal formation using the common channel as a whole

In the system shown in Fig. 1.5 the role of local transmitters is confined to transferring information to the common transmitter which is responsible for matching

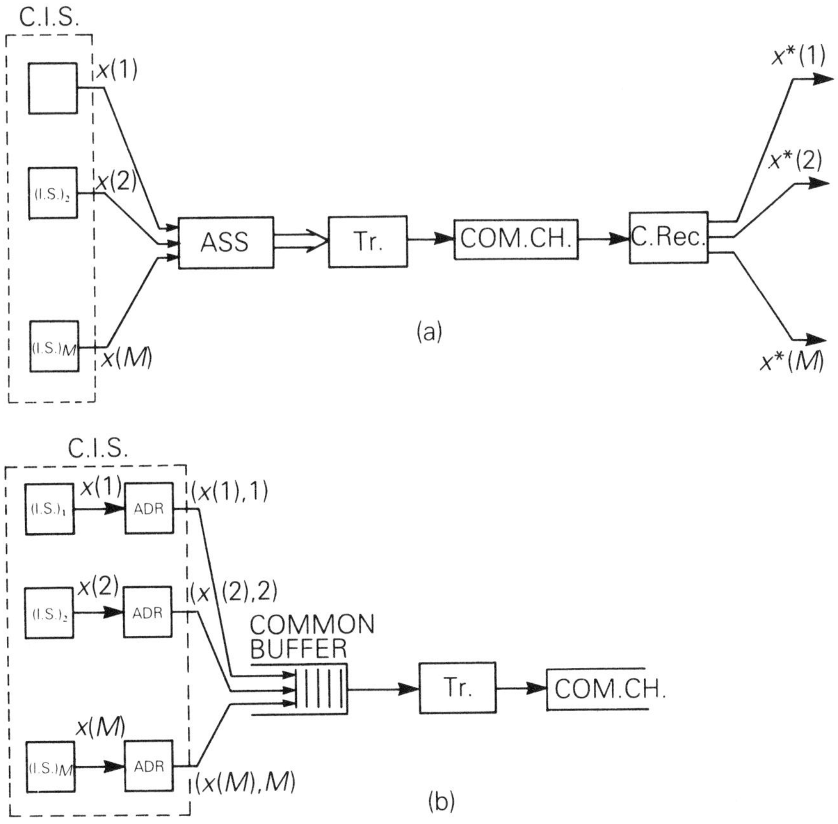

Fig. 1.5 – System with the common transmitter using the common channel as a whole applying (a) batch operation, (b) buffering. $(\text{I.S.})_m$ = information source C.I.S. = collective information source; C.Rec. = common receiver; Tr. = transmitter; ASS = assembly unit; ADR = addressing unit; COM.CH = common channel.

the signal to the common channel. As a result, it operates as if the information sources are situated by the common channel input, forming a collective information source. We can apply batch processing or buffering and sequential operation. In the first case, shown in Fig. 1.5(a), information originating from various sources is assembled into one block. This block is treated as one piece of information, is sent through the common channel as one entity and is recovered as such at the channel output before being broken up into its component pieces of information.

The common transmitter can also operate sequentially using a common buffer, as shown in Fig, 1.5(b). The blocks arriving from various sources are put in this buffer and then, observing some queueing discipline, usually FIFO discipline, are transmitted sequentially. Both for batch processing and buffering we must add to the primary information blocks addresses identifying the source. So the pair (x,m) where x is the primary block of information and m is the number of its source must be registered and transmitted. The block of primary information supplemented with address and treated during its passage as an independent entity is called a **packet**. Figure 1.6 illustrates the structure of a typical packet. Often we divide the information corresponding to one activity cycle of the source into several sub-blocks of equal length, and we use a packet of standard length for such a sub-block.

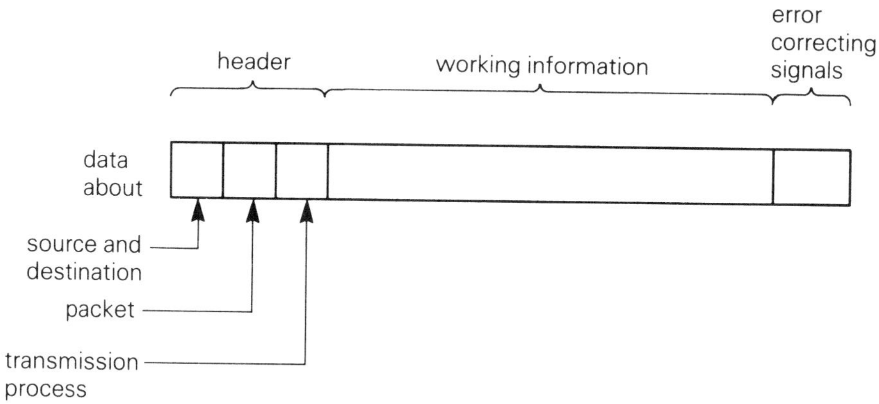

Fig. 1.6 – Structure of a packet.

1.2.3 Systems with separated subchannels – fundamental concepts

The other important system in which the facility at the input of the common channel plays the dominant role in signal forming is the system in which the common channel is split into almost separable subchannels. The basic structure of such a system is shown in Fig. 1.7. The common transmitter is divided into two subsystems. In the subsystem at the common channel input we generate

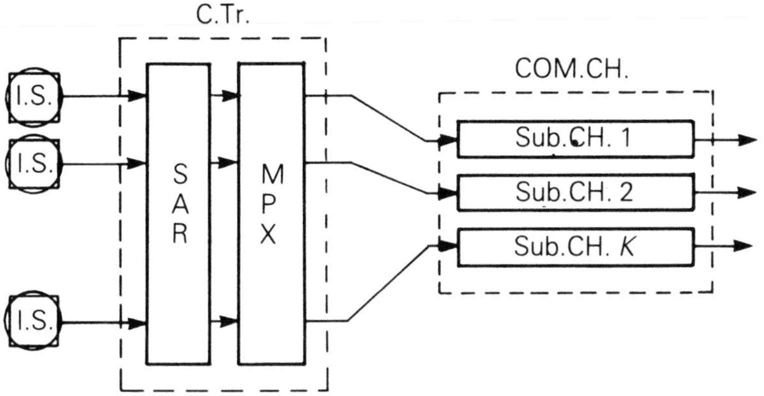

Fig. 1.7 – System with separated subchannels. SAR = Facility realising subchannel assignment rule; MPX = multiplexer.

signals such that the channel becomes, as it were, split into K independent subchannels. This is called channel **multiplexing**. Between the multiplexer and the information sources there is the subsystem which assigns a subchannel to the source. The operating principle of this subsystem is called the **subchannel assignment rule**.

Let S denote a set of signals which can be fed into the channel input. Multiplexing can be interpreted as the selection from the set S of subsets S_k, $k = 1, 2, \ldots, K$ of signals which can be fed into the kth subchannel. Let us assume that the signal at the channel output is the sum of the signal $y'(t)$ which is caused only by the input signals, and the signal $z(t)$ caused by external energy sources; we call $y'(t)$ the **noiseless** output signal, and $z(t)$ the **noise**. Further, let us denote by $\psi_t(\cdot)$ the operation transforming the set of input signals into the noiseless output signal; thus

$$y'(t) = \psi_t[s_1(\cdot), \ldots, s_K(\cdot)] \quad . \tag{1.2.1}$$

If

$$\psi_t[s_1(\cdot), \ldots, s_K(\cdot)] = A \sum_{k=1}^{K} s_k(t) \tag{1.2.2}$$

where A is a constant, the channel is called an **ideal linear channel.** We say that the channels are **ideally separable** if we can faultlessly separate each of the signals $s_k(t)$ from $y'(t)$.

We can show that (see Zadeh, Miller [1.7]) we can divide a channel into ideally separable channels if the subspaces S_k are linearly independent. To obtain the signal $s_k(t)$ we have to project the signal $y'(t)$ onto the subspace S_k.

The projection is most easily performed when the subspaces are orthogonal, i.e. when

$$\int_{t_a}^{t_b} [s_i(t)\, s_j(t)]\, \mathrm{d}t = 0 \tag{1.2.4}$$

for $i \neq j$.

Multiplexing using orthogonal subspaces is called **orthogonal multiplexing.** In practice, two kinds of orthogonal subsets s_k are most commonly used: (a) where the signals from various subsets do not overlap each other in the time domain, (b) those in which the harmonic signal spectra from any two different subsets do not overlap each other in the frequency domain Division of a channel into subchannels based on the sets mentioned in (a) is called **time division multiplexing** (TDM), that based on the sets in (b) is called **frequency division multiplexing** (FDM). These types of system are described widely in the literature (e.g. Doll [1.8]) so we confine ourselves here to a few elucidating comments.

Figure 1.8(a) illustrates TDM. We divide the time axis into time intervals of length T_2, which we call **basic slots.** Each basic slot is divided into K small slots separated by guard intervals which ensure orthogonality. A set consisting of the kth small slot in successive basic slots forms the kth time subchannel. A signal

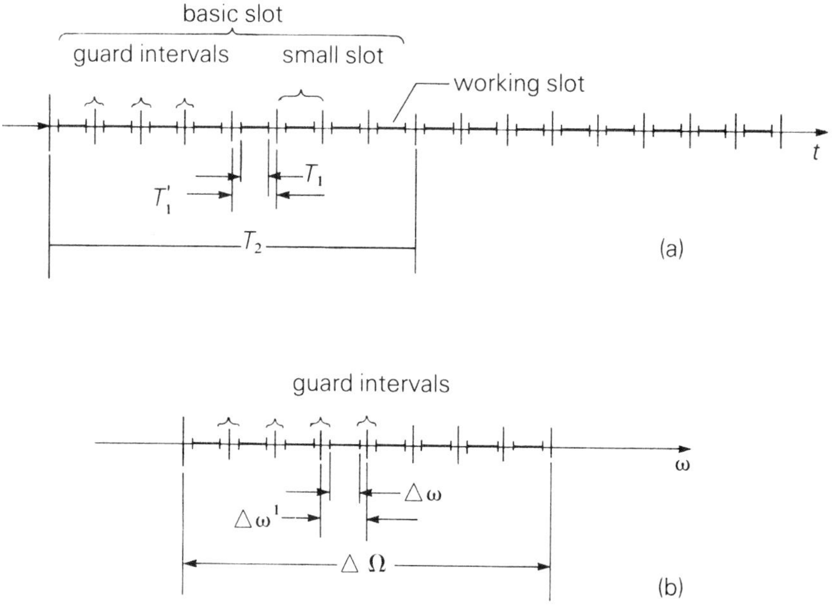

Fig. 1.8 – Organisation of orthogonal subchannels (a) TDM, (b) FDM.

carried by such a subchannel thus takes the form of a sequence of impulses which repeat with a period T_2, and are separated by intervals of length

$$\frac{K-1}{K} \cdot T_2 \ .$$

The projection operation used in TDM is time domain filtering.

In FDM we divide the frequency bands of signals which can be carried by the common channel into sub-bands, as shown in Fig. 1.8(b). Each sub-band corresponds to a frequency subchannel. It is not possible, even theoretically, to exactly satisfy the condition that the spectra of signals having finite duration disappear beyond a finite frequency band. So as to reduce the effect of spectral overlap of signals from various sets S_k we use guard bands, as is shown in Fig. 1.8(b). The projection operation used in FDM is frequency domain filtering.

The second subsystem of a multiaccess system is the subsystem for assigning the subchannel to the source shown in Fig. 1.7. Let:

$\vartheta_\mu(m)$ be the instant the mth source becomes activated for the μth time;
ξ be the information about the state of the system;
k_m be the number of the subchannel assigned to the mth source.

The rule for choosing k_m for given $\vartheta_\mu(m)$, ξ, is called the **subchannel assignment rule**, $K_m(\cdot)$; so

$$\vartheta_\mu(m), \xi \xrightarrow{K_m(\cdot)} k_m \ . \tag{1.2.5}$$

The set of rules

$$K(\cdot) \equiv (K_m(\cdot), \quad m = 1, 2, \ldots, M) \tag{1.2.6}$$

is called the set of subchannel assignment rules. In most cases the system is homogeneous, i.e.:

$$K_m(\cdot) = K_1(\cdot) \tag{1.2.7}$$

$m = 2, 3, \ldots, M$. The multiaccess system is then described by the rule $K_1(\cdot)$.

The simplest type of subchannel assignment rule is the fixed assignment rule according to which each source recieves its subchannel on a permanent basis. Obviously for fixed assignment the number of subchannels K must be equal to the number M of sources, i.e.

$$M = K \ . \tag{1.2.8}$$

Fixed subchannel assignment requires neither the use of s.s.i. nor the adding of source addresses. The disadvantage is that we can improve the common channel utilisation only by increasing the duty ratio of sequences of packets delivered by a single source. This can be done by applying individual buffers as shown in Fig. 1.9, but is costly. The obvious way of avoiding the mentioned disadvantage of the fixed subchannel assignment rule is to make the channel assignment dependent on information about the state of the system. The simplest kind is information which tells us which subchannels are in use and which are not. Thanks to this information, we can divide the set of subchannels into two subsets: NBU, non-busy subchannels, and BU, busy subchannels. A typical example of a flexible subchannel assignment rule using this s.s.i. is:

R1 If a source becomes activated and NBU is not empty, one of the subchannels from NBU is assigned to the source and that subchannel is now included in BU; if NBU is empty, the source has no access to the system. When a source ceases to be active the subchannel assigned to it returns from BU to NBU.

If we use a flexible access rule we cannot state from the received information alone which source has sent it. Therefore we must add to the primary information the address of its source, as in the case of the system with common transmitter.

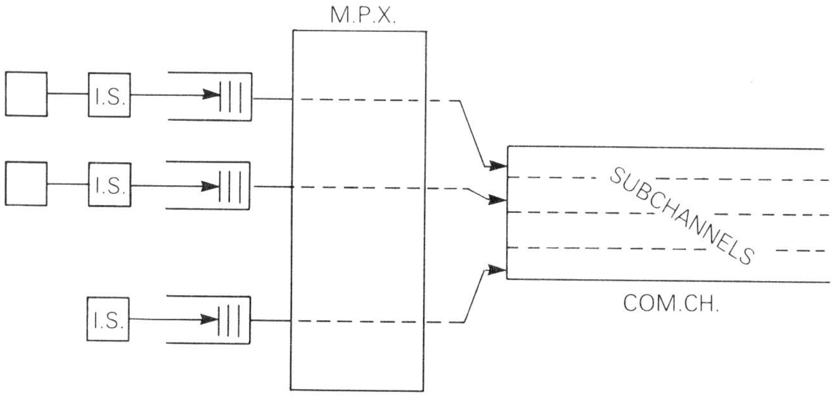

Fig. 1.9 – System with fixed subchannel assignment and with individual buffers. MPX = multiplexer.

1.2.4 Systems with separated subchannels – properties of flexible subchannel assignment

We show now that if we have fewer subchannels than sources, i.e. if

$$M < K \tag{1.2.9}$$

then the flexible access rule R1 permits us to increase substantially the common channel utilisation, even, without buffering. To get insight into the fundamental properties of the rule we introduce several simplifying assumptions:

A1 The properties of all information sources and all subchannels are the same.

A2 When the source feeds its information into a subchannel, the capacity of this subchannel is fully used.

A3 The time taken to assign an idle subchannel to the activated source and that taken to release the subchannel after the source using it has become idle are negligible.

A4 The part of the subchannel capacity needed for transmitting the address is negligible compared with the total subchannel capacity.

A5 No buffering is used.

In view of A5 the information delay is equal to the transmission time, which we consider to be fixed. Thus the system considered here is primarily characterised by the parameters:

ν_1 – duty ratio of the sequence of primary blocks delivered by the information source;

ν – common channel utilisation factor;

P^- – probability that an active source has no access to the channel.

We will show that it is possible to achieve concentration while P^- is reasonably small.

Let $\bar{M}_a$ be the average number of active sources. From definition of ν_1 follows that

$$\nu_1 = \frac{\bar{M}_a}{M} \tag{1.2.10}$$

where M is the number of all sources. From rule R1 it follows that

$$P^- = P(\mathrm{M_a} > K) \tag{1.2.11}$$

where $\mathrm{M_a}$ is a random variable representing the number of sources at a given moment.

The parameter

$$K' \equiv \frac{K - \bar{M}_a}{\bar{M}_a} \tag{1.2.12}$$

can be interpreted as normalised number of channels. Using it we write (1.2.12) in the form

$$P^- = P\,\frac{M_a - \bar{M}_a}{\bar{M}_a} > K' \tag{1.2.13}$$

Next we consider ν. Let $\mathrm{K_{bu}}$ denote the random variable representing the number of busy subchannels: under consideration here we have

$$\mathrm{K_{bu}} \equiv \begin{cases} \mathrm{M_a} & \text{if } \mathrm{M_a} \leqslant K \\ \mathrm{K} & \text{if } \mathrm{M_a} > K\,. \end{cases} \tag{1.2.14}$$

From (1.2.4) it is evident that the average number of busy subchannels

$$EK_{bu} = \sum_{k=0}^{K} [kP(M_a = k)] + KP^- \ . \tag{1.2.15}$$

The common channel utilisation factor:

$$\nu(K) = \frac{EK_{bu}}{K} \ . \tag{1.2.16}$$

From (1.2.15) and (1.2.16) we obtain:

$$\nu(K) = \frac{1}{K} \sum_{k=0}^{K} kP(M_a = k) + P^-(K) \ . \tag{1.2.17}$$

In this notation we indicate that both ν and P^- are dependent on the number of subchannels K. From (1.2.11) it follows that for $K = M$

$$P^-(M) = 0 \tag{1.2.18}$$

and from (1.2.17)

$$\nu(M) = \frac{\bar{M}_a}{M} \tag{1.2.19}$$

From this and (1.2.10) follows that

$$\nu(M) = \nu_1 \tag{1.2.20}$$

which is intuitively obvious, since for $K = M$, no concentration can occur.

The minimum reasonable value for K is 1. If $\bar{M}_a \gg 1$ then from (1.2.12) we see that $K' \approx -1$ and taking into account (1.2.13) we have to expect that $P^-(1) \approx 1$. From (1.2.17) it follows next that $\nu(1) \approx 1$. Thus we conclude that for K increasing from 1 to M, the probability of non-acceptance P^- decreases from 1 to 0 and common channel utilisation decreases from about 1 to ν_1. The rate of decrease depends strongly on the normalised variance

$$\alpha \equiv \frac{\sqrt{\mathrm{var}(\bar{M}_a)}}{\bar{M}_a} \tag{1.2.21}$$

where $\mathrm{var}(\bar{M}_a)$ is the variance of M_a. We show now by an example that $P^-(K)$ decreases more rapidly with K than $\nu(K)$, thus we can achieve concentration keeping $P^-(K)$ small.

1.3 TRANSMISSION OF INFORMATION THROUGH A COMMON CHANNEL – DECENTRALISED SIGNAL FORMATION

Systems with **decentralised signal formation** reduce the role of the common transmitter, or even eliminate it, leaving the organisation of common channel operation to the local transmitters. The structure of such a system is similar to that shown in Fig. 1.4, except that in place of the common transmitter we have a facility for fairly simple processing of the signal emitted by the local transmitters. For example, if the common channel is open space and medium or short radio waves are used, the signals from the local transmitters are simply added.

The rule according to which the local transmitter generates the signal which will be subsequently put into the common channel is called the remote access rule. If we apply remote access rules efficiently the packets coming from various sources can be delivered without excessive delay to their destinations. Therefore we can refer to subchannels even if they are not physically separated. We shall call such subchannels **virtual subchannels** as distinct from the separated subchannels which were considered in the previous section. In real systems, one cannot normally completely eliminate the mutual interference of separated subchannels. Therefore, any differentiation between a separated subchannel and a virtual one is a matter of convention.

In this section we consider the fundamental features of remote access rules, emphasising the role of system state information on which the access decisions are taken.

1.3.1 Fundamental concepts

The signal generated by the mth local transmitter must carry not only the primary information x, but also the address m of the source. It may also depend on the information ξ about system state. So the signal generated by the mth transmitter can be written in the form $s(x,m,\xi;t)$ $t \in \langle t_a, t_b \rangle$, where $\langle t_a, t_b \rangle$ is the time interval reserved for sending the signal. The rule for ordering the signal $s(x,m,\xi;t)$ to information x,m and the auxiliary information ξ is called the access rule of the mth transmitter and is denoted by $S_m(\cdot)$. Thus we have

$$x,m,\xi \xRightarrow{S_m(\cdot)} s(x,m,\xi;t)$$

The operation of a set of local transmitters is characterised by the set of rules

$$S(\cdot) \equiv (S_m(\cdot), \quad m = 1,2,\ldots,M) \tag{1.3.1}$$

The access rule determines signal shaping and timing. In extreme cases of overload the decision may be to not admit the signal into the channel. Often the primary information blocks arrive in batches and the access decision is then the set of individual decisions about signals carrying component blocks. Even if we treat the batch as an entity, the signal carrying it may be a sequence of component signals, e.g. retransmissions. In such cases the individual decisions about component signals can be made either jointly (all at once) or sequentially. A typical example of joint decision making is the batch operation of a system with a common transmitter mentioned in 1.3.1 (see Fig. 1.5(a)). If the individual decisions are made sequentially in time and independently the access rule is called **memoryless.** In general an individual decision may be dependent on decisions made in the past in particular, thus we may have a Markov-type dependence. An example of the system with a common buffer is shown in Fig. 1.5(b).

In the simplest case the decision about the signal is determined completely by the system state information. The rule is then called deterministic. Decision theory shows that in cases where we do not have complete statistical information about the system at our disposal, or where the system operates in a hostile environment, a favourable solution is to apply not a deterministic but a random decision rule. The decision is then taken in two stages. We decided first upon the probability distribution of admissible signal shapes and timings, and in the second stage a random number generator chooses the ultimate signal and its location in time. An example of the randomised remote access rule is that which we consider in Chapter 4 where after a failed transmission a retransmission is started at an instant determined by a random number generator.

So far we have not taken into account the technical aspects of making remote access decisions. One extreme is to make these decisions in a general control unit and to program the local transmitters only to execute these decisions. A completely centralised system would operate like the system with a common transmitter using the whole channel.

The other extreme is where each node makes the decision itself; we call such a system decentralised. There is of course a whole spectrum of systems between these extremes; they are described in Chapters 2 3, and 4.

The most important feature of remote access rules which we will emphasise in this book is the type of information concerning the state of the common channel and nodes on which the access decisions are based. In the simplest case we only have information about the structure of the system, the signals, and statistical properties of the system components for making access decisions. If we only use this fixed information it is called a fixed access rule. A system with fixed access rules can also be described as having free access: each local transmitter feeds in its own signal without considering other transmitters. The system can only operate satisfactorily if the signals are chosen so that if several transmitters are working simultaneously the signals can still be separated at the receiver. One way to achieve this is to use perfectly separable signals, in particular, orthogonal signals. Most important classes of such signals are non-overlapping in time or signals having non-overlapping spectra. A system with such signals is equivalent to one where the channel is split into separable subchannels. The other method is to use signals which are not perfectly separable but which can be recovered correctly using error-correcting codes.

Optimal access decisions can be made if we use the current information about the states of the sources, nodes and channels. This current information is called **system state information** (s.s.i.). If decentralised access rules are applied it is easy to have the current information about the state of the node making the decision. This information is called **local state information.** If the access depends on s.s.i. we call the rule **flexible.** Since we usually try to use s.s.i. to optimise access decisions, we can term flexible rules as **adaptive.** An example of a system applying a flexible rule is the system in which the node monitors the state of the common channel and starts transmission when it finds that the channel is not being used by other transmitters. The features of access rules can be combined, leading to the classification illustrated in Fig. 1.11. Several examples of such combinations will be given in Chapters 2, 3, and 4.

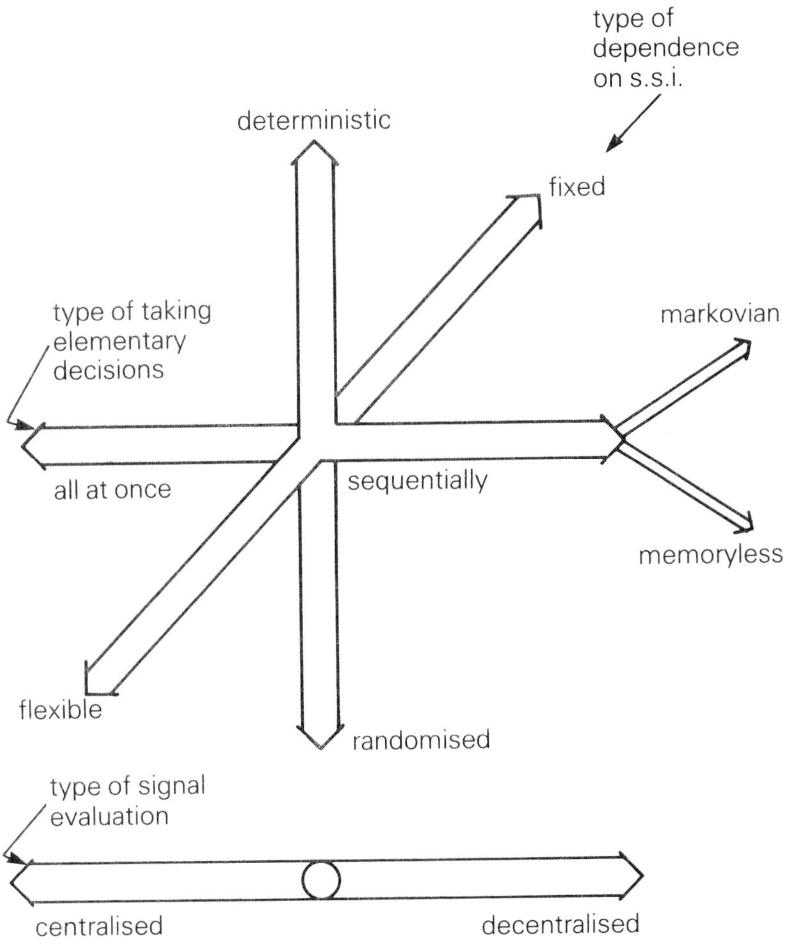

Fig. 1.11 – Features of remote access rules.

So far we have assumed that the information sources are concentrated in an area around the common channel input, the destinations being around the common channel output. A common channel can also be used for linking sources and destinations located along the common channel. This type of system is said to have access '*en route*' and, for an inflow system, take the form shown in Fig. 1.12(a). For an outflow system we have the form illustrated in Fig. 1.12. Both systems can be joined to form an inflow–outflow system with the channel in a loop, as shown in Fig. 1.12(b). In such a system the information centre sends pulses into the channel indicating the sequence of time slots. If the information centre has to transmit a packet, then it is put into a current slot. The local receivers check the addresses of packets flowing past them, and if a packet is addressed to that receiver, it is removed from the slot. If the information centre does not have any packets to transmit, it sends an empty slot. During its journey along the channel, an empty slot can be picked up by a local transmitter which has information to send to the information centre.

Most of the concepts apply to systems with access *en route*. However, we usually require that such systems are simple and therefore local nodes operate only using information which can be obtained by watching packets passing by. Examples of fixed and flexible access rules based on this information will be considered in detail in section 4.3.

1.3.2 The subsystem for state information acquisition and delivery

The operation of a system with flexible access rules depends on the subsystem providing current system state information acquisition and delivery (s.s.i. subsystem). We now consider the fundamental features of these subsystems. Our deliberations will be general so that they are applicable also to general mesh networks.

We first notice that the s.s.i. subsystem is a multiaccess system usually having a similar topology to the working information system which the s.s.i. subsystem is serving. Thus the same general characteristics are found in the s.s.i. subsystem, in particular it can be centralised or decentralised. The s.s.i. subsystem may be based on a separate network of channels, usually though the s.s.i. subsystem uses subchannels of the working information system. If these subchannels are separated, then the situation is as for a separate network. However, if the subchannels are not separated, typically for economic reasons, the s.s.i. subsystem and working system become coupled, which in case of overloading may cause adverse effects.

The states of the network components which the s.s.i. descibes often changes continuously with time. Delivering and using exact information of all such changes would be very costly. Therefore we send only some compressed data about the states, usually samples, taken at **sampling** or **updating instants.** In the simplest case sampling instants are fixed, e.g. taken at a fixed interval. It is more efficient to sample at instants when the state of the sampled process alters;

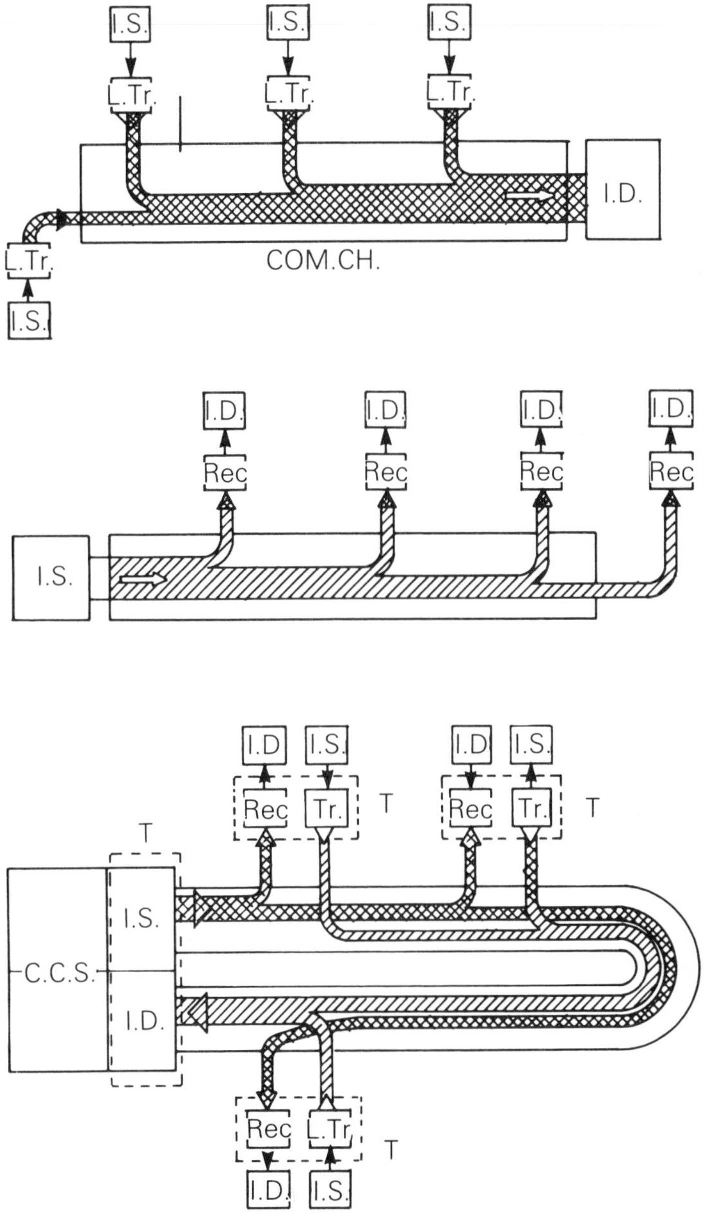

(a)

(b)

(c)

Fig. 1.12 – Systems with access '*en route*' (a) inflow system, (b) outflow system, (c) inflow and outflow loop system. I.S. = information source; L.Tr. = local transmitter; I.D. information destination; Rec. = receiver; C.C.S. = control computer system; T = terminal.

we call this flexible or adaptive sampling. A typical example is predictive-subtractive sampling, in which a new sample is taken when the difference between the values of the process predicted on the basis of previous samples and the real value exceeds a threshold. In the s.s.i. subsystem we have several sources and, in the case of decentralised system, several information–destinations pairs. Therefore we have two types of s.s.i. transmission: (1) **initiated by the source**, (2) **initiated by the user**. In the case of a decentralised system, type 1 transmission is essentially **broadcasting**: a node sends its information to other nodes or to the central control unit, without being asked to do so. Type 2 transmission is based on requests sent to a particular node to send information about its state to a particular destination. The other method is to send a working packet to the systems component. After the packet's arrival the component sends back information about its ability to process packets. We call such systems, **feedback systems**. Classical systems with positive or negative acknowledgement are examples of this system.

Obviously in a system with source-initiated transmission we may indicate not only the destination to which the information source has to send the information about its state, but also require it immediately to take a new sample, thus influencing sampling. The features of s.s.i. are summarised in Fig. 1.13.

It is evident that the more accurate and up to date the s.s.i., the better the decisions about transmission of working packets can be. On the other hand increasing the accuracy and freshness of s.s.i. requires a more sophisticated and

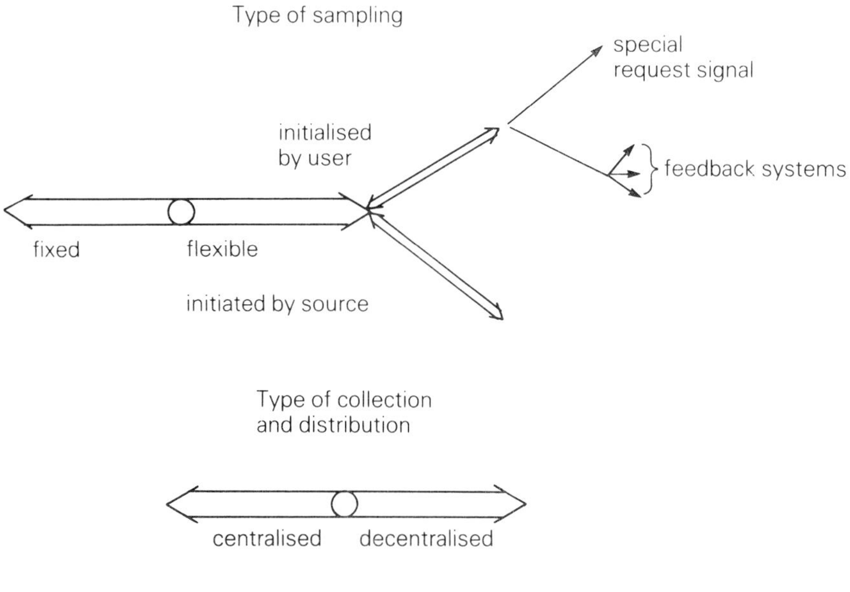

Fig. 1.13 – Fundamental features of s.s.i. subsystems.

therefore more costly s.s.i. subsystem. Therefore with increasing complexity of the s.s.i. subsystem the net profit will first rise and then decline. The optimum choice of the size of s.s.i. subsystem is one of the main topics of this book.

1.4 TRANSMISSION OF INFORMATION THROUGH A NETWORK

In a remote access computer system we usually have at our disposal a network of channels connected by nodes. Such a network structure in a communications system makes it possible to use the channels more efficiently and to substantially increase the reliability of information transmission. In this section we first introduce the fundamental concepts related to transmission through a network, and later we shall consider in more detail the rules according to which packets are guided through the network.

1.4.1 Fundamental concepts

The interconnections of nodes by channels can be decribed by means of a directed graph, whose arcs correspond to channels. Graphs of typical networks are shown in Fig. 1.14. The network in Fig. 1.14(a) is called a **chain** of channels; in Fig. 1.14(b) we have a **bunch** of channels, in Fig. 1.14(c) a **tree** network and in Fig. 1.14(d) a **mesh** network.

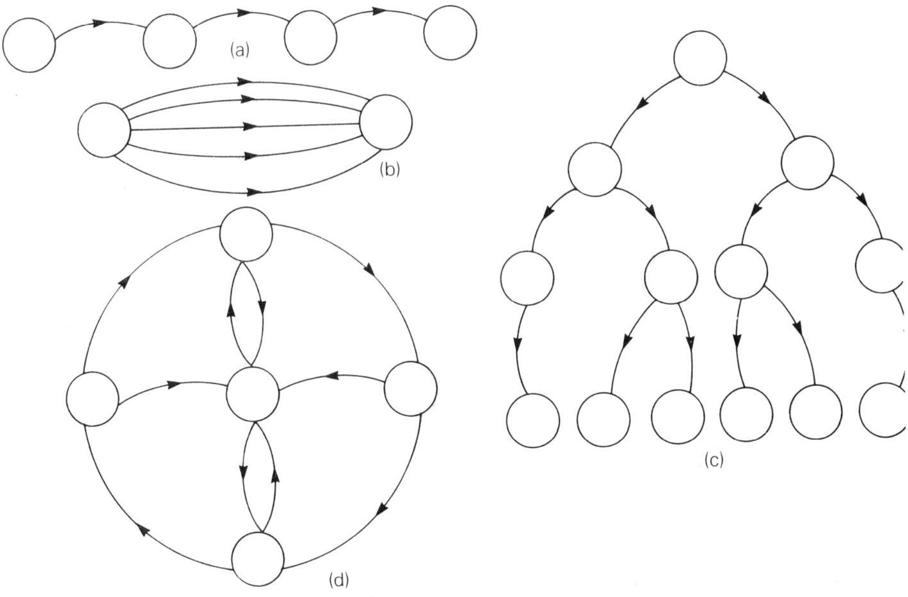

Fig. 1.14 – Typical graphs of networks: (a) chain of channels, (b) bunch of channels, (c) tree network, (d) mesh network.

The required connections between the subsystems of the computing system can also be represented by a graph which we call an **information flow graph.** Examples of such graphs are given in Fig. 1.15. The graph shown in Fig. 1.15(a) corresponds to an inflow information system that in Fig. 1.15(b) corresponds to an outflow system and that in Fig. 1.15(c) to a totally connected system.

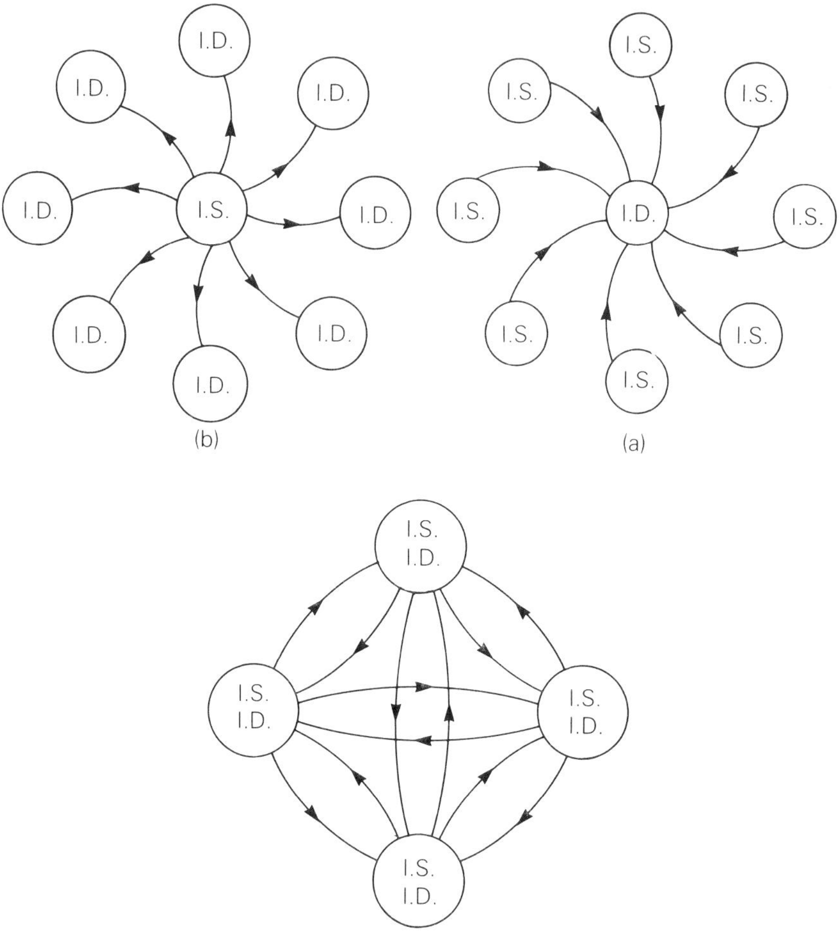

Fig. 1.15 – Typical information flow graphs: (a) inflow system, (b) outflow system, (c) totally connected communication system. I.S. = information source; I.D. = information destination.

The channel network graph need not be the same as the information flow graph. For example, a flow graph having a star structure can correspond to a channel network having a tree structure. The flow graph in Fig. 1.15(a) corresponds to the system with *'en route'*, access shown in Fig. 1.12(a), and that in Fig. 1.15(b) corresponds to the system in Fig. 1.12(b).

Conceptually the simplest way of implementing a given information flow graph is to create a network with a separate channel for each communicating source–destination pair, i.e. a network for which the channel graph and the flow graph are identical. Such a solution would obviously be most uneconomical. Usually we can produce a network whose channel graph has considerably fewer arcs than the flow graph. Information from a given source, denoted by s, is sent to a destination receiving node, denoted by r, along a chain of channels called a **path** and denoted by $\mathcal{P}_{sr}$. Since the channels are used for the transmission of information from several sources paths joining several source–destination pairs may have some channels in common.

In order to describe the operation of a network we have to take into account the fact that the source has periods of activity separated by idle intervals. Two variants of network operation are possible. In the first one, when the source, starts a period of activity, a path is established, for the whole activity cycle. When this cycle is completed, the channels making up the path are released. This variant of network operation is called **circuit switching**. In the second variant, information sent during the activity cycle is divided into smaller units which are supplemented with additional data, to form packets. These packets are sent independently and different packets originating from the same source can be sent along different paths. Since packets appear sporadically at the input of a given channel they are buffered to try to make the best use of channel. The process of sending a packet along a chain of channels is as follows: after arrival at a node, the packet is put into a buffer in which there may already be other packets. The packets are removed in turn and fed into the next channel. This kind of network operation is called both **store and forward** and **packet switching.** The operation of a network in which the store and forward principle is applied is characterised by the **routing rule** according to which the packet is carried through the network. We are now going to consider these rules in more detail.

1.4.2 Routing rules

To forward a packet through a network we have to take signal shaping, timing and routing decisions. This set of decisions we call **packet handling decisions.** Our previous considerations about signal shaping and timing decision in a system with a single common channel apply directly to the mesh network. Although routing decisions do not occur in the systems with a common channel, most features of the routing decisions can be integrated as the 'space domain' counterparts of the signal shaping and timing decisions considered previously. In particular problems of acquisition, transmission and use of **network state information** (n.s.i.) and s.s.i. are quite similar.

The routing determines the path of the packet. It can be considered as a sequence of elementary decisions about moving the packet from node to node. These elementary decisions can be made either all at once or sequentially. In the first case we have pole to pole routing, in the second, node to node routing. In the latter case it is important how strongly routing decisions made in the past can influence future decisions. If the channel chosen at a given node depends only on the destination and source poles, and the instantly available n.s.i., we call the rule **memoryless.** If it depends on the events in the past, we call it a **rule with memory.** The class of rules with memory is quite large. The most important subtypes are the Markovian rules of order corresponding to the number of nodes the packet has 'recently' passed. An example of this type of rule is one which prevents packets from circulating in loops. This example rule may be implemented by storing the indices of the channels traversed by a packet in the packet header, then using these indices to detect that the packet has travelled in a loop. The loop may then be broken by changing the local routing rule, or possibly by destroying the packet.

The routing rule is described as **flexible** if it depends on n.s.i., and **fixed** if it does not. In a real network the n.s.i. is always outdated, not only because it has to be transmitted from distant nodes, but also because it is produced by sampling. The difference between the instant at which the information is available for making a routing decision and the instant it pertains to we call 'delay'. The distance between the place where routing decisions are made and the node to which the n.s.i. pertains is called the 'space range' of the n.s.i. For fixed capacities of channels forming the n.s.i., the delay will increase as the space range increases, and as the channel capacity for transmitting the n.s.i. decreases. As in the case of remote access rules, the routing rules can be deterministic or randomised. If the channel which is chosen is determined solely by the destination pole, the source pole and the available n.s.i., then the rule is called **deterministic**, otherwise it is known as **randomised.**

We have a variety of randomised routing rules. A rule is called **purely random** if there are always at least two channels which can be chosen with probabilities larger than zero and less than one. A more general case is random routing except within a certain neighbourhood. If the destination pole to which the packet is directed does not belong to the neighbourhood of the node at which the packet has just arrived, then the packet is forwarded in a purely random way. If, however, the destination pole lies in the neighbourhood, the packet is forwarded to it in a deterministic way.

The n.s.i. subsystem is a mesh network superimposed on the working packet transmission network. Our previous considerations about the s.s.i. subsystem for a remote access system with a common channel apply directly to the n.s.i. subsystem. This subsystem can apply fixed or flexible sampling, in particular predictive–subtractive sampling.

The transmission of the samples can be either initiated by the node generating the sample, or by the user of n.s.i., i.e. the central control unit in centralised system, or the node making the routing decision in a decentralised system.

The n.s.i. can be collected and evaluated either at a central unit (**centralised n.s.i. subsystem**) or locally at each node (**decentralised n.s.i. subsystem**). Obviously the routing rule and the n.s.i. subsystem should be related. Typically we get the following combinations: pole to pole routing and centralised n.s.i. collection and evaluation giving large delay and space range; node to node routing and distributed n.s.i. collection and routing giving small delay and space range. It is evident that other combinations are possible. For example we could evaluate (centrally) the node to node routing if the speed of packet transmission were much smaller than the transmission speed of the n.s.i. We have such a situation in the case of road traffic where the 'packets' are transported by vehicles but the auxiliary information is sent by radio. Intermediate solutions between pole to pole and node to node solutions are possible, for example the network can be divided into areas, each with a local control unit.

Finally we mention an important feature of routing rules which has no direct counterpart in the subchannel assignment and remote access rules. If a packet may be divided into smaller units, or copied, and the fragments or copies forwarded along different routes, we say that the rule is one of **branched routing**. If the packet is to be forwarded as an indivisible entity, we call the routing rule **branchless.**

As explained in (1.1.1), computer information has a block hierarchic structure. The routing rule for blocks at one level of a hierarchy determines the routing rule for sequences of blocks, thus it determines the routing rule for blocks at a higher level of that hierarchy. The routing rules at different levels of hierarchy can belong to different categories. For example, if the routing for blocks is branchless but flexible then, from the point of view of transmitting sequences of blocks, the rule is one of branched routing. The features of the routing rules introduced here can be combined, yielding a classification as illustrated in Fig.1.16.

1.5 PARAMETERS DESCRIBING A COMMUNICATIONS SYSTEM

In this section we give a general outline of the parameters characterising the operation of a communications system, and methods of defining these parameters. We also define the basic problems of communication system optimisation.

1.5.1 Classification of the quality indices

The parameters characterising the quality of an information transmission system are called the **quality indices** of the system. Economic factors are always of importance and so we introduce economic quality indices. The economic indices

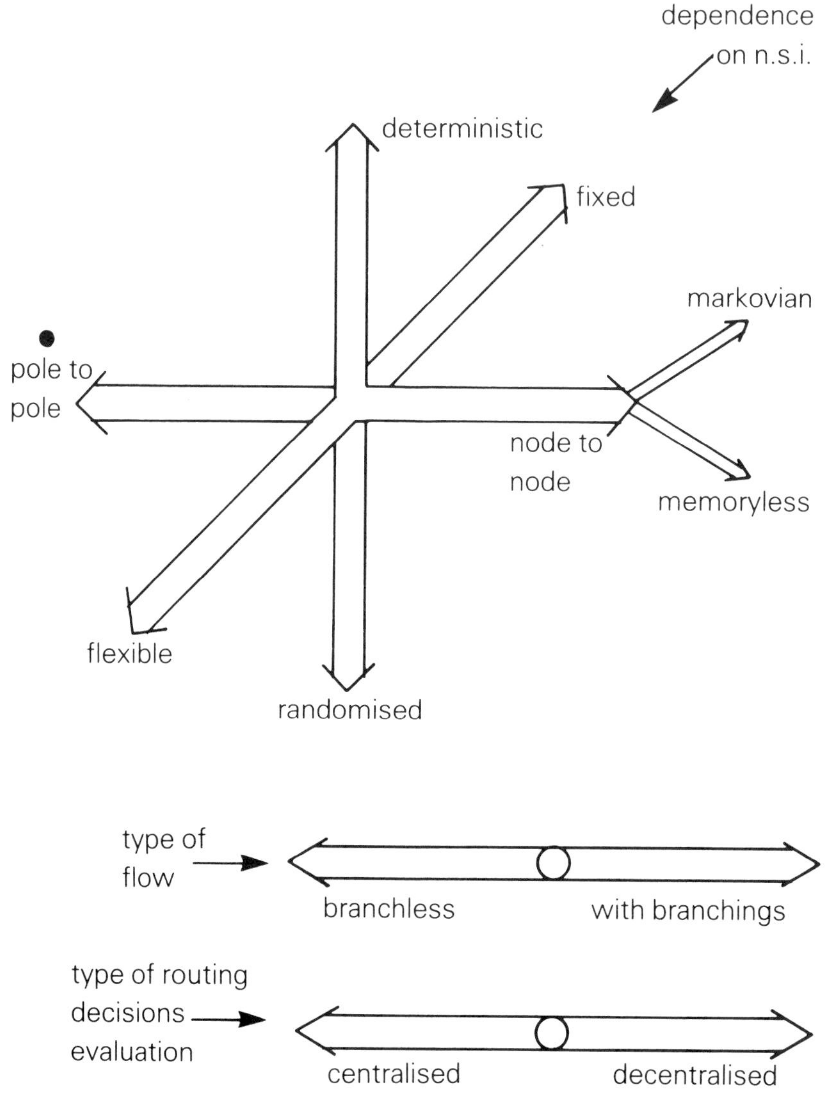

Fig. 1.16 – Fundamental features of routing rules.

connected with the construction and operation of the information system can be divided into two basic groups:

Cost indices related to constructional and operational costs of the information system.

Gain indices related to the gains accruing to the user of an information system as a result of information supplied to him by the system.

These indices, particularly those in the second group, are hard to define precisely or calculate directly, so we usually define secondary indices which, in principle, depend only on the operating rules of the information system. The primary economic indices are fundamentally dependent on these secondary indices. A typical secondary cost index is the number of storage elements which have to be used in the equipment belonging to the information system. This figure is defined by the operating principle of the information system. The storage elements are the costliest parts of the equipment and their construction cost is often the dominant component in the construction cost of the signal processing equipment, hence our primary economic index is derivable from the operating principle.

Of the gain indices we shall pay particular attention to the group of:

Distortion indices for losses incurred by the user of the information system as a result of distortion caused by that system.

We treat distortion indices as a subgroup of B′ gain indices, since the eventual gains made by the user as a result of possessing information depend essentially on the degree to which the information is distorted during its passage through the system. As with cost indices, the distortion indices usually depend not only on the properties of the information system but also on the properties of the higher level system. In order to analyse, as far as is possible, the operating rule of the information system independently of the higher level system we again introduce secondary indices. A typical example of such an index is the delay of information caused by the system. Although they have obvious advantages, secondary indices are often difficult to compare, so it can be difficult to judge whether useful changes in one index are balanced out by adverse changes in another. However by returning to primary economic indices, these difficulties usually disappear.

Even after the introduction of secondary indices, great difficulties often arise in the analysis of the information system as a whole. Therefore we try to examine separately the secondary indices for the individual subsystems of the system by decomposing the analysis and design task into a group of tasks, one for each subsystem. It is not normally possible to bring about a complete decomposition; we can, however, frequently reduce the mutual interaction of the various subsystems to the interdependence of a small number of parameters. We shall give numerous examples of this procedure in later chapters. The situation is relatively straightforward where indices characterising the construction costs of the system are concerned, because we can, to a good approximation, treat the construction cost as the sum of the construction costs of the subsystems.

The situation is more difficult with distortion indices from where there are strong, and often complicated interactions between the subsystems.

1.5.2 Methodology for defining the quality indices

Quality indices are usually defined in two stages. First we introduce a primary index the value of which generally depends not only on the operating rule for the system but also on other factors which are not normally known *a priori.* In the second stage we introduce an operation to remove any dependence on unknown factors and to produce a secondary index. The choice of this operation obviously depends fundamentally on the unknown factors. Therefore we begin by discussing models of these factors which can be parameters, sets of parameters or functions. We use the term quantities for these factors.

The basic model of indeterministic quantities is the probabilistic one, where the unknown quantity is treated as the realisation of a random variable or random process. However, the probabilistic model is not always sufficient hence we classify the system depending upon the knowledge of the probability distribution of the quantity we are interested in. There are two possibilities:

(1) Probability distribution exists (abbreviation E).
(2) Probability distribution does not exist (abbreviation NE).

The first possibility occurs when we are concerned with single unrepeatable observations. We have two further possibilities as regards our knowledge of the quantity and its distribution:

(3) The quantity is known (abbreviation K).
(4) The quantity is not known (abbreviation NK).

Using these four possibilities, we can classify various situations in which unknown quantities are involved. Figure 1.17 shows this classification. The situations illustrated there are divided into levels. On level 1 we have the quantity which interests us. If we know it, we have situation 1.1 and we say that the quantity is determined. If we do not know it, we have situation 1.2, leading to situation: 2.0, the probability distribution of an unknown quantity exists, and 1.3, it does not exist. In situation 1.3 we cannot say anything about the statistical properties of our quantity, we can only know the set of values which this quantity can take.

On level 2, if we know the distribution, we have situation 2.1 and we say that we have complete statistical information about the quantity which interests us, or, in other words, we can apply the Bayes model to that quantity. If we do not know the distribution, then we introduce the concept of the distribution of distributions. If such a distribution does not exist, we have situation 2.3, which is analogous to situation 1.3.

Consider the situation 3.1, where the distribution of distributions exists, and we know it. On the basis of the marginal probability formula, we can calculate the probability density of the quantity we are interested in , so that situation 3.1 reduces to situation 2.1. Obviously, the problem is similar in situation 4.1 etc. Thus situation 2.1 differs fundamentally from situations 1.3, 2.3 etc.

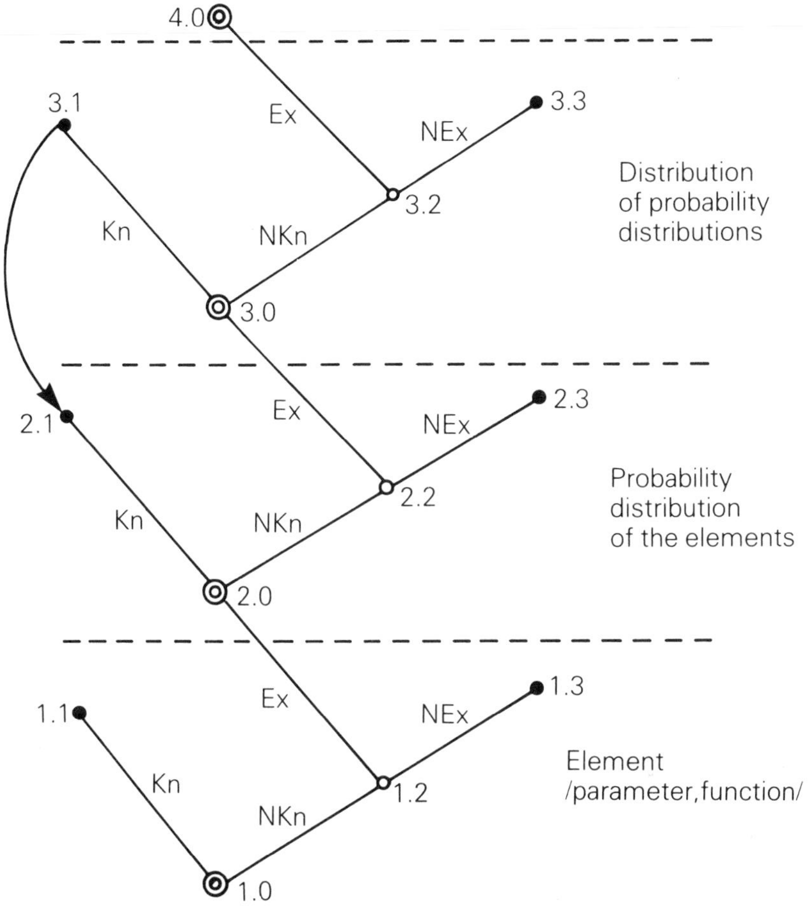

Fig. 1.17 – Classification of situations in which unknown quantities are involved. K = known; NK = not known; E = exists; NE = does not exist.

In general, the primary quality index of a subsystem depends on the mode of operation of the given subsystem and on a certain set of unknown quantities. If $\boldsymbol{a}$ is the set of parameters or function defining this mode and $\boldsymbol{\omega}$ is the set of unknown quantities, we can write down the primary quality index as the function $Q^*(\boldsymbol{a},\boldsymbol{\omega})$. We shall now derive the secondary quality index of the subsystem $Q(\boldsymbol{a})$. To remove the dependence on $\boldsymbol{\omega}$ we introduce the operation $\underset{\omega}{U}$ which we call a **dependence-removing operation.** This operation, acting on the function $Q^*(\boldsymbol{a},\boldsymbol{\omega})$, gives us the function $Q(\boldsymbol{a})$ which is dependent only on $\boldsymbol{a}$:

$$Q(\boldsymbol{a}) \equiv \underset{\omega}{U} Q^*(\boldsymbol{a},\boldsymbol{\omega}) \quad . \tag{1.5.1}$$

The choice of $\underset{\omega}{U}$ depends both on the model of unknown quantities and on the properties of the system we are considering. We shall now illustrate the choice of $\underset{\omega}{U}$ by some examples.

If we have complete statistical information for $\boldsymbol{\omega}$, and we are interested in the long-term behaviour of the system, we choose:

$$\underset{\omega}{U} = \underset{\Omega}{E} \tag{1.5.2}$$

where E is the statistical averaging with respect to the random variable or random process Ω. Definition (1.5.2) leads to the secondary critical function

$$Q(\boldsymbol{a}) = \underset{\Omega}{E}\, Q^*(\boldsymbol{a},\boldsymbol{\Omega}) \tag{1.5.3}$$

Now let us consider the case in which we cannot apply the model with complete statistical information. Let us assume first that the set $\boldsymbol{\omega}$ is given by $\boldsymbol{\omega}_m$, $m = 1, 2, \ldots, M$, i.e. the unknown quantities can have only a finite number of states. We can then frequently introduce the weights α_m which characterise the set $\boldsymbol{\alpha}_m$ so that:

$$\sum_{m=1}^{M} \alpha_m = 1 \tag{1.5.4}$$

whereas the actual values of the function $Q^*(\boldsymbol{a},\boldsymbol{\omega}_m)$ are weighted by means of a power function. This tends to the secondary criterion:

$$Q_\beta(\boldsymbol{a}) \equiv \sum_{m=1}^{M} \alpha_m [Q^*(\boldsymbol{a},\boldsymbol{\omega}_m)]^\beta \;{}^{1/\beta} \tag{1.5.5}$$

where $\beta \geqslant 1$ is a parameter. In the particular case $\beta = 1$ we get the weighted mean

$$Q_1(\boldsymbol{a}) \equiv \sum_{m=1}^{M} \alpha_m\, Q^*(\boldsymbol{a},\boldsymbol{\omega}_m) \tag{1.5.6}$$

If we take the model with complete statistical information for $\boldsymbol{\omega}$, the function $Q(\boldsymbol{a})$ given by equation (1.5.6) will have the same form as in (1.5.3), whereby

$$\alpha_m = P(\boldsymbol{\Omega} = \boldsymbol{\omega}_m)\ . \tag{1.5.7}$$

In practice if we do not know the probabilities $P(\boldsymbol{\Omega} = \boldsymbol{\omega}_m)$, we can often take the empirical frequencies of occurrence of the set $\boldsymbol{\omega}_m$ in place of α_m.

The secondary criterial function $Q_1(\boldsymbol{a})$ does not take into consideration the scattering of values of the function $Q^*(\boldsymbol{a},\boldsymbol{\omega}_m)$ hence we introduce:

$$Q_2(\boldsymbol{a}) \equiv \left[\sum_{m=1}^{M} \alpha_m [Q^*(\boldsymbol{a},\boldsymbol{\omega}_m)]^2\right]^{1/2}\ . \tag{1.5.8}$$

By using the mean $Q_1(\mathbf{a})$ given in (1.5.6), we can write (1.5.8) thus:

$$Q_2(\mathbf{a}) = \sqrt{Q_1^2(\mathbf{a}) + \sum_{m=1}^{M} \alpha_m [Q^*(\mathbf{a},\boldsymbol{\omega}_m) - Q_1(\mathbf{a})]^2} \tag{1.5.9}$$

where $Q_1^2(\mathbf{a})$ is the square of the weighted mean value of the function $Q^*(\mathbf{a},\boldsymbol{\omega}_m)$, and the second term is the weighted square of the scattering.

Taking values of $\beta > 1$ in (1.5.5) we place greater weight on large values of the function $Q^*(\mathbf{a},\boldsymbol{\omega}_m)$. In the limiting case

$$\lim_{\beta\to\infty} Q_\beta(\mathbf{a}) = \max_m Q^*(\mathbf{a},\boldsymbol{\omega}_m) \; . \tag{1.5.10}$$

This function can be interpreted as the result of applying, to $Q^*(\mathbf{a},\boldsymbol{\omega}_m)$, the dependence-removing operations defined by:

$$\underset{\omega}{U} = \max_{\omega\in\Omega} \tag{1.5.11}$$

We shall now give two examples to illustrate the concepts introduced here.

Example 1.5.1 – The quality index of the information recovery rule

Consider the channel in Fig.1.18. $X^*(\cdot)$ is the rule for recovering the information, x^*, from the signal, $\mathbf{y}$, at the channel output, thus $x^* = X^*(\mathbf{y})$.

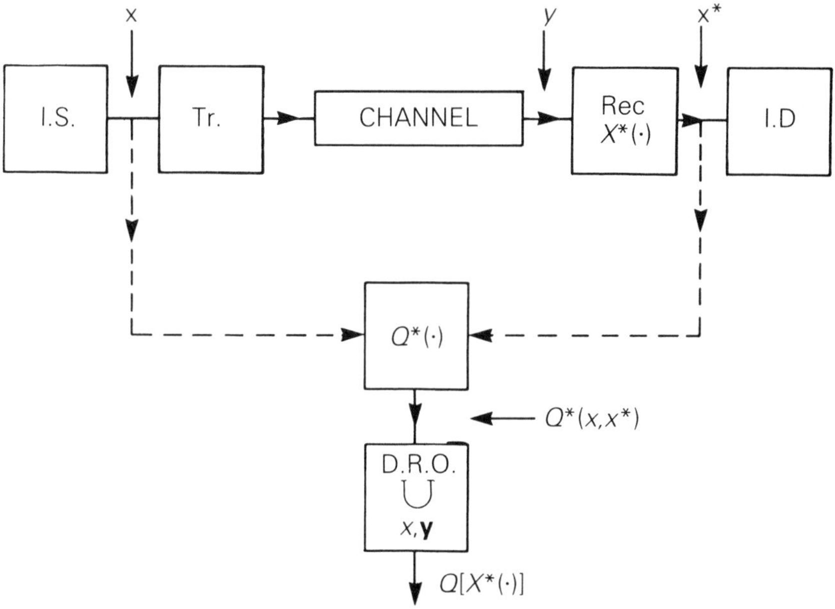

Fig. 1.18 – Illustration of the definition of the parameter characterising the rule $X^*(\cdot)$ of information recovery. I.S. = information source; Tr. = transmitter; D.R.O. = dependence removing operation.

Thus the loss amounts to $Q^*[x, X^*(\mathbf{y})]$. Both x and $\mathbf{y}$ must be treated as unknown quantities; thus $\boldsymbol{\omega} = (x, \mathbf{y})$. Let $\underset{x,\mathbf{y}}{U}$ be the operation to remove the dependence on x and $\mathbf{y}$, giving:

$$Q[X^*(\cdot)] = \underset{x,\mathbf{y}}{U}\, Q^*[x, X^*(\mathbf{y})] \ . \tag{1.5.12}$$

If we have complete statistical information on x and $\mathbf{y}$, and the system is used frequently we may use the statistical averaging operation for $\underset{x,\mathbf{y}}{U}$ thus:

$$Q[X^*(\cdot)] = \underset{\mathrm{X},\mathbf{Y}}{E}\, Q^*[\mathrm{X}, X^*(\mathbf{Y})] \tag{1.5.13}$$

where $\mathrm{X},\mathbf{Y}$ is a random variable modelling $x, \mathbf{y}$. In the particular case where the loss is symmetrical

$$Q[X^*(\cdot)] = P[\mathrm{X} \neq X^*(\mathbf{Y})] \ . \tag{1.5.14}$$

so $Q[X^*(\cdot)]$ is the probability of taking a wrong decision.

Example 1.5.2 – The quality index of a set of routing rules

Consider a network of channels with N poles. Let $\mathcal{R}_{sr}$ be the rule for choosing a route, P_{sr}, from source s to receiving node r; $s, r = 1, 2, \ldots, N$, $s \neq r$. The routing depends on the n.s.i. $\boldsymbol{\xi}$, thus $P_{sr} = \mathcal{R}_{sr}(\boldsymbol{\xi})$.

The time elapsing from the instant the packet was delivered by the source s to the instant when it reaches the destination r, called briefly 'delay', is used as the primary parameter. This delay can be written as:

$$\tau_1(P_{sr}, \boldsymbol{\sigma}_{sr}) = \sum_{(u,v)\in P_{sr}} \tau_1[(u,v), \boldsymbol{\sigma}(u,v)] \tag{1.5.15}$$

where† (u,v) denote the channel; $\boldsymbol{\sigma}(u,v)$ the state of the channel including the input buffer and $\boldsymbol{\sigma}_{sr} = (\boldsymbol{\sigma}(u,v); (u,v) \in P_{sr})$ the state of the path along which the packet is being sent.

In terms of the routing rule the delay is $\tau_1[\mathcal{R}_{sr}(\boldsymbol{\xi}), \boldsymbol{\sigma}_{sr}]$. Like the previous example we take $\underset{\xi,v}{U}$ as the statistical averaging operation. Thus our primary parameter is the average delay:

$$\tau[\mathcal{R}_{sr}(\cdot)] = \underset{\Xi,\Sigma_{sr}}{E}\, \tau_1[\mathcal{R}_{sr}(\boldsymbol{\Xi}, \boldsymbol{\Sigma}_{sr})] \tag{1.5.16}$$

† Throughout this book symbols related to a path are denoted by a symbol with subscripts indicating the first and last node of the path, e.g. σ_{sr}, while symbols related to channels we denote by symbols followed by brackets containing the channels input and output nodes, e.g. $\sigma(u,v)$.

where Ξ, Σ_{sr} are random variables or processes representing ξ and σ_{sr}. The operation of the whole network is described by the set of routing rules

$$\mathbf{R}(\cdot) \equiv [R_{sr}(\cdot);\ s,r = 1,2,\ldots,N \quad s \neq r] \tag{1.5.17}$$

and the delay parameter (with the dependence on s,r removed) is:

$$\bar{\tau}[\mathbf{R}(\cdot)] = \underset{s,r}{U} \tau [R_{sr}(\cdot)] \ . \tag{1.5.18}$$

If we take the operation of weighted summation (1.4.6) for U we obtain:

$$\bar{\tau}[\mathbf{R}(\cdot)] = \sum_{s=1}^{N} \sum_{\substack{r=1 \\ s \neq r}}^{N} \alpha_{sr} \tau [R_{sr}(\cdot)] \tag{1.5.19}$$

We often take α_{sr} as the relative flow intensity of the packets sent between this pair of poles, where:

$$\alpha_{sr} = \frac{X_{sr}}{\sum_{i=1}^{N} \sum_{\substack{j=1 \\ j \neq i}}^{N} X_{ij}} \tag{1.5.20}$$

and X_{sr} is the average intensity of flow from sr.

Often we are interested in the worst case delay so we use the operation defined by (1.5.11) to give:

$$\tau[\mathbf{R}(\cdot)] = \max_{s,r} \tau [R_{s,r}(\cdot)] \tag{1.5.21}$$

1.6 NETWORK OPTIMISATION PROBLEMS

In this section we describe a methodology for formulating optimisation problems. We consider the hierarchy of optimisation problems which arise in the design of a communications network for a remote processing system, and the links between these problems. Finally we present an outline of the remainder of the book.

1.6.1 Methodology for formulating optimisation problems

The operating rule of a system is determined by a set of parameters or functions, denoted by a and known as the describing set. The set of permissible describing sets for a system is determined by the constraints imposed on the operating rule and is denoted by A. We optimise for the routing rule by introducing an ordering relation in the set A such that we can find a set, $\mathbf{a}_0 \in A$, where $\mathbf{a}_0 \geqslant \mathbf{a}\ \forall\ \mathbf{a} \in A$. In practice, we introduce an ordering relation, based on the quality indices discussed in the previous section, by means of the synthetic index Q_{synt}, and by saying that $\mathbf{a}_i > \mathbf{a}_j$ if $Q_{\text{synt}}(\mathbf{a}_i) < Q_{\text{synt}}(\mathbf{a}_j)$. The index Q_{synt} which can be interpreted as the net gain to the system's owner, is a function of the secondary indices,

$$Q_{\text{synt}} \equiv F(Q_1, Q_2, \ldots, Q_j) \qquad (1.6.1)$$

where Q_j, $j = 1, \ldots, J$ are the secondary indices.

The optimisation is circumscribed by **technical feasibility constraints** denoted by $\mathcal{C}_{\text{tech}}$. These constraints comprise in particular the **physical feasibility constraints** $\mathcal{C}_{\text{ph}}$ which require that the decision made at a given instant depends only on events which happened in the past. The optimisation problem therefore assumes the form:

> In the set $\mathcal{A}$, which is determined by the technical feasibility constraints $\mathcal{C}_{\text{tech}}$, we have to find the set $\mathbf{a}_0$ for which the synthetic index achieves its extreme value (minimum or maximum, depending on the meaning of the index).

We denote this optimisation problem by† OP $\mathbf{a}, Q_{\text{synt}} \mid \mathcal{C}_{\text{tech}}$, with the obvious notation. However, for the same reasons as before, we prefer to formulate the optimisation problems in terms of the secondary indices. We do this in the following way:

(a) we consider one of the indices, which we denote by Q_1, to be the fundamental index;
(b) we require that the remaining indices, denoted by $Q_2, Q_3, \ldots, Q_J$ remain inside fixed intervals, or take fixed values – we denote this set of constraints by $\mathcal{C}_Q$.

The optimisation problem now takes the form:

> In the set of describing parameters $\mathbf{a}$ determined by the constraints $\mathcal{C}_Q$ and $\mathcal{C}_{\text{tech}}$ we have to find the set $\mathbf{a}_0$ for which the criterion Q_1 achieves its extreme value

which we denote by OP $\mathbf{a}, Q_1 \mid \mathcal{C}_Q, \mathcal{C}_{\text{tech}}$.

A third approach is to simultaneously take into account the set of quality indices $Q_1, Q_2, \ldots, Q_J$, and search for describing sets satisfying the constraints $\mathcal{C}_{\text{tech}}$ such that decreasing each index Q_j is possible only by simultaneously increasing at least one of the remaining indices. The set of describing sets having this property is called the set of **polyoptimal solutions** (or solutions optimal in the sense of Pareto).

† Here and subsequently we apply shorthand notation: Optimisation Problem – Variable – Criterion | Constraints.

1.6.2 Optimisation problem hierarchies

When designing a communications network in teleprocessing systems, a hierarchy of optimisation problems emerges, namely, the problems of optimising:

(1) the rules for feeding signals into a channel or subchannel used for sending signals from just one source, especially those for modulation, coding and acknowledgements;
(2) the rules for feeding signals into a common channel, especially for muli-access, multiplexing and subchannel assignment;
(3) the rules for forwarding a packet through the network, especially routing and flow controls;
(4) the choice of the channel and subchannel capacities in the network;
(5) the choice of the network topology.

The first three of these problems relate to the design of a node in a teleprocessing network, and the other two relate to the design of the network as a whole.

We now give some examples to illustrate the above-mentioned problems. As the first example, we take the problem of optimisating the rule $X^*(\cdot)$ with index $Q[X^*(\cdot)]$ from Example (1.5.1). The optimisation problem for this rule can be written as OP $X^*(\cdot), Q \mid C_{\text{tech}}$, where C_{tech} are the constraints that the rule should be implemented by a certain type of equipment.

For our second example, we take the problem of optimising the channel capacity for sending packets with fixed statistical properties from a single source through a single channel, i.e. problem (1). Such a problem can arise in the point-to-point transmission of packets, or as an isolated problem in the general task of network optimisation.

We further assume that the rule for feeding packets into a channel is fixed and consists of FIFO-type buffering. As critical function we take a synthetic quality index defined by:

$$Q \equiv \kappa_1 - \kappa_2 \tag{1.6.4}$$

where κ_1 is the charge the owner of the system makes to the user for sending the information, and κ_2 is the cost which the owner incurs in sending the information. We assume that the charge κ_1 depends chiefly on the delay τ with which the information is delivered, which we indicate by writing $\kappa_1(\tau)$. For very small τ, the delay is negligible to the user, so the owner of the system can make the maximum possible charge. As τ increases, the value of the information to the user decreases because it is not so up-to-date, so the system's owner is forced to charge less. If the delay is very great, the information may be completely useless to the user, and so he cannot be charged. This relationship is illustrated in Fig. 1.19(a).

The costs which the owner of the system incurs chiefly depend upon the channel capacity C which we indicate by writing $\kappa_2(C)$. A typical graph of the

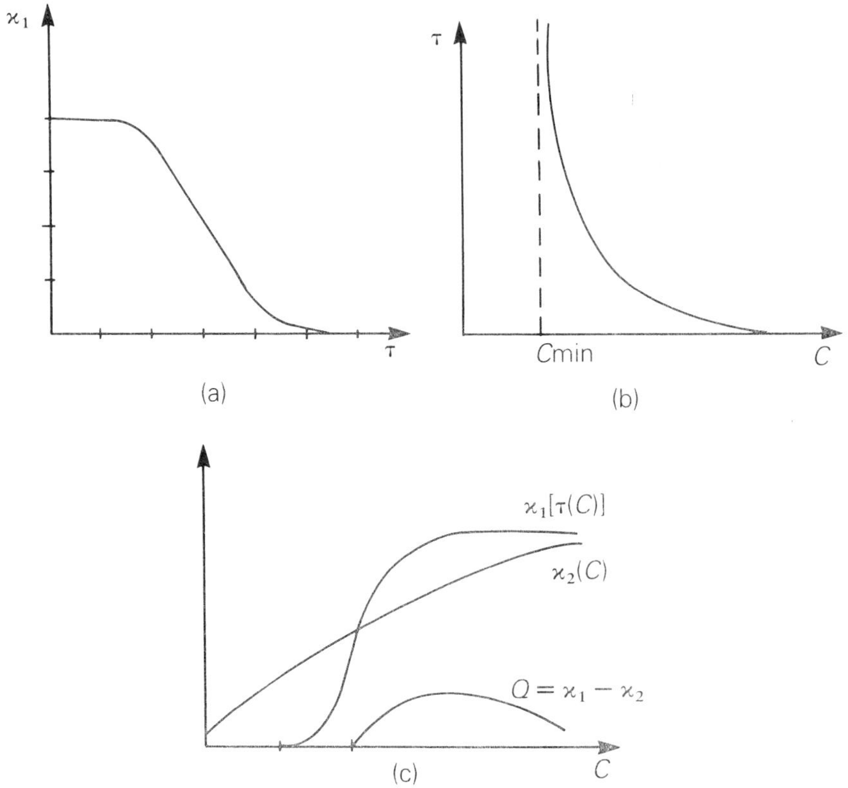

Fig. 1.19 – Typical dependences of: (a) charge κ_1 the owner of the system makes to the user on the average information delay τ_1; (b) the average delay τ on channel capacity C; (c) cost κ_2 incurred by the owner for renting the channel, the charge $\kappa_1[\tau(C)]$, and the profit on the channels.

function $\kappa_2(C)$ is shown in Fig. 1.19(c). If the transmission rule and statistical properties of the information are fixed, τ depends primarily on the capacity C. A typical relationship is shown in Fig. 1.19(b). The parameter $C_{\min}$ can often be interpreted as the mean rate of sending information. Since the delay τ is a function of the capacity, and since the profit depends on τ, the profit ultimately depends on C. The relationship $\kappa_1[\bar{\tau}(C)]$ resulting from Figs. 1.19(a) and (b) is shown in Fig. 1.19(c). We see that the optimisation problem OP CQ has a unique solution.

We now give an example of optimising the set of routing rules $\boldsymbol{R}(\cdot) = (R_{sr}(\cdot), s \neq r)$ which we considered in Example 1.5.2. We shall assume that.

(1) the statistical properties of the information sources are given;
(2) the topology of the connections and the set $\boldsymbol{C} = (C_1, \ldots, C_K)$ of channel capacities C_k, $k = 1, \ldots, K$ are given;

(3) as criterial function we take τ as defined by 1.5.21.

The optimisation problem defined by these constraints can be written in the form OP$\boldsymbol{R}(\cdot), \tau \mid C_{\text{tech}}$.

1.6.3 Relationship between the optimisation problems

The sequencing of optimisation problems introduced on page 57 corresponds to the hierarchy of these problems. Often the higher numbered problems are not relevant because the properties of the network to which they pertain are fixed. For example, the connection topology and the channel capacities may be predetermined, so that we can only choose the rules of node operation, i.e. only problems (1), (2), and (3) occur.

It is important to note that we cannot always decompose a higher numbered problem into a set of simpler, lower numbered, problems. By way of example, let us take the (type 2) problem of optimising a set $\boldsymbol{S}(\cdot) = (S_m(\cdot), m = 1,2,\ldots,M)$ of rules for feeding signals generated by local transmitters into a common channel. As criterion, we take the delay and we assume that the properties C_{COM} of the common channel are fixed thus OP$\boldsymbol{S}(\cdot), \bar{\tau} \mid C_{\text{COM}}$ arises. The optimisation problem for an isolated subsystem consisting of a local transmitter and a channel CH_m, carrying signals from this transmitter to the common channel, is a problem of type 1 and can be written in the form OP $S_m(\cdot)$ $\tau_m \mid C_{CH_m}$ where τ_m is the parameter characterising the delay of packets transmitted by the mth local transmitter. The problem OP $\boldsymbol{S}(\cdot)$, $\bar{\tau} \mid C_{\text{COM}}$ can be regarded as the set OP $\boldsymbol{S}_m(\cdot)$, $\bar{\tau} \mid C_m$, where C_m is the mth virtual subchannel, but we cannot directly use the solution of problems from level 1 to solve this set of problems. The difficulty is that for a multiaccess system the properties of a virtual channel for the mth transmitter depend on the transmission rules of the remaining local transmitters. If we assume, that the system is homogeneous in the sense that the operating rules of all local transmitters are the same, then when changing the transmission rule of a given transmitter we also change the transmission rules of the remaining transmitters, and so change the properties of the virtual channel. The simultaneous consideration of both changes is usually very complicated and so we often apply an heuristic method to simplify optimisation problems of this type. This method is based on the principle of adaptation, which we now describe briefly. We first optimise the rule according to which the isolated subsystem operates assuming that the set of properties of this subsystem $\boldsymbol{\Pi}$, which is reality depends on other subsystems is fixed. The optimum operating rule for the subsystem usually is dependent on $\boldsymbol{\Pi}$, thus we denote this rule by $R_0\,[(\cdot), \boldsymbol{\Pi}]$.

Next we introduce auxiliary facilities which continuously estimate the properties $\boldsymbol{\Pi}$, initially assumed to be fixed and known. Let $\boldsymbol{\Pi}^*$ be these estimates. These estimates are based either on data which the subsystem obtains or on data about the properties of the system as a whole. Obviously, to realise this principle, we have to introduce an auxiliary subsystem for collecting and transmitting the auxiliary information required to derive $\mathbf{\Pi}^*$. The structure of the subsystem considered above is shown in Fig. 1.20.

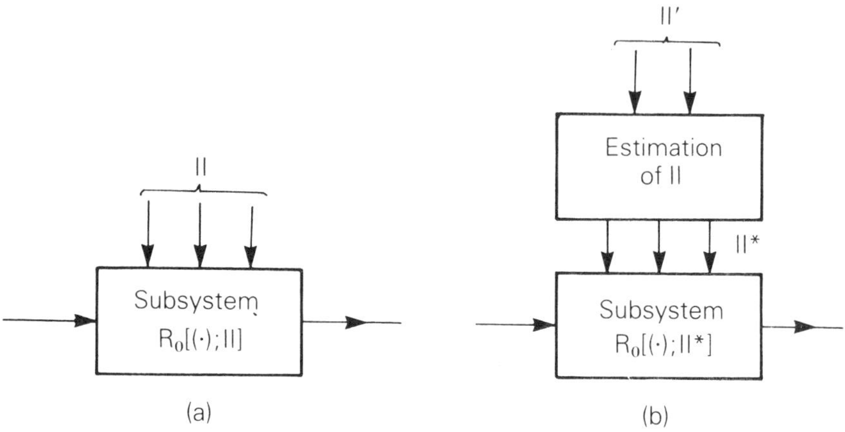

Fig. 1.20 – The structure of an adaptive system. Systems realising: (a) fixed optimum rule; (b) and adaptive rule. Π = set of properties of the subsystem considered depending on the states of other subsystems; Π' = the set of primary data about the other subsystems.

The principle of adaptation is frequently applied in practice. For example the routing rule used in the ARPA network is based on the assumption that the delays introduced by individual channels are constant and known. In reality, delays caused by channels are variable in time and are unknown in advance. The use of the principle of adaptation leads to the following rule:

(a) we estimate the packet time through the individual channels;
(b) we treat these estimates as real, fixed packet passage times, and we find the route for which the total estimated time is as small as possible.

1.7 OUTLINE OF THE BOOK

In this book we present a number of problems of computer communication network analysis and optimisation. The book consists of two parts. In the first comprising Chapters 2, 3 and 4 we consider systems with a common channel, in the second, comprising Chapters 5, 6, 7 and 8 we deal with mesh networks. The necessary mathematical background and details of more lengthy calculations are given in appendices. We pay great attention to common channel systems for three reasons. Firstly, they are used for autonomous systems and for almost isolated component subsystems in a larger system. Secondly, the system with a single channel and several users can be considered as an approximate model of a node and a channel in a general mesh-type computer communications system. Thirdly, by analysing and optimising the multiaccess system, we encounter and can explain most of the problems of sharing information transportation resources between many users.

When considering the transmission of information through the common channel, we will emphasise the role of the information about the state of the system (s.s.i.). The material in Chapters 2, 3 and 4 is ordered according to the amount of system state information which is used. In Chapter 2, after a general introduction to the problems of remote access, we consider systems in which little or no s.s.i. is used. These are systems with separated subchannels and systems with free access in which a user enters the common channel without taking other users into account.

In Chapters 3 and 4, we deal with remote access systems with a single channel in which system state information is used. We consider first the simplest system in which we still apply free access, but a feedback channel provides information about the quality of transmission through the common channel. Then in Chapter 4 we deal with a variety of systems in which auxiliary information about state of local transmitters is available. These are systems with so-called carrier-sensing, polling and reservation.

The last part of Chapter 4 is devoted to loop systems in which the information sources and local transmitters are located along the common channel. Again, various types of organisation of local transmitter operation will be considered.

Chapters 5, 6 and 7 are devoted to the problem of routing packets through a network. In Chapter 5, we start with algorithms for finding the shortest path in a directed graph. These algorithms are useful in subsequent parts of the book, for solving routing rule optimisation, and channel capacity assignment and optimisation problems. Next we consider fixed routing in a network whose state is known precisely and in a network with complete statistical information available. Of course, such models are oversimplified, but they are good starting points for determining efficient routing rules for more exact models of real networks in which we take into account the lack of knowledge of the network state. Here we use the general principle of adaptation formulated previously.

If the statistical properties of the information sources are known and the rule for routing the individual packet is given, we can evaluate the less detailed properties of the packet flow, in particular the pattern of average intensities of flows passing through the network channels. Further, if we introduce an index characterising the quality of the flow pattern in such a way that this index is an increasing function of the index characterising the quality of the rule for routing a single packet, then the optimum flow pattern will correspond to the optimum routing rule. This observation can be very useful in the search for the best possible routing rule when we cannot solve its optimisation problem directly.

In Chapter 6 we therefore consider the problems of optimising the average flow through a network. We start with constraints imposed on the flow and then go on to its optimisation. We shall also deal with the optimisation of the average flow described by the relative intensities of flows coming out of a node. Such a description of the average flow corresponds to the decentralised routing of a packet from node to node. Finally we will present a methodology for finding the routing for individual packets based on the optimum average flow.

When designing a routing rule, we usually have to take into account the fact that the total loading of the network varies, so we have to introduce measures easing the adverse effects of overloading; these will also be discussed in Chapter 7. We will start with a classification of methods of congestion control and then consider the most important ones in more detail.

In the chapters mentioned above we assume that the network topology and the channel capacities are given; thus we deal with the optimisation problems on levels 2 and 3 mentioned on page 57. In the last chapter we shall discuss problems of channel capacity optimisation, and topology, i.e. problems on levels 4 and 5. We start with relatively simple problems of optimising tree network capacities. For such networks it is also possible to give efficeint algorithms for determining the topology of the tree network. Next, we shall deal with the problem of finding optimum capacities of channels in a mesh network having a fixed topology.

REFERENCES

[1.1] Abramson, N., and Kuo, F. F., (eds.), (1972), *Computer Communication Networks*, Prentice-Hall, Englewood Cliffs.

[1.2] Schwartz, M., (1977), *Computer Communication Network Design and Analysis*, Prentice-Hall, Englewood Cliffs.

[1.3] Davies, D. W., and Barber, D. L. A., (1976), *Communication Networks for Computers*, Wiley, London.

[1.4] Hobbs, L. C., (1972), Terminals, *Proc. IEEE*, **60**, 1273–1284.

[1.5] Fuchs, E., and Jackson, P. E., (1970), Estimates of distributions of random variables for certain computer communications traffic models, *Comm. of ACM*, **13**, 752–757.

[1.6] Dedick, A. L., Fuchs, E., and Jackson, P. E., (1971), Data traffic measurements for inquiry – response computer communication systems, *Proc. of the IFIP Congress Ljubljana, 1971, Booklet TA-4, Hardware and Systems*, 79–83.

[1.7] Zadeh, L. A., and Miller, K. S. (1952), Fundamental aspects of linear multiplexing, *Proc. I.R.E.*, **40**, 1091–1097.

[1.8] Doll, D., (1978), *Multiplexing and Concentration*, Prentice-Hall, Englewood Cliffs.

[1.9] Kleinrock, L., (1975), *Queueing Systems*, 2 vols., Wiley, New York.

2

Open systems with a common channel

In this and the next two chapters we consider systems with a common channel, arranged according to the amount of s.s.i. used for making access decisions. Here we discuss the simplest open systems in which no information about the state of the common channel is available. Firstly, we consider in more detail the parameters characterising the system, in particular the delay they introduce. Next we analyse the systems with centralised signal formation, namely systems with a common buffer and systems with separated orthogonal subchannels and fixed subchannel assignment. In the following two subsections we deal with open systems with decentralised signal formation using continuous and pulsed signals. Since no s.s.i. is used in these systems they may be also called open free access systems.

2.1 PARAMETERS CHARACTERISING THE SYSTEM

The general considerations from section 1.5 on the parameters characterising information systems apply directly to the multiaccess systems. We consider first the delay which is the fundamental distortion index. Next we deal with other distortion indices and finally with cost indices.

2.1.1 Parameters characterising the delay

To define the parameters characterising the delay we must specify the operations performed on the signal. Our considerations will be quite general, so that they are applicable to the more sophisticated remote access systems which we will consider in the two subsequent chapters. The general block diagram of the source–destination link is shown in Fig. 2.1.

The primary block delivered by the source is stored in the input memory. From here it is transferred to the buffer and then to the transmitter whose first component is the coder, and the second the modulator. In the coder a packet consisting of bits is formed. Then bit by bit it is transferred to the modulator. The transfer of signals is controlled by the node control unit (NCU). In the case of an open system the decisions of NCU are based solely on the local information

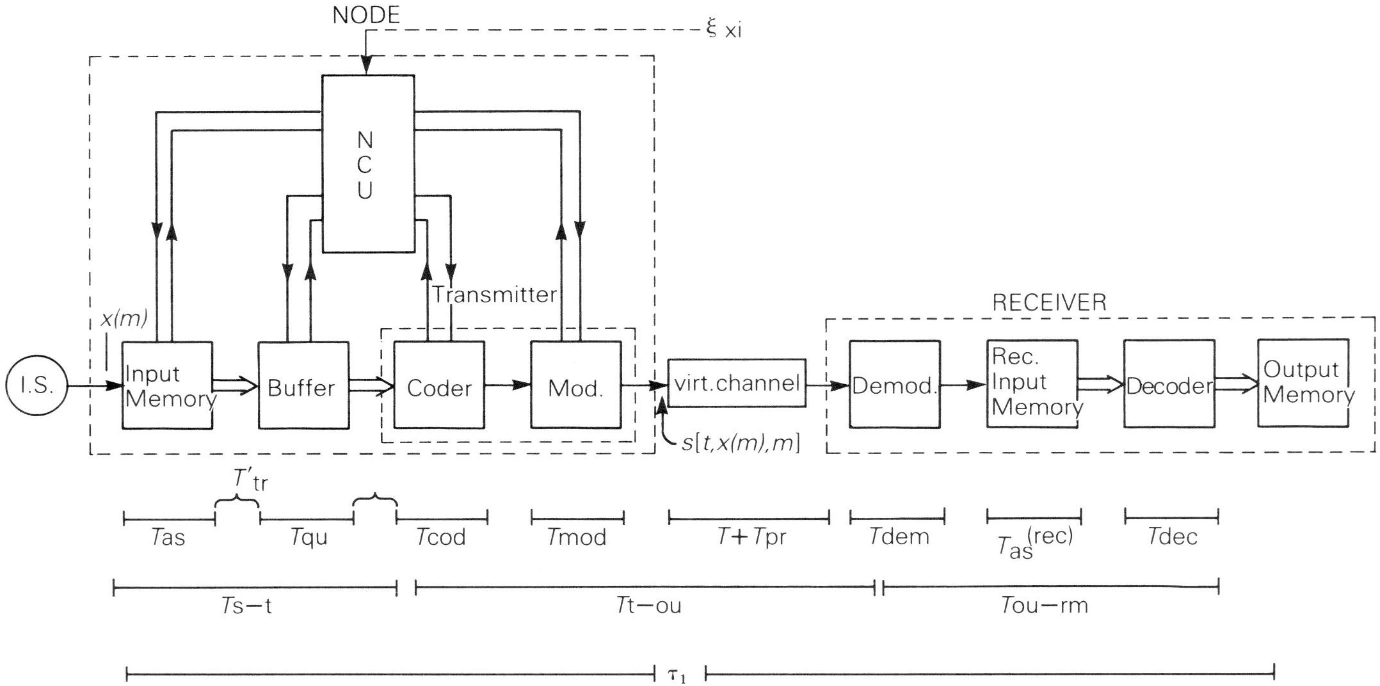

Fig. 2.1 – Model of a link in a multiaccess system. NCU = node control unit; Mod. = modulator; virt. channel = virtual channel; Demod. = demodulator; τ_1 = packets delay; T_{as} = assembly time; T_{qu} = queueing time; T = signal duration; T_{pr} = propagation time; T_{tr} = transfer times; T_{s-t} = source transmitter; T_{t-ou} = transmitter–channel output; T_{ou-rm} = channel output - receiver output memory.

about the state of all the components of the node. In other systems the system state information ξ is also available and used. At the output of the virtual channel we have the receiver with its components indicated on Fig. 2.1.

We call the time elapsing from the instant when the primary packets is stored in input memory to the instant when the recovered packet is stored in the reciever's output memory the **packet delay.** Denoting the delay by τ_1 we have

$$\tau_1 = T_{s-t} + T_{t-ou} + T_{ou-rm} \tag{2.1.1}$$

where

T_{s-t} is the time elapsing from the instant when the primary packet was delivered by the source to the instant when it is put in the transmitter source–transmitter transfer time; (hence the subscript s–t);

T_{t-ou} is the time elapsing from the instant when the packet was put in the transmitter to the instant when it is completely delivered to the output of the channel transmitter – channel output transfer time – (hence the subscript t–ou);

T_{ou-rm} is the time elapsing from the instant when the packet arrived at the channel output to the instant when the primary block is stored in the receiver's output memory (hence the subscript ou–rm).

We have

$$T_{s-t} = T_{as} + T_{qu} + T'_{tr} \tag{2.1.2a}$$

$$T_{t-ou} = T_{cod} + T_{mod} + T + T_{pr} + T''_{tr} \tag{2.1.2b}$$

$$T_{ou-rm} = T_{dem} + T_{dec} + T'''_{tr} \tag{2.1.2c}$$

where

T_{as} is the time required to assemble the primary packet in the input memory;
T_{qu} is the time spent by the packet in the queue in the buffer (queueing delay);
T_{cod} is the introduced by the coder;
T_{mod} is the delay introduced by the modulator;
T is the duration of the signal carrying the packet through the channel;
T_{pr} is the propagation time through the channel;
T_{dem} is the delay introduced by the demodulator;
T_{dec} is the delay introduced by the decoder;
T'_{tr}, T''_{tr}, T'''_{tr} are the total times of transferring the signal between the blocks forming the chains s–tr, tr–ou, ou–rm.

The times defined are illustrated on Fig. 2.1. The double lines represent parallel data transmission, since it is usually very rapid T'_{tr}, T''_{tr}, T'''_{tr}, T_{cod}, T_{dec} are negligibly small compared with other components. Delays introduced by the modulator and demodulator are about a bit duration, thus also small. The essential component of the delay introduced by the receiver is the time taken to store the signal in the input memory which is approximately equal to signal duration T. However, the received packet can be registered a byte at a time as the signal is still being fed into the channel. Therefore, if we take into account the time of feeding the signal into the channel, which is equal to signal duration T, we do not need to include the time taken to store the signal at the receiver's input memory a component of packet delay. From the above remarks it follows that the delay

$$\tau_1 = T_{as} + T_{qu} + T_{tr} + T + T_{pr} \tag{2.1.3}$$

where T_{tr} is the total time of transferring the signal between node components.

Analysing and comparing various systems it is convenient to use the normalised delay

$$\tau_1' \equiv \frac{\tau_1 - T_c}{T_{ref}} \tag{2.1.4}$$

where T_c is a constant component of delay independent of the system.

> We call the reference time, T_{ref}, the minimum duration of the signal carrying the packet through the common channel, on the assumption that the channel is used only for transmission of that packet. (2.1.5)

Usually we take

$$T_{con} = T_{pr} \tag{2.1.6}$$

The delay depends in general on the information $x(m)$ the packet is carrying, the state $\boldsymbol{\sigma}$ of the system and on the access rule $S_m(\cdot)$. Thus we can write $\tau_1\{S_m[x(m)_1\xi],\boldsymbol{\sigma}\}$. Removing the dependence on $x(m)$ and $\boldsymbol{\sigma}$ (see point 1.5) we obtain the parameter characterising the rule $S_m(\cdot)$ from the point of view of packet delay. We denote it by $\tau[S_m(\cdot)]$. If we apply the model with complete statistical information and take as DR statistical averaging, using (2.1.3) we obtain

$$\tau[S_m(\cdot)] = \bar{T}_{as} + \bar{T}_{qu} + \bar{T}_{tr} + \bar{T} + T_{pr} \tag{2.1.7}$$

The symbols with the bar denote statistical averages.

The operation of all local transmitters is described by the set of rules

$$\boldsymbol{S}(\cdot) \equiv (S_m(\cdot); \quad m = 1, 2, \ldots, M) \ .$$

To obtain the parameter $\bar{\tau}[\boldsymbol{S}(\cdot)]$ characterising the set of rules $\boldsymbol{S}(\cdot)$ we have to remove the dependence of $\tau[S_m(\cdot)]$ on m. Introducing the weighting coefficients α_m similarly to (1.5.19) we define:

$$\bar{\tau}[S(\cdot)] = \sum_{m=1}^{M} \alpha_m \tau[S_m(\cdot)] \quad . \tag{2.1.8}$$

Assuming 2.1.7 we obtain the normalised delay

$$\tau'[S_m(\cdot)] = \frac{\bar{T}_{as} + \bar{T}_{qu} + \bar{T}_{tr} + \bar{T}}{T_{ref}} \quad . \tag{2.1.9}$$

In open systems the total transfer time is negligible, thus the normalised delay is

$$\tau'[S_m(\cdot)] = \frac{\bar{T}_{as} + \bar{T}_{qu} + \bar{T}}{T_{ref}} \ldots \tag{2.1.10}$$

2.1.2 Other parameters characterising the system

The fundamental distortion index is the delay considered previously. The other distortion index is the probability of erroneous recovery of the information as defined by formula (1.5.14). The secondary parameter upon which this probability depends is the capacity C_m of the virtual channel linking the mth transmitter with an output of the common channel. The parameter characterising the set of transmission rules is the efficiency of using the common channel capacity

$$\zeta_c \equiv \frac{\sum_{m=1}^{M} C_m}{C} \tag{2.1.11}$$

C being† the common channel capacity.

An important parameter characterising distortions is P^- the probability of not admitting information into the system or rejecting before delivering to the destination. This is essentially a secondary parameter because the non-accepted message is usually stored in an external memory until it can be put into the system. The delay connected with such a procedure obviously depends essentially on P^-.

The secondary parameters characterising the construction cost of the system are the common channel capacity and the memory capacity of the buffers. If the

† Here and subsequently we denote the parameters characterising the subchannel with a subscript symbol usually 'm', with corresponding parameters for the common channel with the same symbol, but without a subscript.

channel capacity is fixed, the cost to the user of sending a bit of information is a decreasing function of the ratio

$$\nu \equiv \frac{X}{C} \tag{2.1.12}$$

where X (in bit/s) is the rate of information transmission through the common channel and C(bit/s) is the common channel capacity. We call ν the efficiency of channel utilisation and we take it as the fundamental secondary cost parameter.

2.2 SYSTEMS WITH CENTRALISED SIGNAL FORMATION

We consider now systems with a common buffer and transmitter and systems with fixed assignment of separated orthogonal subchannels using individual buffers.

Our interest in systems with fixed access and orthogonal subchannels is justified by their simplicity. In particular they require no addressing. The system can also be considered as a model for systems with decentralised signal formation using orthogonal signals not overlapping in time of frequency domains. We first consider the homogeneous system and next we deal with the optimum assignment of subchannel capacities in a non-homogeneous system.

2.2.1 Systems with a common buffer

We consider here the system shown in Fig. 1.5(a). If the capacity of the common buffer is sufficiently large, the probability of block non-acceptance can be made very small; but this happens at the expense of introducing queueing delay. Therefore we concentrate on the relationships between the common channel utilisation factor and the average delay. We must distinguish the packets coming from various sources placed in the common buffer. We do so by including the source number in the packet. To number the sources we need

$$N_{\text{ad}} \equiv \lceil \log_2 M \rceil \tag{2.2.1}$$

bits, where $\lceil u \rceil$ denotes the smallest integer greater than u.

We now consider a rule of system operation which is a modification of rule R1 from section 1.2.3:

R1 The source address is added to the primary information block delivered by the source. The packet formed is put into the common buffer. The queueing discipline is FIFO. As soon as a subchannel completes transmission, the packet at the head of the queue is put into that subchannel.

Analysing the system we assume

A1 The information delivered by the mth source is a sequence of blocks; the sequence of starting instants forms a Poisson process of intensity λ_m.

A2 A block consists of a fixed number N_m of bits.
A3 The sequences of blocks emitted by individual sources are statistically independent.
A4 The system is homogeneous, i.e. $\lambda_m = \lambda_1 = \text{const.}$, $N_m = N_1 = \text{const.}$, all subchannels have the same properties, the rules of feeding signals into the subchannels are the same:

From A2 it follows that the number of bits forming the packet is

$$N_p = N_{ad} + N_1 \quad . \tag{2.2.2}$$

We define:

$$\zeta_{ad} = \frac{N_\lambda}{N_p} \tag{2.2.3}$$

as the addressing efficiency.

Since the overlapping of independent Poisson sequences again yields a Poisson sequence, it follows from A1 and A3 that the starting instants of the packets arriving at the common buffer form a Poisson process of intensity

$$\lambda = \sum_{m=1}^{M} \lambda_m \quad . \tag{2.2.4}$$

Let C be the common channel capacity in bit/s, then:

$$T_1' = \frac{N_x + N_{ad}}{C} \tag{2.2.5}$$

is the duration of a packet together with its address:†

$$T_1 = \frac{N_x}{C} \tag{2.2.6}$$

would be the duration of the packet if it only carried the working information:

$$\nu' = \lambda T_2' \tag{2.2.7a}$$

is the duty ratio of the signals in the common channel, and:

$$\nu = \lambda T_2 \tag{2.2.7b}$$

is the common channel utilisation factor, taking into account the working information only.

† Parameters without primes (′) correspond to working information only and those with primes to working information plus additional factors such as addresses or guard space.

From (2.2.2) and (2.2.3) we have

$$\nu = \zeta_{ad}\nu' \ . \tag{2.2.8}$$

To obtain normalised delay we use (2.1.10). For the rule considered

$$\bar{T}_{as} = 0 \tag{2.2.9}$$

The queueing time is obtained from (A.1.36)

$$\bar{T}_{qu} = T_1' \frac{1}{2(1-\nu)} \tag{2.2.10}$$

and the reference time

$$T_{ref} = T_1 \tag{2.2.11}$$

From (2.1.10), (2.2.7)–(2.2.11) we obtain

$$\tau_{CB}' = \frac{1}{2}\frac{1}{\zeta_{ad}-\nu} + \frac{2}{\zeta_{ad}} \tag{2.2.12}$$

(suffix CB reminds us that we consider the system with a common buffer). The dependence of τ_{CB}' on ν is of the type

$$f(\tau) = \frac{1}{\zeta - \nu} + a \tag{2.2.13}$$

where $0 < \zeta < 1$, and $a > 0$ are two constants. Diagrams of $f(\tau)$ are shown in Fig. 2.2.

It is possible to split the common channel into $K > 1$ separate subchannels and to put the packet at the head of the common queue into a non-busy subchannel as soon as one is available. Such a system would be quite complicated, in particular we need to apply addressing. On the other hand it can be expected (and proved rigorously) that the delay for the previously considered system with the non-split common channel is smaller than for the system with a common buffer and separated subchannels. Therefore we will not consider such systems here.

In our reasoning we have assumed that the blocks are solid. We now take into account the hierarchic nature of information. Assuming that a block of order b is a set of blocks of order $b+1$, separated by idle intervals. The blocks of the highest order B are solid. For blocks of order b we denote:

$T_x(b)$ – the average duration of the block;
$N_x(b)$ – the average number of information bits carried by the block;
$N_{max}(b)$ – the maximum number of bits the block could carry if it were solid;

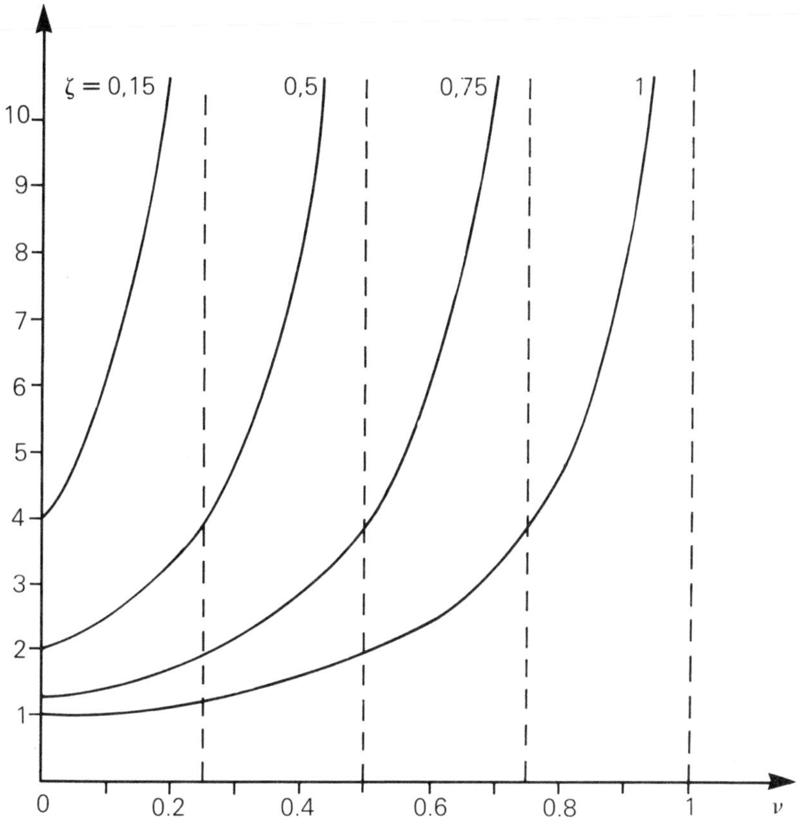

Fig 2.2 – Diagrams of function $(\zeta - \nu)^{-1} \tau a$.

$T_{b+1}(b)$ – the joint average duration of a block of order b consisting of blocks of order $b+1$.

We call

$$\nu_i(b) \equiv \frac{T_{b+1}(b)}{T_x(b)} \tag{2.2.14}$$

the internal duty ratio and

$$\zeta_x(b) = \frac{N_x(b)}{N_{\max}(b)} \tag{2.2.15}$$

block utilisation efficiency. From the definitions it follows that $\nu_i(B) = \zeta_x(B) = 1$, and

$$\zeta_x(b) = \nu_i(b)\,\nu_i(b+1)\,\ldots\,\nu_i(B-1) \tag{2.2.16}$$

We now assume that blocks are coded into packets, the block of order b being considered as solid. Let us denote by

$T(b)$ – the duration of the packet if it carried only the primary block (without address);

$T'(b)$ – the duration of the packet carrying the block and the address.

It is

$$T(b) = \frac{1}{C} N_{\max}(b) \tag{2.2.17a}$$

$$T'(b) = \frac{1}{C} (N^*_{\max}(b) + N_{\text{ad}}) \tag{2.2.17b}$$

The addressing efficiency

$$\zeta_a(b) = \frac{T(b)}{T'(b)} \tag{2.2.18}$$

From (2.2.17) we have

$$\zeta_a(b) = \frac{N_{\max}(b)}{N_{\max}(b) + N_{\text{ad}}} \tag{2.2.19}$$

Let $\nu'(b)$ be the duty ratio of the sequence of packets carrying blocks order b put into the channel. It is

$$\nu'(b) = \lambda(b)\, T'(b) \tag{2.2.20}$$

where $\lambda(b)$ is the intensity of blocks of order b. During a time T only $T\lambda(b)N(b)$ information bits are transmitted, but the channel could carry CT bits. Thus

$$\nu(b) = \frac{\lambda(b)N(b)}{C} \tag{2.2.21}$$

is the common channel utilisation. From (2.2.20), (2.2.18), (2.2.17), (2.2.15) we have

$$\nu = \zeta_a \zeta_x \nu' \tag{2.2.22}$$

The queueing time is given by (A.8.36):

$$T_{\text{qu}} = T'(b) \frac{1}{2[1 - \nu'(b)]} \tag{2.2.23}$$

The reference time

$$T_{\text{ref}} = \frac{N_x(b)}{C} = \zeta_a \zeta_x T'(b) \tag{2.2.24}$$

From (2.1.10) we obtain the normalised delay

$$\tau'(b) = \frac{1}{2}\left[\frac{1}{\zeta(b)-\nu} + \frac{2}{\zeta(b)}\right] \tag{2.2.25}$$

where

$$\zeta(b) \equiv \zeta_a(b)\zeta_x(b) \tag{2.2.26}$$

is the overall efficiency including addressing and 'porosity' of the blocks. Obviously the delay is smaller the larger $\zeta(b)$ is. If b grows from 1 to B then block size $N_{\max}(b)$ decreases and from (2.2.19) we see that addressing efficiency $\zeta_a(b)$ decreases. On the other hand from (2.2.16) we see that block utilisation $\zeta_x(b)$ increases with b. Thus we can expect that there is an optimum block order level b_o minimising $\zeta(b)$ and thus minimising the normalised delay.

2.2.2 Systems with fixed subchannel assignment

We now deal with a fixed subchannel assignment system with individual buffers, which is shown in Fig. 1.11. For such a system the number of channels is equal to the number of sources:

$$K = M \tag{2.2.27}$$

In view of homogeneity assumption A4 a parameter characterising the set of rules $\boldsymbol{S}(\cdot)$ is the same as the corresponding parameter characterising a rule $S_m(\cdot)$. In particular $\bar{\tau}[\boldsymbol{S}(\cdot)] = \tau[S_m(\cdot)]$. Therefore we consider only $\tau[S_m(\cdot)]$ and denote it briefly τ with a subscript denoting the system. We consider TDM first let:

T_1' be the duration of the small slot, including the guard interval;
T_1 the duration of the working part of the small slot (briefly 'working slot');
T_2 be the duration of the large slot.

This notation is illustrated in Fig. 1.9. We have

$$T_2 = MT_1' \tag{2.2.28}$$

We assume the following operating rule:

R2 A block arriving from the mth source is put into the mth buffer. The queue discipline is FIFO. The block at the head of the queue is transferred to the channel in the next small slot corresponding to the mth subchannel.

In addition to A1–A4 we assume:

A5 The information block fits into the working slot and uses it capacity completely.

The common channel capacity utilisation is:

$$\zeta_c = \frac{MT_1}{T_2} = \frac{T_1}{T_1'} \tag{2.2.29}$$

In view of the assumption made we apply formula (A.1.36) for the buffer operating cyclically with period T_2, which gives the average queueing delay

$$\bar{T}_{qu} = T_2 \frac{1}{2(1-\nu_1)} \tag{2.2.30}$$

where ν_1 is the working slot utilisation factor; from the homogeneity assumption (A4) we write ν_1 rather than ν_k.

Notice that $\bar{T}_{qu} \to T_2/2$ when $\nu_1 \to 0$. This is because the packet must on average wait $T_2/2$ for its slot. For the system considered

$$\bar{T}_{as} = 0 \ . \tag{2.2.31}$$

From definition 2.1.5 it follows that the reference time is:

$$T_{ref} = T_1 \ . \tag{2.2.32}$$

Under assumptions A4 and A5 the common channel utilisation:

$$\nu = \nu_1 \zeta_c \tag{2.2.33}$$

Because $\nu_1 \leqslant 1$, we must have

$$\nu < \zeta_c \ . \tag{2.2.34}$$

Substituting 2.2.18, 2.2.21 in 2.1.10 we obtain the normalised delay

$$\tau'_{TDM} = \frac{M}{2}\left[\frac{1}{\zeta_c - \nu} + \frac{2}{M}\right] . \tag{2.2.35}$$

Now consider a system using FDM. The whole frequency band $\Delta\Omega$ is divided into M bands of width $\Delta\omega'$ corresponding to single subchannels. Thus

$$\Delta\omega' = \frac{\Delta\Omega}{M} \ . \tag{2.2.36}$$

Only band $\Delta\omega$ is used for sending information, the remainder, i.e. $\Delta\omega' - \Delta\omega$ is the guard bandwidth.

We assume the following rule of system operation:

R3 A block arriving from the mth source is put into the mth buffer. The queue discipline is FIFO. The transmission of the block at the head of the queue begins as soon as the transmission of the previous block ends.

We assume now:

A5″ If the block is transmitted through the subchannel the capacity of the subchannel is used completely.

The common channel capacity utilisation factor

$$\zeta_c = \frac{\Delta\omega}{\Delta\omega'} \; . \tag{2.2.37}$$

In view of the assumptions made we apply formula (A.2.20) for the buffer operating continuously, which gives us:

$$T_{qu} = T_3 \frac{\nu_1}{2(1-\nu_1)} \tag{2.2.38}$$

where T_3 is the duration of the packet in the subchannel and ν_1 is its utilisation ratio.

Usually the rate of transmission is proportional to the bandwidth of the channel. Thus the rate of a transmission through the common channel is $\Delta\omega/\Delta\Omega$ times larger than through the subchannel. Therefore we take:

$$T_{ref} = \frac{\Delta\Omega}{\Delta\omega} T_3 \tag{2.2.39}$$

From (2.2.24), (2.2.25), (2.2.17) we have

$$T_{ref} = \frac{\zeta_c T_3}{M} \tag{2.2.40}$$

Taking into account that 2.2.19 holds for rule R2 from (2.1.10), (2.2.26), (2.1.28) we obtain the normalised delay

$$\tau_{FMD} = \frac{M}{2} \frac{1}{\zeta_c - \nu} \; . \tag{2.2.41}$$

From (2.2.35) and (2.2.41) we see that for both TDM and FDM the dependence of τ' on ν is of type (2.2.12) and thus is illustrated by Fig. 2.2. The delay for TDM and FDM fixed access systems differ only slightly, FDM being better.

However, we assumed that the FDM subchannel operates continuously. If we assume that it operates cyclically with period T_3, the difference would be still slight, but in favour of TDM.

Comparing (2.2.14), (2.2.13), (2.2.29) we see that addressing efficiency ζ_{ad} is the counterpart of channel capacity utilisation ζ_c in fixed access systems applying time and frequency division. Both ζ_{ad} and ζ_c are of similar orders of magnitude, but τ'_{CB} is much smaller than τ'_{TD} and τ'_{FD} since the factor M does not occur. Thus a system with common buffer using the channel as a whole is essentially better than systems with separated subchannels and fixed subchannel assignment.

2.2.3 Optimisation of channel capacity division in an inhomogeneous system with fixed assignment

We consider systems where the rates of information emission $\lambda_m \bar{N}_m$ are different. We again assume A1, A3 (see page 68), but in place of A2 we take:

A2′ The number of bits forming each block is a random variable which can be approximated by a continuous variable having an exponential probability distribution of mean $\bar{N}_m$.

That is we assume that the blocks are independent Poisson-exponential sequences; the justification for making such an assumption was given in section 2.3. We consider here the operating rule R2 (page 73). To simplify the notation in this section, we shall not take into account the guard intervals. We take the cost κ of the common channel as the index characterising the system construction and we assume that

$$\kappa = \sum_{k=1}^{K} \varphi_k C_k \tag{2.2.42}$$

where C_k, $k = 1, 2, \ldots, K$ is the capacity of the kth subchannel and φ_k, $k = 1, 2, \ldots, K$ are fixed coefficients.

We take the delay as the parameter characterising the quality of information transmission. The parameter characterising the delay for the whole system we define using (1.5.5), which gives us

$$\bar{\tau}_\beta = \left[\sum_{k=1}^{K} \alpha_k \tau_k^\beta\right]^{1/\beta} \tag{2.2.43}$$

where τ_k is the average delay of packets forwarded through the kth link; $\alpha_k \geqslant 0$ are weighting coefficients, $\sum_{k=1}^{K} \alpha_k = 1$, and $\beta \geqslant 1$ is a fixed parameter.

As the weighting coefficient we take the relative average intensity, i.e. we take

$$\alpha_k = \frac{\lambda_k}{\sum_{l=1}^{K} \lambda_l} \tag{2.2.44}$$

As was discussed in section 1.4.2, for $\beta = 1, \bar{\tau}_1$ can be interpreted as the weighted delay, for $\beta = 2$, as the mean square root of the delay, for $\beta \to \infty, \bar{\tau}_\beta$ approaches the largest τ_k.

We limit ourselves to the parameters κ and $\bar{\tau}_\beta$. Thus $OP_{\min} C, \bar{\tau}_\beta | \kappa = \hat{\kappa}, C \geqslant 0$ arises where $C = \{C_k, k = 1, 2, \ldots, K\}$ is the set of subchannel capacities and $C \geqslant 0$ denotes $C_k \geqslant 0, k = 1, 2, \ldots, K$. If in (2.2.19) we take $\alpha_k = 1 = \text{const.}$, the problem considered becomes† $OP_{\min} C, \bar{\tau}_\beta | \sum_{k=1}^{K} C_k = C, C \geqslant 0$ where C is the common channel capacity.

We consider first $OP_{\min} C, \bar{\tau}_\beta | \kappa = \hat{\kappa}$, disregarding the constraints $C \geqslant 0$. We shall discover that the capacities which are solutions to this simplified problem are non-negative and are thus solutions to the primary optimisation problem.

Let us first express τ_k as a function of C_k. Under assumptions A1, A2, A3, A5, we can use formula (A.2.19) which gives us:

$$\tau_k = \frac{N_k}{C_k - \lambda_k \bar{N}_k} . \tag{2.2.45}$$

Using (2.2.43) and (2.2.44) we can express τ_β as a function of C_k:

$$\bar{\tau}_\beta = \left[\left(\sum_{k=1}^{K} \lambda_k \right)^{-1} \sum_{k=1}^{K} \lambda_k \left(\frac{\bar{N}_k}{C_k - \lambda_k \bar{N}_k} \right)^{\beta} \right]^{1/\beta} \tag{2.2.46}$$

The solutions of $OP_{\min} C, \tau_\beta | \kappa = \hat{\kappa}$ must satisfy the system of equations

$$A\kappa \frac{\partial}{\partial C_k} (\bar{\tau}_\beta + A\kappa) = 0 \tag{2.2.47}$$

for $k = 1, 2, \ldots, K$ and the equation

$$\sum_{k=1}^{K} \varphi_k C_k = \hat{\kappa} \tag{2.2.48}$$

† This problem was formulated and solved for $h = 1$ by Kleinrock [2.1] and for arbitrary $h \geqslant 1$ by Meister *et al.* [2.2], [2.3].

The parameter A which appears here is the Lagrange multiplier. This set of equations can be solved in a closed form (see Appendix A.3). The solution depends on the exponent β. Let $C_{ko}(\beta)$ be the optimum capacity for the kth subchannel for a given value of β. For $\beta = 1$ and $\beta = \infty$ we have:

$$C_{ko}(1) = \lambda_k N_k + \Delta\kappa \frac{(\lambda_k \bar{N}_k / \varphi_k)^{1/2}}{\sum_{l=1}^{K} (\lambda_l \bar{N}_l / \varphi_l)^{1/2}} \tag{2.2.49}$$

$$C_{ko}(\infty) = \lambda_k N_k + \Delta\kappa \frac{\bar{N}_k}{\sum_{k=1}^{K} \varphi_k \bar{N}_k} \tag{2.2.50}$$

where

$$\Delta\kappa \equiv \kappa - \kappa^* \tag{2.2.51}$$

$$\kappa^* \equiv \sum_{k=1}^{K} \varphi_k \lambda_k \bar{N}_k \ . \tag{2.2.52}$$

The condition that a solution exists is:

$$\Delta\kappa > 0 \ . \tag{2.2.53}$$

The parameters κ^* and $\Delta\kappa$ occurring here are straightforward to interpret. The minimum channel capacity for which the channel utilisation factor $\nu_k = 1$ is $\lambda_k \bar{N}_k$. A channel with $\nu_k = 1$ cannot operate satisfactorily since the buffers would introduce infinite delays, hence the channel construction cost must be greater than κ^*. The parameter $\Delta\kappa$ is equal to this excess, thus (2.2.51) must hold. Formulae (2.2.49) and (2.2.50) show that the optimum capacity is equal to the magnitudes of the flow intensities $\lambda_m \bar{N}_m$ (bit/s) plus an addition proportional to the excess $\Delta\kappa$. For the criterion τ_1 the proportionality coefficient is in turn proportional to the square root of the intensity $\lambda_m \bar{N}_m$.

2.3 OPEN FREE-ACCESS SYSTEMS WITH CONTINUOUS SIGNALS

In this section and the next we deal with open systems in which the common channel is not divided into subchannels and the local transmitters introduce their signals without taking into account the other local transmitters. The essential difference between this type of system and that of section 2.2, is that this type of system allows several transmitters to start transmitting simultaneously. Therefore we must be able to recover the applied signals even though they may overlap, and thus become distorted.

In free access systems where several transmitters use the common channel, the signal coming from a given transmitter may become distorted in two ways: (a) by external factors, e.g. thermal noise, impulse noises; these are called **external disturbances**, and (b) by signals coming from other transmitters, i.e. by **interference.** Since, in general, we assume that the system is homogeneous, changing the type of signal used by each local transmitter will alter the interference, and hence the quality of information transmission. This causes significant differences between the behaviour of free-access systems where many transmitters use a common channel, and that of systems in which the channel is used by only one transmitter. Since the distortion introduced depends on the kind of signals used in free-access system, the relationships between parameters characterising the system differ qualitatively from those of single transmitter systems.

When using a system without separated subchannels, we assume that distortion of information may occur, but we try to ensure that the probability of this is small. Thus we achieve a separation of the channels into virtual subchannels.

In this section we first illustrate the fundamental properties of free remote access system by the example of a system using randomly chosen realisations of a continuous gaussian process† as the transmitted signals; these signals we call **randomly chosen continuous signals.**‡ Because of the technical difficulties involved in their generation and optimal reception, such signals are not suitable for practical systems. However, a system using these signals is relatively easy to analyse, and helps us to gain an insight into the general properties of free remote access systems. More practical systems will be discussed in the next section.

2.3.1 Model of the system with continuous signals

A1 The information delivered by the mth source is a sequence of primary blocks; the sequence of starting instants forms a Poisson process of intensity λ_m.

A2 A primary block consists of a fixed number N_1 of bits.

A3 The sequences of primary blocks emitted by individual sources are statistically independent.

A4 The system is homogeneous.

As is well known from communication theory, we can counteract the random noise in the channel more efficiently, the more bits of information are assembled in a block and sent as a unit. The length of the block needed to obtain the desired probability of error depends essentially on the properties of the noise

† Randomly chosen continuous signals were used first for the analysis of multiaccess systems by Fulton [2.4].

‡ Instead of signals generated by a random signal generator we may also consider signals generated by a deterministic signal generator, generating signals having properties similar to the realisation of a random process (e.g. feedback shift register followed by a suitable linear filter). Such signals are called pseudorandom signals, as are the signals used in the system considered in this section.

in the channel, while the length of the primary blocks delivered by the source depends only on the properties of the source. In general, the length of the block, favourable from the point of view of error protection, is much greater than the length of primary blocks of information delivered by thc source. To avoid this we assume that $B \geqslant 1$ consecutive primary blocks are assembled into a secondary block. To the secondary block we add the address. The address requires $N_{ad} = \log_2 M$ bits (see 2.2.1). Let us denote by N the number of primary information bits carried by the packet. It is

$$N = BN_1 \tag{2.3.1}$$

The packet carries

$$N_p = N + N_{ad} \tag{2.3.2}$$

bits, where N_{ad} is the number of address bits, given by (2.2.1). The addressing efficiency defined by (2.2.25) is

$$\zeta_{ad} = \frac{N}{N_p} \,. \tag{2.3.3}$$

We assume that

A5 We take as signals (S_x, m, t) carrying the packets the segments of duration T of randomly chosen realisations of the low-band gaussian process $S_x(t)$ having a power spectral density

$$S_x(\omega) = \begin{cases} S_x(0) & \text{for } |\omega| \leqslant 2\pi(\Delta f) \\ 0 & \text{for } |\omega| > 2\pi(\Delta f) \end{cases} \tag{2.3.4}$$

where $S_x(0)$ is a constant and Δf the width of the frequency band occupied by the signals.

We assume that the node operates according to the rule R1 consisting of subrules:

R1.1 Primary blocks coming from the source are put into a buffer which we call the assembly buffer. If B primary blocks are collected in the assembly buffer, the address is added and the packet is formed.

R1.2 The packet is put into the buffer which cooperates in the usual way with the transmitter on the FIFO discipline.

The structure of the node realising this rule and an example of signals formed according the this rule is shown in Fig. 2.3(a).

We assume further:

A6 The common channel is a linear one. The signal at the channel output has the form

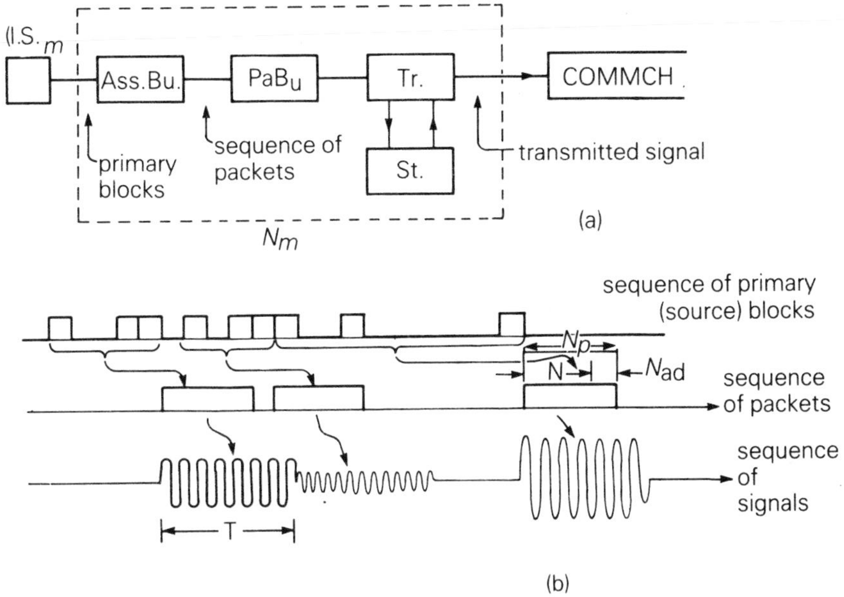

Fig. 2.3 – Illustration of rule 1 of section 2.4. (a) Block diagram of the node: Ass. Bu. = packet assembly buffer; Pa-Bu = packet buffer; Tr. = transmitter; St. = storage of waveforms carrying the packets. (b) Typical sequence of signals; number of blocks assembled into a packet $B = 3$.

$$y(t) = \sum_{m=1}^{M} \alpha_m(t) s[x(m), m, t] + z(t) , \qquad 0 \leqslant t \leqslant T \tag{2.3.5}$$

where $\alpha_m(t)$ is the function describing the fact that the transmitter operates intermittently, defined by the formula

$$\alpha_m(t) = \begin{cases} 1 & \text{if the } m\text{th transmitter is operating} \\ 0 & \text{if the } m\text{th transmitter is idle} \end{cases} \tag{2.3.6}$$

and $z(t)$ is the external noise; a model of the system corresponding to this example is shown in Fig. 2.4(a).

A7 The noise $z(t)$ is the realisation of the stochastic gaussian process $Z(t)$ of spectral density

$$S_z(\omega) = \begin{cases} S_z(0) \text{ for } \omega \leqslant 2\pi(\Delta f) \\ 0 \quad \text{ for } \omega > 2\pi(\Delta f) \end{cases} \tag{2.3.7}$$

where $S_z(0)$ is a constant.

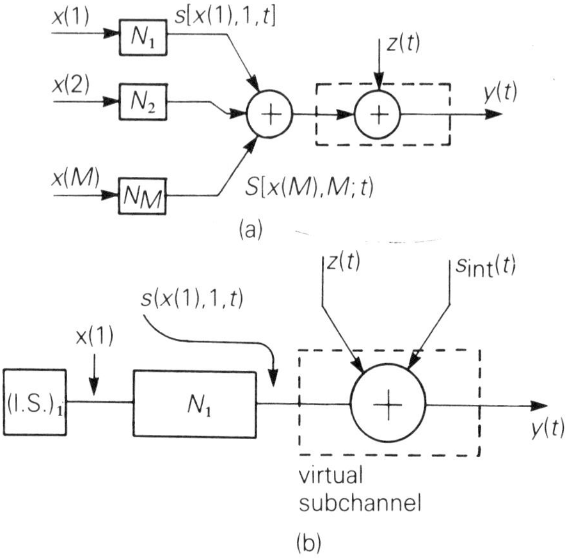

Fig. 2.4 – Model of (a) the system with continuous signals and linear common channel, (b) single link.

We assume further that:

A8 The process representing the state of the mth transmitter (operating, idle) is stationary, the processes representing the states of local transmitters are mutually independent.

The second part of A8 will be satisfied if no local transmitter has any information about the operation of the other transmitters. Let ν_{tr} be the duty ratio of signals transmitted by the mth transmitter; in view of the homogeneity assumption, it does not depend on m. Obviously:

$$\nu_{tr} = EA_n(t) \tag{2.3.8}$$

where $A_n(t)$ is a process representing $\alpha_n(t)$.

Let us consider the transmission of information from a given source, say the source with number $m = 1$. The received signal can be put in the form

$$y(t) = s(x_1, 1, t) + S_{int}(t) + z(t) \tag{2.3.9}$$

where

$$s_{int}(t) \equiv \sum_{m=2}^{M} \alpha_m(t)\, s[x(m), m, t] \ . \tag{2.3.10}$$

The model of the virtual subchannel considered is shown in Fig. 2.4(b). The signal $s_{int}(t)$ we call **interference.**

The statistical properties of information sources completely define the statistical properties of the process $S_{int}(t)$ representing $s_{int}(t)$. However, we introduce the following assumption:

A9 The interference given by (2.3.10) is a realisation of the stationary gaussian process of power spectral density

$$S_{int}(\omega) = \begin{cases} \sum_{m=2}^{M} \nu_{tr} S_x(0) = (M-1)\nu_{tr} S_x(0) & \text{for} \quad |\omega| \leqslant 2\pi(\Delta f) \\ 0 & \text{for} \quad |\omega| > 2\pi(\Delta f) \end{cases} \tag{2.3.11}$$

We introduce the multiplier ν_{tr} into the above summation because the mth transmitter only works during a ν_{tr}th part of the time. Assumption A9 has an heuristic character and is only approximately satisfied in this system by assumptions A1–A8, but the approximation is good, especially for large values of M. Under assumptions A8 and A9, the transmitted signal in the virtual subchannel is overlapped by gaussian noise

$$Z_1(t) = Z(t) + S_{int}(t) \tag{2.3.12}$$

where $S_{int}(t)$ is the process representing the interference given by (2.4.10). The spectral density of $Z_1(t)$ is

$$S_{z1}(\omega) = \begin{cases} S_z(0) + (M-1)\nu_{tr} S_x(0) & \text{for} \quad |\omega| \leqslant 2\pi(\Delta f) \\ 0 & \text{for} \quad |\omega| > 2\pi(\Delta f) \end{cases} \tag{2.3.13}$$

2.3.2 The capacity of a virtual subchannel

Even under the simplifying assumptions introduced it does not seem possible to evaulate the fundamental parameters of the system in a closed form. Therefore we shall use the approximate formulae which apply when the duration of the signals T is large. In these formulae the capacity of the virtual channel plays a fundamental part.

In this section we evaluate the capacity of the virtual subchannel and the efficiency of common channel capacity utilisation defined by (2.1.14). We first deal with the system considered previously. Then we show that a simple form of local transmitter coordination, which keeps the total power of signals fed into the common channel at a constant level, significantly improves the common channel capacity utilisation.

Under assumptions A7 and A9 we can use Shannon's formula for calculating the virtual subchannel capacity

$$C = \Delta f \log_2 \left(1 + \frac{W_s}{W_n}\right) \tag{2.3.14}$$

where Δf is the bandwidth occupied by the signal, W_s is the power of the noiseless signal, and W_n is the power of the additive gaussian noise. From (2.4.1) we see that for W_s we have to take $W_{s1} = 2(\Delta f)S_x(0)$, and from (2.4.13) it follows that for W_n we have to take $W_Z + (M-1)\nu_t W_{s1}$ where $W_Z = 2(\Delta f)S_z(0)$ is the power of the external noise $z(t)$. From (2.3.11) we detain the virtual subchannel capacity

$$C_1 = \Delta f \log_2 \left(1 + \frac{W_{s1}}{W_z + (M-1)\nu_1 W_{s1}}\right) \tag{2.3.15}$$

The average power of noiseless signals in the common channel is the sum of the signal powers due to the local transmitters. Using equation (2.3.14) and taking

$W_s = \sum_{m=1}^{M} W_{sm}$, $W_n = W_z$ we obtain the common channel capacity:

$$C = \Delta f \log_2 \left(1 + \frac{M\nu_{\text{tr}} W_{s1}}{W_z}\right) . \tag{2.3.16}$$

Under the homogeneity assumption A4, the efficiency of using the common channel capacity is:

$$\zeta_c = \frac{MC_1}{C} \tag{2.3.17}$$

The fundamental parameter characterising the signals is the product of the signal duration and bandwidth:

$$N_{\text{df}} \equiv 2T(\Delta f) \tag{2.3.18}$$

which we interpret as the **number of degrees of freedom.** If N_{df} is fixed the characteristic parameter is the ratio of signal power to that of the noise:

$$\rho_1 \equiv \frac{W_{s1}}{W_z} \tag{2.3.19a}$$

If N_{df} can vary the characteristic parameter is the ratio of signal energy to noise energy per degree of freedom:

$$\rho_{e1} \equiv \frac{E_{s1}}{E_z} \tag{2.3.19b}$$

in which:

$$E_{s1} \equiv TW_{s1} \tag{2.3.20a}$$

and

$$E_z \equiv W_z/(\Delta f) \tag{2.3.20b}$$

are the signal energy per degree of freedom and noise respectively.

For fixed N_{df} substituting in (2.4.17) we obtain the efficiency of the common channel capacity utilisation:

$$\zeta_c = \frac{M \log_2 \{1 + \rho_1 [1 + (M-1)\rho_1]^{-1}\}}{\log_2(1 + M\rho_1)} \tag{2.3.21}$$

and for variable N_{df}:

$$\zeta_c = \frac{M \log_2 [1 + \rho_{e1} N_{df} + (M-1)\rho_{e1}]^{-1}}{\log_2(1 + M\rho_{e1}/N_{df})} \tag{2.3.22}$$

Figure 2.5(a) illustrates equation (2.3.21) for the most unfavourable care when $\nu_t = 1$.

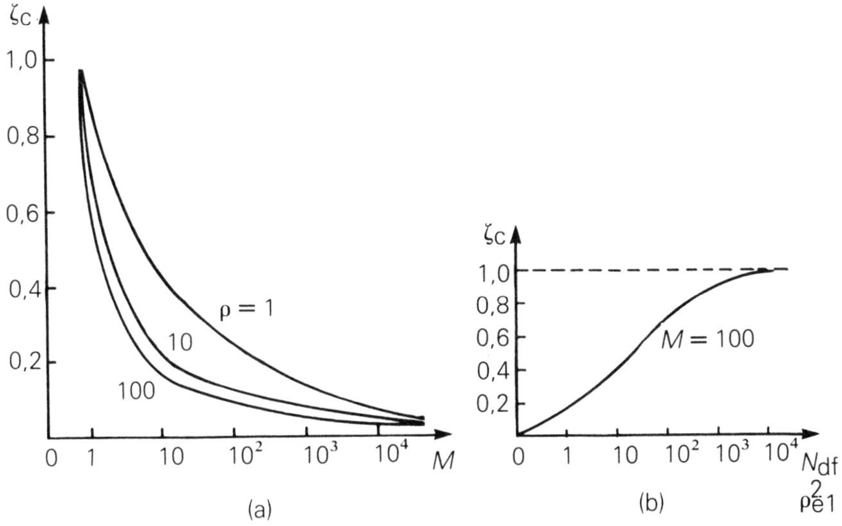

Fig. 2.5 – Dependence of the efficiency of using the common channel capacity ζ_c in an open free-access system on (a) the number of information sources M; ρ = external noise/single local transmitter average power ratio, fixed; (b) parameter N_{df}/ρ_{e1} where N_{df} is the number of degrees of freedom, ρ_{e1} = external noise/single local transmitter average energy per degree of freedom ratio, on M.

The efficiency of common channel capacity utilisation, at a fixed value of ρ_1, reduces as M increases because of increased interference. From Fig. 2.4(b) we see that ζ_c approaches 1 as N_{df} gets bigger, for fixed M. We can interpret this in the following way. If the number of dimensions of signal space, from which we choose white noise realisations, is suitably large, then these signals are approximately orthogonal, and the efficiency of orthogonal systems (without time or frequency guard intervals) is equal to 1. This may be justified theoretically.

Next, let us deal with a modification of the system described above, whereby we introduce relatively simple coordination of transmitter operation. Modifying A7 assume:

A10 The power of the signal from each transmitter is controlled by a central unit so that the power of the composite signal introduced into the average common channel, W_z, is constant.

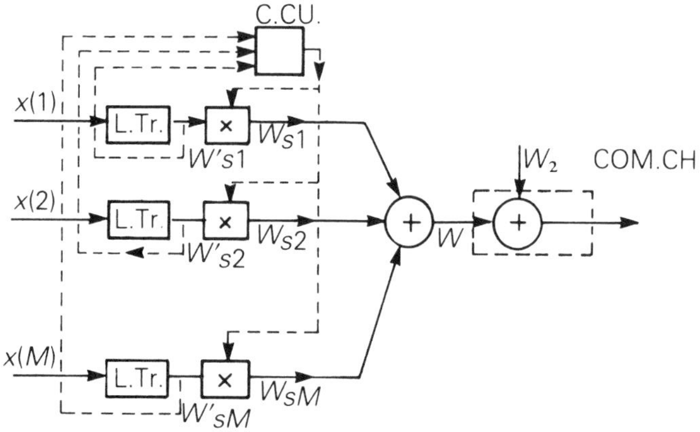

Fig. 2.6 – Model of a system with continuous signals and control of total common channel input power, N' = node operating with fixed power, CCU = central control unit, controlling power total.

A system like this† is shown in Fig. 2.6. Let W'_{sm} denote the primary power of the signal generated by the mth transmitter. The average power at the output of the centrally controlled element

$$W_{sm} = \alpha \nu_{tr} W'_{sm} \tag{2.3.23}$$

where

$$\alpha \equiv \frac{W}{\sum_{m=1}^{M} W'_{sm}} \tag{2.3.24}$$

† It can be shown (e.g. Aein [2.5]) that the system considered here is a good model for the instantaneous phase in a system using phase keyed signals and a hard limiting transponder, as, for example, in satellite relay stations.

In such a situation,

$$\sum_{m=1}^{M} \nu_{tr} W'_{sm} = W = \text{const.} \tag{2.3.25}$$

Using again formulae (2.3.12), (2.3.15) after some elementary algebra, for fixed N_{df}:

$$\zeta_c = \frac{M \log_2 \{1 + \rho[M + (M-1)\rho]^{-1}\}}{\log_2 (1+\rho)} \tag{2.3.26}$$

and for variable N_{df}:

$$\zeta_c = \frac{M \log_2 [1 + \rho_e N_{df} M + (M-1)\rho_e]^{-1}}{\log_2 1 + \rho_e / N_{df}} \tag{2.3.27}$$

where

$$\rho \equiv \frac{W}{W_z} \tag{2.3.28}$$

is the ratio of the total power introduced into the common channel to that of the external noise, and

$$\rho_e \equiv \frac{E}{E_z} \;. \tag{2.3.29}$$

is the energy ratio, where E_z is given by formula (2.3.29), and $E = WT$.

It is evident from formula (2.3.26) that if ζ_c is treated as a function of the number of sources M, there exists a limit:

$$\zeta_c(\infty) \equiv \lim_{M \to \infty} \zeta_c(M) \tag{2.3.30}$$

and

$$\zeta_c(\infty) \equiv \frac{\rho}{(1+\rho) \log_2 (1+\rho)} \tag{2.3.31}$$

Graphs of the dependence (2.3.26) are shown in Fig. 2.7 and we see that $\zeta_c(\infty) > 0$. From Fig. 2.7 we see that as $M \to \infty$ for an uncoordinated system, hence we see that coordination is beneficial. It is easy to check that the dependences between ζ_c and N_{df} described by formulae (2.3.27) and (2.3.22) are qualitatively similar. The efficiency becomes the greater, the larger the product $N_{df}\rho_e^{-1}$, so a centrally coordinated system is the better, the greater the number of degrees of freedom of the signal, or the better the channel.

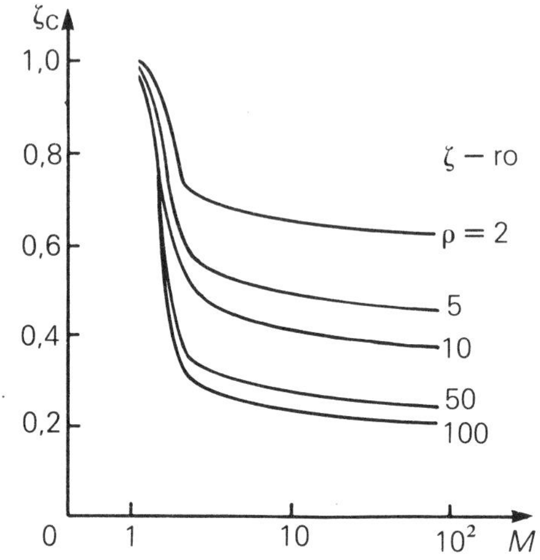

Fig. 2.7 – Dependence of the efficiency of using the common channel capacity ζ_c on the number of information sources M for a remote access system with control of total common channel input power W; ρ = external noise/total input power ratio.

2.3.3 Relationships between the fundamental parameters of systems with continuous signals

We first evaluate the probability of erroneous packet recovery and the information delay.

Because of interference, errors are inherent in systems with non-separable subchannels, even if the common channel is ideal. Let P_e be the probability of error when the optimum inforamtion recovery rule is applied. On assumption A9 this is minimum Milbert distance rule. Probability P_e depends in a complicated way on the set of transmitted signals. However, if the duration of the signals T is large and probability of error depends heavily on the virtual subchannel capacity and on the rate of information transmission by the active transmitter

$$X_{tr} \equiv \frac{N_p}{T} \tag{2.3.32}$$

where N_p is the number of bits the packet consists of. Under assumptions A6 and A9 we can apply Shannon's formulae (see Shannon [2.6]):

$$P_e \cong \Phi\left(\sqrt{\chi N_{df}}\,\frac{X_{tr} - C_1}{2(\Delta f)}\right) \tag{2.3.33}$$

where $\Phi(u)$ is the normal distribution with unit variance,

$$N_{df} = 2T(\Delta f) \tag{2.3.34}$$

is the number of signal degrees of freedom given by (2.3.16), (Δf) is the signals bandwidth, C_1 (bit/s) is the virtual subchannel capacity evaluated on the assumption that average transmitted power is W_{s1}

$$\chi \equiv 2\rho \frac{1+\rho}{2+\rho} \tag{2.3.35a}$$

where

$$\rho \equiv \frac{W_{s1}}{W_z + (M-1)\nu_{tr} W_{s1}} \tag{2.3.35b}$$

is the ratio of signal power to the power of total noise which is the sum of external noise and interference. Formula (2.3.33) is valid if

$$X_{tr} < C_1 \tag{2.3.36}$$

However, the difference $C_1 - R_{tr}$ must not be large (for details, see Shannon [2.6]). From (2.3.33), (2.3.34), we have:

$$T = \frac{A(P_e)}{(C_1 - X_{tr})^2} \tag{2.3.37}$$

where

$$A(P_e) \equiv [\Phi^{-1}(P_e)]^2 \frac{4\Delta f}{\chi} \tag{2.3.38}$$

and $\Phi^{-1}(u)$ is the inverse function of $\Phi(u)$.

From (2.3.37) we see that in order to obtain the imposed probability of error of the optimum rule of recovering information, the duration of the signals T used must grow as $C_1 - X_{tr}$ diminishes and becomes large as X_{tr} approaches C_1.

Substituting (2.3.37) in (2.3.32), we obtain the equation

$$(TC_1)^2 - 2(TC_1)(N_p + A(P_e)/2C_1) + N_p^2 = 0 \tag{2.3.39}$$

The only solution for T satisfying the obvious condition

$$X_{tr} < C_1 \tag{2.3.40}$$

is

$$T = \frac{N_p + N_r}{C_1} \tag{2.3.41}$$

where

$$N_r \equiv A(P_e)/2C_1 + \sqrt{\left(\frac{A(P_e)}{2C_1}\right)^2 + N_p \frac{A(P_e)}{2C_1}} \tag{2.3.42}$$

The parameter N_r can be interpreted as the number of redundant bits which must be introduced to transmit N_p information bits with error probability P_e using signals of finite duration. The parameter

$$\zeta_s \equiv \frac{N_p}{N_p + N_r} \tag{2.3.43}$$

can thus be interpreted as the efficiency of carrying the information by the signal; we call this signal efficiency (hence the subscript 's'). From (2.3.41) and (2.4.43), we get

$$T = \frac{1}{C_1 \zeta_s} N_p \tag{2.3.44}$$

$$X_{tr} = \zeta_s C_1 \tag{2.3.45}$$

Thus if we take T given by (2.3.44) we can transmit N_p bits of information with probability of error P_e.

We now consider packet delay. For the system considered the assembly time $\bar{T}_{as}$ must be taken into account as in (2.1.16). The primary block stays in the assembly buffer until B primary blocks arrive. The average time spent in the assembly buffer is therefore one half of the average time elapsing between the arrival of B consecutive primary blocks; this latter time is $(B-1)\lambda_1^{-1}(0)$. Thus

$$\bar{T}_{as} = \frac{1}{2}(B-1)\lambda_1^{-1} \tag{2.3.46}$$

Let us denote by ν_{tr} the duty ratio of transmitted signals. Since λ_1/B is the intensity of packet arrivals, it is

$$\nu_{tr} = T\frac{\lambda_1}{B} \tag{2.3.47}$$

Using this we put (2.3.46) in the form

$$\bar{T}_{as} = \frac{T}{2}\frac{B-1}{B\nu_{tr}} \tag{2.3.48}$$

The starting instants of packets are no longer poissonian. The rather complicated expression for the average time spent by packets in the buffer can be found in Saaty [2.7]. However, with a good approximation we can take it as

$$\bar{T}_{qu} = A_1(B)\,T\frac{\nu_{tr}}{2(1-\nu_{tr})} \tag{2.3.49}$$

The coefficient $A_1(B)$ is about one. We have $A_1(1) = 1$ and then formulae 2.3.49 and A.2.22 coincide, as they should. The time needed to transmit a bit through the common channel is C^{-1}. Since the signal carries $N = BN_1$ information bits, the reference time defined by 2.1.11 is

$$T_{ref} = \frac{N}{C} \tag{2.3.50}$$

From (2.3.3), (2.3.17), (2.3.32), (2.3.45) we have

$$T_{ref} = \frac{\zeta T}{M} \tag{2.3.51}$$

where

$$\zeta \equiv \zeta_{ad}\zeta_c\zeta_s \tag{2.3.52}$$

is overall efficiency, including addressing, capacity and signal utilisation efficiencies.

Let us denote

ν – common channel utilisation;
ν_1 – virtual subchannel utilisation;
X_1 – rate of working information delivery by a source (bits/s);
X_{a1} – rate of delivery of working information and addressing by a node.

It is

$$\nu = \frac{MX_1}{C} \tag{2.3.53}$$

$$\nu_1 = \frac{X_1}{C_1} \tag{2.3.54}$$

$$X_1 = \lambda_1 N_1 \tag{2.3.55}$$

$$X_{a1} = \frac{\lambda_1}{B} N_p \ . \tag{2.3.56}$$

If the transmitter operated continuously the rate of transmission would be X_{tr} given by (2.3.32). Thus the ratio X_1/X_{tr} is the duty ratio of transmitted signals, i.e.

$$\nu_{tr} = \frac{X_1}{X_{tr}} \ . \tag{2.3.57}$$

From the definition it follows that

$$X_1 < X_{a1} \leqslant X_{tr} < C_1 \tag{2.3.58}$$

Formulae 2.3.53–2.3.58 and (2.3.1), (2.3.3), give us

$$\nu = \zeta \nu_{tr} \ . \tag{2.3.59}$$

From (2.1.16), (2.3.46), (2.3.49), (2.3.51), (2.3.58) for the considered open free-access system we obtain the normalised delay

$$\tau'_{FA} = \frac{M}{2\zeta}\left[\frac{\zeta(B-1)}{\zeta B} + A_1(B)\frac{\nu}{\zeta - \nu} + 2\right] \tag{2.3.60}$$

The parameter ζ, and in turn, the normalised delay τ', depend in a complicated way on primary system parameters. We will now analyse in more detail the dependence of τ' on the fundamental parameter B determining the size of the packet. From (2.3.45), (2.3.43) and (2.3.2) we have

$$X_{tr} = C_1 \frac{BN_1 + N_{ad}}{BN_1 + N_{ad} + N_r} \tag{2.3.61}$$

The parameter $N_{ad} = \log M$ is determined uniquely by the number of sources M while N_r is determined according to (2.3.42) by the probability of error P_e. Thus for the fixed parameters M and P_e, B and R_{tr} determine each other. Investigating the dependence of τ' on B is therefore equivalent to investigating the dependence of τ' on R_{tr}. From (2.3.58) it follows that

$$X_{a1} < X_{tr} < C_1 \tag{2.3.62}$$

Let us suppose that both X_{a1} and C_1 are fixed. We can change R_{tr} by changing the error correcting code used. Let us suppose first that

$$X_{tr} = X_{a1} + \epsilon \tag{2.3.63}$$

where ϵ is a small number and postive. From (2.3.34), (2.3.57) it follows that the difference $C_1 - X_{tr}$ is large. Thus the block duration, T which is necessary in order to achieve the desired error probability P_e, is small. However, from (2.3.57) we see, that ν_{tr} is large, and from (2.3.49) follows that $\bar{T}_{qu}$, and τ'_{FA} are large too. In the second extreme case, we take

$$X_{tr} = C_1 - \epsilon \tag{2.3.64}$$

where ϵ is again a small positive number. In this case the difference

$$X_{tr} - X_{a1} = C_1 - X_{a1} - \epsilon \tag{2.3.65}$$

is large ν_{tr} is small and T_{qu} is small too. However, because $C_1 - R_{tr}$. is small from (2.4.37) follows the signal duration T, must be large. Thus the dependence of τ on X_{tr} is as shown in Fig. 2.8, and the optimum value of R_{tr} lies inside the interval determined by condition (2.3.62).

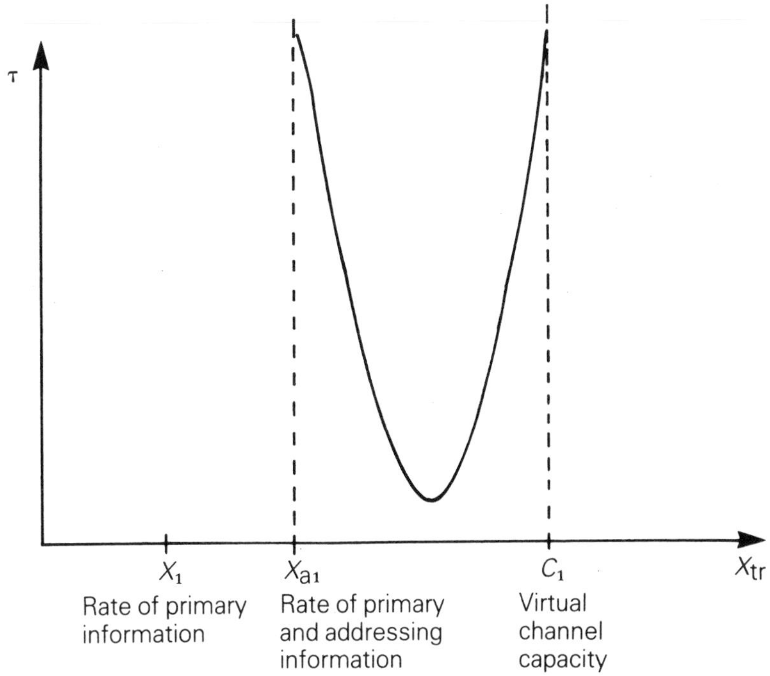

Fig. 2.8 – Typical dependence of the normalised delay τ' on the rate of information transmission by the active transmitter X_{tr}. X_{a1} = rate of transmission by the node of working and information and addressing; C_1 = virtual subchannel capacity.

In our deliberations, we have assumed that the virtual channel capacity C_1 is fixed. As we explained previously, due to the homogeneity assumption A4, changing the duty ratio ν_{tr} also changes the interference and ultimately the capacity C_1. However, as may be seen from (2.3.13) and (2.3.14), C_1 depends on ν_{tr} only logarithmically. Thus the changes of C_1 with ν_{tr} are small so the conclusions we drew for fixed C_1 hold qualitatively when we take into account the dependence of C_1 on ν_{tr}.

2.4 OPEN FREE-ACCESS SYSTEMS WITH SIGNALS HAVING SMALL DUTY RATIOS

In this section we shall deal with multiaccess systems using sequences of elementary, usually binary, signals known as code sequences. Code sequences for which the duty ratio is (a) close to unity and (b) much less than unity are of interest here. The use of type (a) code sequences generally require complicated coding and decoding apparatus. The asymptotic properties of multiaccess systems using type (a) code sequences are analogous to those for systems with pseudorandom continuous signals. This is because, for such sequences, the probability of errors in an optimised system behaves in the same way as that (given by (2.3.35)) for pseudorandom continuous signals.† Far simpler from the point of view of both the transmission and the near optimal recovery of information are systems which use type (b) code sequences. We now deal with this type of system. We first consider fundamental properties of code sequences with small duty ratios, and then derive the capacity of a virtual subchannel in a system in which such signals are used. In the second part of this section we discuss briefly the principles of choice of systems parameters.

2.4.1 Description of the system and its fundamental parameters – signals having a small duty ratio

We introduce the assumption:

A1 The system is homogeneous.
A2 The system operates synchronously.

As in the previous section, we assume that the primary blocks are assembled into secondary blocks. The secondary block, augmented by the address, forms the packet (see also Fig. 2.3). We assume that the signal carrying the packet is a sequence of binary elementary signals. Let T be the duration of the signal carrying the packet and T_0 the duration of the elementary signal. The number of elementary binary signals forming the total signal is

$$N_e \equiv T/T_0 \tag{2.4.1}$$

Obviously, N_e must be greater than or equal to the number N_p of information and addressing bits forming the packet. We assume that the signal has the form:

$$S(x,m;t) = A(x,m;t)\cos(\omega_0 t + \psi) \qquad t \in \langle 0,T \rangle \tag{2.4.2}$$

where

$$A(x,m;t) = \sum_{n=1}^{N_e} a_n(x,m)\, g[t-(n-1)T_0] \tag{2.4.3}$$

in which $g(t)$ is the elementary signal, and the coefficients $a_n(x,m)$ are binary. We shall assume that they are 0 and 1. A typical signal $A(x,m;t)$ is shown in Fig. 2.9.

† The properties of free multiaccess systems using both (a) and (b) types of code signals were investigated deeply in the study [2.8], the properties of systems applying signals of type (b) were analysed in a series of papers by Sommer [2.9]–[2.11]. Recent trends of research in the field of free multiaccess systems can be found in the proceedings of the conference: New Concepts in Multi-user Communication, sponsored by NATO Advanced Study Institute and held in 1980 in the UK.

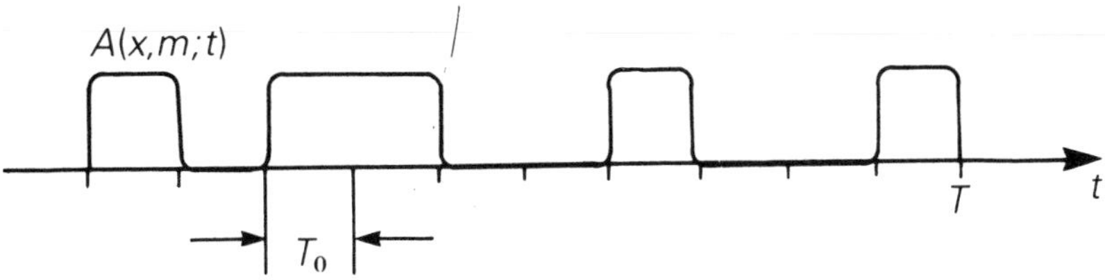

Fig. 2.9 – Examples of envelope $A(x_1 m_1 t)$ given by (2.4.3).

The time interval $\langle 0,T\rangle$ is called the basic slot, while the intervals $\langle (n-1)T_0, nT_0\rangle$ are briefly referred to as 'slots'. If $a_n(x,m) = 1$, we say that the nth slot is active. Let N_a be the number of active slots. The ratio

$$\nu_i \equiv \frac{N_a}{N_e} \tag{2.4.4}$$

is the **internal duty ratio of the signal** (compare (2.2.14)). As in the previous section we shall take the randomly chosen signals as the model of the signals considered. We shall assume that the coefficients $a_n(x,m)$ are realisations of a sequence of mutually independent binary variables such that the probability of choosing 1 is ν_i. As is well known, if N_1 is sufficiently large, the number of different signals obtained in such a way is approximately

$$L \approx 2^{N_e H(\nu_i)} \tag{2.4.5}$$

where $H(P)$ is the entropy of the binary probability distribution with probability P. Since we have 2^{N_p} different packets,

$$2^{N_p} \approx L \ . \tag{2.4.6}$$

From (2.4.5) and (2.4.6) we have

$$N_p = N_e H(\nu_i) \ . \tag{2.4.7}$$

We assume that the node again operates according to the rule R1. As in the previous section, let ν_{tr} be the duty ratio of signals transmitted by a single transmitter, the signals being considered as solid. Finally, let ν_{ov} be the overall duty ratio of the signals generated by the transmitter, taking into account both the internal and the between-signal 'porosities'. Obviously,

$$\nu_{ov} = \nu_i \cdot \nu_{tr} \ . \tag{2.4.8}$$

Analysing the system we assume:

A3 The local channel does not introduce any distortion.

A4 A binary signal (0 – no impulse, 1 – impulse) appears in the nth elementary slot at the common channel output.

A5 The common channel is a symmetrical, binary, stationary and memoryless channel; the probability of error caused by external factors is P_{ex}.

A6 The facility at this input of the common channel operates according the rule: If at least one of the local transmitters introduced an impulse into the nth slot, then an impulse is introduced into the nth slot of the common channel, otherwise no impulse is sent.

The system considered is shown in Fig. 2.10(a).

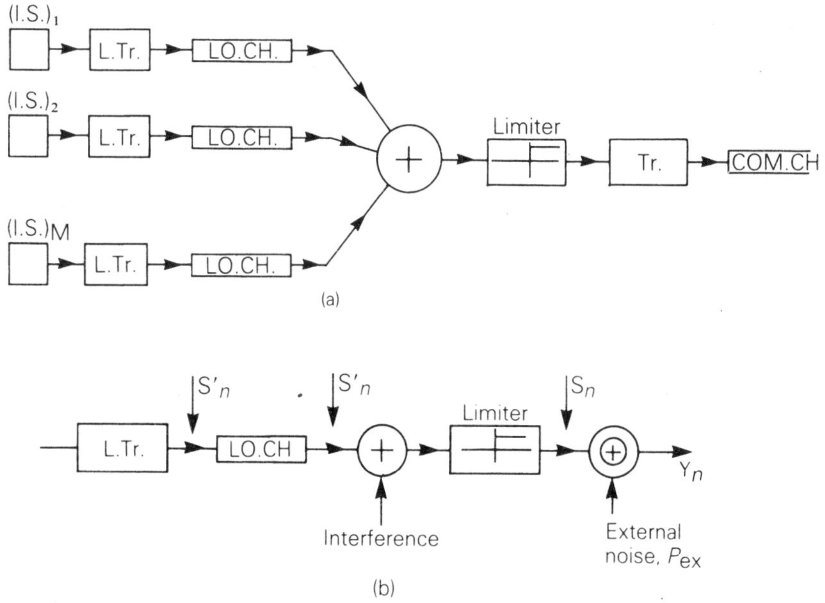

Fig. 2.10 – Model of a free remote access system with pulsed signals and limiter, (a) general, (b) of virtual subchannel. L.Tr. = local transmitter; LO.CH. = local channel: S'_n, S_n, Y_n = binary signals. ⊕ denotes mod 2 addition.

2.4.2 The capacity of a virtual subchannel

As in the case of continuous signals, virtual channel capacity, and related to it, channel capacity utilisation ζ_c are important secondary parameters determining the probability of error.

Without loss of generality we can consider the first virtual subchannel. A block diagram of this channel is shown on Fig. 2.10(b). Let us denote by P_1 the probability that a given transmitter puts its impulse in a given slot. Assuming that the coefficients are chosen randomly we see that

$$P_1 = \nu_{\text{ov}} \tag{2.4.9}$$

where ν_{ov} is the overall duty ratio introduced previously.

The statistical properties of the interference are determined by the assumptions we made, but we make the following simplifying assumption:

A7 The interference in different small slots is statistically independent.

This assumption is satisfactory if the elementary signals constitute a realisation of sequences of independent random variables, and if the number of transmitters causing interference is large. Let Y_n and S'_n be the random variables representing the common channel output signal and the local channel input (and output) signal in the nth slot. The properties of the virtual subchannel are described by $P(Y_n = y \mid S'_n = s)$, so we now calculate these probabilities. Let us take the probability $P(Y_n = 1 \mid S'_n = 1)$. From the equation for marginal probability we have:

$$\begin{aligned} P(Y_n = 1 \mid S'_n = 1) &= P(Y_n = 1, S_n = 0 \mid S'_n = 1) \\ &+ P(Y_n = 1, S_n = 1 \mid S'_n = 1) = \\ &P(Y_n = 1 \mid S_n = 0, S'_n = 1)\, P(S_n = 0 \mid S'_n = 1) \\ &+ P(Y_n = 1 \mid S_n = 1, S'_n = 1) \times P(S_n = 1 \mid S'_n = 1)\ . \end{aligned} \tag{2.4.10}$$

As can be seen from Fig. 2.10 and assumption A6 the event $S_n = 0$ under the condition $S'_n = 1$ is impossible, hence $P(S_n = 1 \mid S'_n = 1) = 1$. From Fig. 2.10 it can be further seen that

$$P(Y_n = 1 \mid S_n = 1, S'_n = 1) = P(Y_n = 1 \mid S_n = 1) = 1 - P_e \tag{2.4.11}$$

and:

$$P(Y_n = 0 \mid S'_n = 1) = P_{\text{ex}} \tag{2.4.12}$$

Also we have:

$$\begin{aligned} P(Y_n = 1 \mid S'_n = 0) &= P(Y_n = 1, S_n = 0) \mid S'_n = 0) + \\ &+ P(Y_n = 1, S_n = 1 \mid S'_n = 0) \\ &= P(Y_n = 1 \mid S_n = 0)\, P(S_n = 0 \mid S'_n = 0) \\ &+ P(Y_n = 1 \mid S_n = 1)\, P(S_n = 1 \mid S'_n = 0)\ . \end{aligned}$$

According to assumption A6 the event $S_n = 0$ under the condition $S'_n = 0$ can occur only when none of the other transmitters use the nth slot. Therefore

$$P(S_n = 0 \mid S'_n = 0) = (1 - P_1)^{M-1} \tag{2.4.14}$$

From (2.5.13) we get:

$$P(Y_n = 1 \mid S'_n = 0) = \\ P_{ex}(1-P_1)^{M-1} + (1-P_{ex})[1-(1-P_1)^{M-1}] \quad (2.4.15)$$

These probabilities, $P(Y_n = y \mid S'_n = s')$, completely described the virtual subchannel. We begin the evaluation of the virtual subchannel capacity by calculating the amount of information, I_M, sent by the common channel per elementary slot (binary signal). According to the homogeneity assumption:

$$I_M = M I_1 (Y_n : S'_n) \quad (2.4.16)$$

where $I_1(Y_n : S'_n)$ is the amount of information about the variable Y_n which is carried by the variable S'_n. Knowing the *a priori* probability $P(S' = s')$ and the conditional probabilities previously derived, I_M can be calculated.

We first consider I_M as $M \to \infty$. If the probability P_1 is constant, the capacity $I_M \to 0$ and the efficiency $\zeta_c \to 0$ as $M \to \infty$. More realistically we consider P_1 (and therefore N_{df}) changing with M, so as to keep constant the probability of one of the M transmitters using the slot under consideration. We call this probability the non-activity probability and denote it by P_{na}. From this definition it follows that:

$$P_{na} = (1-P_1)^M \ . \quad (2.4.17)$$

It is not difficult to show (see for example Sommer's paper [2.9]) that under the condition $P_{na} = \text{const.}$, there exists a limit:

$$I_\infty \equiv \lim_{M \to \infty} I_M \quad (2.4.18)$$

where:

$$I_\infty = \{P_{ex} \log_2 [P_{ex} + (1-2P_{ex})P_{na}] + (1-P_{ex}) \log_2 [(1-P_e) - \\ -(1-2P_{ex})P_{na}] - [P_{ex} \log_2 P_{ex} + (1-P_{ex}) \ln (1-P_e)]\} \log_2 P_{na} \ . \quad (2.4.19)$$

The dependence of I_∞ on P_{na} at fixed P_{ex} is shown graphically in Fig. 2.11. I_∞ reaches a maximum, which for $P_{ex} = 0$ is

$$P^*_{na} = 0.5 \ . \quad (2.4.20)$$

For finite values of M, the calculation of I_M is difficult. Figure 2.12 shows the dependence of I_M on P_1 at fixed M with $P_{ex} = 0$. For each M there is a value P^*_1, maximising I_M. Where M is large ($M > 50$), P^*_1 is obtained to a good approximation by substituting equation (2.4.17) in (2.4.20):

$$P^*_1 = 1 - 2^{-1/M} \ . \quad (2.4.21)$$

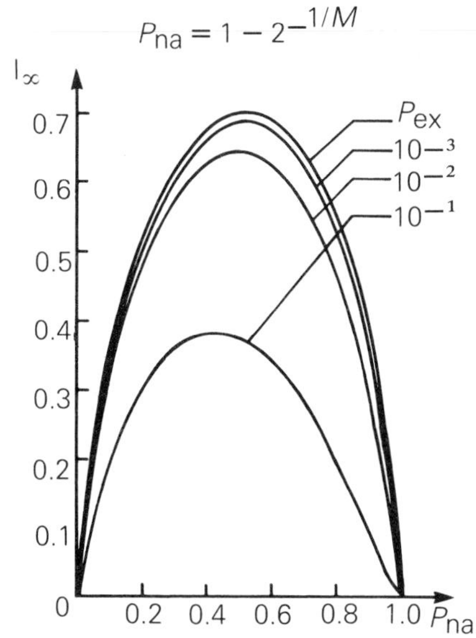

Fig. 2.11 – Dependence of the symptotic amount of statistical information I_∞ carried by the virtual subchannel on the probability P_{na} that no transmitter is active in a given slot; P_{ex} = probability of binary error caused by external noise.

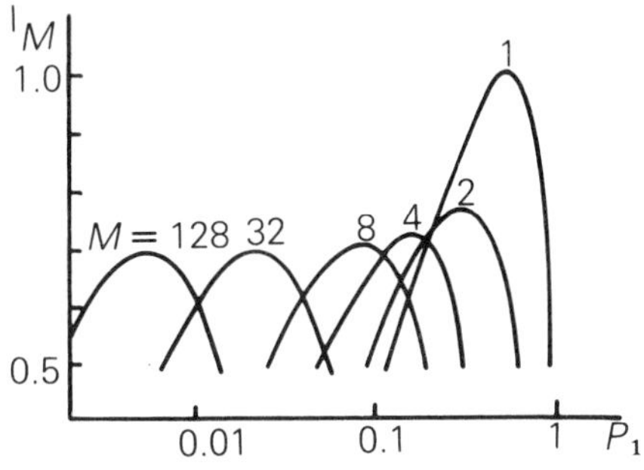

Fig. 2.12 – Dependence of the amount of statistical information I_M carried by the virtual subchannel on the probability P_1 that a slot is filled; M = number of information sources.

For $M \gg 1$ we have

$$P_1^* \approx \frac{\log 2}{M} \ . \tag{2.4.22}$$

If we substitute P_1^* instead of P_1 in the expression for $I_1(\mathrm{Y}:\mathrm{S}')$, we obtain the virtual subchannel capacity C_1. Next, taking $C = N_e C_b(P_{ex})$, where $C_b(P_{ex})$ is the capacity of the binary, symmetrical, memoryless channel, we obtain the efficiency of using the common channel capacity, ζ_c defined by (2.1.11). The dependence of ζ_c on P_{ex} at fixed M is shown in Fig. 2.13(a), and the dependence of ζ_c on M with $P_{ex} = 0$ is given in Fig. 2.13(b). From Fig. 2.13(a) we may conclude that in the case of small values of P_{ex}, the efficiency ζ_c almost does not depend on P_{ex}. This can be explained by the fact that in this system the chief cause of capacity reduction is the interference coming from other transmitters and not the external noise. The slight improvement in efficiency with increasing values of P_e is due to the fact that if P_{ex} takes large values, the effect of interference coming from the remaining transmitters becomes less. One has to remember that, according to equation (2.4.21), by increasing M we also reduce P_1^* so as always to get the maximum shown in Fig. 2.12.

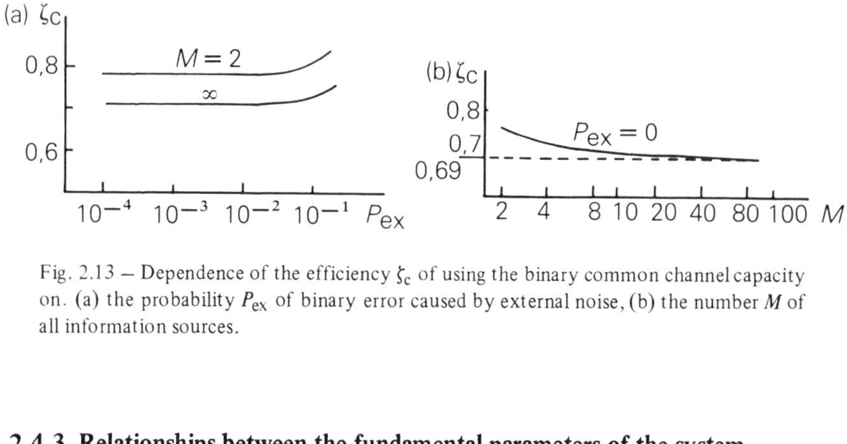

Fig. 2.13 – Dependence of the efficiency ζ_c of using the binary common channel capacity on. (a) the probability P_{ex} of binary error caused by external noise, (b) the number M of all information sources.

2.4.3 Relationships between the fundamental parameters of the system

We now briefly consider the parameters characterising the operation of the system and we will indicate how the fundamental parameters should be chosen. As in the previous section, we first introduce the rates of transmission characterising the system. However, we now take not the rate per second but the rate per elementary slot. We denote the latter by a prime ($'$). The rate of primary information transmission coming from a single source is:

$$X_1' = T_0 X_1 = T_0 \lambda_1 N_1 \tag{2.4.23}$$

and the rate of primary information and addressing

$$X_{a1}' = T_0 X_{a1} = \zeta_{ad}^{-1} X_1' \tag{2.4.24}$$

where X_1 and X_{a1} are given by (2.3.55) and (2.3.56) respectively, and ζ_{ad} is the addressing efficiency given by (2.3.3).

The transmission rate of the active transmitter is

$$X'_{tr} = N_p/N_e \ . \tag{2.4.25}$$

From (2.4.7) we have

$$X'_{tr} = H(\nu_i) \ . \tag{2.4.26}$$

$$X'_{a1}/X'_{tr} = \nu_{tr} \tag{2.4.27}$$

where ν_{tr} is the duty ratio of the sequence of signals generated by the transmitter, the signals being considered as solid.

To achieve high channel capacity utilisation the overall duty ratio ν_{ov} should take ν^*_{ov} given by (2.4.21). Thus we must get:

$$\nu_i \cdot \nu_{tr} = \nu^*_{ov} \ . \tag{2.4.28}$$

From (2.4.27), (2.4.26) and (2.4.23) we have

$$\nu_{tr} H \frac{\nu^*_{ov}}{\nu_{tr}} = X_1 T_0 \ . \tag{2.4.29}$$

From this formula we see that for a fixed rate X_1(bit/s) we can change the duty ratio ν_{tr} only by changing the slot duration T_0. Thus we are free to change independently only T_0 and the number of elementary signals N_e. As in the continuous case, this latter parameter is interrelated with the probability of error P_e. The probability of error is given the asymptotic formula

$$P_e \cong A \exp(-N_e \alpha) \tag{2.4.30}$$

where α is a growing function of the rate margin $C'_1 - R'_t$ (the detailed properties of A and α can be found in, for example, Fano [2.13]. Thus for fixed P_e, the number of bits N_e forming the packet is a decreasing function of the margin $C'_1 - X'_{tr}$. Therefore, as in the continuous case, if the value of X'_{tr} is close to that of C'_1 we must use signals in which N_e is large, which for fixed T_o causes that the signal duration and thus the delay are large. If, however, we take X'_{tr} close to X'_{a1} the number of packets in the buffer is large and thus the delay again becomes large. Thus the dependence of the packets passage time on the duty ratio ν_{tr} is as shown in Fig. 2.7. From (2.4.28)we see next that an internal duty ratio exists ν^*_i which minimises the average delay.

From our discussion in the last two subsections, we can draw the following conclusions: (1) it is possible to use the common channel for transmitting packets from several sources with transmitters operating in a completely uncoordianted fashion; (2) the dependence of the normalised packets passage in the open free-access system on the common channel utilisation is similar in nature to that in systems with separated subchannels; however, the fundamental parameter ζ which is the overall efficiency coefficient may be much smaller than the channel utilisation coefficient ξ_c in the system with separable channels; (3) in the free-access open systems there is an optimum rate of transmission by an active transmitter which in turn determines the optimum size of the packet. If the rate is large and the margin between it and the virtual channel capacity is small, we have to take large packets to achieve the desired probability of error. However, if the rate is small, the duty ratio if signals transmitted approaches unity and the packets spend a lot of time in the buffer; (4) an optimal internal duty ratio exists for pulsed signals: it corresponds to a compromise between the large number of elements helping to identify the signal and the small packet size reducing the interference.

REFERENCES

[2.1] Kleinrock, L., (1964), *Communication Nets – Stochastic Message Flow and Delay*, McGraw-Hill, New York.

[2.2] Meister, B., Muller, H. R., and Rudin, H. R., (1971), New optimization criteria for message-switching networks, *IEEE Trans. on Comm. Technology*, **COM-19**, 256–260.

[2.3] Meister, B., Muller, H. R., and Rudin, H. R., (1972), On the optimization of message-switching networks, *IEEE Trans. on Comm.*, **COM-20**, 8–14.

[2.4] Fulton, F. F., (1967), *Channel Utilisation by Intermittent Transmitters*, Stanford Electronics Laboratory Res. Rap. 1235.

[2.5] Aein, J. M., (1964), Multiple access to a hard-limiting communication satellite repeater, *IEEE Trans. on Space Electronics and Telemetry*, **SET 10**, 159–167.

[2.6] Shannon, C. E.,(1959), Probability of error for optimal codes in a gaussian channel, *Bell. Syst. Techn. J.*, **38**, 3, 611–650.

[2.7] Saaty, T. L., (1961), *Elements of Queuing Theory*, McGraw-Hill, New York.

[2.8] Aein, J. M., and Schwartz, J., W. (eds.), (1965), *Multiple Access to a Communication Satellite with a Hard Limiting Repeater*, Institute for Defence Analysis Rept. R-108, Arlington.

[2.9] Sommer, R. C., (1966), Asynchronously multiplexed channel capacity, *Proc. of the IEEE*, **54**, 79–80.

[2.10] Sommer, R. C., (1968), High efficiency multiple access communication through a signal processing repeater, *IEEE Trans. on Comm. Techn.*, **COM-16**, 222–282.

[2.11] Sommer, R. C., (1966), A coded RADA system, *Proc. of the IEEE*, **54**, 1196–1197.

[2.12] Sommer, R. C., (1968), Time-frequency RADA signalling with a random number of active subscribers, *Proc. of the IEEE*, **58**, 212–213.

[2.13] Fano, R. M., (1961), *Transmission of Information*, Wiley, New York.

3

Feedback systems with a common channel

In this and in the next chapter we continue to consider remote access systems with a single common channel. The subsections are ordered according to the amount of information about state of the channel available at the node. In sections 3.1 and 3.2 we consider the simple feedback system with asynchronous, and synchronous access. In section 3.3 we deal with systems in which the nodes besides the feedback information have information if the common channel is busy or not.

3.1 ASYNCHRONOUS SYSTEMS WITH FEEDBACK

In this section we will consider systems using feedback information, ξ_f indicating whether or not a packet clashed with another in transmission.† We first describe the system, then derive the dependence of the packet intensity in the common channel on the intensity of packets passing successfully through the channel. Knowing this dependence, we can evaluate the average number of retransmissions needed to successfully deliver the packet to its destination, and thus permits us to evaluate the average packet delay, and its dependence on the channel utilisation factor. Finally we consider the case when nodes are distributed over an area. In the last subsection we will consider aspects of the distribution in space of the nodes of the system, and we show that it can cover only a limited circular area, with the destination in the centre. The nodes outside that circle are not able to transmit the packet successfully, despite many attempts.‡

As we mentioned, we will derive in this section only the fundamental relationships for the asynchronous access system, introducing several simplifying assumptions. In the following section we first consider in an analogous way the

† This type of system was first analysed and implemented by N. Abramson [3.1] and was called the ALOHA system.

‡ Abramson [3.2] who discovered this effect, noticed the analogy to the story from Greek mythology, and called the circular area the Sisyphus circle.

synchronous access system. However, next we will analyse the synchronous access system in more detail, removing in particular, the essential simplifying assumption about packet independence. We will also study the stability of the system. It will be shown that the synchronous access system is superior to the free access system, so the more detailed analysis of the asynchronous access system would be involved and it can be expected that the results of such an analysis would be almost exact counterparts of the more detailed analysis of the synchronous access system; therefore we will not carry out here the more detailed analysis of the asynchronous access system.

3.1.1 Description of the system

The block diagram of an asynchronous access system with feedback (AAF) is shown in Fig. 3.1 and the structure of the node in Fig. 3.2. The rule for operating the node is:

(1) Packet delivered by the source (called the primary packet) is put into the entrance buffer.
(2) The auxiliary information ξ_f about the quality of transmission can take one of the forms

ξ^+ – transmission was successful,
ξ^- – transmission was unsuccessful.

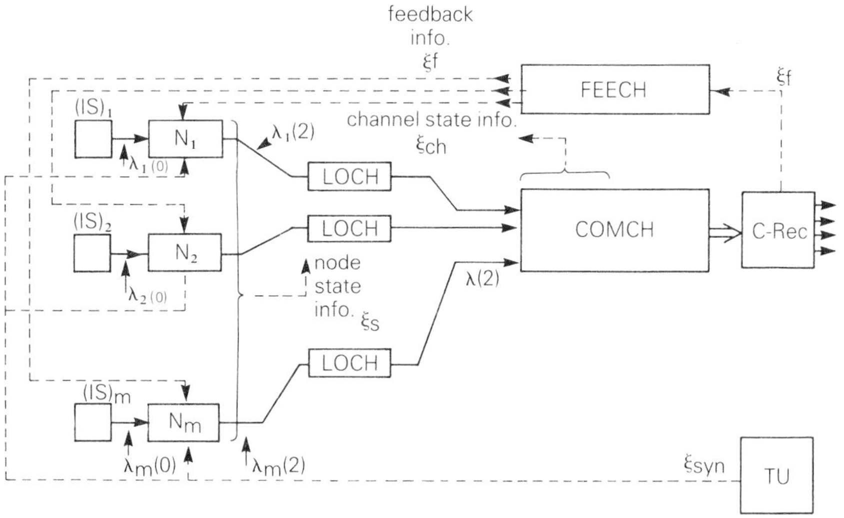

Fig. 3.1 – Block diagram of systems with feedback. $(\mathrm{IS})_m$ = mth information source; N_m = mth mode; LOCH = local channel; FEECH = feedback channel; COMCH = common channel; C-Rec = central receiver; TU = timing unit. Broken lines indicate the system identification information flow.

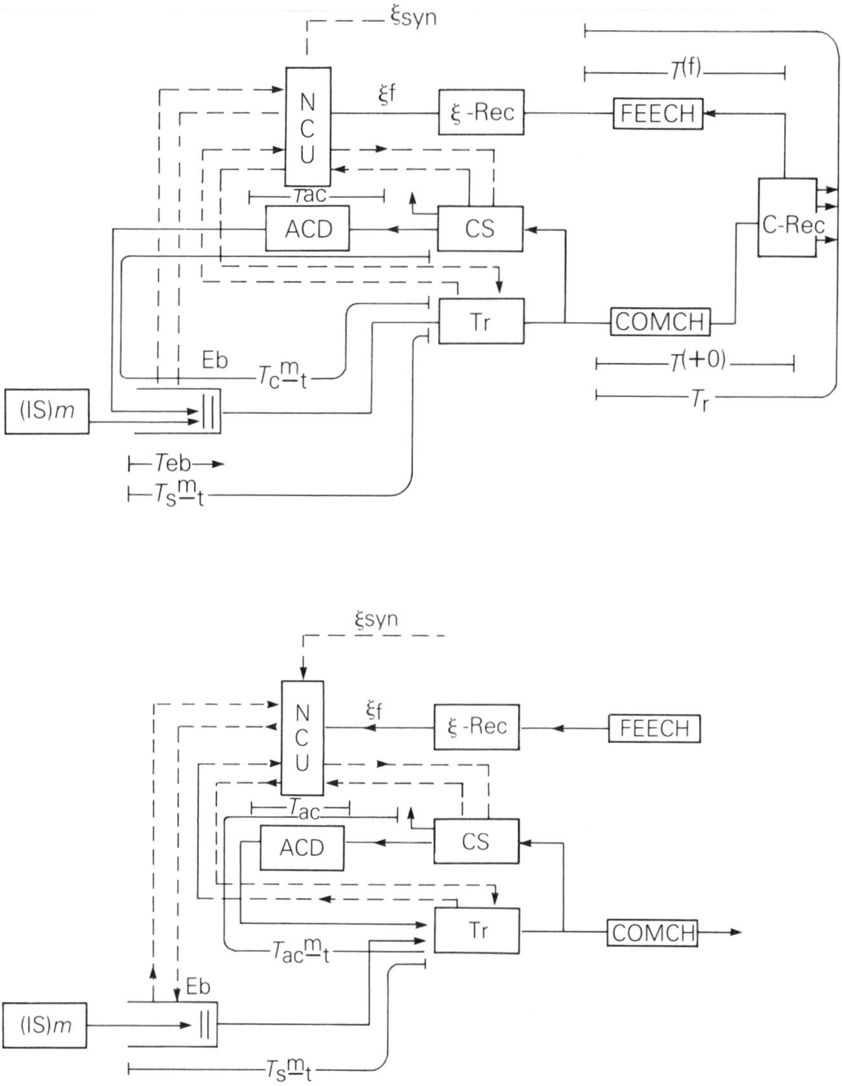

Fig. 3.2 – Structure of a node in a system with feedback, using (a) subrules (3.1a), (5.1a), (b) subrules (3.1b), (5.1b). $(IS)_m$ = mth information source; Eb = entrance buffer; Tr = transmitter; NCU = node control unit; ACD = anticollision delay unit; CS = copy storage; ξ-Rec = ξ_{fch} information receiver; FEECH = feedback channel; COMCH = common channel; interrupted lines indicate internal state identification and control. In the asynchronous access system, the ξ_{syn} information is not available. Thin lines indicate the paths along which the delays defined in section 3.1.3 arise.

The copy of the packet fed into the common channel is put into the copy storage (CS).

(2.1) If $\xi_f = \xi^+$ then the copy is destroyed.
If $\xi_f = \xi^-$ then the copy is transferred to the anticollision delay unit (ACD unit).

(3) At the ACD unit the anticollision delay T_{ac} is chosen. After this time elapses the copy is either.

(3.1a) transferred to the entrance buffer (Eb), or

(3.1b) obtains the highest priority in the node.

(4) The entrance buffer operates according to first in, first out (FIFO) discipline, treating the primary packets and copies equally.

(5) As soon as the transmitter has completed the transmission of the previous message the node control unit puts the packet of highest priority into the transmitter.

(5.1a) If subrule (3.1a) is applied then the packet (primary or copy) at the head of the queue in the entrance buffer has the highest priority in the node.

(5.1b) If subrule (3.1b) is applied then the primary packet in the front of the queue at the entrance buffer becomes the highest priority but only after the ξ^+ information about the previous packet arrived.

If the round trip delay $T_r \gg T$ then it would be wasteful to keep the transmitter idle until the feedback signal returns. We then apply subrules (3.1a) and (5.1a). However, doing so we allow several packets to be 'in flight' at once so that sequencing of recovered packets may be changed as shown in Fig. 3.3(a), and we have to apply packet numbering. If T_r is about T then it pays to avoid problems with sequencing by prohibiting the transmission of a new packet before the previous one is successfully sent. Subrules (3.1b) and (5.1b) do this. A typical transmission in such a case is shown in Fig. 3.3(b).

If $T_r < T$ then a ξ^- decision may be taken before the transmission of the packet is completed. In such a case we interrupt the transmission. Therefore we can always assume that after the arrival of ξ^- information the transmitter is ready to transmit a new packet.

If two nodes which transmitted unsuccessfully started retransmitting their packets simultaneously, a new collision would certainly occur. To avoid this we introduce the **anticollision delay** T_{ac}. This can be chosen such that each node always introduces a different delay, e.g. the mth node introduces the delay $T_{ac} = mT$, but this is unfair. To achieve fairness, a random delay is usually introduced by applying the subrule:

(3.2) Anticollision delay at node m is chosen at random by the random variable T_m.

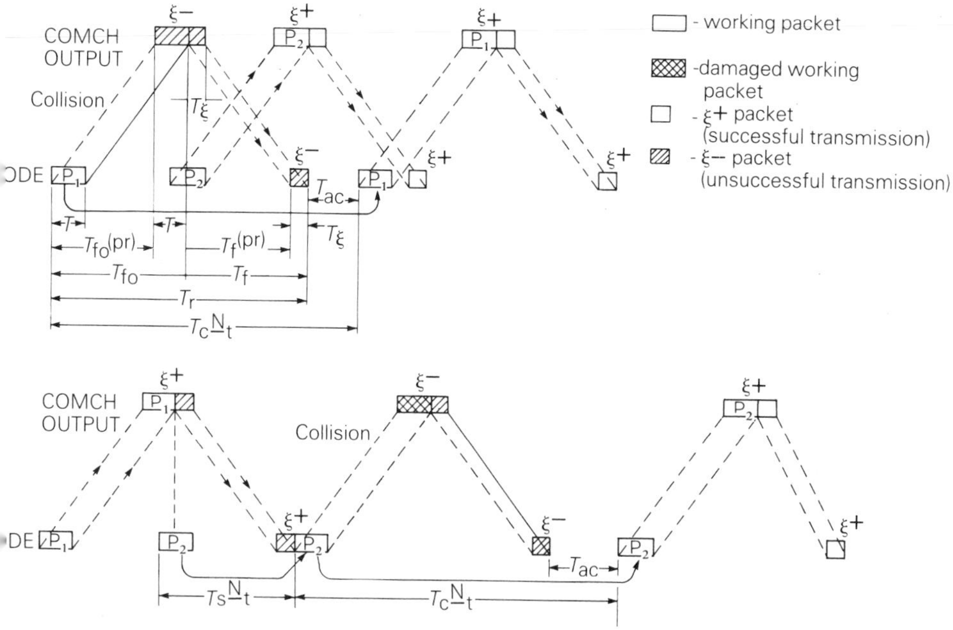

Fig. 3.3 – Typical transmission process in access system with feedback: (a) subrules (3.1a), (5.1a), (b) 3.1b), (5.1b).

Describing the rules we assumed that both positive and negative acknowledgements (ξ^+ and ξ^-) concerning packet transmission are sent. However, we often only return a positive acknowledgement ξ^+, and assume ξ^- if a ξ^+ has not been returned within a timeout period, T_{out}.

3.1.2 Derivation of the approximate relationships between the total flow intensity and the intensity of successful transmissions

To analyse the system considered we have to specify the properties of the information source. We will assume here that:

A1 The sequence of starting instants of primary packets from the mth source is Poisson distributed, with density† $\lambda_m(0)$.

A2 The stochastic processes corresponding to the various sources are statistically independent.

A3 The properties of the system are constant.

† Subsequently we introduce various classes of packets. We call a new packet delivered by the source a class 0 packet. Hence the notation $\lambda_m(0)$. In the previous chapter, where no division into classes was introduced we used the simple notation λ_m.

The sources satisfying A1, A2 we call poissonian independent sources, and the systems satisfying A3, we call stationary.

We further assume that:

A4 Each packet has the same duration T.

A5 The random variables T_m, $m = 1, 2, \ldots, M$ representing the anticollision delay are statistically independent and they have the same probability distribution. The probability distribution of T_m is uniform within the interval $\langle 0, ZT \rangle$ where Z is a systems parameter called the **randomisation index.**

A6 Even a partial overlapping of two or more packets is detected; this always generates the information ξ^- which reaches the nodes which sent the packets.

A7 External noise is present in the common channel, which can cause the packet to be corrupted and ξ^- to be generated. We denote the probability of such an event by P_{ex}. The external noise is statistically independent of the packets in the common channel.

The exact analysis of the system operating according to subrules A1–A7 is complicated. To get an insight into the fundamental properties of the system, we next introduce a number of simplifying assumptions. The first is:

A8 The probability that a primary packet or any copy will collide with another packet is the same.

We call this assumption the uniform collision assumption. The uniform collision assumption is quite restrictive, since if we had no anticollision delay a pair of packets which collided once would collide again with probability 1. Thus there is in general another probability of a primary collision and of a repeated collision. However, we show in the next section that when the randomisation index Z is sufficiently large, we can expect the results derived using assumption A8 to be quite accurate.

We call a packet delivered by the source a **class 0 packet**, a packet which is transmitted successfully a **class 1 packet**, while any packet put in the channel whether it is involved in a collision or going through successfully, a **class 2 packet**. We use indices to denote the parameters characterising classes of packets. In particular, we denote by

$\lambda_m(i)$ – the intensity of class i, $i = 0, 1, 2$, packets coming from the mth node.

We further assume that:

A9 The capacity of the entrance buffer is infinite.

A10 The average number of packets in the entrance buffer and of copies in the storage are finite.

Under these assumptions each packet delivered by the source will ultimately be transmitted successfully. Thus:

$$\lambda_m(1) = \lambda_m(0) \tag{3.1.1}$$

Let us denote by P_m^- the probability of packet collision. In view of the uniform collision assumption which does not depend on packet class:

$$\lambda_m(2) = \lambda_m(1) + \lambda_m(2)P_m^- \tag{3.1.2}$$

The transmission of a copy we call a retransmission. Let us denote the average number of retransmissions by $\bar{H}_m$. We write (3.1.2) alternatively in the form:

$$\lambda_m(2) = \lambda_m(1) + H_m\lambda_m(1) \ . \tag{3.1.3}$$

Thus

$$\bar{H}_m = \frac{\lambda_m(2)}{\lambda_m(1)} - 1 \tag{3.1.4}$$

and from (3.1.2) we have:

$$\bar{H}_m = \frac{P_m^-}{1-P_m^-} \ . \tag{3.1.5}$$

We will now derive this relationship in another way. Under assumption A9 the probability that after exactly h successful transmissions a successful one will follow is $(P_m^-)^h(1-P_m^-)$. Thus:

$$\bar{H}_m = \sum_{n=1}^{\infty} h(P_m^-)^h(1-P_m^-) = \frac{P_m^-}{1-P_m^-} \ . \tag{3.1.6}$$

Considering all the transmitters:

$\lambda(i)$ – is the intensity of all ith class packets in the common channel.†

From the definitions it follows that:

$$\lambda(i) = \sum_{m=1}^{M} \lambda_m(i) \qquad i = 0,1,2 \ . \tag{3.1.7}$$

If (3.1.1) holds, then:

$$\lambda(1) = \lambda(0) \ . \tag{3.1.8}$$

In most cases the homogeneity assumption is satisfied.

† Here and subsequently we denote a parameter characterising the common channel with the same symbol as the parameters characterising the local channel but without subscript m.

A11 All information sources have the same properties and all nodes apply the same rule of operation.

On this assumption $\lambda_m(i) = \lambda(i)/M =$ const. and formulae (3.1.4), (3.1.2), take the form

$$\lambda(2) = \lambda(1) + \bar{H}\lambda(1) \quad (3.1.9)$$

$$\lambda(2) = \lambda(1) + P^-\lambda(2) \quad (3.1.10)$$

where P^- denotes the probability of packet collision which, in view of A11, does not depend on m. Notice that P^- is a function of $\lambda(2)$, which we indicate by writing $P^-[\lambda(2)]$. We can interpret (3.1.10) as shown in Fig. 3.4. This clearly shows that as far as packet intensities are concerned, we have a situation analogous

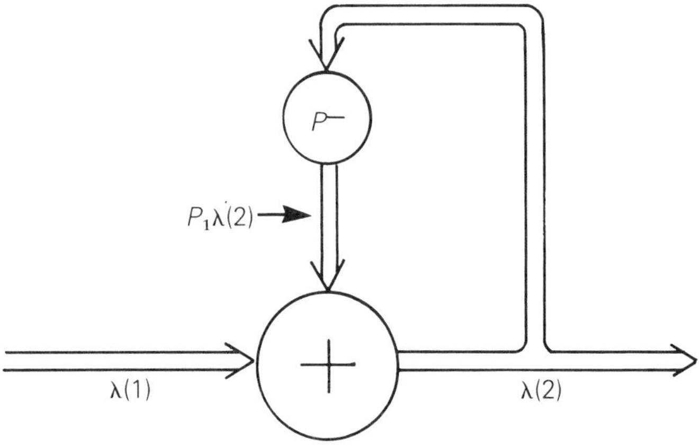

Fig. 3.4 – Graphic interpretation of the relationship between the intensity of packet flow and multiplexing and feeding. (1), total intensity of successful packets flow; (2), flow intensity of all packets (primary, retransmissions); P = probability of arrival of ξ^- information.

to the one in a circuit with non-linear feedback. To find the dependence between $\lambda(2)$ and $\lambda(1)$ we have to determine the dependence of $P^-[\lambda(2)]$ on $\lambda(2)$, which is determined by the statistical properties of the flow in the common channel. This is unequivocally determined by the assumed statistical properties of the information sources and the operating rules of the system. However, we introduce the further assumption:

A12 The model of the starting instants of the packets making up the joint flow in common the channel is a Poisson process.

We will now show that, under assumptions A9, A12 the relationship between $\lambda(1)$ and $\lambda(2)$ can be easily derived. Let Y_c denote a binary random variable representing the effect of packet collisions. $Y_c = 1$ if a given packet overlaps with another packet, and $Y_c = 0$ if there is no overlap. Furthermore, let Y_{ex} be a random variable representing the effect of external noise in the common channel, with values as above. From the definition of the random variable Y_{ex} and A7 it follows that:

$$P(Y_{ex} = 1) = P_{ex} \quad . \tag{3.1.11}$$

The decision ξ^- is taken either if $Y_c = 1$ or if $Y_c = 0$ and $Y_{ex} = 1$. Thus the probability of making ξ^- decision is:

$$P^- = P(Y_c = 1) + P(Y_c = 0, Y_{ex} = 1) \tag{3.1.12a}$$

which we can put in the form

$$P^- = 1 - P(Y_c = 0) + P(Y_c = 0)\,P(Y_{ex} = 1) \tag{3.1.12b}$$

$P(Y_c = 0)$ is the probability that, in a time interval of length $2T$, no other transmitter starts transmitting a packet. We call this interval the **collision zone** – see Fig. 3.5. Under assumption A12 this is the probability that an event in a

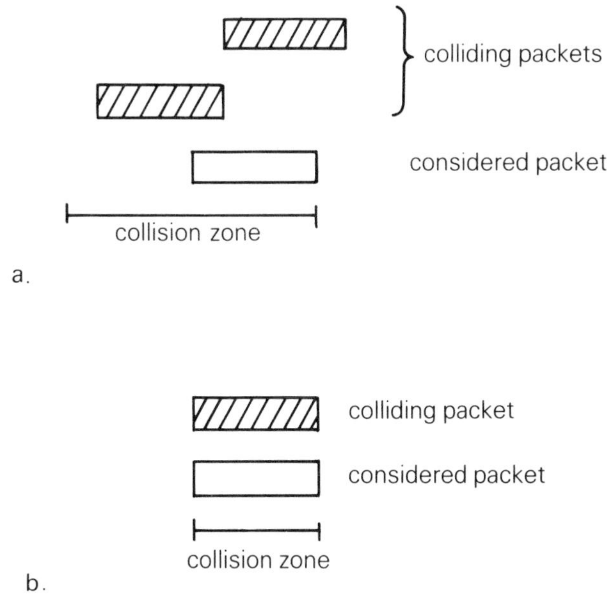

Fig. 3.5 – Collision zones: (a) free access system, (b) synchronised system.

Poisson process does not occur in the collision zone. Since the duration of the zone is $2T$ we have:

$$P(Y_c = 0) = \exp[-2T\lambda(2)] \quad (3.1.13)$$

Ultimately:

$$P^-[\lambda(2)] = 1 - \exp[-2T\lambda(2)] + P_{ex} \exp[-2T\lambda(2)] \quad (3.1.14)$$

Let us now introduce the normalised intensities of packets in the common channel

$$\nu(i) \equiv \lambda(i)T \qquad i = 1, 2 \ . \quad (3.1.15)$$

If no collisions occur $\nu(2) < 1$, and can be interpreted as the duty ratio of the packets in the common channel. Since $\lambda(1)$ is the intensity of successful transmissions, it is always:

$$\nu(1) < 1 \ . \quad (3.1.16)$$

The parameter $\nu(1)$ can be interpreted as the duty ratio of successfully transmitted packets. Using formula (3.1.14) and the normalised intensities we write (3.1.9) in the form:

$$\nu(1) = (1 - P_{ex})\nu(2) \exp[-2\nu(2)] \quad (3.1.17)$$

When we do not have to take external noise into account, i.e. when $P_{ex} = 0$, this formula simplifies to

$$\nu(1) = \nu(2) \exp[-2\nu(2)] \quad (3.1.18)$$

The dependence of $\nu(1)$ on $\nu(2)$ for fixed values of P_{ex} which result from (3.1.18) are shown in Fig. 3.6(a). From these diagrams we see that, at first, $\nu(2)$ increases with $\nu(1)$. However after the critical value 0.5 any further increase of $\nu(2)$ causes a decrease in $\nu(1)$. Thus two values of $\nu(2)$ correspond to these values of $\nu(1)$ less than the maximum. We can expect these two values of $\nu(2)$ to correspond to the following situations:

(a) there are few packets in the channel; these are mainly packets transmitted for the first time, and collisions are fairly rare
(b) there are many packets which are for the most part packets which have been retransmitted several times, and collisions between them are frequent.

Situation (b) can be expected to be unstable and the channel may become blocked, thus we are only interested in the dependence of $\nu(2)$ on $\nu(1)$ in the range $0 \leqslant \nu(2) \leqslant 0.5$. This dependence is shown in Fig. 3.6(b). From Fig. 3.6(a) it is evident that for a fixed value of P_{ex} there exists a maximum value $\nu_{max}(1, P_{ex})$.

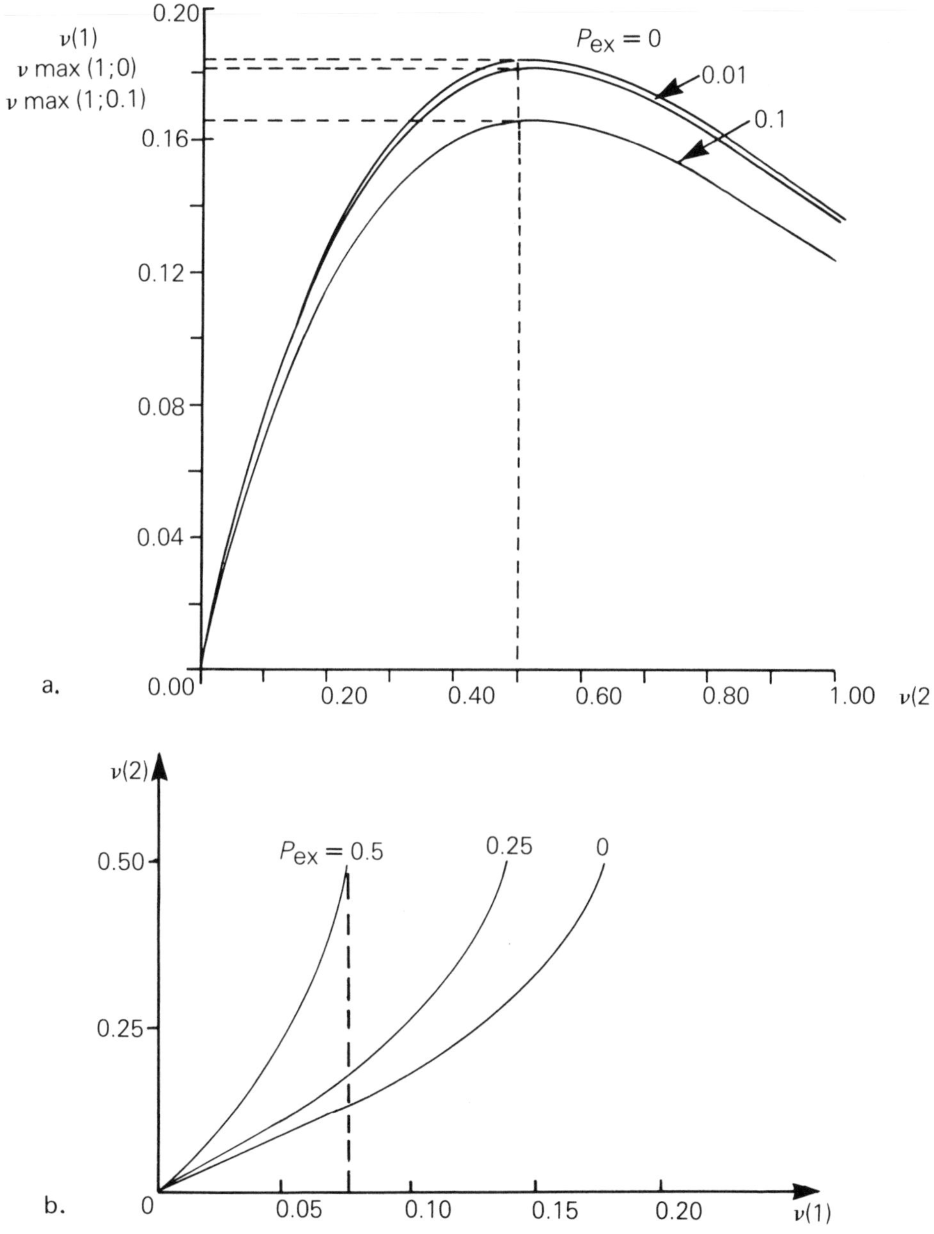

Fig. 3.6 – Relationship between the normalised intensity of successful transmissions $\nu(1)$ (channel utilisation factor) and the normalised intensity of all transmissions $\nu(2)$. P_{ex} = probability of external noise. (a) dependence of $\nu(2)$ on $\nu(1)$, (b) dependence of $\nu(1)$ on $\nu(2)$, within the range $\langle 0, \nu_{max}(1, P_{ex})\rangle$.

The maximum $\nu_{\max}(1)$ of $\nu_{\max}(1, P_{ex})$ is reached for $P_{ex} = 0$, and

$$\nu_{\max}(1) = \frac{1}{2e} \ . \tag{3.1.19}$$

This conclusion can be formulated in such a way that the maximum value of the channel utilisation factor for packets successfully transmitted is $1/2e \approx 0.18$.

3.1.3 Average packet delay

Let us denote by $\tau_1(H)$ the packets delay when we have H retransmissions. We have:

$$\tau_1(H) = T_{s-t} + H(T_r + T_{c-t}) + T_{fo} \tag{3.1.20}$$

where

$$T_{fo} = T + T_{fo}^{(pr)} \tag{3.1.21a}$$

$$T_f = T_\xi + T_f^{(pr)} \tag{3.1.21b}$$

$$T_r = T_{fo} + T_f \tag{3.1.21c}$$

and

T_{s-t} – is the time elapsing from the instant the primary packet is delivered by the source to the instant its transmission starts: the source – transmitter transfer time;

T_{c-t} – is the delay from receiving the packet: the copy–transmitter transfer time;

T – is the working packet duration;

T_ξ – is the duration of the packet carrying the ξ information;

$T_{fo}^{(pr)}$, $T_f^{(pr)}$ are the propagation times through the forward and feedback channels respectively;

T_{fo} – is the time taken to send the working packet through the forward channel;

T_f – is the time taken in the feedback channel;

T_r – is the round trip time.

The definitions introduced are illustrated in Figs. 3.2 and 3.3.

Similarly as in Chapter 2 instead of $\tau_1(H)$ it is more convenient to use the normalised delay

$$\tau_1'(H) = \frac{\tau_1(H) - T_{fo}^{(pr)}}{T} \tag{3.1.22}$$

On the assumption that the number of retransmissions does not depend on the copy transfer process, we average (3.1.20) and obtain the average packets delay:

$$\tau \equiv \bar{T}(1) + \bar{H}\bar{T}_c \tag{3.1.23}$$

where

$$\bar{T}(1) = T_{\text{s-t}} + T_{\text{fo}} \tag{3.1.24a}$$

is the delay of a successful (class 1) packet, while

$$\bar{T}_{\text{c}} = \bar{T}_{\text{c-t}} + \bar{T}_{\text{r}} \tag{3.1.24b}$$

is the delay of a copy and $\bar{H}$ is the average number of retransmissions. The average normalised delay

$$\tau' = \frac{\bar{T}_{\text{s-t}}}{T} + \frac{\bar{H}\bar{T}_{\text{c}}}{T} + 1 \ldots \tag{3.1.25}$$

We will now consider in more detail the components of (3.1.25). We have:

$$\bar{T}_{\text{s-t}} = \bar{T}_{\text{eb}} \tag{3.1.26}$$

where $\bar{T}_{\text{eb}}$ is the average time spent in the entrance buffer. If we use the buffer for retransmission (subrules (3.1a), (5.1a)) we can approximately evaluate T_{eb} using the well-known formula A.2.22 for a continuously emptied buffer and taking $\lambda_m(2)$ as packet intensity. Thus we have:

$$\bar{T}_{\text{eb}} = \frac{T}{2}\frac{\nu_m(2)}{1-\nu_m(2)} \tag{3.1.27}$$

where $\nu_m(2)$ is the normalised packet intensity. We have

$$\bar{T}_{\text{c-t}} = \bar{T}_{\text{ac}} + \bar{T}_{\text{ac-t}} \tag{3.1.28}$$

where $\bar{T}_{\text{ac-t}}$ is the time needed to transfer the copy from the anticollision delay unit to the transmitter.

If we use the entrance buffer for copies (subrules (3.1a), (5.1a)) then

$$\bar{T}_{\text{ac-t}} = \bar{T}_{\text{eb}} \tag{3.1.29a}$$

If we retransmit directly (subrules (3.1b), (5.1b)) then

$$\bar{T}_{\text{ac-t}} = 0\ . \tag{3.1.29b}$$

From A2 we have:

$$\bar{T}_{\text{ac}} = T\frac{Z}{2} \tag{3.1.30}$$

Finally, let us consider the average number of retransmissions. As we have shown in subsection 3.1.1 (see formula (3.1.4)), we have:

$$\bar{H} = \frac{\lambda(2)}{\lambda(1)} - 1 = \frac{\nu(2)}{\nu(1)} - 1 \tag{3.1.31}$$

Using (3.1.25), (3.1.30), (3.1.31), we ultimately get the normalised delay

$$\tau' = \frac{T_{s-t}}{T} + \left(\frac{\nu(2)}{\nu(1)} - 1\right)\left(\frac{T_{ac-t}}{T} + \frac{Z}{2} + T'_r\right) + 1 \qquad (3.1.32)$$

where $T'_r = T_r/T$ is the normalised round-trip time. For the homogeneous system (A11), it

$$\nu_1(2) = \frac{\nu(2)}{M} \qquad (3.1.33)$$

where $\nu(2)$ is the normalised intensity of the total flow in the common channel. When $M \gg 1$, we have $\nu_1(2) \ll 1$ and from (3.1.27) it follows that both $\bar{T}_{s-t} \ll T$ and $\bar{T}_{ct-t}/T \ll 1$. Thus (3.1.32) simplifies to

$$\tau' = 1 + \beta\left(\frac{\nu(2)}{\nu(1)} - 1\right) \qquad (3.1.34)$$

where

$$\beta \equiv T'_r + \frac{Z}{2} \; . \qquad (3.1.35)$$

Using the formula we obtain the dependence of τ' on $\nu(1)$ and parameter β. This dependence is shown in Fig. 3.7. Obviously τ' is smaller, the smaller Z is. However,

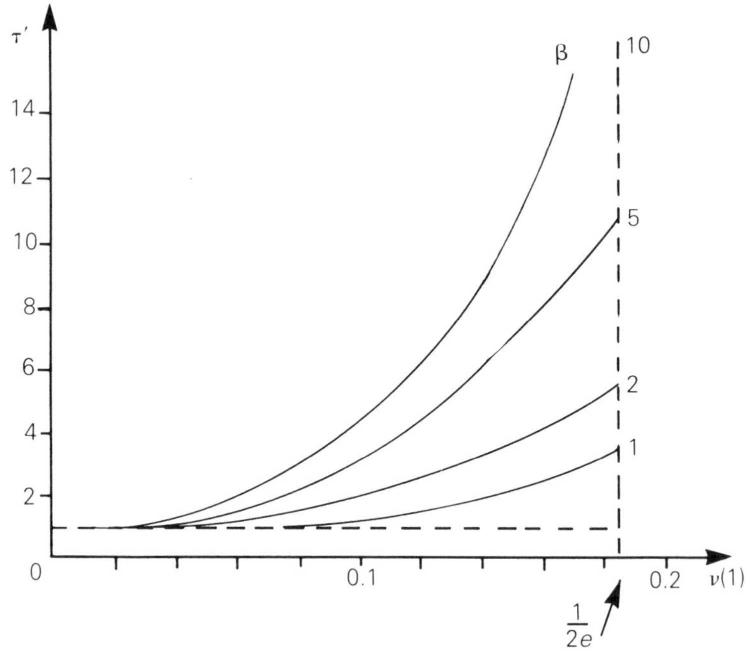

Fig. 3.7 – Dependence of the normalised packet passage time τ'/T, channel utilisation $\nu(1)$ and parameter β.

this is true only for large Z since for small Z repeated collisions would be very frequent, thus the uniform collision assumption and formula (3.1.5) would not hold, but we can expect that the packet delay would be large. To choose an optimum value for Z, we have to study in more detail the relationship between $\nu(2)$ and $\nu(1)$ without resorting to the simplifying uniform collision assumption A8. We make this analysis in the next section, showing that values of Z of the order of a few units are satisfactory.

3.1.4 Spatial properties of systems with feedback

The information sources and nodes which we were discussing earlier are usually distributed over an area around the central node to which information is directed. As a result, signals bringing packets from different nodes are of different power when they reach the central node. If we transmit signals with redundancy increasing error immunity, we normally get a threshold value for the signal-to-noise ratio above which the quality of information transmission is very good. So, for example, if a weak signal overlaps a strong signal node, the probability that the information carried by the strong signal will be incorrectly recovered is very small. We shall now examine the effect of this on the relationship between the normalised intensity of all packets and the normalised intensity of successful transmissions. We shall be using a model in which the nodes are located fairly close to each other. Instead of using intensities, it is appropriate to use spatial densities. At this point we will introduce some assumptions about the sources. We assume that they are poissonian and independent (A3, A4), the packets have equal duration T and:

A13 The sources, and therefore the nodes, are located close enough to each other for time to be regarded as being continuously distributed.

We also assume that there is no external noise, that the system is homogeneous, and that:

A14 If a packet sent by a node at a distance l from the central node overlaps a packet sent by a node at a distance αl from the central node, where $\alpha \geqslant 1$, the packet from the first node will be correctly received, but the second will not be.

As a result of A14 we introduce the concept of packet density per unit area, which we define as follows:

$$\lambda'(\mathrm{i}) \equiv \frac{\lambda(i, \delta S)}{\gamma(\delta S)} \qquad (3.1.36)$$

$i = 0, 1, 2$, where $\lambda(i, \delta S)$ is the packet intensity from nodes located in the small region δS, and $\gamma(\delta S)$ is the area of that region. Next we define the normalised densities:

$$\nu'(i) \equiv T\lambda'(i) \tag{3.1.37}$$

From assumptions A9, A10 we have

$$\nu'(1) = \nu'(0) \ . \tag{3.1.38}$$

We further assume:

A15 The normalised densities depend only upon the distance of the centre of the area δS from the central node (see Fig. 3.8); as a result of this we write $\nu'(i,r)$.

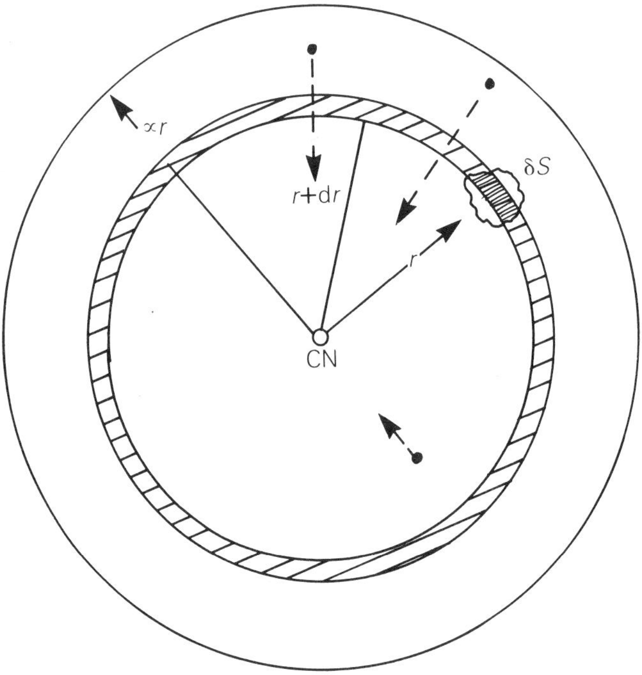

Fig. 3.8 – Illustration of the definition of the density of packet flow.

Using the uniform collision assumption (A8) and that about the Poisson character of packet flow A2, A3. We can now derive the fundamental relationship between the normalised densities $\nu'(1,r)$ and $\nu'(2,r)$. Let:

$C(r)$ – be the circle of radius r; the central node is at the centre of the circle;

$\lambda[i, C(r)]$ – be the intensity of ith class packets coming from nodes located within the circle $C(r)$.

Transmission from a node N_1, in $C(r)$, will be successful if it is not overlapped by any packet from nodes in $C(\alpha r)$. The intensity of such packets is $\lambda[2, C(\alpha r)]$, and no collision with the packet from node N_1 will take place if none of the nodes within $C(\alpha r)$, apart from N_1 starts to transmit during the collision zone. The probability of this happening is:

$$\exp\{-2T\lambda[2, C(\alpha r)]\}$$

As in the relationship (A15) for the normalised density of packets coming from nodes lying within a ring of radii $l, l + \mathrm{d}l$ (see Fig. 3.8), we have:

$$\nu'(1,r)\cdot 2\pi r\,\mathrm{d}r = \nu'(2,r)\cdot 2\pi r\,\mathrm{d}r\cdot\exp\{-2T\lambda[2, C(\alpha, r)]\} \tag{3.1.39}$$

From the definition of $\lambda[2, C(\alpha r)]$ and assumption A14 we get:

$$\lambda[2, C(\alpha r)] = 2\pi\int_0^{\alpha r} l\lambda'(2,R)\,\mathrm{d}R\ . \tag{3.1.40}$$

Having substituted this expression in (3.1.39), we finally obtain

$$\nu'(2,r) = \nu'(1,r)\exp\left[-4\pi\int_0^{\alpha r}\nu'(2,r')\,\mathrm{d}r'\right] \tag{3.1.41}$$

Differentiating both sides of this equation, and substituting for the exponential term from (3.1.41) we get:

$$\frac{\mathrm{d}\nu'(1,r)}{\mathrm{d}r}\nu'(2,r) = \frac{\mathrm{d}\nu'(2,r)}{\mathrm{d}r}\nu'(1,r) - 4\pi r\alpha^2\nu'(1,r)\nu'(2,r)\nu'(2,\alpha r) \tag{3.1.42}$$

This is the basic differential equation, derived by N. Abramson [3.2], linking the normalised flow intensities of all packets and of successfully transmitted packets. In order to illustrate the relationships resulting from this differential equation, we shall examine a particular example, assuming that

$$\nu'(0,r) = \text{const.} \tag{3.1.43}$$

and that

$$\alpha = 1 \tag{3.1.44}$$

i.e. interference from weaker signals may be neglected.

From A15 and (3.1.42), we can rewrite (3.1.38) as:

$$\frac{d\nu'(2,r)}{dr} = 2\pi r[\nu(2,r)]^2 \ . \tag{3.1.45}$$

Integrating we obtain:

$$\nu'(2,r) = \frac{1}{A - 2\pi r} \tag{3.1.46}$$

where A is an integration constant. We can rewrite this equation in the following form:

$$\nu'(2,r) = \frac{\nu^*(2,0)}{1 - 2\pi\nu^*(2,0)r} \tag{3.1.47}$$

where $\nu^*(2,0)$ is the value of the normalised packet density from the area surrounding the central node. Let:

$$r_{cr} \equiv \sqrt{\frac{1}{2\pi\nu'(2,0)}} \tag{3.1.48}$$

Equation (3.1.47) can be written in the form

$$\nu'(2,r) = \frac{1}{1-(r/r_{cr})^2} \tag{3.1.49}$$

For $r < r_{cr}$, the density $\nu'(2,r) > 0$, and therefore the intensity $\lambda(2,r)$ of all packets in one unit of area remains constant, but for $r \to r_{cr}$, the intensity $\lambda'(2,r) \to \infty$. Thus we can only send packets from nodes which are less than l_{cr} from the centre. This happens because the number of collisions and therefore the number of retransmissions increases with distance from the central node. As l_{cr} is approached, retransmissions dominate, and these preclude the collision-free transmission of packets from nodes located at a distance greater than l_{cr}.

3.2 SYNCHRONOUS ACCESS SYSTEM

In a synchronous access system with feedback (abbreviated SAF) the channel has slots during which the nodes may transmit. In SAF systems either a transmission is successful or a complete collision occurs, whereas in AAF systems partial collisions are possible. Since we assumed that partial collisions destroy the packet completely, and they are more frequent than complete collisions, we may expect SAF systems to be more efficient.

The section starts with a description of the system, then gives an analysis of the system similar to that performed for AAF systems in the previous section.

In the second section we give a more exact analysis of the dependence of packet delay on channel utilisation, and in the third section we consider SAF system stability.

3.2.1 Description of the system

The channel is divided into slots of duration T equal to the packet length, and packets must be placed in these slots. Thus packet transmission can start at times

$$t_j = jT \qquad j = 1, 2, \ldots \,. \tag{3.2.1}$$

In view of this we change assumption A4 from section 3.1 assuming that

A4′ The random variable representing the anticollision delay $T_m = ZT$, where Z is a discrete variable, taking integer values $z = 1, 2, \ldots, Z$ with equal probabilities

$$P(Z = z) = \begin{cases} 0 & \text{for } Z \leqslant 0,\ z > Z \\ \dfrac{1}{Z} & \text{for } 1 \leqslant z \leqslant Z \end{cases} \tag{3.2.2}$$

We first derive the fundamental relationships between the intensity $\nu(2)$ of all packets in the channel and the intensity $\nu(1)$ of successful transmissions. We assume that the sources are poissonian and independent (A2, A3), and that the system is homogeneous. We also assume that the packets are coded so that they cannot be destroyed by noise. We use the terms class 0, 1, 2 packets (delivered by the source, going successfully through, any in the common channel). Let:

$P_m(i), i = 0, 1, 2$ be the probability that a packet coming from the mth node is a class i packet;

$\lambda_m(i)$ be the intensity of class i packets put into a slot by the mth transmitter.

We have

$$P_m(0) = \lambda_m(0)T \tag{3.2.3}$$

We further assume that the system is stationary A4 and stable (A10) and that the buffer capacities are infinite (A9). On such assumptions every primary packet delivered by the source will ultimately be transmitted successfully. Hence:

$$P_m(1) = P_m(0) \tag{3.2.4}$$

For $i = 1, 2$. Let us denote

$$\nu_m(i) \equiv T\lambda_m(i) \tag{3.2.5}$$

as normalised intensity.

From this definition, it follows that:

$$\bar{\Lambda}_m = P_m(i) = \nu_m(i) \tag{3.2.6}$$

For the system as a whole $\lambda(i)$ is the total intensity of class i packets, and

$$\nu(i) = T\lambda(i) \tag{3.2.7}$$

is the normalised intensity. Obviously:

$$\lambda(i) = \sum_{m=1}^{M} \lambda_m(i) \tag{3.2.8}$$

$$\nu(i) = \sum_{m=1}^{M} \nu_m(i) \tag{3.2.9}$$

From (3.2.4), (3.2.6) follows that

$$\lambda(1) = \lambda(0) \tag{3.2.10}$$

We now derive the fundamental relationship between $\nu(2)$ and $\nu(1)$. The statistical properties of packet flow in the channel are determined by the properties of the sources and by the system operating rules. However, we introduce again the simplifying uniform collision assumption which for SAF system takes the form:

A8′ The occurrence of a class 2 packet in a given slot is independent of events in other slots.

From this assumption it follows that the probability of collision is the same for a primary packet and for a copy. Similarly as is the case for A8 we can expect that A8′ is acceptable if the randomisation index Z in (3.2.2) is large.

The transmission of a packet transmitted in the jth slot by the mth source will be succesful if no other source is transmitting a packet. Thus

$$P_m(1) = P_m(2) \sum_{m=1}^{M} [1 - P_m(2)] \tag{3.2.11}$$

For the homogeneous system all the probabilities are independent of m, thus we can rewrite (3.2.11) as:

$$P_1(1) = P_1(2)[1 - P_1(2)]^{M-1} \tag{3.2.12}$$

Using (3.2.6) we have:

$$\nu_1(1) = \nu_1(2)[1 - \nu_1(2)]^{M-1} \tag{3.2.13}$$

From homogeneity and (3.2.9) it follows that:

$$\nu_1(i) = \frac{\nu(i)}{M} \tag{3.2.14}$$

Using this, we can rewrite (3.3.13) as

$$\nu(1) = \nu(2)\left[1 - \frac{\nu(2)}{M}\right]^{M-1} \tag{3.2.15}$$

For $M \to \infty$ we have:

$$\nu(1) = \nu(2)\exp\left[-\nu(2)\right] \tag{3.2.16}$$

This formula can be also derived using (3.1.10) which holds for SAF. On the simplifying assumption A8′ the probability of collision is

$$P^- = 1 - \exp\left[-\nu(2)\right] \tag{3.2.17}$$

Substituting it in (3.1.6) and using (3.1.3) we obtain (3.2.1).

A graph of (3.2.16) is shown in Fig. 3.9. It can be easily proved that for SAF systems the maximum value of $\nu(1)$ is $1/e$. Figure 3.9 also shows the curve

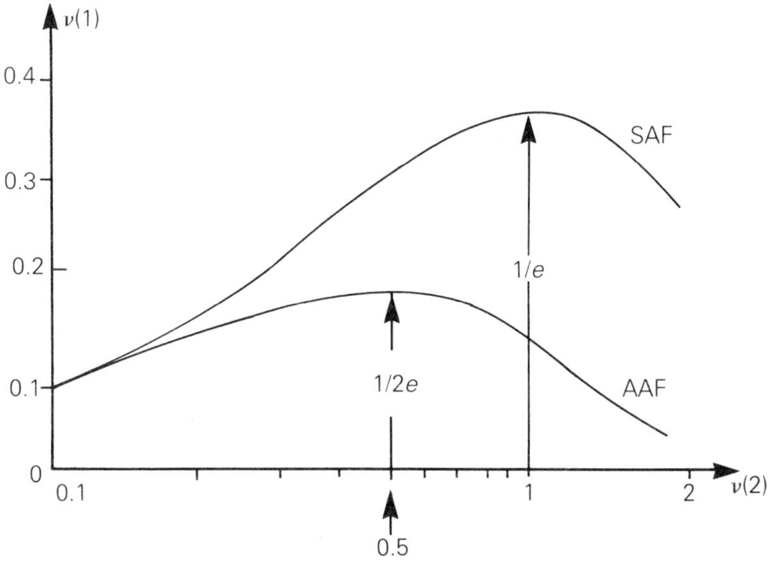

Fig. 3.9 – Dependence of the normalised intensity $\nu(1)$ of successful transmisions channel utilisation factor on the intensity $\nu(2)$ of all packets in the common channel. Limiting case, independent packet collisions, no external noise. AAF = asynchronous access system; SAF = synchronous access system, common channel sensing.

for an AAF system with $P_{ex} = 0$ from Fig. 3.5(b). We see that synchronisation of the system doubles the maximum intensity of successful transmissions. Obviously the doubled collision zone is the primary reason for the inferiority of AAF systems.

3.2.2 More exact relationships between the normalised packet intensities and packet delay

In the following two subsections we shall replace the previously introduced simplifying assumptions by more realistic ones. We first remove the uniform collision assumption, we analyse in more detail the collisions, so that we can take into account the different character of primary packet and copy collision. Such an analysis will enable us to determine the desirable value for the randomisation index Z. The second fundamental simplifying assumption was that that the system is stationary. Removing this assumption and analysing changes of the state of the system we formulate the conditions which must be satisfied so that the system is stationary and stable. However, we keep assumption A12 that the total flow in the common channel is poissonian.

We start with the analysis of the relationship between $\nu(1)$ and $\nu(2)$ as defined previously.

Let us consider the following events:

SP the successful transmission of a primary packet (abbreviation: primary successful).

SC the successful transmission of a copy (abbreviation: successful copy).

Also let:

$$\mathbf{P}^+_{pr} \equiv \mathbf{P}\,(\text{successful primary}) \tag{3.2.18a}$$

$$\mathbf{P}^+_{c} \equiv \mathbf{P}\,(\text{successful copy}) \tag{3.2.18b}$$

Relationship (3.1.4) (between $\lambda(1)$, $\lambda(1)$ and the average number of retransmissions) still holds therefore we analyse the random variable H representing the number of retransmissions. Under the independence assumption A4 we have:

$$P(\mathrm{H} = h) = (1 - P^+_{pr})(1 - P^+_c)^{h-1} P^+_c \tag{3.2.19}$$

The average number of retransmissions

$$\bar{H} = \sum_{h=1}^{\infty} hP(\mathrm{H} = h) = \frac{1 - P^+_{pr}}{P^+_c} \tag{3.2.20}$$

We see that (3.1.6) is a special case of (3.2.20) with $P^+_{pr} = P^+_c = 1 - P^-_m$.

We evaluate first P^+_{pr}. We assume that the node considered places its primary packet in the jth slot, and we introduce the events:

no collision with a primary packet delivered by another node (abbreviation: no primary–primary collision);
no collision with a copy (abbreviation: no primary–copy collision).

We have

$$P^{+}_{\mathrm{pr}} = P(\text{successful primary}) = P(\text{no primary–primary collision}) \times P(\text{no primary–copy collision}) \quad (3.2.21)$$

No primary–primary collision occurs if no other node than the one considered tries to place its primary packet in the jth slot. This is illustrated in Fig. 3.10(a). In view of assumption A3 (Poisson source)

$$P(\text{no primary–primary collision}) = \exp[-\nu_{\mathrm{a}}(1)] \quad (3.2.22)$$

where

$$\nu_{\mathrm{a}}(1) \equiv \frac{M-1}{M}\nu(1) \quad (3.2.23)$$

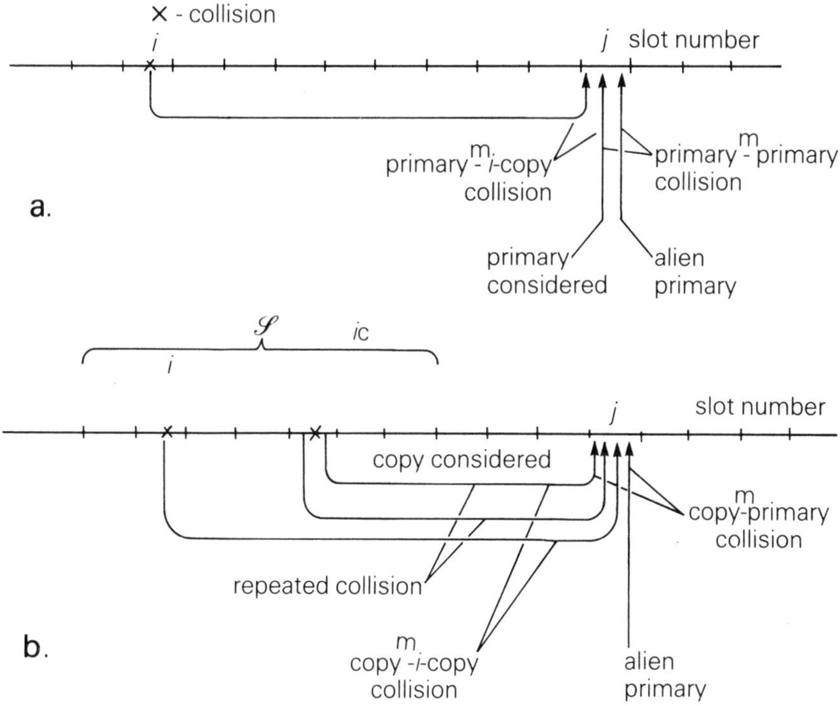

Fig. 3.10 – Illustration to the definition of the events (a) primary–primary, primary–copy collision, (b) copy–primary repeated collision, copy–i-copy collision. The cross denotes a collision in the past.

is the normalised intensity of all primary packets delivered by sources other than the considered one (alien packets – hence the subscript a).

Let us denote by C the set of numbers of such slots preceding the jth slot, that a copy resulting from a collision in a slot $i \in C$ could be located in jth slot. From (3.2.2) it follows that C contains Z elements. We consider the event

no collision with a copy which was caused by a collision in ith slot (abbreviation: no primary–i-copy collision).

(see Fig. 3.10). We have:

$$P(\text{no primary–copy collision}) = \bigcap_{i \in C} P(\text{no primary–}i\text{-copy collision}) = [P(\text{no primary–}i\text{-copy collision})]^Z \quad (3.2.24)$$

Let us denote by l_i the number of packets which were located at the ith slot, $i \in C$, delivered by nodes other than the one considered. There is no primary–i-copy collision if either there was no collision at ith slot, i.e. if either $l_i = 0$ or $L_i = 1$, or if $l_i \geqslant 2$, and the anticollision delay was so chosen that the copy is not located in the jth slot. Thus

$$P(\text{no primary–}i\text{-copy collision}) = P(L_i = 0) + P(L_i = 1) + \sum_{l=2}^{\infty} P(L_i = l)\left(1 - \frac{1}{Z}\right)^l \quad (3.2.25)$$

On the assumption A12 L_i is a Poisson variable, thus

$$P(L_i = l) = \frac{[\nu_a(2)]^l \exp[-\nu_a(2)]}{l!} \quad (3.2.26)$$

where

$$\nu_a(2) = \frac{M-1}{M}\nu(2) \quad (3.2.27)$$

is the normalised total intensity of packets coming from all nodes other than the one considered.

After some manipulation from (3.2.25), (3.2.26) we obtain

$$P(\text{no primary–}i\text{-copy collision}) = \exp\frac{-\nu_a(2)}{Z} + \frac{\nu_a(2)}{Z}\exp[-\nu_a(2)] \quad (3.2.28)$$

Putting this and (3.2.22) into (3.2.21) we obtain the probability P_{pr}^+. For M, large $\nu_a(1) \approx \nu(1)$ and $\nu_a(2) \approx \nu(2)$, it can be checked that:

$$\lim_{Z \to \infty} P_{pr}^+ = \exp[-\nu(2)] \quad (3.2.29)$$

Next we evaluate the probability P_c^+ of successful copy transmission. Similarly to (3.2.21) we have

$$P_c^+ = P(\text{successful copy}) = P(\text{no copy–primary collision}) = P(\text{no copy–copy collision}) \quad (3.2.30)$$

Similar to (3.2.22)

$$P(\text{no copy–primary collision}) = \exp[-\nu_a(1)] \quad (3.2.31)$$

It is

$$P_c^+ = P(\text{no copy–copy collision}) = P(\text{no repeated collision}) \times \bigcap_{i \in C - i_c} P(\text{no copy–}i\text{-copy collision}) = P(\text{no repeated collision}) \times P(\text{no copy–}i\text{-copy collision})^{-Z-1} \ldots \quad (3.2.32)$$

Repeated collision we call the collision of the copy considered with another copy caused by the same collision in slot i_c, which caused our copy see Fig. 3.10. The collisions in slots $C - i_c$ we call alien collisions, and the copies caused by these collisions we call **alien copies.** The probability of repeated collision is by definition a conditional probability, on the condition that in slot i_c an earlier collision has occured. Let us denote by l_{i_c} the number of packets other than the considered one which were involved in that collision. Similarly to the last component on RHS of (3.2.25) we have

$$P(\text{no repeated copy collision}) = \sum_{l=1}^{\infty} P(\mathrm{L}_{i_c} = l \mid \mathrm{L}_{i_c} \geqslant 1)\left(1 - \frac{1}{Z}\right)^l \quad (3.2.33)$$

For $l \geqslant 1$ the conditional probability we obtain from the formula

$$P(\mathrm{L}_{i_c} = l \mid \mathrm{L}_{i_c} \geqslant 1) = \frac{P(\mathrm{L}_{i_c} = l,\ \mathrm{L}_{i_c} \geqslant 1)}{\mathrm{P}(\mathrm{L}_{i_c} \geqslant 1)} = \frac{\mathrm{P}(\mathrm{L}_{i_c} = l)}{\mathrm{P}(\mathrm{L}_{i_c} \geqslant 1)} \quad (3.2.34)$$

The variable L_{i_c} is again the Poisson variable with p.d. given by (3.2.26). Using this, after some manipulation we obtain.

$$P(\text{no repeated copy collision}) = \left\{\exp\left[\frac{-\nu_a(2)}{Z}\right] - \exp[-\nu_a(2)]\right\}\{1 - \exp[-\nu_a(2)]\}^{-1} \quad (3.2.35)$$

Notice that if we were not to apply anticollision delay, taking $Z = 1$, then the probability of no repeated copy collision would be 0, thus we would have a new collision, while for $Z \to \infty$ the probability of no repeated collision is almost 1, thus almost certainly no repeated collision would occur.

We next consider the probability of no collision between our copy and an alien copy caused by a collision in ith slot, $i \neq i_c$. It is

$$P(\text{no copy--}i\text{-alien copy collision}) = P(\text{no primary--}i\text{-copy collision}) \tag{3.2.36}$$

Formulae (3.2.30), (3.2.31), (3.2.35), (3.2.36) and (3.2.28) give us the probability P_c^+ of successful copy transmission. It can be checked that for large M:

$$\lim_{Z\to\infty} P_c^+ = \exp[-\nu(2)] \tag{3.2.37}$$

This together with (3.2.29), gives a strict justification of the uniform collision assumption which we introduced in section 3.1.1.

From our consideration it follows that both for large M P_{pr}^+ and P_c^+ are functions of $\nu(1)$, $\nu(2)$ and the randomisation index Z, thus we write $P_{pr}^+[\nu(1), \nu(2), Z]$ and $P_c^+[\nu(1), \nu(2), Z]$.

Putting these functions into (3.2.20) we obtain† from (3.1.9) the dependence $\nu(1) = \Psi_1[\nu_1(2), Z]$. The curves illustrating this dependence are shown in Fig. 3.11. The curve, $Z = \infty$, is the curve SAF shown in Fig. 3.3. It can be shown that, for a quite wide range of $\nu(2)$ and Z to a good approximation:

$$\begin{aligned} \nu(1) &\cong A(Z)\cdot\Psi_1(\nu(2), \infty) \\ &\cong A(Z)\nu(2)\exp[-\nu(2)] \end{aligned} \tag{3.2.38}$$

where $A(Z)$ depends only on Z.

From Fig. 3.11 there follows the important conclusion that, even for small values of Z, the throughput is little below the maximum.

We will now consider the average delay. It is evident that formula (3.1.32) can be applied. The important component of the times T_{s-t} and T_{ac-t} is now the waiting time for the next slot. This time has a uniform probability distribution in the interval $\langle 0, T\rangle$, thus its average value is $T/2$. This is usually much larger than the time the packet spends in the entrance buffer (the copy, if subrules (3.1b), (5.1b) are applied). Thus we take

$$\bar{T}_{s-t} = \bar{T}_{ac-t} = \frac{1}{2}T \tag{3.2.39}$$

From (3.1.32) and from relationship $\nu(1) = \phi_1[\nu(2), Z]$ we obtain ultimately:

$$\tau' = \Psi_2[\nu(1), Z] \ . \tag{3.2.40}$$

† The formulae for $\Psi_1[\nu(2), Z]$ were first derived by Lam; see [3.3].

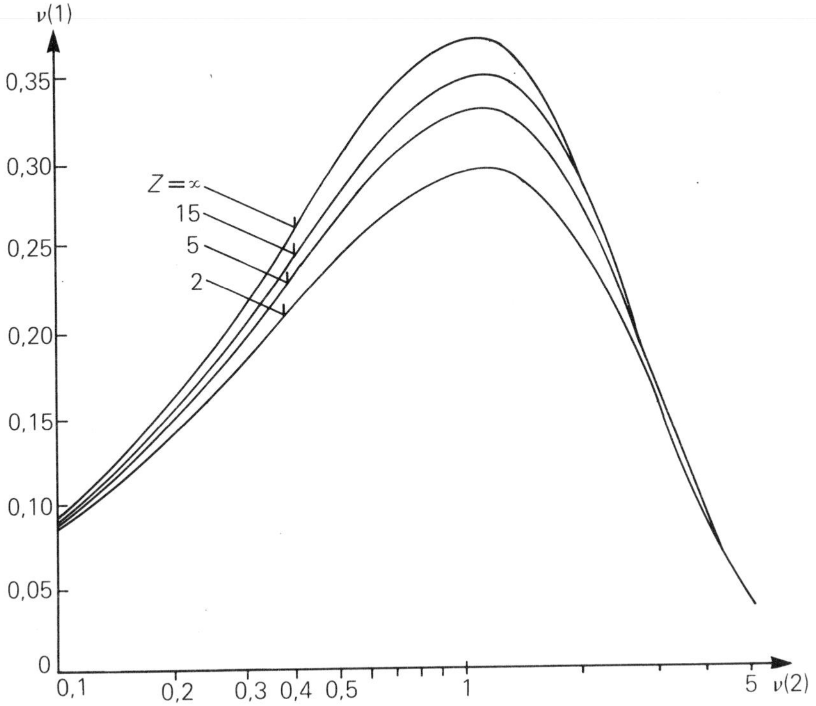

Fig. 3.11 – Relationship between the normalised intensity $\nu(1)$ of successfully transmitted packets and the normalised intensity $\nu(2)$ of all packets in the channel, and the randomisation index Z.

A typical dependence of τ' on $\nu(1)$ and Z is shown in Fig. 3.12. It can be proved (see Lam [3.3]) that for $\nu(1) \to 0$ the average number of retransmissions

$$\bar{H} \cong \frac{Z\nu(1)}{Z-1} \tag{3.2.41}$$

Using this and (3.2.39) we have, from (3.1.32),

$$\tau' \cong 1.5 + \frac{Z\nu(1)}{Z-1}\left[T_r' + \frac{Z+1}{2}\right] \tag{3.2.42}$$

From Fig. 3.12 it can be seen that this is a good approximation for $\nu(1) \leqslant 0.2$.

It can easily be seen that both for AAF and for SAF for a given value of $\nu(1)$, a value of Z exists which minimises τ'. In particular, evaluating $d\tau'/dZ$ from (3.3.42) we see that for $\nu(1) \to 0$, the optimum value Z_0 of Z minimising τ' is the largest integer such that $Z^2 - 3Z - -2T_r' \leqslant 0$. For large $\nu(1)$ it does not seem

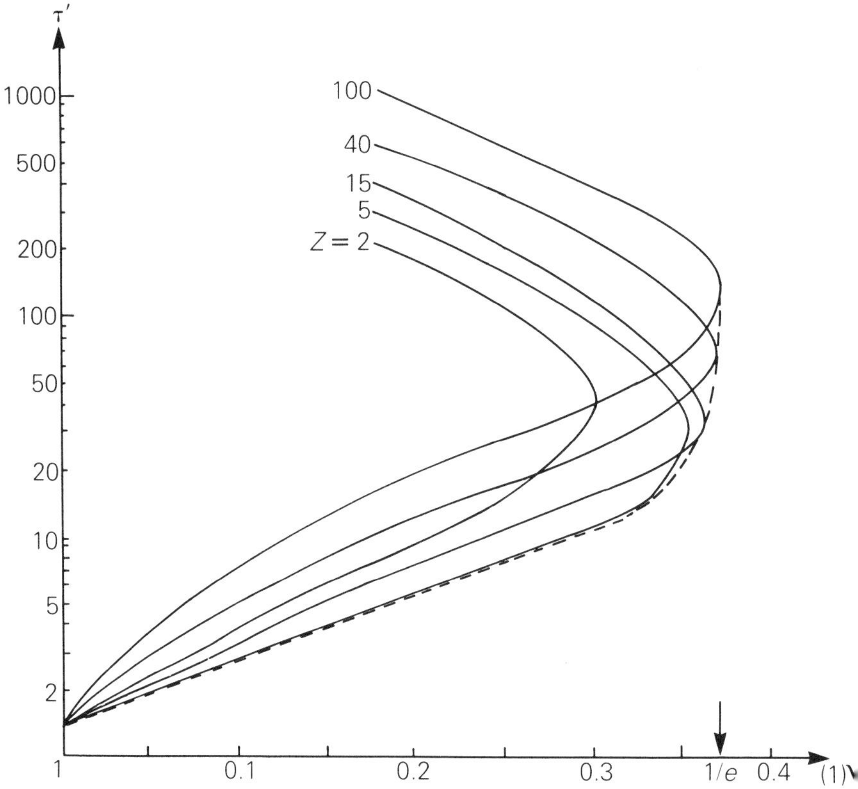

Fig. 3.12 – Typical dependence of the normalised delay τ' on the normalised intensity $\nu(1)$ of successful transmissions. Z = randomisation index, $T_r' = 12$.

possible to obtain the optimum value $Z^*[\nu(1)]$ in the closed form. The dotted line in Fig. 3.12 shows the relationship $\nu = \Psi_2\,[\nu(1), Z_0\,[\nu(1)]$ where $Z_0^*[\nu(1)]$ is the value of Z minimising τ for fixed $\nu(1)$. To obtain the minimum delay $\Psi_2\{\nu(1), Z_0[\nu(1)]\}$ we must have an adaptive feedback system with a facility for estimating $\nu(1)$ then calculating $Z^*[\nu(1)]$. All nodes have then to use $Z^*[\nu(1)]$ as randomisation index.

3.2.3 Stability of the system

We now analyse the stability of synchronous systems. The idea is not to evaluate the averages $\nu(1)$, $\nu(2)$ and τ directly as we did previously, but to consider conditional averages corresponding to a fixed state of the system.† We assume that

† The method was given by Kleinrock, Lam [3.4].

we have an SAF system without the entrance buffer and therefore in place of subrule 1 we take the subrule

1′ The packet delivered by the source is put into the transmitter only if the transmission of the previous packet has been completed and no copy remains in the copy store. If these conditions are not satisfied the packet is lost, and the transmitter is said to be blocked.

We next introduce the concept of system state:

We say that the system is in state σ_l if exactly l transmitters are blocked.

Let us denote

$\nu(1) = \lambda(1)T$ – normalised intensity of successful transmission;

$\nu(1\,|\,l)$ – normalised intensity of successful transmission on the condition that the system is in state σ_l;

Obviously

$$\nu(1) = \sum_{l=0}^{M} \nu(1\,|\,l)P(\sigma_l) \tag{3.2.43}$$

where $P(\sigma_l)$ is the probability of state σ_l. The average number of blocked transmitters

$$\bar{L}_{\text{bl}} = \sum_{l=1}^{M} lP(\sigma_l) \tag{3.2.44}$$

Let us denote by τ_{s} the average time spent by the packet in the system. If it is in a stable state we can apply Little's theorem which gives us

$$\bar{L}_{\text{bl}} = \tau_{\text{s}}\lambda(1) \tag{3.2.45}$$

The normalised delay (including packet duration):

$$\tau' = \frac{\bar{\tau}_{\text{s}}}{T_1} + 1 = \frac{\bar{L}_{\text{bl}}}{\nu(1)} + 1 \tag{3.2.46}$$

From (3.2.44)–(3.2.46) we see that to find $\nu(1)$ and τ' we have to evaluate $P(\sigma_l)$, and $\nu(1\,|\,l)$ for $k = 0, 1, \ldots$. We consider $P(\sigma_l)$ first.

The statistical properties of the system depend on the properties of the sequence of packets put into the channel and they in turn depend on the probability distribution of the time interval between successive retransmissions. Let us denote by VT the random variable representing this interval, V being a discrete random variable. Since the time interval considered is the sum of the round trip delay and the anticollision delay, which has the p.d. given by (3.2.2) we have

$$P(V = v) = \begin{cases} 0 \text{ for } 0 \leqslant v \leqslant N_r \\ \frac{1}{Z} \text{ for } N_r \leqslant v \leqslant N_r + Z \\ 0 \text{ for } v \geqslant N_r + Z + 1 \end{cases} \tag{3.2.47}$$

where v is integer and $N_r \equiv T_r/T_1$ is the round trip delay measured in slots. The analysis of the system with time interval between successive retransmissions having the probability distribution (3.2.47) would be prohibitively complicated.

Kleinrock and Lam [3.4] proposed to take instead of (3.2.47) the geometrical p.d.

$$P(V = v) = P_{at}(1 - P_{at})^{v-1} \tag{3.2.48}$$

The parameter P_{at} can be interpreted as probability that a retransmission will be attempted in the next slot (hence the subscripts). Obviously the shape of both p.d.s is quite different. However, Kleinrock and Lam [3.4] concluded from simulation experiments, that the ultimate results obtained for the geometrical probability distribution are close to those observed in simulation experiments with the real probability distribution (3.2.47), if the mean value for both probability distributions are the same. For p.d. (3.2.47) we have $\bar{V} = N_r + (Z+1)/2$ while for the geometrical p.d. $\bar{V} = P_{at}^{-1}$. Hence taking

$$P_{at} = \frac{1}{N_r + (Z+1)/2} \tag{3.2.49}$$

we can expect that the results obtained for the system in which time interval between successive retransmissions has the geometrical p.d. with parameter P_{at} given by (3.2.49) will be with good accuracy valid for the real system. As is well known assuming the geometrical probability distribution is equivalent to assuming that

A4′ Having a packet to retransmit we do this in the actual slot with a fixed probability P_{at}.

If we decided not to retransmit in the actual slot, we try in the next and so on. On assumption A2 (Poisson starting instants) the sequence $\sigma(t_j)$ of states of the node is a Markov chain. From the theory of Markov chains it is known that under quite general assumptions for large j the probability distribution of the state $\sigma(t_j)$ does not depend on either j or on the initial state $\sigma(t_1)$. This asymptotic probability distribution is called stationary. The stationary probabilities are determined by Chapman–Kolmogorov equations:

$$P(\sigma_k) = \sum_{m=0}^{M} P[\Sigma(t_{j+1}) = \sigma_k \mid \Sigma(t_j) = \sigma_l]\, P(\sigma_l) \tag{3.2.50}$$

$k = 1, 2, \ldots, M$, where $P[\Sigma(t_{j+1}) = \sigma_k \mid \Sigma(t_j) = \sigma_l]$ are the transition probabilities. We will now evaluate them.

Suppose that the set of transmitters is in state σ_l for the duration of the jth slot. It can move to state σ_{l-1}, in the $j+j$th slot, if one and only one of the l blocked transmitters has sent its packet, and no primary packets have entered the system. The transmitters remain in state σ_l if: no blocked transmitter sent a packet and exactly one primary packet entered the system; no primary packets entered the system, no blocked transmitter transmitted; or two or more transmitters transmitted. The set of transmitters changes to the state σ_{l+1} if at least one of the blocked transmitters sends a packet, and at least one packet from an unblocked transmitter enters the channel. In such a situation, this transmitter becomes blocked. Finally, the system state becomes σ_{l+m} where $m \geqslant 2$, if unblocked transmitters send new packets.

$$P[\Sigma(t_{j+1}) = \sigma_k \mid \Sigma(t_j) = \sigma_k] = \begin{cases} 0\,, & k \leqslant l-2\,; \\ kP_{at}(1-P_{at})^{k-1}(1-P_1)^{M-k}\,, & k = k-1\,; \\ (1-P_{at})^k(M-k)P_1(1-P)^{M-k-1} + \\ \quad + [1-kP_{at}(1-P_{at})^{k-1}](1-P_1)^{M-k}\,, & k = l\,; \\ (M-k)P_1(1-P_1)^{M-k-1}[1-(1-P_{at})^k]\,, & k = l+1\,; \\ \binom{M-k}{l-k} P_1^{l-k}(1-P_1)^{M-l}\,, & k \geqslant l+2\,. \end{cases} \tag{3.2.51}$$

where $P_1 = P_m(0)$ is the probability that a primary packet is delivered by a source. Assuming that $M \to \infty$, and $MP_1 = \nu = \text{const.}$, these equations take the form:

$$P[\Sigma(t_{j+1}) = \sigma_k \mid \Sigma(t_j) = \sigma_l] = \begin{cases} 0\,, & k \leqslant l-2\,; \\ kP_{at}(1-P_{at})^{l-1}\exp(-\nu)\,, & k = l-1\,; \\ (1-P_{at})^l \exp(-\nu) + \\ \quad + [1-lP_{at}(1-P_{at})^{l-1}]\exp(-\nu)\,, & k = l\,; \\ \nu\exp(-\nu)[1-(1-P_{at})^l]. & k = l+1\,; \\ (\nu^{k-l})/[(k-l)!]\exp(-\nu)\,, & k \geqslant l+2 \end{cases} \tag{3.2.52}$$

Knowing the transmission probabilities and solving the Chapman–Kolmogorov equations (3.2.50) we obtain the stationary probabilities $P(\sigma_l)$ of system states. To obtain from (3.2.43), (3.2.44), (3.2.46) the fundamental parameters $\nu(1)$

and τ' we have to find the conditional intensity $\nu(1|l)$. Evaluating it we will also be able to draw important conclusions about system stability.

Since in a slot only one packet can go successfully through we have

$$\nu(1\,|l) = P(\text{successful transmission}\,|\,\sigma_l) \tag{3.2.53}$$

where $\nu(1|l)$ is the conditional intensity of successful packets, introduced earlier. We have:

$$P(\text{successful transmission}\,|\,\sigma_l) = P(\text{no primary collision}\,|\,\sigma_l) + \\ + P(\text{no copy collision}\,|\,\sigma_l) \tag{3.2.54}$$

No primary (copy) collision will occur if; (1) none of the l blocked nodes attempts to retransmit its copy, (2) one and only one non-blocked node places its primary packet in the slot. Thus

$$P(\text{no primary collision}) = (1-P_{\text{at}})^l(M-k)P_1(1-P_1)^{M-l-1} \tag{3.2.55}$$

No copy collision will occur if one and only one of the blocked transmitters tries to retransmit its copy and none of the non-blocked transmitters transmits a primary packet. Thus

$$P(\text{no copy collision}) = lP_{\text{at}}(1-P_{\text{at}})^l(1-P_1)^{M-l}\ . \tag{3.2.56}$$

Let us denote by $\nu(0\,|l)$ normalised intensity of primary packets put into the system in the state σ_l. In accordance with the subrule 1′ (see page 131) only a non-blocked transmitter can accept a new packet. Thus:

$$\nu(0\,|l) = (M-l)P_1 \tag{3.2.57}$$

Using (3.2.54)–(3.2.56) we have from (3.2.53)

$$\nu(1|\,l) = (1-P_{\text{at}})^l\nu(0\,|l)\left[1-\frac{\nu(0\,|l)}{M-l}\right]^{M-l-1} + \\ + lP_{\text{at}}(1-P_{\text{at}})^{l-1}\left[1-\frac{\nu(0\,|l)}{M-l}\right]^{M-l} \tag{3.2.58}$$

If:

$$\nu(l) > \nu(1\,|\,l) \tag{3.2.59}$$

on average more packets are put in, than go successfully through. Similarly, if

$$\nu(1\,|\,l) < \nu(l) \tag{3.2.60}$$

l must decrease. Thus σ_l is stable if:

$$\nu(0\,|l) = \nu(1\,|\,l) \tag{3.2.61}$$

Let $\nu_s(1 \mid l)$ be the normalised intensity of input (and output) for which the state σ_l is stable. From (3.2.58) and (3.2.61) it follows that $\nu_s(1 \mid l)$ satisfies the equation

$$\nu = (1-P_{at})^l \nu \left[1-\frac{\nu}{M-l}\right]^{M-l-1} + lP_{at}(1-P_{at})^{l-1}\left[1-\frac{\nu}{M-l}\right]^{M-l} \tag{3.2.62}$$

Using this equation we can determine $\nu_s(1 \mid l)$ from l, or vice versa. In most cases $M \gg 1$, so that:

$$\left[1-\frac{\nu}{M-l}\right]^{M-l-1} \approx \left[1-\frac{\nu}{M-l}\right]^{M-l} \approx \exp(-\nu) \tag{3.2.63}$$

and equation (3.2.64) takes the form:

$$\nu = (1-P_{at})^l \nu \exp(-\nu) + lP_{at}(1-P_{at})^{l-1}\exp(-\nu) \tag{3.2.64}$$

l is an integer, but to simplify these considerations, we will assume that it is a continuous variable. The sets of points corresponding to solutions of (3.2.64) for fixed P_{at} form curves as shown in Fig. 3.13. They are labelled with values of Z (which determines Q).

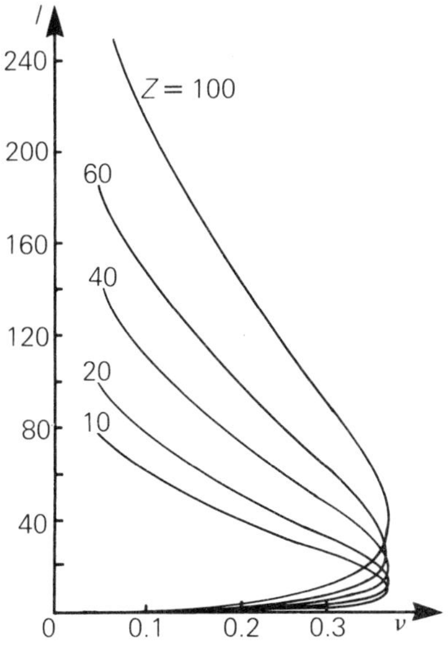

Fig. 3.13 – Equilibrium curves on the ν, l plane, where l is the number of blocked transmitters, drawn while treating l as a continuous variable, Z is the randomisation index, $N_r = 12$; the parameter P_{at} is calculated from (3.2.49).

Equation (3.2.57) can be represented on the ν, l plane as a straight line $\nu = (M - l)P_1$. This line is called the **system load characteristic**. The position of this line with respect to the equilibrium curve defined by (3.2.64) indicates the behaviour of the system. Figure 3.14(a) presents the first possibility. Suppose that l transmitters are blocked and that $\nu(l)$ corresponds to point A′ on Fig. 3.14(a). Since $\nu(l) > \nu(1 \mid l)$ A′ will move in the direction shown by the arrow. The converse applies to point A″ and movement takes place in the opposite direction. Thus, in the situation shown in Fig. 3.14(a) point A is the stable state of the system.

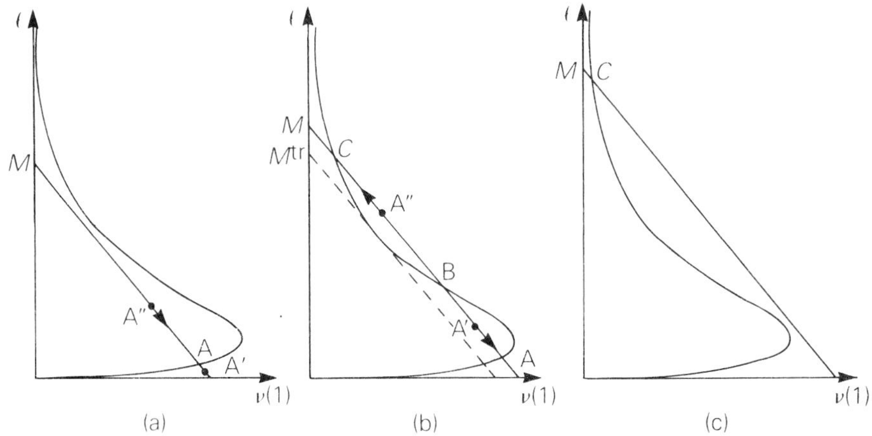

Fig. 3.14 – Types of systems state: (a) stable, (b) unstable, (c) stable, clogged, states. A = stable or locally stable; B = unstable; c = clogged. The curves are equilibrium lines for Z = const., straight lines are line for M_{cr}.

Figure 3.14(b) illustrates a second possibility. The arrows show the tendency of state changes. State B is obviously unstable, small deviation from it will cause the system to drift away from state B. Intensity of successful transmissions in state A and the number of blocked nodes is large, thus the delay is reasonably low; therefore we call it the **operation state**. If the deviation from state A is small the system state will return to A. However, if deviation brings the state in to the interval (B, C) the system state will move toward state C. Thus A is a **locally stable state**. Similarly C is locally stable, but from the point of view of packets transmission the system in state C is useless: the intensity of packets going through is very small and the delay very large. Therefore C corresponds to the **clogged system**.

From (3.2.51) it follows that there exists a positive but small probability that the system returns from state C to state A. Thus the system illustrated in Fig. 3.14(b) would exhibit bistable behaviour jumping between locally stable states A and C. Since it can be shown that the average time spent in the clogged state is much longer than in the operating state, the whole system characterised by Fig. 3.14(b) must be classified as unstable. The system characterised by Fig. 3.14(c) is obviously stable, but useless since it stays in the clogged state.

Fluctuations in the influx of packets cause deviations from the stable state. However, if the deviations are not very large we can take the parameters characterising the stable state as an approximation of the averages $\bar{L}_{bl}$ and $\nu(1)$. Using such simplification we can draw qualitative conclusions about system's properties. They should, however, be checked by simulation.

Let us first consider the effect of changing the randomisation index Z. We assume that both the number of sources M and the intensity of primary packet delivery are fixed, thus the operating line is fixed, but we alter Z. Such a situation is illustrated in Fig. 3.15(a). We see from it that parameter Z has a critical effect on stability. If we start with a stable system and decrease Z, then starting at a critical value $Z_{cr}(M)$ the system becomes unstable, while the previously mentioned tendency to move into the clogged state grows. It is best to take Z slightly larger than the minimum value Z_{cr} ensuring stability. These qualitative considerations confirm numerical results. Typical digrams of $\nu(1)$ and versus Z are shown in Fig. 3.15(a). We see that for $Z < Z_{cr}$ the delay rapidly grows with Z while the intensity of successful transmissions decrease. The intensity $\nu(1)$ for $Z > Z_{cr}$ is rather independent of Z, delay τ', grows only slowly with Z; this is obvious since the average anticollision delay grows.

Next let us assume that randomisation index Z, and thus the equilibrium contour, is fixed, the system operating point is fixed and we change the number M of nodes; thus we change the load line as shown in Fig. 3.16. Let us notice that if we increase M then in order to keep the operating point fixed we have to decrease the probability of new packet arrival P_1. From Fig. 3.16 we see that as long as M does not exceed a critical M_{cr}, the system is stable, but for larger M it becomes unstable. This conclusion is quite interesting since it shows that the stability depends not only on the total intensity of packets put into the common channel but also on the number M of nodes.

It is evident that the stability considerations force us to operate with quite a low $\nu(1)$ corresponding to the situation when only one stable state exists (Fig. 3.14(a)). The obvious way to improve the common channel utilisation is to operate at the locally stable state A shown in Fig. 3.14(b) and to introduce an auxiliary mechanism to bring the system back to that state if it starts to drift to the clogged state C. This can be done by two means: (1) by restricting the access of primary packets; (2) by increasing temporarily the randomisation index Z, increasing average delay but making the system stable. Restricting access of new packets is a common method of counteracting the congestion which we will consider in detail in Chapter 7 and is realized by an admission rule. This rule, based on the information ξ about the state of the system makes the binary admission decision which is either α^- – the primary (new) packet must not

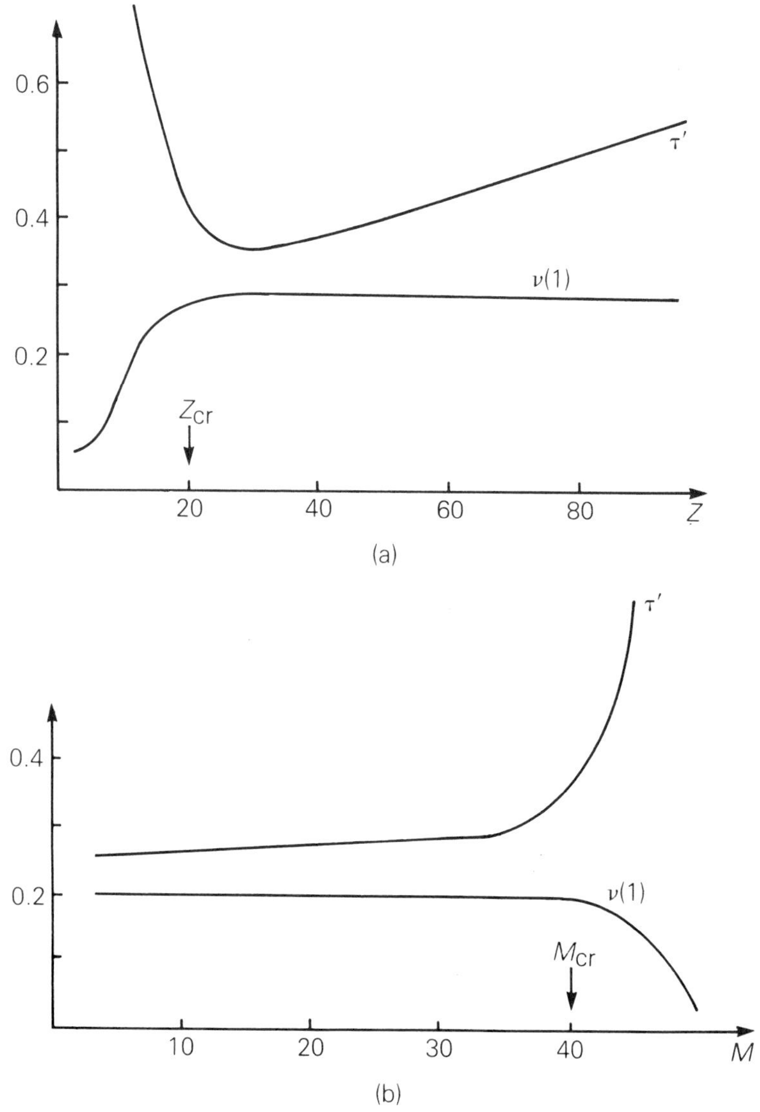

Fig. 3.15 – Typical dependence of the normalised intensity $\nu(1)$ of successful transmissions and the normalised delay on: (a) randomisation index Z, (b) number of nodes M, total intensity fixed.

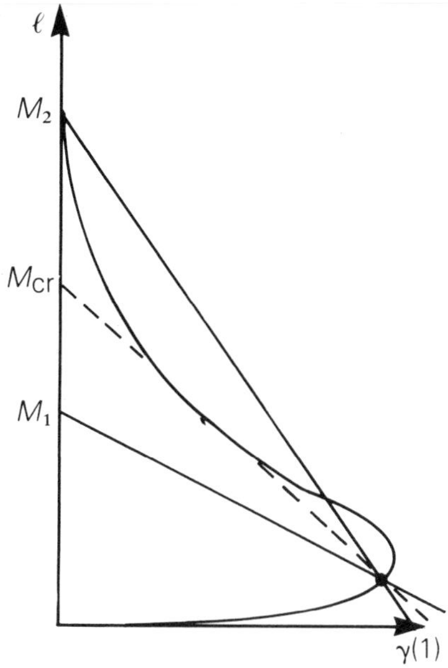

Fig. 3.16 – Characterisitics of system with variable load line, randomisation index Z and $\nu(1)$ for the operating point fixed.

enter the node—or α^+ – it is permitted to enter it. Notice that decision α^+ does not mean that the transmission of the packet starts, since according to subrule 1′ it can still be rejected. Typical is the admission rule:†

$$A_m(\xi) = \begin{cases} \alpha^+ & \text{if } L^*(\xi) < L \\ \alpha^- & \text{if } L^*(\xi) \geqslant L \end{cases} \tag{3.2.65}$$

where $L^*(\xi)$ is the estimate of the number of all packets in the system waiting for retransmission based on ξ, and L is a threshold. In an extreme case we could implement a subsystem collecting information about the states of nodes. Then ξ would be the exact number L of blocked transmitters. Obviously if the system is in the state σ_l then $L = l$. We can, however, estimate L just by watching the common channel. The intensity of all packets in the channel is the sum of admitted primary packets and of retransmissions, thus

$$\nu(2\,|\,l) = \nu(0\,|\,l) + lP_{at} = (M-l)P_1 + lP_{at} = MP_1 - l(P_1 + P_{at}) \tag{3.2.66}$$

Thus $L^* < L$ is equivalent to the inequality $\nu^* > \nu$ where ν^* is an estimate of $\nu(2\,|\,l)$ and the threshold $\nu = MP_1 - L(P_1 + P_{at})$. Suppose the node observes I_w

† This one and other access control rules were analysed first by Kleinrock, Lam [3.4], Part II.

slots preceding the actual one (this set of slots is called the window, hence the subscript w) and I_0 among them are idle. The ratio

$$\nu^* = 1 - \frac{I_0}{I_w} \tag{3.2.67}$$

is obviously an estimate of $\nu(2\,|\,l)$. The admission rule (3.2.65) is equivalent to the rule

$$A_m(I_0) = \begin{cases} \alpha^+ & \text{if} \quad \nu^* \geqslant \nu \\ \alpha^- & \text{if} \quad \nu^* < \nu \end{cases} \tag{3.2.68}$$

The other method to stop the system from drifting to the clogged state is to change the randomisation index Z. Let us denote by Z_{ls} the randomisation index corresponding to the locally stable state A shown in Fig. 3.14(b) and by $Z_s > Z_{ls}$ the randomisation index corresponding to the stable state A, shown in Fig. 3.14(a). Similar to`the admission rule (3.2.68) is the rule for controlling Z

$$Z_m(\xi) = \begin{cases} Z_{ls} & \text{if} \quad L^*(\xi) < L \\ Z_s & \text{if} \quad L^*(\xi) \geqslant L \end{cases} \tag{3.2.69}$$

Both mechanisms for peventing the system from becoming clogged can be combined. An example is the rule:

$$\begin{aligned} A(\xi) &= \alpha^+, Z_m(\xi) = Z_{ls} && \text{if} \quad L^*(\xi) \leqslant L_1 \\ A(\xi) &= \alpha^+, Z_m(\xi) = Z_s && \text{if} \quad L_1 < L^*(\xi) < L_2 \\ A(\xi) &= \alpha^-, Z_m(\xi) = Z_s && \text{if} \quad L^*(\xi) \geqslant L_2 \end{aligned} \tag{3.2.70}$$

where $L_1 < L_2$ are two thresholds.

3.3 SYSTEMS WITH ACCESS CONTROLLED BY THE CHANNEL STATE

In this section we consider systems in which information ξ_{ch}, which tells us whether or not the local transmitters are operating. We call ξ_{ch} the **channel state information** and we say that the system has **channel state controlled access** (CHSCA). Our analysis follows the same pattern as for the two previous systems.

3.3.1 Description of the system

It is desirable that the time, T_{ch}, taken for the channel state information to reach the transmitter is small compared with the packet duration T, i.e.:

$$T_{ch} < T \tag{3.3.1}$$

We assume that this condition is satisfied. We will next assume that ξ_{ch} can take one of the forms:

ξ_{bu} – common channel busy;
ξ_{nbu} – common channel not busy (idle).

Apart from the feedback information ξ_{fee} and the channel state information ξ_{ch}, we may also have synchronising information ξ_{syn} permitting the synchronisation of the entire operation of the local transmitters. Since it would not be reasonable to take any action during the intervals smaller than the transit time T_{ch} of the channel state information, we assume that the period T_0 of synchronisation pulses is T_{ch}, i.e.

$$T_0 = T_{ch} \ . \tag{3.3.2}$$

The synchronising pulses determine the slots of duration T_0. In view of (3.3.2), we call these slots **minislots.**

The synchronised channel state controlled access rule (abbreviation: SCHSA) consists of subrules 1–4, as for AAF, but instead of 5 it uses the subrule:

6 In jth minislot a decision α, based on the information $\xi_{ch}(j)$, is made about the transmission of the packet with the highest priority. The decision is either

α_{im} – transmission should start immediately, i.e. at the beginning of the the next minislot, or
$\alpha_w(z)$ – we should wait, no transmission should be attempted during the next z minislots.

Possible α decision-making rules are:

6a If $\xi_{ch}(j) = \xi_{nbu}$ then decide α_{im}.
If $\xi_{ch}(j) = \xi_{bu}$ then choose z as a realisation of a random variable Z and decide $\alpha_w(z)$.

6b If $\xi_{ch}(j) = \xi_{bu}$ then we refrain from action until first ξ_{nbu} information arrives.
If $\xi_{ch}(j) = \xi_{nbu}$ then the decision $\alpha(j)$ which can be either α_{im} or $\alpha_w(1)$ is chosen randomly accordingly to probability

$$P_{im} = P(\alpha = \alpha_{im}) \tag{3.3.3}$$

If $\alpha(j) = \alpha_{im}$ the packet is transmitted. If, however, $\alpha(j) = \alpha(1)$ then we wait until the next slot. If $\xi_{ch}(j+1) = \xi_{nbu}$ we act as in jth slot. If, however, $\xi_{ch}(j+1) = \xi_{bu}$ we choose z as the realisation of the random variable Z and decide $\alpha_w(z)$.

A node operating according to this rule is shown in Fig. 3.17.

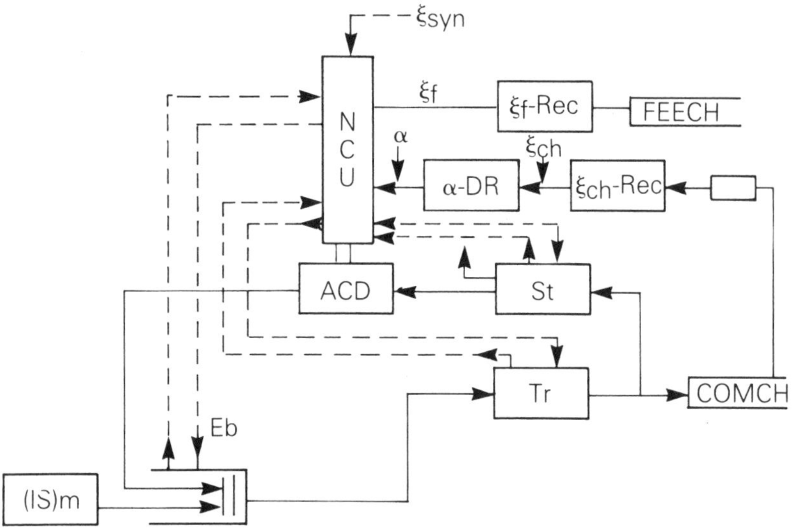

Fig. 3.17 – Structure of the node is the channel state controlled access system. Notation as in Fig. 3.1.

If transmission were started immediately the channel became idle – then, since all nodes use the same rule, with large probability several nodes would transmit their packets at once, causing a collision. Two ways of avoiding such an unfavourable effect are possible: (a) after noticing that a transmission is going on the transmitter refrains from checking the channel state, and thus from attempting a transmission for a randomly chosen time. This is the idea behind subrule 6a which we call a **non persistent rule.** (b) When the channel becomes idle, the transmitters do not try to transmit their packet immediately, but allow a random mechanism to decide the transmission time. This idea behind subrule 6b, which we call a **P_{im}-persistent rule.**

Suppose, that $\xi_{ch}(j) = \xi_{bu}$ but $\xi_{ch}(j+1) = \xi_{nbu}$, thus a transmission was completed at jth minislot. If we apply the non-persistent rule decision $\alpha_w(z)$ is taken and it can happen that during $(j+1)$th slot and some successive ones the channel remains idle, while our transmitter has a packet to transmit. This disadvantage of the non-persiting rule is avoided in rule 6b.

Without ξ_{ch}, if we sent the packet when the channel was busy ξ_{fee} would tell us that a collision had occurred. Thus, when $\xi_{ch} = \xi_{bu}$, it is reasonable to proceed as we do in a SAF system when a collision has occurred. Thus the procedure determined by subrule 6b corresponds to the introduction of the anticollision delay in systems with feedback. Therefore we assume that:

A16 The random variable Z appearing in subrule 6b has the same probability distribution as that determining the anticollision delay mentioned in subrule 3.

To simplify the description we considered the synchronised version of the channel state controlled access system. It is evident that we can remove the restriction that the transmission should start at the beginning of a minislot, which gives us an asynchronous channel state controlled access rule (ACHA).

3.3.2 Relationships between the packet intensities and the delay

We will now illustrate the method of analysing systems using channel state information, taking as our example the non-persistent rule. The analysis will correspond to that of subsections (3.1.2), (3.2.1). We assume that the sequences of packets delivered by the source are poissonian (A3) and independent (A4), the system is stable and the buffer capacities are infinite (A7, A8). We introduce five classes of packet defined in Table 3.1. Notice that a packet can change its type several times.

Table 3.1.

Type number, j	Description of packet type
0	Primary (delivered by the source).
1	Successful transmitted packets.
2	Packets put into the common channel.
3	Packets which have had a collision in the common channel.
4	Packets trying to enter the common channel (in accordance with subrule 6 of CHSCA rule).
5	Packets not admitted because the common channel is busy (in accordance with subrule 6b for $\xi_{ch}(j) = \xi_{bu}$).

We denote the intensity of packets of type j delivered by the mth source by $\lambda_m(j)$ and the intensity of all the type j packets in the system by $\lambda(j)$. From the definitions, it follows that:

$$\lambda_m(2) = \lambda_m(1) + \lambda_m(3) \tag{3.3.4}$$

$$\lambda_m(4) = \lambda_m(2) + \lambda_m(5) \tag{3.3.5}$$

and

$$\lambda(j) = \sum_{m=1}^{M} \lambda_m(j) \tag{3.3.6}$$

Since all packets are eventually transmitted

$$\lambda_m(1) = \lambda_m(0) \tag{3.3.7}$$

$\lambda_m(0)$ is the intensity of packets delivered by the mth source. The transmission time of a type 1 packet is given by

$$\bar{T}(1) = \bar{T}_{s-t} + T_{fo} \tag{3.3.8}$$

where T_{s-t} is defined on page 114 and T_{fo} is given by (3.1.21a). For type 3 packets, the average transmission time is:

$$\bar{T}(3) = T_{fo} + T_f + \bar{T}_{ac} \tag{3.3.9}$$

where T_{fo}, T_f are transmission times defined by (3.2.3) and $\bar{T}_{ac}$ is the average anticollision delay.

For a type 5 packet, the delay (in view of subrule 6b) is:

$$\bar{T}(5) = \bar{T}_{ac} \ . \tag{3.3.10}$$

Since all packets are eventually transmitted the fraction of packets of type $i = 3,5$ is $\lambda(i)/\lambda(1)$. The overall average transmission time is:

$$\tau = \bar{T}(1) + \frac{\lambda(3)}{\lambda(1)} \bar{T}(3) + \frac{\lambda(5)}{\lambda(1)} \bar{T}(5) \ . \tag{3.3.11}$$

We will now evaluate the intensities $\lambda(i)$, $i = 2, 3, 4, 5$, starting with the relationship between $\lambda(4)$ and $\lambda(1)$. We assume that

A12′ The starting instants of class 4 packets form a Poisson process.

$\lambda(4)$ is the intensity of that process. The method for obtaining the relationship between $\lambda(4)$ and $\lambda(1)$ was given by Kleinrock [3.5] Part I. We introduce the two system states:

σ_{nbu} – the system is idle (no local transmitter is operating);
σ_{bu} – the system is busy (at least one transmitter is operating).

We denote the time interval during which the system remains in state σ_l by $T(\sigma_l)$. The states σ_{nbu} and σ_{bu} alternate, and we call two consecutive time intervals $T(\sigma_{nbu})$, $T(\sigma_{bu})$ the **system operating cycle.** Let $\bar{T}(\sigma_{nbu})$, $\bar{T}(\sigma_{bu})$ be the average of $T(\sigma_{nbu})$ resp. $T(\sigma_{bu})$, and let T_{cy} be the average duration of the system operating cycle.

$$\bar{T}_{cy} = \bar{T}(\sigma_{nbu}) + \bar{T}(\sigma_{bu}) \ . \tag{3.3.12}$$

We now introduce:

$P(1)$ – the probability that a successful transmission occurs during a system operating cycle.

The mode of operation is such that at most one successful transmission occurs in one cycle. Thus $P(1)$ is equal to the average number of successful packet transmissions during a system cycle, and hence

$$P(1) = \lambda(1)\bar{T}_{cy} \ . \tag{3.3.13}$$

Suppose now that the system is in state σ_{nbu}, then at $t = 0$ transmitter 1 starts to transmit its packet denoted P_1 and the system passes to state σ_{bu} as shown in Fig. 3.18. The local transmitters will be informed about this after time T_{ch}.

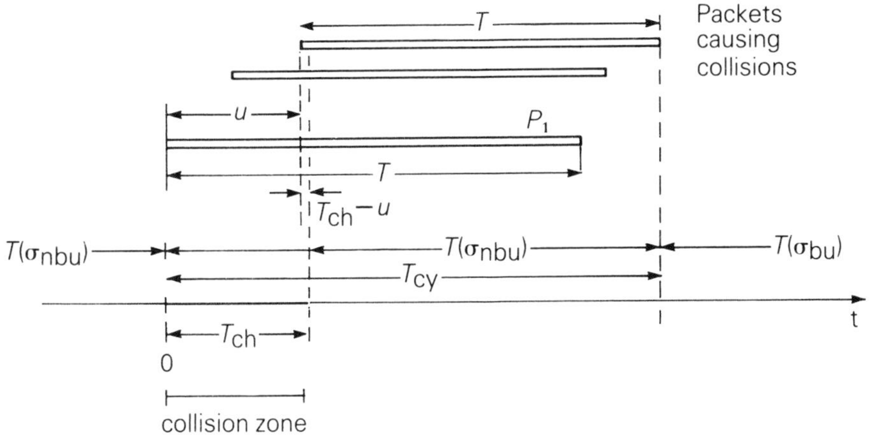

Fig. 3.18 – Illustration to the derivation of a formula (3.3.18).

During the time interval $\langle 0, T_{ch}\rangle$ they may start to transmit and cause a collision, so the interval $\langle 0, T_{ch}\rangle$ is the **collision zone**. From assumption A12′ and the definition of $\lambda(4)$, it follows that the probability that no local transmitter other than the mth one starts to transmit in the collision zone is $\exp[-\lambda(4)T_{ch}]$. Thus:

$$P(1) = \exp[-\lambda(4)T_{ch}] \tag{3.3.14}$$

To evaluate $\bar{T}_{ch}$ we first evaluate $T(\sigma_{nbu})$; From A12′, we see that:

$$\bar{T}(\sigma_{nbu}) = [\lambda(4)]^{-1} \ . \tag{3.3.15}$$

Next we consider the busy intervals. If a transmitter other than number 1 starts transmitting at time u, $0 \leqslant u \leqslant T_{ch}$, this transmission will last until $u + T$, and the other transmitters will learn about the end of the transmission at $u + T + T_{ch}$. Thus if we define U as the random variable representing the instant at which the last transmitter starts its operation in the collision zone, the averge duration of the busy period is:

$$\bar{T}(\sigma_{bu}) = \bar{U} + T + \bar{T}_{ch} \tag{3.3.16}$$

where $\bar{U}$ is the average value of U. If $U \leqslant u$, where $0 \leqslant u \leqslant T_{ch}$, then we know that no transmissions start in the time interval $\langle u, T_{ch} \rangle$. Thus

$$P(U < u) = \exp[-\lambda(4)(T_{ch} - u)] \tag{3.3.17}$$

$$P(U < 0) = 0$$

and the average is

$$\bar{U} = \int_0^{T_{ch}} u \, dP(U < u) = T_{ch} - \frac{1}{\lambda(4)}\{1 - \exp[-\lambda(4)T_{ch}]\} \tag{3.3.18}$$

Putting (3.3.14)–(3.3.16), (3.3.18) into (3.3.13) we obtain the desired relationship between $\lambda(1)$ and $\lambda(4)$. Introducing the normalised intensities,

$$\nu(j) = T\lambda(j) \tag{3.3.19}$$

for $j = 3, 5$ and the normalised transmission time for ξ_{ch}

$$T'_{ch} = \frac{T_{ch}}{T} \tag{3.3.20}$$

we can write this relationship in the form

$$\nu(1) = \frac{\nu(4)\exp[-T'_{ch}\nu(4)]}{\nu(4)(1 + 2T'_{ch}) + \exp[-T'_{ch}\nu(4)]} \tag{3.3.21}$$

Obviously $\nu(1)$ is the common channel utilisation factor. This relationship is illustrated in Fig. 3.19 for various T'_{ch}.

We can now find the dependence of the other packet intensities on $\lambda(2)$. Let $P_{ref} \equiv 1 - P_{im}$ be the probability that the NCU refrains from attempting to transmit a packet. By definition:

$$\lambda(5) = P_{ref}\lambda(4) \tag{3.3.22}$$

and

$$\lambda(2) = (1 - P_{ref})\lambda(4) \; . \tag{3.3.23}$$

The transmission of packets arriving either when the system is non-busy, or during the collision zone, is not postponed. The other $M - 1$ transmitters are not yet aware that one has started to transmit, so:

$$1 - P_{ref} = \frac{T_{ch} + \bar{T}(\sigma_{nbu})}{T \quad \bar{T}_{cy}} \; . \tag{3.3.24}$$

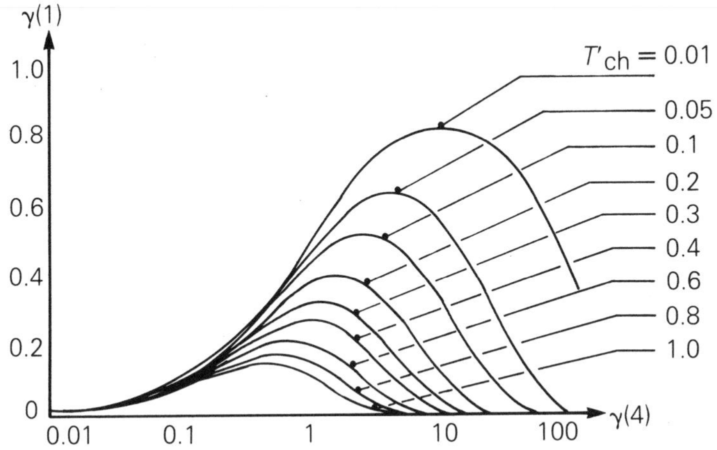

Fig. 3.19 – Dependence of the normalised intensity $\nu(1)$ of packets going successfully through on the intensity $\nu(4)$ of packets attempting transmission for the non-persistent free access channel state controlled system T'_{ch}, normalised channel state information delay uniform collision assumption.

The analysis of the ACHA system can be extended to other types of channel state controlled access systems, in particular to the SCHA system described in section 3.3.1 (see Kleinrock [3.5]). Figure 3.20 shows the results of this analysis, and provides a comparison with the AAF and SAF systems.

We stressed in Chapter 1 that it is essential to analyse the delay of system state information on which access decisions are based for a multiaccess system. We denote it by τ_ξ and define:

$$\tau_\xi = \begin{cases} T_r & \text{for AAF and SAF} \\ T_{ch} & \text{for CHA systems} \end{cases} \tag{3.3.25}$$

Comparing the systems we assume that τ_ξ for asynchronous and synchronous feedback systems are the same; we denote it $(\tau_\xi)_f$ and assume that

$$(\tau_\xi)_{ch} = \frac{1}{2}(\tau_\xi)_r \tag{3.3.26}$$

We first consider the dependence of the maximum intensity of packets passing successfully through the channel on the normalised system state information delay $\tau'_s = T_a/T_{ref}$. Such dependences for AAF, SAF, ACHA following from formulae (3.1.25), (3.1.26), (3.2.19), (3.2.21) and for SCHA based on formulae given in Kleinrock [3.5] is shown in Fig. 3.21. From this figure we draw the important conclusion that for small τ'_ξ the systems using the channel state

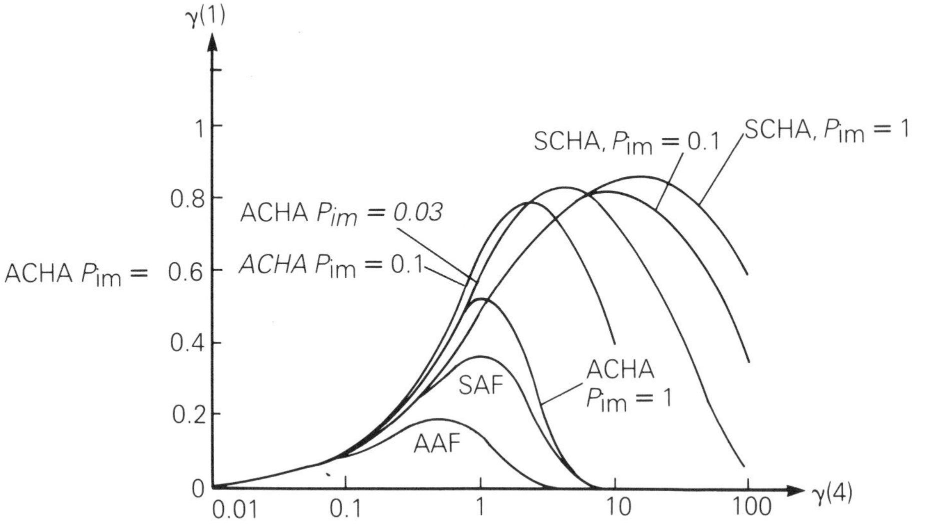

Fig. 3.20 – Dependence of the normalised intensity $\nu(1)$ of packets going successfully through on the normalised intensity $\nu = \nu(4)$ of packet attempting transmission for the system using ξ_{ch} information; $A(S)$CHA P_{im} = persistent asynchronous (synchronous) access channel state controlled access, P_{im} + probability of immediate attempt at transmission. In the case of AAF and SAF, $\nu = \nu(2)$ is the normalised intensity of all packets put in the channel; $\tau'_{\xi} = 0.01$.

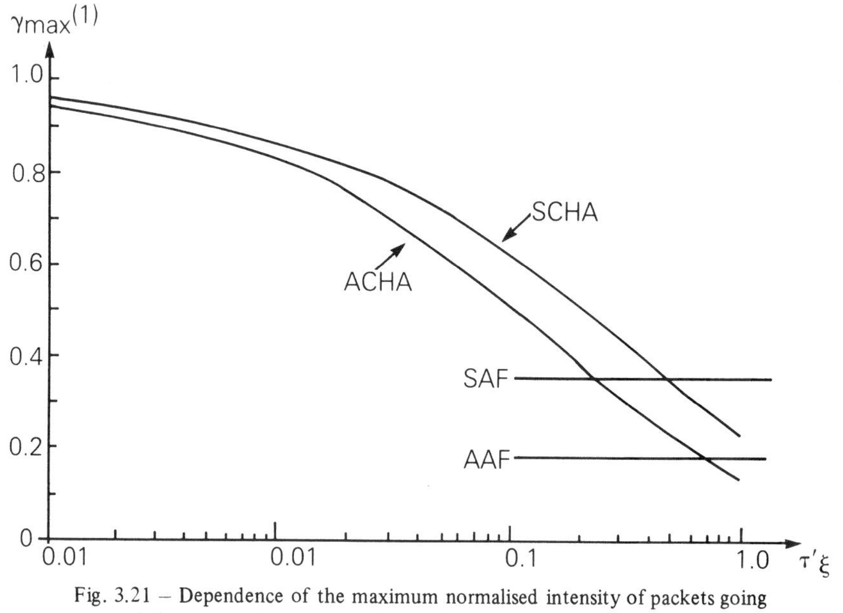

Fig. 3.21 – Dependence of the maximum normalised intensity of packets going successfully through in systems with feedback on the normalised channel state information delay time τ'_{ξ}. $Z = \infty$.

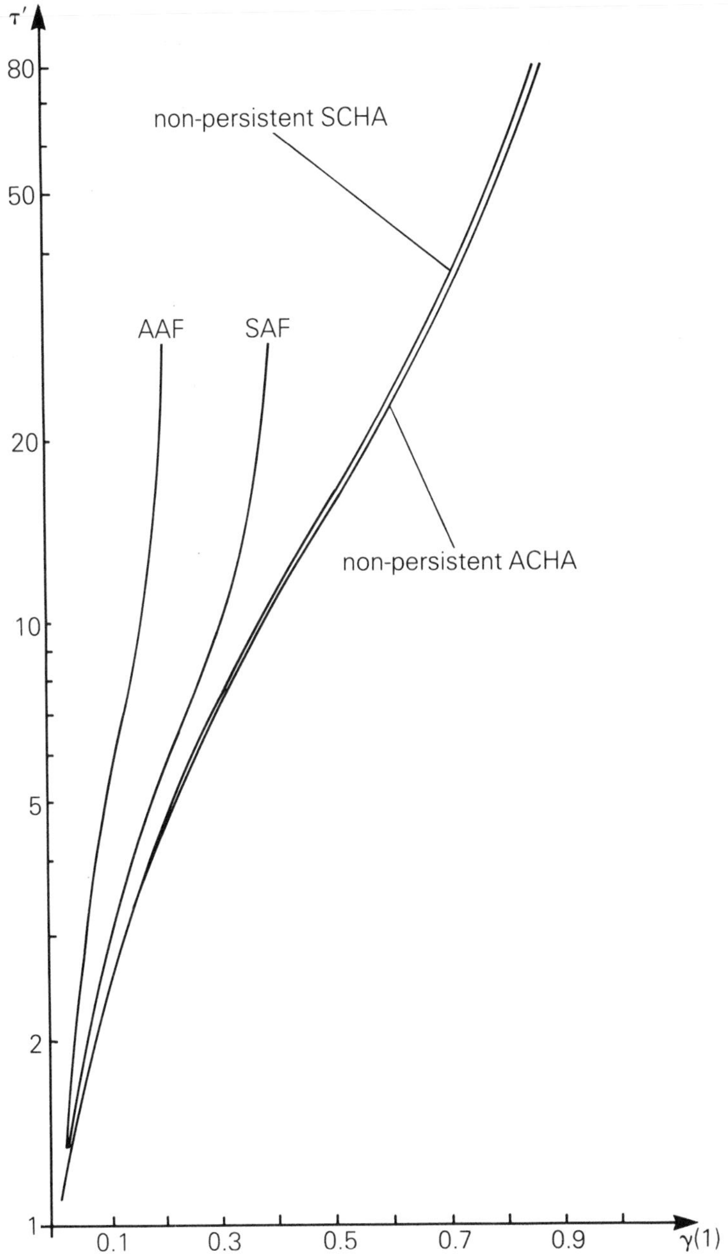

Fig. 3.22 – Dependence of the normalised delay τ' on the normalised intensity $\nu(1)$ of successful transmissions; for medium range systems, $\tau'_\xi = 0.001$, based on Staniszewski [3.6].

information are definitely superior from the point of view of the maximum achievable intensity of packets passing successfully through.

However, for τ'_ξ of order of 0.5 the CHA systems become inferior to systems with feedback which do not use channel state information. This can be explained by the fact that making decisons on the basis of greatly outdated information ξ_{chs} is worse than disregarding such information. In general, if we have more information for making decisions, the quality of the decision will be better, provided we use the information in an optimal way.

To compare the various remote access systems from the point of view of packet passage time we will take two values of the normalised system information delay, namely we will take $\tau'_\xi = 0.002$ and $\tau'_\xi = 0.02$, considering the small-range case. The comparison of the non-persistent channel state controlled systems and the feedback systems information is shown in Fig. 3.22. We see from it that for small- and medium-range cases the systems with channel state controlled access are superior from the point of view of delay.

We have hitherto considered a simple model of systems with common channel state information. The most limiting assumption we made was that the propagation time of ξ_{ch} information does not depend on the node which occupies the common channel. In a real system, the nodes may be dispersed over an area so large that some transmitters may be beyond the horizon with respect to others and thus the information that they feed into the common channel cannot reach those other transmitters. Kleinrock called this problem the problem of hidden transmitters. A method of preventing the difficulties arising from such transmitters was proposed and described in Kleinrock [3.5], Part II.

REFERENCES

[3.1] Abramson, N., (1970), The ALOHA system – Another alternative for computer communications, *Fall. Joint. Comp. Conf. AFIPS Conf. Proc.*, **37**, 281–285.

[3.2] Abramson, N., (1977), The throughput of packet broadcasting channels, *IEEE Trans. on Comm.*, **COM-25**, 117–127.

[3.3] Kleinrock, L., Lam, S. S., (1973), Packet-switching in a slotted satellite channel, *AFIPS Conf. Proc. 1973*, **42**, National Computer Conference, 703–710.

[3.4] Kleinrock, L., Lam, S. S., (1975), Packet-switching in a multiaccess broadcast channel: I. Performance evaluation; II. Dynamic control procedures, *IEEE Trans. on Comm.*, **COM-23**, 410–422, 891–904.

[3.5] Kleinrock, L., Tobagi, F. A., (1975–77), Packet switching in radio channels: Part I – Carrier sense multiple-access modes and their throughput-delay characteristics; Part II – The hidden terminal problem in carrier sense multiple-access and the busy-tone solution; Part III – Polling and (dynamic) split-channel reservation multiple access; Part IV – Stability considerations and dynamic control in carrier sense multiple-access, *IEEE Trans. on Comm.*, **COM-23**, 1400–1416, 1417–1433; **COM-24**, 832–845; **COM-25**, 1103–1119.

[3.6] Staniszewski, A., (1979), The role of system identification information in remote multiaccess system, Doctorial Dissertation, Kraków.

4

Common channel systems with coordinated node operation

In this chapter we continue to consider remote multiaccess systems in which several nodes transmit their information through a common channel. In the feedback systems considered in the previous chapter packet collision is possible. However, the systems which we are going to consider in this chapter are organised so that collisions are not possible. This is achieved by coordinating the operation of the transmitters.

In the first section of this chapter we consider systems which use polling, and tokens for the use of the common channel. In the second section we consider the family of systems which use reservation techniques to achieve coordination. In the last section we consider systems with *en route* access.

4.1 SYSTEMS WITH POLLING

In systems using polling the nodes are permitted to use the common channel in turn. Whilst the common channel is being used all other nodes are prohibited from putting their packets into the channel. After the transmitting node has completed its cycle of operation, the next node is allowed to use the common channel whilst the remainder must stay idle.

The system consists of two subsystems: (1) the subsystem for transmitting the working information; and (2) the polling subsystem for collecting and distributing information about the beginning and end of the node operation. We can have both centralised and decentralised versions of the system. The former is known as hub polling, the latter, roll-call polling. These systems can work either synchronously or asynchronously.

4.1.1 Description of the system

We first consider an asynchronous centralised polling system with the control unit at the channel output. A block diagram of such a system is shown in Fig.4.1. The central control unit (CCU) sends permit information, ξ_{per}, to all nodes.

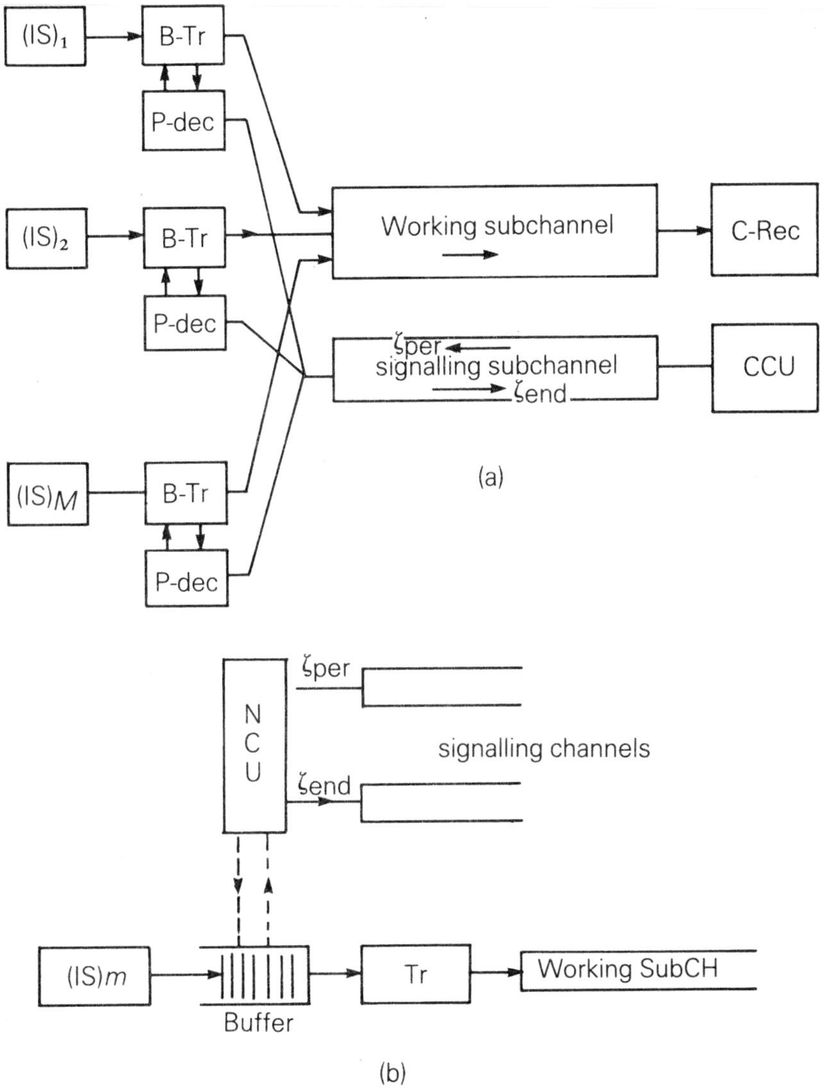

Fig. 4.1 – Centralised system with polling. (a) Block diagram. (b) Structure of the node. P-dec, polling decision unit; $N_m, m = 1, 2, \ldots, N$ node; NCU, node control unit; CCU, central control unit; C-rec, control receiver.

ξ_{per} can take the values ξ_m, $m = 1, 2, \ldots, M$, where ξ_m means that the mth transmitter is permitted to start transmitting packets. After the mth transmitter has completed transmission of its packets, it sends the signal ξ_{end} to the CCU, which then sends ξ_{m+1}. The procedure is continued cyclically by sending ξ_1 after

ξ_M. This asynchronous, centralised polling (ACP) rule is defined more precisely by the set of subrules:

1. A packet delivered to the mth node is put into its buffer.
2. When $\xi_{per} = \xi_m$, the mth node control unit removes packets from its buffer according to a FIFO discipline.
3. When the buffer is empty, ξ_{end} is sent to the CCU.
4. If $\xi_{per} = \xi_m$ and the buffer at the mth node is empty, ξ_{end} is sent immediately.

The block diagram of a node operating according to this rule is shown in Fig. 4.1(a), and a typical packet transmission process is illustrated in Fig. 4.2(a).

In a decentralised version, the nodes themselves pass the permit round. A typical transmission process in the decentralised system is shown in Fig. 4.2(b).

In a synchronised system, we divide the time axis into slots of duration

$$T_1 = T \tag{4.1.1}$$

where T is the duration of the packet. Synchronous access systems operate in the same way as the asynchronous systems described above, except that every packet is located in a slot.

All these systems operate cyclically. The length of the cycle, as seen by a particular node, is called the **system operating cycle** and is designated T_{cy}.

We first describe in more detail the operation of the synchronous system. Let:

$t_i = iT_1, i = 0, 1, \ldots$ be the starting instant of the $(i+1)$th slot;
$\langle t_{i-1}, t_i \rangle, i = 1, 2, \ldots$ be the ith slot;
j be the index of the system cycle;
$I_m(j)$ be the number of the first slot in the jth cycle after the mth node has received ξ_m;
$I'_m(j) - 1$ be the number of last slot filled with the packets delivered by the mth source in the jth cycle:

$$\vartheta_m(i) = T_1 I_m(j) \tag{4.1.2a}$$

and

$$\vartheta'_m(i) = T_1 I'_m(j) \tag{4.1.2b}$$

be the corresponding slot starting times;
$l_m(t_i)$ be the number of packets in the buffer at an instant just before t_i;
$\Lambda_m(t', t'')$ be the number of packets delivered by the mth source in the time interval $\langle t', t'' \rangle$.

The above definitions are illustrated in Fig. 4.3.

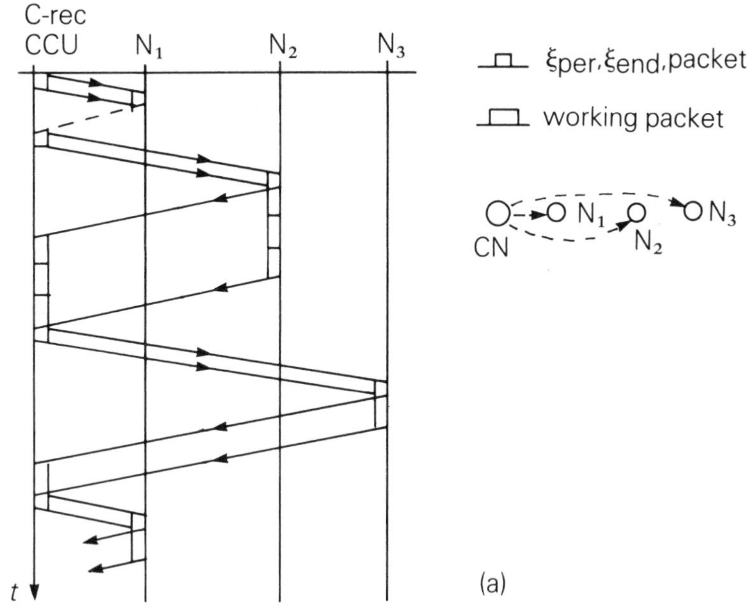

(a)

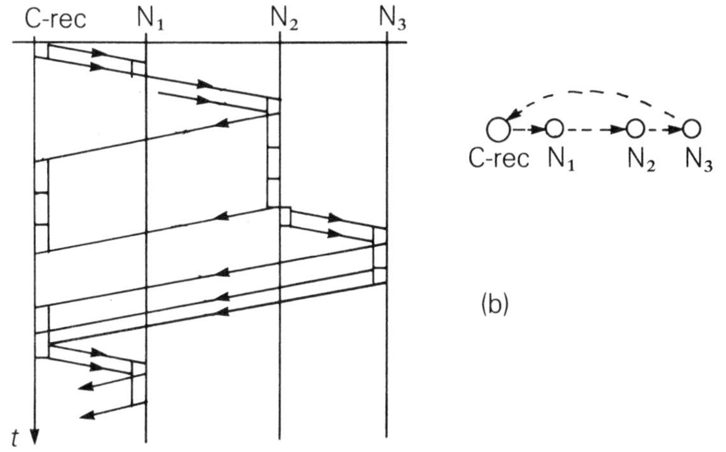

(b)

Fig. 4.2 – Typical transmissions in a polling system. (a) Centralised version central control unit located at the control receiver. (b) Decentralised version. Notation as on Fig. 4.1. N_m, mth node.

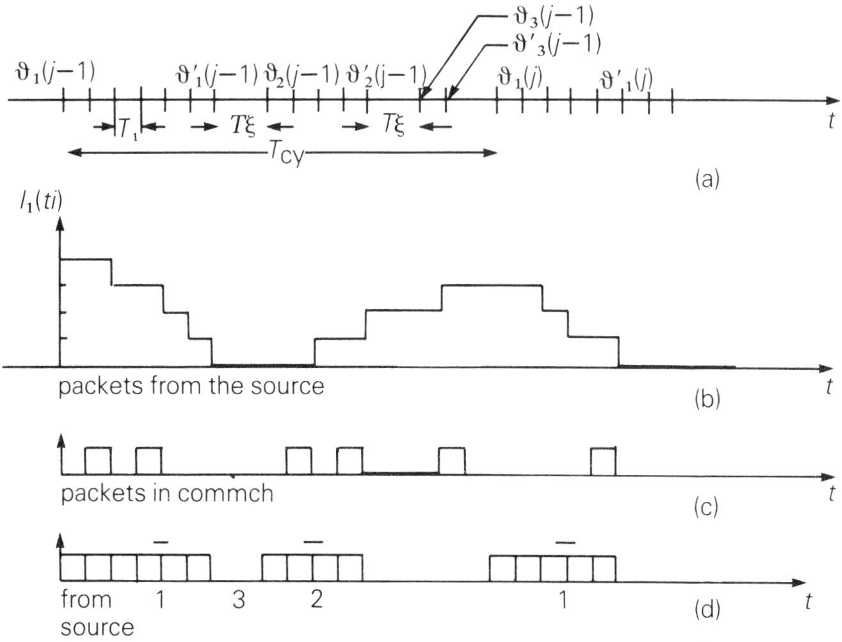

Fig. 4.3 – Packet sequence in a synchronous polling system with $M = 3$ nodes. (a) Timing. (b) Number of packets in the buffer at the first node. (c) Packets delivered by the first source. (d) Packets in the common channel.

From the ACP rule adapted to synchronous operation it follows that:

$$
l_m(t_i) = \begin{cases} l_m[\vartheta_m(j)] + \Lambda_m[\vartheta_m(j), t_i] - [t_i - \vartheta_m(i)]/T_1 & \text{for } \vartheta_m(j) \leqslant t_i \leqslant \vartheta'_m(j) \quad \text{(a)} \\ 0 \quad \text{for } t_i = \vartheta'_m(j) & \text{(b)} \\ \Lambda_m[\vartheta'_m(j), t_i] \quad \text{for } \vartheta'_m(j) < t_i < \vartheta_m(j) & \text{(c)} \end{cases} \tag{4.1.3}
$$

Part (a) of this formula says that, when a node is transmitting the number of packets in the buffer is the number which was there when transmission started, augmented by new packets delivered by the source and diminished by the number of slots which have passed since the $\vartheta_m(j)$th slot. Part (b) is reaffirmation of the definition of $\vartheta'_m(j)$; part (c) says that, while node is not using the channel, all packets delivered by the source are accumulated in the buffer.

After the transmission of the last packet, ξ_{end} is sent. Let:

$T_e^{(\text{pr})}$ be the propagation time of the packet carrying ξ_{end};

T'_e be the duration of the signal carrying ξ_{end};

T_e be the total time elapsing between sending ξ_{end} and its reaching the central station.

Obviously,

$$T_e = T_e^{(pr)} + T_e' \tag{4.1.4}$$

We define similarly the times $T_{per}^{(pr)}$, T_{per}', T_{per} characterising the transmission of ξ_{per}. We have

$$T_{per} = T_{per}^{(pr)} + T_{per}' \tag{4.1.5}$$

and we write

$$T_{pol} = T_e + T_{per} \tag{4.1.6a}$$

for the total polling information transport time i.e. the total time elapsing between the $(m-1)$th node completing its operation and the mth being informed that it can start transmitting.

In the case of a system operating synchronously the packet must wait for the next slot. Thus

$$T_{pol} = T_1 \left\lceil \frac{T_e + T_{per}}{T_1} \right\rceil \tag{4.1.6b}$$

From our considerations it follows that the blocks of packets transmitted along the common channel by successive nodes are separated by idle intervals of duration T_{pol}. Typical examples of packet sequences described by (4.1.4) are shown in Fig. 4.3.

We next consider systems operating asynchronously. As previously, we define

$\vartheta_m(j)$ as the time at which ξ_m reaches the mth node during the jth system cycle;
$\vartheta_m'(j)$ as the time following $\vartheta_m(j)$ when the buffer first becomes empty.

The operation of the system differs from that of the synchronous system, only in that $\vartheta_m(j)$ and $\vartheta_m'(j)$ are not multiples of a fixed interval. Hitherto we have considered the centralised system. In the case of the decentralised system there is no need to send the ξ_{end} information. After completing its operation each node has only to transmit the permit information the next node. Thus in case of the asynchronous decentralised system, the polling information transport time is.

$$T_{pol} = T_{per} \tag{4.1.7a}$$

where T_{per} is given by (4.1.6a). Similarly to (4.1.6b) for the synchronous operation

$$T_{pol} = T_1 \left\lceil \frac{T_{per}}{T_1} \right\rceil \tag{4.1.7b}$$

The transportation time T_{pol} depends in general on the distance between nodes m and $m+1$. Similarly, as in the case of centralised system, we shall subsequently assume that it is constant.

4.1.2 Parameters characterising the system

We assume that:

A1 The system is homogeneous, i.e. all nodes operate according to the same rule, and all sources have the same statistical properties.

A2 The system is stationary, i.e. the statistical properties of the system state do not depend on the system cycle number, and the average numbers of packets in the buffers is finite.

The fundamental secondary parameter characterising the polling system is the average duration of the cycle. We give a simple derivation of it.

Let $\Lambda_m(T_{cy})$ be the average number of packets delivered by the mth source during one system cycle (hence index 'cy'). In view of the homogeneity assumption,

$$\Lambda_m(T_{cy}) = \bar{L}_{cy} = \text{const.} \tag{4.1.8}$$

By definition:

$$\bar{L}_{cy} = \lambda_1(0)\bar{T}_{cy} \tag{4.1.9}$$

where λ_1 is the intensity of packets delivered by a source and $\bar{T}_{cy}$ is the average duration of the cycle. During the time interval $\langle \vartheta_m(i-1), \vartheta_m(i) \rangle$ polling information must be sent M times, and a total of $M\bar{L}_{cy}$ working packets must be transmitted. Thus:

$$\bar{T}_{cy} = M\lambda_1(0)\bar{T}_{cy} + MT_{pol} \tag{4.1.10}$$

We denote by:

$$\nu_1 = \lambda_1(0)T_1 \tag{4.1.11}$$

the normalised intensity of packets delivered by a source during one slot. The parameter

$$\nu = M\nu_1 \tag{4.1.12}$$

is the common channel utilisation factor. From (4.1.11), (4.4.10) we have:

$$\bar{T}_{cy} = \frac{MT_{pol}}{1-\nu} \; . \tag{4.1.13}$$

The normalised packet delay defined by (2.1.18) is

$$\tau' = \frac{T_{s-t}}{T} + 1 \tag{4.1.14}$$

where T_{s-t} is source–transmitter passage time. We assume that

A.1.1 The sources are poissonian and independent.
A3 Packets have fixed duration $T = T_1$.

To simplify the analysis we replace subrule 2 by the subrule:

2′ Packets delivered by the mth source after permit ξ_m arrives wait in the buffer until the next cycle.

For systems with subrule 2′ the period of collecting packets which are transmitted in a batch is the period between two successive ξ_e signals, while with subrule 2 between two successive ξ_{per} signals. In Appendix A.4 the average $\bar{T}_{s-t}$ is derived.† From (A.4.15), (A.4.20) and (4.1.14) we obtain.

$$\tau' = \frac{[1+(\nu/M)]}{2[1-(\nu^2/M)]}\left[M(M-1)\left[\frac{2}{T'_{pol}}\left(\frac{\bar{T}_{cy}}{T_1}\right)^{-1} + 2\frac{\nu}{M}T'_{pol} + \left(\frac{\nu}{M}\right)^2\left(\frac{\bar{T}_{cy}}{T_1}\right)^2\right] + \right.$$

$$\left. + M\,(T'_{pol})^2\left(\frac{\bar{T}_{cy}}{T_1}\right)^{-1} + 2\frac{\nu}{M} + \nu\right] + 1 \tag{4.1.15}$$

where $T'_{pol} = T_{pol}/T_1$ is the normalised polling information total passage time, $\bar{T}_{cy}$ is the average system cycle duration given by (4.1.14), and ν is the channel utilisation factor. Typical diagrams of the relationship (4.1.15) are shown in Fig. 4.4 by continuous lines. As follows from the formula, the normalised delay T'_{pol} depends on the channel utilisation factor ν and on the normalised polling information passage time τ'_p; it is also highly dependent on the number of nodes M.

Konheim and Meister [4.2] were able to analyse the synchronous system and obtained the normalised delay

$$\tau' = \frac{\nu}{2(1-\nu)} + \frac{M-\nu}{2M} + T'_{pol}\frac{M-\nu}{2(1-\nu)} + \frac{T_{cy}}{T_1} + 1 \tag{4.1.16}$$

where $T'_{pol} = T_{pol}/T$ is the normalised polling time and T_{pol} is given by (4.1.6b) resp. (4.1.7b).

† The derivation is based on Hayes and Sherman [4.1].

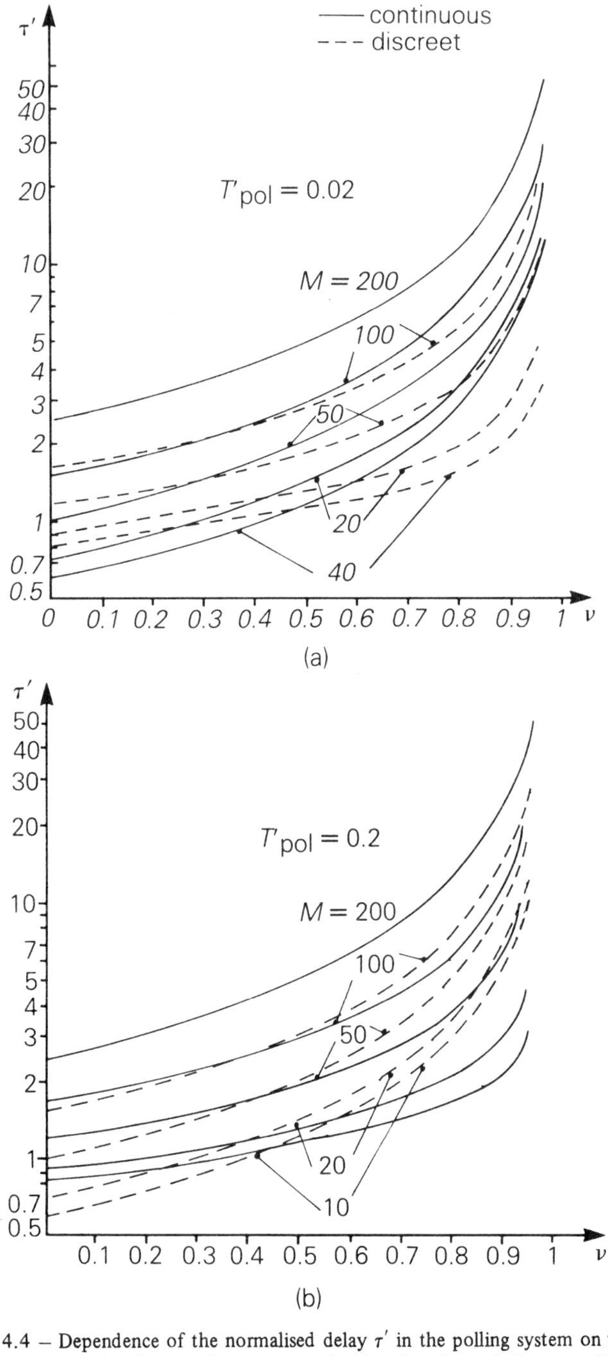

Fig. 4.4 – Dependence of the normalised delay τ' in the polling system on the common channel utilisation factor ν, number M of nodes and the normalised polling information passage time T'_{pol}. Continuous lines, asynchronous access; interrupted lines, synchronous access. (a) $T'_{pol} = 0.02$; (b) $T'_{pol} = 0.2$.

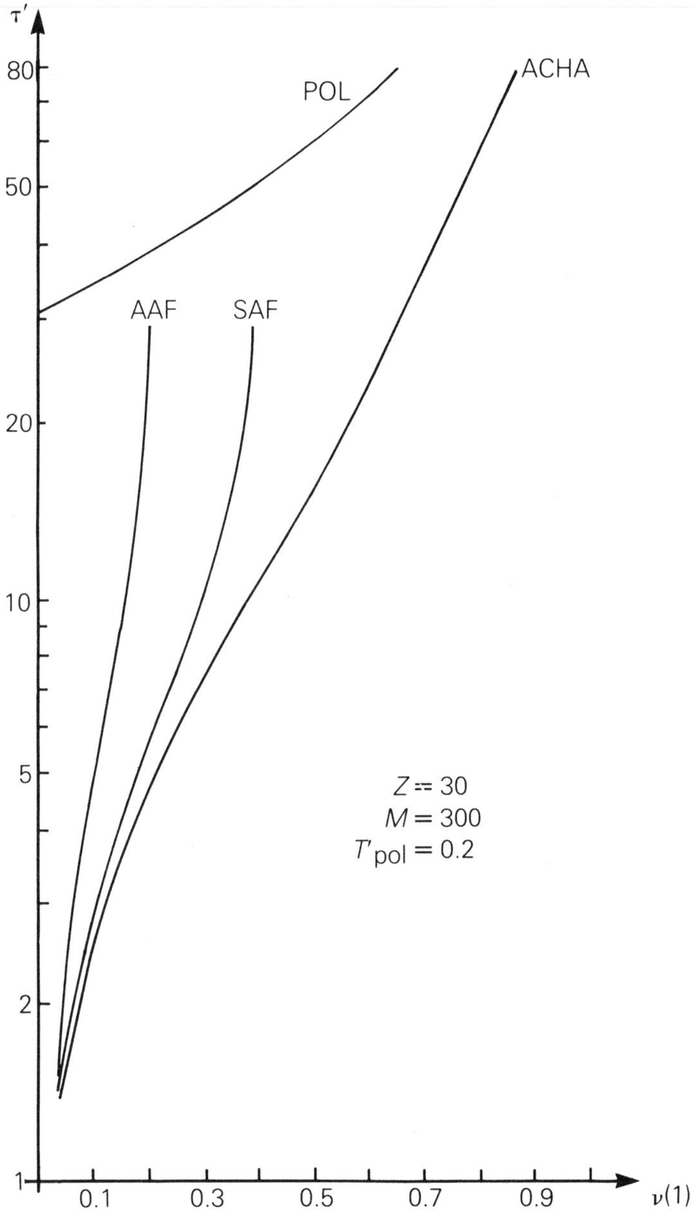

Fig. 4.5 – Dependence of normalised delay τ' on channel utilisation ν for various access systems; $Z = 30$, $M = 300$, $T'_{pol} = 0.2$; AAF, SAF, asynchronous, synchronous access systems with feedback; ACHA, asynchronous channel state controlled access system; POL, decentralised synchronous access system with polling $M = 300$. Based on Staniszewski [3.6].

The diagrams of τ' versus ν given by (4.1.16) are shown in Fig. 4.4 as interrupted lines. From (4.1.13) we see that T_{cy}/M is proportional to T'_{pol}, thus both for the asynchronous and synchronous systems the delay τ' depends strongly on T_{pol}. From (4.1.6) and (4.1.7) it follows that the decentralised system is definitely superior to the centralised since T_{pol} is smaller for the decentralised system not only because we need not transmit ξ_{end} but also because T_{per} is usually smaller for the decentralised system.

Comparing systems with feedback and systems with polling we take for the latter

$$\tau_\xi = T_{pol} \tag{4.1.17}$$

and we assume

$$T_{pol} = T_f \ . \tag{4.1.18}$$

The comparison follows from Fig. 4.5, where we assumed for feedback systems randomisation index $Z = 30$ and $\tau_\xi = 0.2T$. We see that in the range where the systems with feedback can operate, the polling system is inferior, although it can operate quite effectively over a certain range where systems with feedback cannot. The system with polling remains inferior to the ideal system with the channel state controlled access. The serious drawback of the system with polling is that the delay for that system depends strongly not only on channel utilisation $\nu(1)$ but also on the number of the nodes M. Thus, if we have many nodes with small normalised intensities, the polling system is disadvantageous.†

4.2 RESERVATION SYSTEMS

A reservation system consists of two subsystems: (a) the reservation subsystem, and (b) the working packets transmission subsystem. The common channel is divided into the working and reservation subchannels serving these subsystems. The reservation subsystem usually needs both forward and feedback channels, but the working system only needs a forward channel. Flexible or fixed division of the common channel into the working and reservation subchannels is possible. An example of a flexible division is one where the whole common channel is used by the reservation subsystem when no working packets are being transmitted, but when data transmission starts, only a part of the common channel is used for reservation packets. The subchannel for the reservation subsystem we can also divide into sub-subchannels and assign them in a fixed way to the local transmitter, or we can use a free access without separated sub-subchannels. In a system with flexible common channel division into working and reservation

† Another comparison of polling systems can be found in Kleinrock and Tobagi [3.5] Part III.

subchannels we may change the access rules to the reservation subchannel, or the type of common channel division may itself vary. An example of such a system will be described in detail in the second subsection; other systems were considered by Kleinrock and Tobagi [3.5] Part III.

We can use either decentralised or centralised implementation of the reservation and working subsystems. For example, both these systems are centralised if we have one control centre which collects all reservation packets, makes the decisions about scheduling the working packets and controls the local transmitters. Such a system would be suitable for a satellite capable of complex signal processing. In a decentralised system, the reservation packets are watched by all the local transmitters, which make their own scheduling decisions, based on an understanding of how the other transmitters work. The broadcasting ability of a satellite repeater can be used to deliver the reservations packets to all local transmitters.

4.2.1 Description of a reservation system with flexible channel division†

We assume that there are two kinds of packet in the system: (a) large packets carrying the working information; (b) small packets, carrying reservation information or an acknowledgement, or short, high priority messages for users.

The system can be in one of two states: σ_v, the vigilance state, or σ_w, the working state. When the system is in the vigilance state only small packets can be sent and the system operates as a synchronous system with feedback (described in subsection 3.2.1). The timing pulses have period T_0 and are generated centrally. The slots which they define are called minislots (see Fig. 4.6(a)). We assume that one small packet fills one minislot. The timing during the working state is shown in Fig. 4.6. Three types of slot are generated: (1) a large slot of duration T_2, (2) a basic slot of duration T_1, and (3) a minislot of duration T_0. A large slot is divided into $K_w + 1$ basic slots. The K_w initial slots are called working slots (hence the subscript 'w'), and the last slot is a reservation slot. A reservation slot is divided into K_r minislots. We thus have:

$$T_2 = (K_w + 1)T_1 \tag{4.2.1}$$

$$T_1 = K_r T_0 \tag{4.2.2}$$

We assume that the s.s.i. subsystem delivers for each node binary information about the systems state: vigilant σ_v or working σ_w. When the system is in the σ_w-state the node is informed about the number of the next, as yet unreserved slot.

† The system considered was proposed and first analysed by Roberts [4.3].

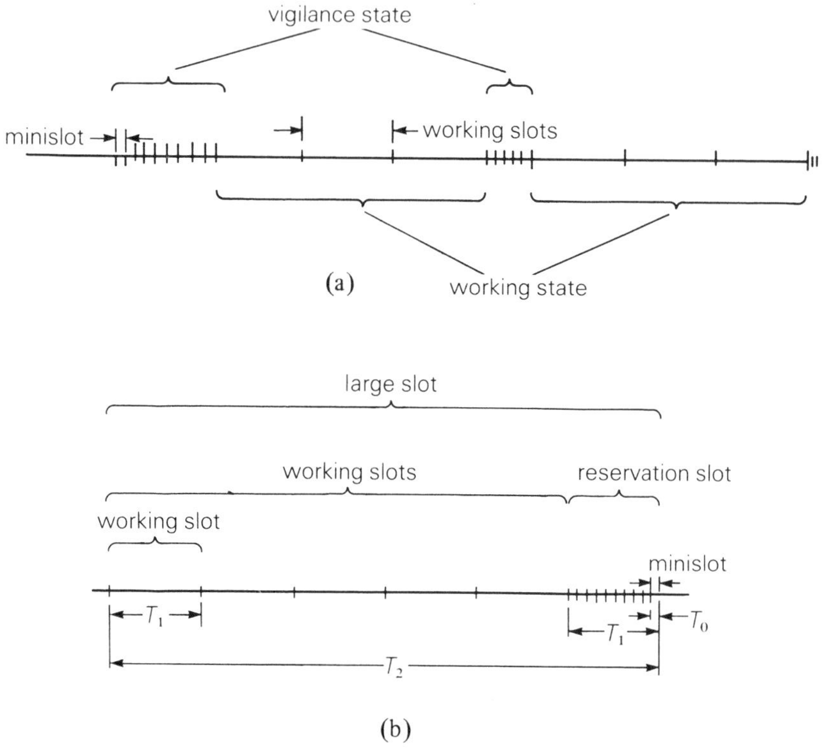

Fig. 4.6 – Timing in a reservation system: (a) general; (b) inside the large slot.

In the centralised version of the s.s.i. subsystem each node sends to the control unit (CCU) information about the size of the batch it has to transmit. The CCU keeps a record of all previous reservations and it sends back to the node considered the numbers of slots which are assigned to it.

In the decentralised version each node broadcasts information about the size of the batch of its packets and all nodes register this information. Thus every node can determine itself the next unreserved slots. Both in the centralised and decentralised system the node obtains the feedback information ξ_f informing it if the reservation signal was involved in a collision or not.

The rule of node operation is:

1 If a batch of working packets arrives then:
  1.1 It is placed in the working packet entrance buffer.
  1.2 A small packet specifying the size of the batch is generated.
2a If the system is in vigilance state then:
  2.1a The small packet is transmitted according to SAF rules.
  2.2a After ξ^+ information returns the system passes into the working state.

2b If the system is in the working state then:

2.1b The small packet is transmitted according to SAF rules modified so that:

2.1.1b The first attempt of transmission in the minislot is chosen at random among the minislots of the first available reservation slot.

2.1.2b Retransmitting with an anticollision delay we count successive minislots passing if necessary to the next reservation slot.

2.2b After ξ^+ returns the node locates packets forming the batch in the next non-reserved slots (the reservation subsystem delivers data about these slots).

2.3b If after transmission of the last packet for which reservation was made no new ξ^+ signal returns to any node then the system passes into vigilance state.

The block diagram of the node implementing this rule is shown in Fig. 4.7 with examples of transmissions in Fig. 4.8.

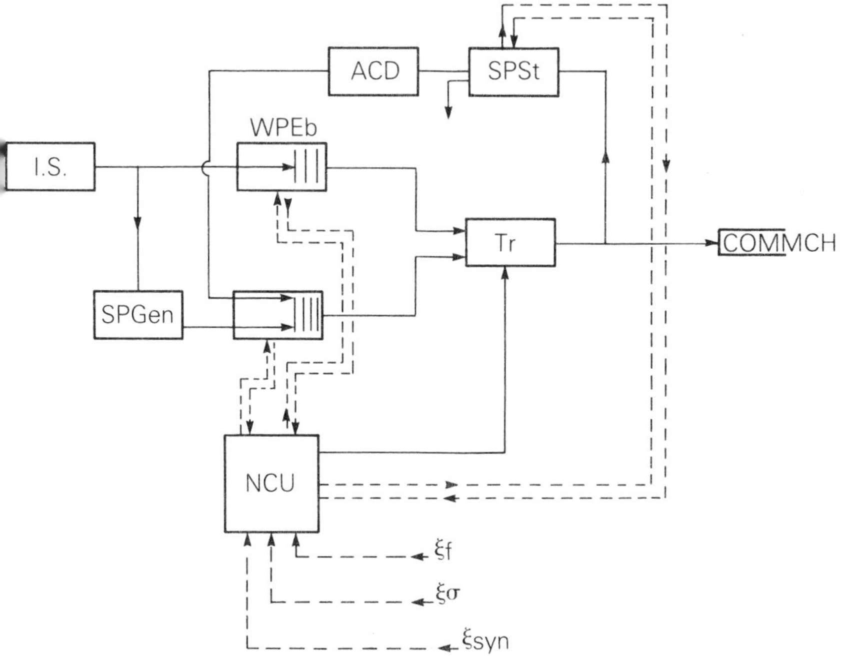

Fig. 4.7 – Structure of the node in the reservation system operating according to the reservation rule. I.S., information source; WPEd, working (small) packet entrance buffer; SPGen, small packet generator; SPSt, small packet storage; ACD, anticollision delay; NCU, node control init; ξ_σ, system state information (v or w).

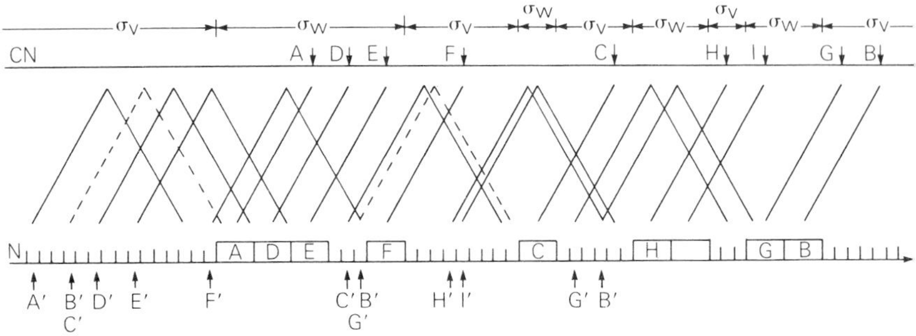

Fig. 4.8 – Example of transmissions in systems operating according to Res. 1 rule. CN, control node; N, local node; $K_r = K_w = 3$; σ_V, σ_W, vigilance, working states.

The aim of choosing the first minislot randomly in the subrule 2.1.1b is similar to the case of the persisting rule, to avoid a pile-up of packets in the first minislot in the reservation slot.

In order to analyse systems operating according to this rule, we assume:

A1 The system is homogeneous.

A2 The source delivers batches of packets which form a Poisson process of intensity $\lambda_{b1}(0)$. The number of packets in a batch is a realisation of the random variable B. The random variables corresponding to various batches are statistically independent.

A3 The starting times of primary reservation packets and of their retransmitted copies form Poisson processes of intensity λ_{1s}. The process correspond to various nodes are independent.

A4 The capacities of the entrance buffers are infinite but the average number of packets in the buffers are finite.

Let us denote:

$$a \equiv \frac{\lambda_{1s}(0)}{\lambda_{b1}(0)} \tag{4.2.3}$$

If only one small packet corresponds to one batch $a = 1$. In general we may have additional traffic of small packets; then $a > 1$.

It is evident that the average delay for working packets depends on the reservation time, so we derive the reservation time first. The analysis follows that for the synchronous access system with feedback presented in section 3.2.1.

4.2.2 Small packet intensities

We denote the parameters characterising the reservation subsystem in the vigilance state and in the working state by the indices V, and W respectively. To remind us that the parameters characterise small packets, we use the subscript index s. As in Chapter 3, the index 1 denotes the parameters characterising packets which are successfully transmitted, and the index 2 denotes all packets, both primary and copies. For example:

$\nu_s(1, V)$ is the normalised intensity of small packets which are successfully transmitted in the vigilance state.

Let us start with the intensities of small packets in the vigilance state. The difficulty in the analysis is that the duration of the state depends on the process of packet transmission: however, we will analyse the system assuming that this state lasts indefinitely. The total intensity of small packets delivered by all the local transmitters is $\lambda_s(0) = M\lambda_{s1}(0)$. In view of assumption A4 every primary small packet is ultimately transmitted successfully. Thus the normalised intensity of successfully transmitted packets in the vigilance state is:

$$\nu_s(1, V) = \lambda_s(0)T_0 \tag{4.2.4}$$

The system operates in the same way as the synchronous access system described in section 3.2, so we can directly apply the results from that section. Using formula (3.2.35) we can find $\nu_s(1, V)$ in terms of the normalised intensity of all packets $\nu_s(2, V)$:

$$\nu_s(1, V) = A\nu_s(2, V)\exp[-\nu_s(2, V)] \tag{4.2.5}$$

where the constant A depends on the anticollision randomisation index Z.

Next we consider the small packet intensities in the working state, again assuming that this state lasts for ever. The total intensity of the packets delivered by all sources is again $\lambda_s(0)$. Under subrule 1.2, the primary small packets generated during the first K_W working slots are put into the entrance buffer and are taken out only when the first reservation slot starts. On average, there are $\lambda_s(0)K_WT_1$ such packets. During the reservation slot, another $\lambda_s(0)T_1$ packets are generated. Thus normalised intensity of the successfully transmitted small packets is:

$$\nu_s(1, W) = \lambda_s(0)(K_W + 1)T_0 \ . \tag{4.2.6}$$

For the case considered, relationship (4.1.18) holds, and so we have.

$$\nu_s(1, W) = A\nu_s(2, W)\exp[-\nu_s(2, W)] \tag{4.2.7}$$

where A again depends on the anticollision randomisation index Z.

4.2.3 Small packet delay

We derive the average small packet delay for both the vigilance and working states. For the vigilance state which we assume to last permanently we can use formula (3.1.20) with slight modifications. We are now interested in the arrival of the auxiliary information ξ^+ so instead of $T_{(fo)}$ we have to take the round trip propagation time T_r. Using (3.1.31) we thus have:

$$\tau(V) = T_{s-t}(V) + T_{rt}(V) + \left[\frac{\nu_s(2, V)}{\nu_s(1, V)} - 1\right][T_{ac}(V) + T_{ac-t}(V) + T_r(V) \tag{4.2.8}$$

Assuming that the duration of small packets in the forward and feedback channels is the same, equal to T_0, we have

$$T_r(V) = 2[T_0 + T_t^{(pr)}] \tag{4.2.9}$$

Average anticollision delay is

$$\bar{T}_{ac} = \frac{T_0 Z}{2} \tag{4.2.10}$$

Since we apply subrule 3.1 of 3.1.1 it is:

$$\bar{T}_{s-t}(V) = \bar{T}_{ac-t}(V) = \bar{T}_{eb}(V) + \frac{T_0}{2} T_0 \tag{4.2.11}$$

where $\bar{T}_{eb}(V)$ is the average waiting time in small packets entrance buffer, and $T_0/2$ is the average waiting time for the next slot.

If $\nu_{eb}(2, V)$ is the normalised intensity of all small packets entering the entrance buffer during the vigilance state, then:

$$\nu_{eb}(2, V) = \frac{1}{M} \nu_s(2, V) \ . \tag{4.2.12}$$

We can approximate $\bar{T}_{eb}(V)$ by formula (A.1.30). Thus

$$\bar{T}_{eb} = T_0 \frac{\nu_{eb}(2, V)}{2[1 - \nu_{eb}(2, V)]} \ . \tag{4.2.13}$$

We consider next the delay for small packets in the working state. As previously, we assume that this state lasts permanently. We use again formula (3.1.20) which gives us:

$$\bar{\tau}(W) = \bar{T}_{s-t} + T_r(W) + \left[\frac{\nu_s(2, W)}{\nu_s(1, W)} - 1\right][\bar{T}_{ac} + \bar{T}_{ac-t} + \bar{T}_r(W)] \tag{4.2.14}$$

Again

$$\bar{T}_{s-t}(W) = \bar{T}_{ac-t}(W) = \bar{T}_{eb}(W) \tag{4.2.15}$$

and

$$T_r(W) = T_r(V) \; . \tag{4.2.16}$$

To evaluate $\bar{T}_{eb}(W)$ we have to consider a buffer out of which packets can be taken out only during bunches of K_r minislots separated by intervals of duration $K_w T_1$; we call such an operation **intermittent**. As an approximation of the buffer operating intermittently we introduce an auxiliary buffer operating rhythmically.

Only one small packet is located in each slot of the auxiliary system. The packets taken out of the auxiliary system are not transmitted but are kept in storage. After the arrival of a reservation slot. These packets are transferred into the corresponding minislots and transmitted. The relationship between the primary system and the auxiliary one is illustrated in Fig. 4.9. It is evident that from the point of view of packet delay and channel utilisation the auxiliary system is a reasonably good model of the primary one. Since the number of auxiliary buffer cycles and the number of minislots during the large slot should be same, it must be that

$$T_1' = \frac{T}{K_r} \; . \tag{4.2.17}$$

The slot utilisation for the auxiliary buffer should be the same as the minislot utilisation, thus

$$\nu_{s1}(2, W) = \frac{1}{M}\nu(2, W) \; . \tag{4.2.18a}$$

Formula (A.2.17) gives the average queuing time in the auxiliary buffer

$$\bar{T}_{qu} = T_1' \frac{1}{2[1 - \nu_{s1}(2, W)]} \; . \tag{4.2.18b}$$

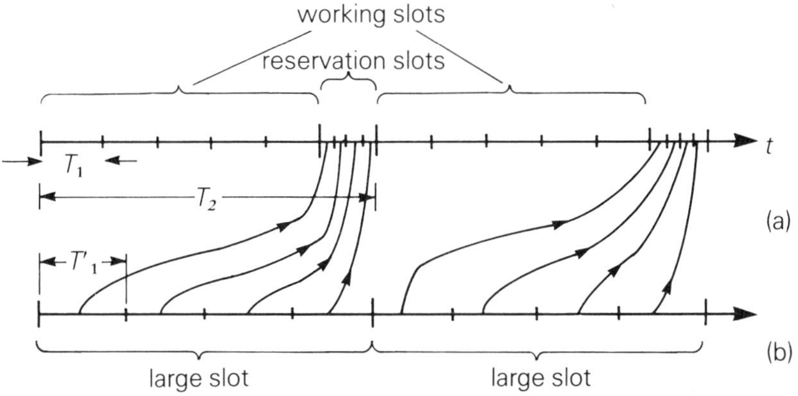

Fig. 4.9 – Timing in the primary and the auxiliary system.

The average waiting time in the storage is $(T_2 - T_1)/2$. Thus with good approximation the average queueing time in the entrance buffer operating intermittently is

$$\bar{T}_{eb} = \bar{T}'_{qu} + \frac{(T_2 - T_1)}{2} = \frac{T_0}{2}\left[\frac{K_w + 1}{1 - \nu_{s1}(2, W)} + K_r K_w\right] \quad (4.2.19)$$

Next let us consider the anticollision delay. In the working state batches of minislots which can be used for small packet transmission are separated by working slots, which are idle from the point of view of small packet transmission. We assume that the ratio Z/K_r is an integer, where Z is the minislot randomisation factor and K_r is the number of minislots in reservation slot. We next assume that the minislot is chosen randomly in two stages. Firstly we choose the number of reservation slots for which the copy is delayed from the range $0, 1, \ldots, Z/K_r$. Secondly we choose the number of the minislot inside this reservation slot with uniform probability from the range $1, 2, \ldots, K_r$. The average anticollision delay is:

$$\bar{T}_{ac} = \frac{T_1}{2} + \frac{Z}{2I} T_2 = T_2 \frac{1}{K_w + 1} + \frac{Z}{K_r} \; . \quad (4.2.20)$$

Substituting (4.2.9), (4.2.15–20) in (4.2.14) we obtain the average small packet delay $\tau(W)$ in the working state. Hitherto we evaluated the conditional averages $\bar{\tau}(V)$ and $\tau(W)$. The average small packet delay is

$$\tau_s = P(\Sigma = \sigma_v)\tau(V) + P(\Sigma = \sigma_w)\tau(W) \quad (4.2.21)$$

where Σ is the random variable representing system state. Obviously

$$P(\Sigma = \sigma_v) = 1 - P(\Sigma = \sigma_w) \; . \quad (4.2.22)$$

To evaluate the probability $P(\Sigma = \sigma_w)$, we consider a long time interval $\langle 0, T\rangle$, and denote by $\bar{T}(W)$ the average time in the interval $\langle 0, T\rangle$ during which the system is in the working state. We have:

$$P(\Sigma = \sigma_w) = \frac{\bar{T}(W)}{T} \; . \quad (4.2.23)$$

Let us denote by $\lambda_w(0)$ the average intensity of all working packets, put into the system. In view of assumption A2

$$\lambda_w(0) = M\lambda_{b1}(0)\bar{B} \quad (4.2.24)$$

where $\bar{B} = EB$ in the average number of packets in a batch. During the time interval $\langle 0, T\rangle$; an average of $\lambda_w(0)T$ working packets are generated by the source. To transmit them we need on average $\lambda_w(0)T/K_w$ large slots. Thus $\bar{T}(W) = \lambda_w(0)TT_2/K_w$ and

$$P(\Sigma = \sigma_v) = \nu_w \qquad (4.2.25)$$

where

$$\nu_w \equiv \frac{\lambda_w(0)T_2}{K_w} = \lambda_w(0)\frac{K_w+1}{K_w}T_1 \ . \qquad (4.2.26)$$

If the channel stayed permanently in the working state then ν_w would be the working slot utilisation factor; hence the subscript 'w'.

4.2.4 Transmission of working packets

We now discuss the delay of batches of packets. Let τ_{ba} be the average time elapsing from the instant the source started to deliver the batch to the instant when its reception is complete. We have:

$$\tau_{ba} = \bar{T}^{(ba)}_{s-t} + T^{(pr)}_f + T_{ba} \qquad (4.2.27)$$

where

$\bar{T}^{(ba)}_{s-t}$ is the average time taken to transfer the batch from the source to the transmitter;

$\bar{T}_{ba}$ is the total duration of packets forming the batch;

$T^{(pr)}_f$ is the forward channel propagation time.

In view of subrules 1.2, 2.1, we have:

$$\bar{T}_{s-t} = \bar{T}_{res} + \bar{T}_{qu} \qquad (4.2.28)$$

where

$\bar{T}_{res}$ is the reservation time,

$\bar{T}_{qu}$ is the queuing time of the batch.

The reservation time is just the small packet delay

$$\bar{T}_{res} = \tau_s \ . \qquad (4.2.29)$$

The results of making reservations is that packets from all nodes are placed in a virtual common queue. From the point of view of the packets which got reservations the system considered is equivalent to the system with common buffer and a common transmitter shown in Fig. 2.8. The time $\bar{T}_{qu}$ is the average time the packet spends in the virtual common buffer therefore we call it **queueing time.**

Since the working slots are separated by reservation slots the virtual common buffer operates intermittently. We can analyse it as the small packet entrance buffer operating in the working state, assuming that it is equivalent to the buffer operating rhythimically with a storage.

The period of operation of the equivalent buffer is

$$T_1' = \frac{K_w + 1}{K_w} T_1 . \tag{4.2.30}$$

The normalised intensity of arriving working packets is

$$\lambda_w(0) T_1' = \lambda_w(0) \frac{K_w + 1}{K_w} T_1 = \frac{\lambda_w(0) T_2}{K_w} = \nu_w \tag{4.2.31}$$

the last equality following from (4.2.26). As an approximation for the average time spent by the batch in the equivalent buffer we take the Pollaczek formula

$$\bar{T}_{qu}' = T_1' \sqrt{\frac{B^2}{(\bar{B})^2} \frac{\nu_w}{2(1-\nu_w)}} . \tag{4.2.32}$$

As an approximation for the time spent in the time spent in the storage we take $T_1/2$. Thus we take

$$\bar{T}_{qu} = \bar{T}_{qu}' = T_1/2 . \tag{4.2.33}$$

Substituting (4.2.21), (4.2.28), (4.2.29), (4.2.33) in (4.2.27) gives us the batch delay τ_{ba} as a function of K_w, K_r, Z and the normalised intensity of all working packets passing the common channel which is

$$\nu = \lambda_w(0) T_1 = \frac{K_w}{K_w + 1} \nu_w \tag{4.2.34}$$

Since we have no overlapping of working packets $\nu(1)$ is the common channel utilisation factor used in previous sections.

Hitherto we considered the transmission of the whole batch. The delay of a single packet characterises the normalised delay

$$\tau' = \frac{\tau_{ba}}{\bar{B} T_2} \tag{4.2.35}$$

4.2.5 Choice of system parameters

In the reservation system described we have to choose the parameters K_w, K_r, Z. The principles for choosing Z are similar to those discussed in subsection 4.2.3. Parameters K_w and K_r are related. It follows from (4.2.11) that the largest possible value of the minislot utilisation i.e. the average number of small packets per minislot $\nu_s(1, W)$ is A/e. Thus we can at most obtain $K_r A/e$ successful batch reservations per large slot. During that slot an average of $K_w/\bar{B}$ batches can be sent. This number must not surpass the number of successful reservations, so we must get:

$$\frac{K_w}{\bar{B}} \leqslant \frac{K_r A}{e} \tag{4.2.36}$$

or, equivalently,

$$K_r \geqslant K_w \frac{e}{A\bar{B}} \ . \tag{4.2.37}$$

Since using a value of K_r larger than the minimum determined by RHS of (4.2.37) would mean the inefficient use of the reservation subchannel, we will assume that

$$K_r = \frac{K_w e}{\bar{B}A}(1+\epsilon_1) \tag{4.2.38}$$

where ϵ_1 is a small safety margin. Both T_{res} and T_{qu} depend on the number K_w of working slots per large slot. The reservation time T_{res} increases with K_w as the loading of the reservations slot increases. However, the fraction of the common channel capacity used for large packet transmission is $K_w/1 + K_w$. It increases with K_w, which causes the queueing time T_{qu} to decrease. We can choose K_w either to minimise the packet delay or to maximise the efficiency of use of the channel bandwidth.

To get some insight into the properties of this reservation system, we again take our standard system as an example. We obtain practically the same curves for the small range system with $\tau'_\xi = 0.02$ as for the medium range system with $\tau'_\xi = 0.2$ showing that the average delay in the reservation system does not depend critically on the propagation time. Diagrams of such typical dependences are shown in Fig. 4.10. As may be expected, the delay increases with K_w for small channel utilisation. However, for large utilisation, the average waiting time is large and the system saturates. Increasing K_w shifts the saturation point towards larger values of the channel utilisation ν.

4.2.6 Reservation upon collision system

Figure 4.10 shows the dependence of the packet normalised delay τ' on the common channel utilisation ν for the reservation and feedback systems. From it we can conclude that, for small $\nu(1)$, systems with feedback are definitely better than reservation systems, while for larger $\nu(1)$, the reverse is true. The reason for the unfavourable performance of the reservation system for small ν is that we spend time making a reservation even when this is not recessary because collisions are rare. This would suggest a hybrid system which would operate as a free access system when no collisions occur and as a reservation system when collisions do occur. A family of systems based on such an idea was proposed by Fratta [4.4].

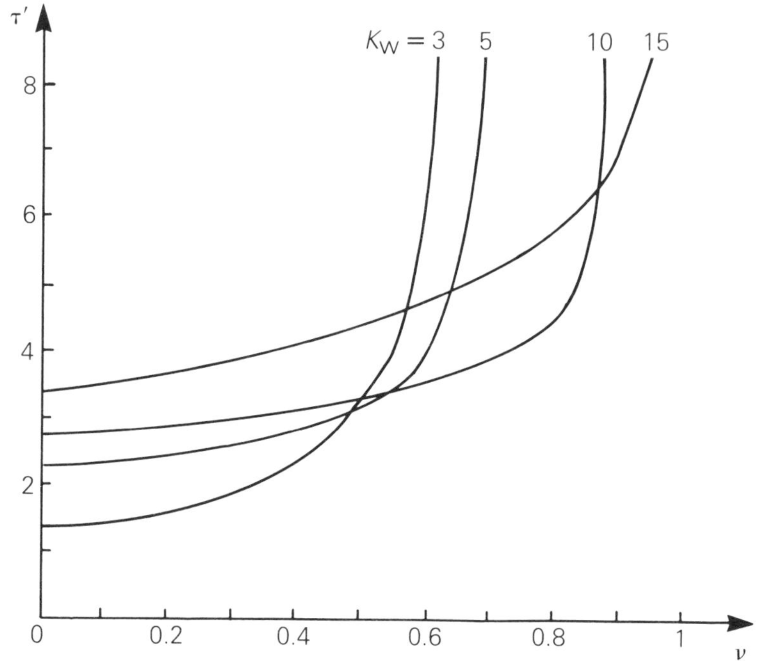

Fig. 4.10 – Typical dependence (a) of the normalised delay τ' on the common channel utilisation factor ν and (b) the number K_w of working slots per large slot is the system with reservation.

The system must be organised so that when collisions take place we can find out which nodes sent packets, so that reservations can be made for them. In the centralised and synchronised version of the system which we are going to describe, that goal is achieved by dividing the basic slot into two subslots: (a) a working slot and (b) a reservation slot. The subchannel formed by the reservation slots is called the **reservation subchannel** and it is used to identify the packets sources in such a way that they cannot be destroyed in the channel. This can be achieved by dividing the reservation subchannel into sub-subchannels and assigning them to the nodes in a fixed way (methods descibed previously, e.g. 2.2). Let us denote by ξ the information about system state. It can take the forms: ξ_r, the system is in the reservation state; or ξ_f, it operates as a feedback system. A central control unit controls the system state by sending information ξ. The system operates according to the reservation upon collision rule (RUC):

1.1 If the node received $\xi = \xi_f$ then it uses the working subchannel as a synchronous access system with feedback.

1.2 If $\xi = \xi_r$ then the node proceeds as follows:
  1.2.1 Newly arrived packets are put into an auxiliary buffer.
  1.2.2 Packets which have collided are transmitted according to a centrally determined schedule.

1.3 After the information ξ_f has arrived, the node operates according to subrule 1.1. A random anticollision delay is introduced for packets taken out of the auxiliary buffer, so they are treated as new packets delivered by the source.

The system central control unit (CCU) operates according to the following rule:

1.4 The CCU watches the working channel. If it observes a collision then
  1.4.1 It sends ξ_r to all nodes.
  1.4.2 It determines the numbers of the working slots in which the collided packets should be transmitted and informs the nodes.
  1.4.3 The CCU also informs the nodes when to revert to subrule 1.1.

Figure 4.11 shows typical behaviour for such a system. This rule has been analysed by Fratta [4.4].

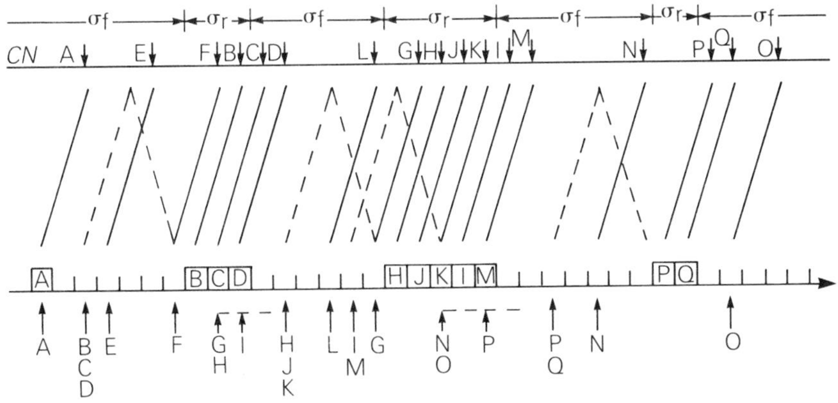

Fig. 4.11 – Typical transmission in the reservation upon collision system. σ_f, free access state, σ_r, reservation state.

Various modifications of the RUC rule are possible and some were considered by Fratta [4.4].

Finally we compare all the rules so far considered, using the example of the standard small and medium range systems we have often used before, in Fig. 4.12. We conclude from these figures that for the example chosen, the reservation upon collision system is the best. However, when considering the complexity of the systems, and thus their reliability, other much simpler systems are also of importance.

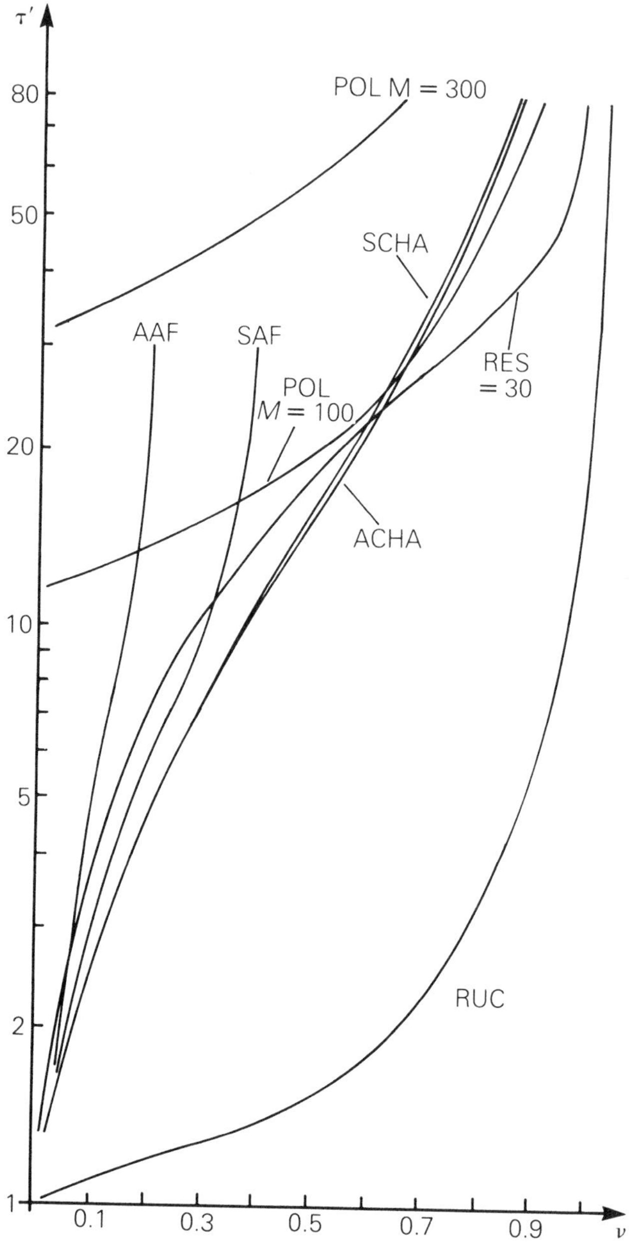

Fig. 4.12 – Dependence of the normalised delay τ' on the normalised intensity ν of packets going through the common channel without collisions AAF (SAF) asynchronous (synchronous) access systems with collision. SCHA, synchronous channel state controlled system; SCP, synchronous access centralised polling system; Res, reservation system with flexible comch division, RuC, reservation upon collision system (based on Staniszewski [3.6]).

4.3 SYSTEMS WITH CONTINUOUS ACCESS *EN ROUTE*

Systems with *en route* access were described in general in Chapter 1.† We consider centralised outflow systems and inflow–outflow systems which are a superposition of the inflow and outflow systems see Fig. 1.11. In general, a node consists of the local source, local transmitter, local destination and local receiver; similarly the set consisting of the central source, central destination, transmitter and receiver will be called the central node. We call the set of rules on which such systems operate the **packet handling rules.**

In this section we first consider the fundamental features of packet handling rules. Next we discuss the fundamental parameters characterising these rules, and outline the methods for analysing them. In the second subsection we analyse systems in which a packet, once located in its slot, travels to its destination undisturbed. In the last subsection we consider systems in which it is possible to interrupt a packet's journey and to use the emptied slot to transmit a packet of higher priority.

4.3.1 Fundamental properties of systems with access *en route*

As for multiaccess systems, system identification information (s.i.i.) is essential for the operation of systems with access *en route.* The handling of packets generated by the transmitter's own source and of packets in transit is based on this information. We usually require that systems with access *en route* are simple so we assume that:

A1 The packet handling decisions are based solely on the data carried by the packets passing through the node considered, in particular that number of the source and destination of the packets.

We consider only systems with synchronous access where the central node generates narrow pulses (with a period T_1) which are sent into the common channel to determine the sequence of slots. We assume that:

A2 A packet fits exactly into a slot.

Let $t_m(j)$ be the instant at which the jth, $j = 1, 2, \ldots$ timing pulse reaches the mth, $m = 1, 2, \ldots, M$ node (see Fig. 4.13). We have:

$$t_m(j+1) - t_m(j) = T_1 \tag{4.3.1}$$

whereas the difference $t_{m+1}(j) - t_m(j)$ is the time which the nth timing pulse takes to travel between the mth and the $(m+1)$th node.

To classify the packet handling rules and hence systems with access *en route* we first describe the fundamental features of the rules. We will first consider the

† Most typical systems with access *en route* are loop systems, for a review of such systems and methods of their analysis see Pierce [4.5], Kobayoshi, Konheim [4.6].

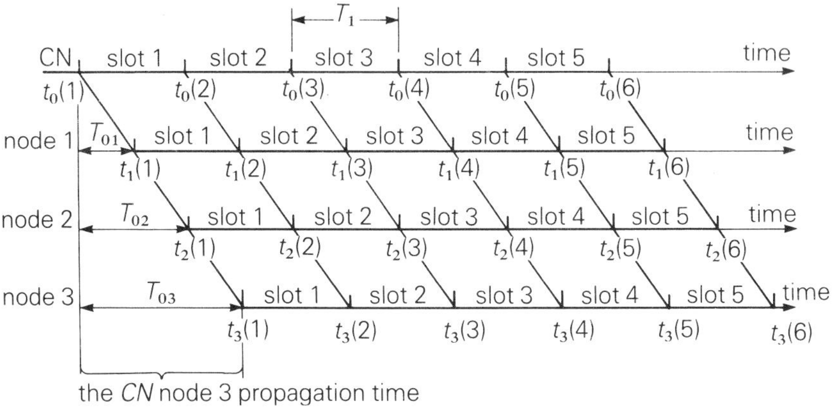

Fig. 4.13 – Timing in access *en route* systems CN, central node.

structure of the node realising the rule shown in Fig. 4.14. The packets from the channel known as external packets) are sent to the address and the priority checking unit. If this node is the external packet's destination then the slot is freed. If the external packet is addressed to another node then the priority of the packet is compared with the priorities of other packets in the node. The packet of the highest priority is put into the transmitter. If this is not the external packet, the external packet is stored in the buffer.

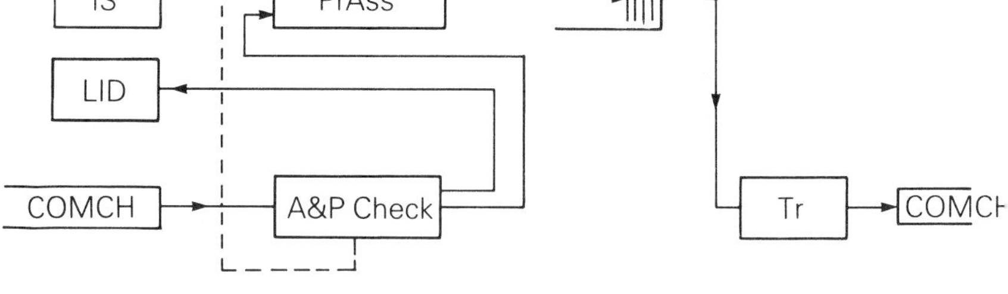

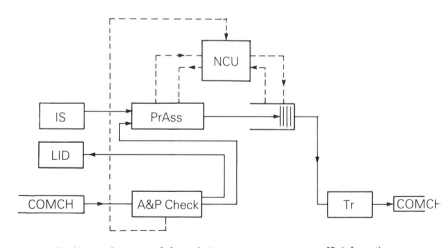

Fig. 4.14 – Structure of the node in access *en route* systems. IS, information source; LID, local information destination; NCU, node control unit; Tr, transmitter; PrASS, priorities assignment unit; A & P, address and priority checking unit.

If we give the highest priority to every external packet, then once a packet is located in a slot, it will travel in that slot to its desination. An internal packet can thus only be located in an empty slot. This rule is called the rule of ***en route* access without interruption.** If a packet can be removed from its slot and replaced by a packet with higher priority, the operating rule is known as ***en route* access with interruption.**

We now consider in more detail packet handling rules without interruption. These rules can be classified as having either fixed or flexible access. With fixed access we have a system operating cycle comprising M slots, often called a large slot. The duration of the large slot is:

$$T_2 = MT_1 \quad . \tag{4.3.2}$$

The mth, $m = 1, 2, \ldots, M$, slot inside a given system operating cycle is assigned to the mth terminal. A packet generated by the mth source (or directed to the mth destination) can be put into the mth slot only. Thus a packet coming from (or directed to) the mth node will be sent in the slot with the number

$$j_m(i) = m + iM \tag{4.3.3}$$

$i = 0, 1, 2, \ldots$. The structure of the slot sequence is thus the same as in the system with separated time subchannels and fixed node-subchannel assignment rule which was considered in section 2.3. From (4.3.2) and (4.3.3) it can be seen that the ith slot for the mth node reaches the mth node at the instant:

$$\vartheta_m(i) = \vartheta_m(0) + j_m(i)T_2 \tag{4.3.4}$$

where $\vartheta_m(0)$ is the instant at which the zeroth slot for the mth node, reaches its own node. From formulae (4.3.1)–(4.3.3) we get:

$$\vartheta_m(i+1) - \vartheta_m(i) = T_2 \tag{4.3.5}$$

The above notation is illustrated in Fig. 4.15.

For an inflow and outflow system we need to decide to re-use a slot after the packet has been taken out. It is quite difficult for a node to remove a packet directed to it and to insert a new packet into the same slot. Because of this difficulty many systems allow freed slots to remain empty. A system which does not re-use empty slots is said to operate **without slot release**, and one which does re-use empty slots operates with **slot release.** Slot release permits the common channel to be used more efficiently but at the price of increased node complexity. We always assume that the central node applies the packet handling rule with slot release.

We now consider systems which allow interruption. Here the nodes must be able to replace one packet by another in a given slot, i.e. we have slot release.

The packet handling rule admitting interruption is described by the subrules of assigning priorities to the packets. An example is a subrule in which: (1) the

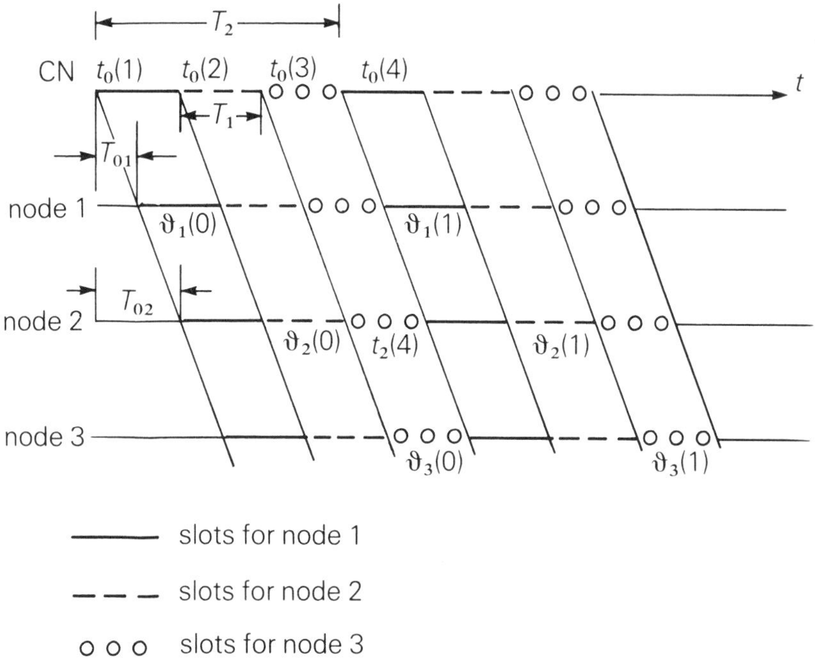

Fig. 4.15 – Timing in a system with fixed access.

priority is higher the greater the number the destination node, (2) for packets directed to the same node the second order priority is higher, the smaller the number of the source is.

Such priorities simply mean that a packet obtains higher priority the further it is from the source to the destination.

From the practical point of view, the most important systems are inflow and outflow systems in which terminals send tasks to the computing system located at the central node, and the central node sends back an answer. In such a system the packets are generated in batches and the statistical properties of the batches produced by the terminal and the central node may differ greatly. The parameter characterising the batches is:

$$\psi = \frac{\bar{B}_{m0}}{\bar{B}_{0m}} \tag{4.3.6}$$

where $\bar{B}_{m0}$ is the average batch size for packets travelling from the mth terminal to the central node, and $\bar{B}_{0m}$ is the average size for the opposite direction. We may exploit the difference in the batch sizes by using different rules for handling packets travelling in opposite directions.

The inflow and outflow systems are characterised by the total time T'_m elapsing between the task being delivered to the terminal and the terminal obtaining the complete answer, minus the computation time. We call T'_m the response delay. It is:

$$T_m = T_{m0} + T_{0m} \tag{4.3.7}$$

where T_{m0} is the time taken to transmit the batch from the mth terminal node to the central node, and T_{0m} is the time taken to transmit the reply. In the subsequent sections, we will derive the relationships between the packet (or batch) passage time and the common channel utilisation factor for various types of packet handling rules.

4.3.2 Rules for handling packets without interruption

In this section we analyse inflow systems operating without interruption. In addition to A1, assume the following about the source:

A3 The packets are delivered in batches, and the number of packets in a batch is represented by the random variable B. The random variables corresponding to the various batches are independent.

A4 The process representing the number of batches generated at mth node during the time interval $\langle 0, t\rangle$ has independent stationary increments; the processes for $m \neq n$ are independent.

As a special case of A2, we assume:

A3′ The source delivers only single packets (B = 1).

and as the special case of A.3,

A4′ The model of the starting instant is a stationary Poisson process of intensity† λ_m.

In most of our discussions we also assume homogeneity:

A5 All terminal sources have the same statistical properties; under A3′ we get λ_m = const.

We assume the following about the system:

A6 The system is an inflow system without interruption.

A7 The capacity of each buffer is infinite.

† According to notation principles used previously we should write $\lambda_m(0)$. Since in the systems considered here no collisions occur we have only one class of packets and we write λ_m.

We first consider fixed access rules, then flexible access rules. In each case we first take a simple model assuming single packet arrivals (A3′), and then a general model for batch arrivals.

We start with the fixed access rule and single packet arrivals. The working slots are grouped into large slots of duration $T_2 = MT_1$. Let:

$l_m(t)$ be the number of the packets in the buffer at $t \neq \vartheta_m(i)$, where $\vartheta_m(i)$ is given by (4.3.4), and

$l_m[\vartheta_m(i)]$ be the number of packets in the buffer just before $\vartheta_m(i)$ the start of the ith slot,

From systems operation rules follows:

$$l_m[\vartheta_m(i+1)] = \{l_m[\vartheta_m(i)] - 1\}^+ + \Lambda_m^{(2)}(i) \tag{4.3.8}$$

where $\Lambda_m^{(2)}(i)$ is the number of packets delivered by the mth source in the time interval $\langle\vartheta_m(i), \vartheta_m(i+1)\rangle$, and

$$u^+ = \begin{cases} u & \text{if } u \geqslant 0 \\ 0 & \text{if } u < 0 \end{cases} . \tag{4.3.9}$$

Notice that according to (4.3.5), the interval $\langle\vartheta_m(i), \vartheta_m(i+1)\rangle$ has a duration T_2. That is why we introduce the superscript 2 in $\Lambda_m^{(2)}(i)$.

As we show in Appendix A.1, if we assume A3 and A4, we can express the stationary probability distribution of the random variable $l_m[\vartheta_m(i+1)]$ in terms of the probability distribution of $\Lambda_m^{(2)}(i)$, and thus calculate the average L_m. As is shown in Appendix A.1, an essential role is played by the parameter

$$\nu_m \equiv E\Lambda_m^{(2)}(i) \tag{4.3.10}$$

which,† assuming stationarity, does not depend on the slot number i. In order to interpret ν_m, let us notice that the ratio

$$\lambda_m = \frac{E\Lambda_m^{(2)}(i)}{T_2} \tag{4.3.11}$$

can be interpreted as the intensity of packets delivered by the source. Thus ν_m can be taken to be the normalised intensity of packets delivered by the mth source, or the average number of packets per slot delivered by the source. As can be seen in Appendix 1, if

$$\nu_m < 1 \tag{4.3.12}$$

† We write ν_m not $\nu_m(0)$ – see footnote page 181.

L_m is finite. In such a case, every packet delivered by the source ultimately goes through the channel. Thus, since collisions cannot occur using this access rule, ν_m can also be interpreted as the duty ratio of the packets in the sequence of slots assigned to the mth terminal. Appendix 1 shows that if ν_m satisfies (4.3.12), we get;

$$\bar{L}_m[\vartheta_m(i)] = \frac{1}{2}\frac{\operatorname{var}(\Lambda_m^{(2)})}{1-E\Lambda_m^{(2)}} + \frac{1}{2}E\Lambda_m^{(2)} \tag{4.3.13}$$

By definition, $L_m[\vartheta_m(i)]$ is the number of packets just before the arrival of the ith slot. In the period between the slot starts, no packets are removed so the average number $L_m(t)$ of packets in the buffer at time t is as shown in Fig. A.2. Since on average $E\Lambda_m^{(2)}(i)$ new packets arrive during the slot, $\bar{L}_m(t)$ averaged over time, which we denote by $\bar{\bar{L}}_m$, is:

$$\bar{\bar{L}}_m = \bar{L}_m[\vartheta_m(i)] - \frac{1}{2}E\Lambda_m^{(2)}(i) \tag{4.3.14}$$

Let us now assume that the arrival instants of packets from the source form a Poisson sequence. From (4.3.13), (4.3.14) we then have

$$\bar{L}_m = \frac{\nu_m}{2(1-\nu_m)} \ . \tag{4.3.15}$$

From Little's theorem, we obtain the average queueing time spent by the packet in the mth buffer:

$$\tau_{wm} = \frac{\bar{L}_m}{\lambda_m} \ . \tag{4.3.16}$$

From (4.3.15) we ultimately obtain the passage time of the packet coming from the mth source:

$$\tau_m = T_2\frac{1}{2(1-\nu_m)} + T_1 \ . \tag{4.3.17}$$

We now consider batch arrivals, and we assume that:

A8 The random variable B representing the number of packets in the batch has a geometric probability distribution, i.e. $P(\mathrm{B} = b) = (1 - P_1)b^{P_1}$ where $0 \leqslant P_1 < 1$.

The average number of packets in the batch

$$\bar{B} = \frac{1}{1-P_1} \ . \tag{4.3.18}$$

In order to find τ_m we consider a test batch consisting of b packets delivered at t' just before the beginning of the next slot and directly evaluate the average time $\bar{\tau}_m(b)$ between t' and sending the last packet in the batch. Using embedded Markovian chain theory, it can be shown (see Pawlikowski [4.7]) that:

$$\tau_m(b) = (\bar{L}_m[\vartheta_m(i)] - E\Lambda_m^{(2)} + \mathrm{b} - 1)T_1 + \frac{M+1}{2} T_2 \tag{4.3.19}$$

where, as previously we denote

$\bar{L}_m[\vartheta_m(i)]$ as the average number of packets in the buffer just before the arrival of a new 'own' slot,

$\Lambda_m^{(2)}$ as the number of batches delivered during the large slot.

Taking into account (4.3.13) formula (4.3.19) simplifies to:

$$\tau_m(b) = \frac{1}{2}\left[\frac{\operatorname{var}[\Lambda_m^{(2)}(i)]}{1 - E\Lambda_m^{(2)}(i)} - \frac{1}{2}E\Lambda_m^{(2)}(i) + b - 1\right] T_2 + \frac{M+3}{2} T_1 \tag{4.3.20}$$

Under assumption (A8) we obtain:

$$\tau_m(b) = \left[\frac{1}{2}\,\frac{\lambda_m(1+P_1)T_2}{1-P_1-\lambda_m T_2} - \frac{1}{2}\,\frac{\lambda_m T_2}{1-P_1} + \upsilon - 1\right] T_2 + \frac{M+3}{2}\,T_1 \tag{4.3.21}$$

From these formulae we see that in the case of a homogeneous system, i.e. when $\nu_m = \nu_1 =$ const. the packet passage time does not depend on the node number m. This can be easily explained since: (1) subchannels corresponding to various nodes are used in the fixed access system independently, (2) we defined the packets passage time as the sum of the packets waiting time and its durations, but without taking into account the propagation time. Notice that if the number b of packets in the batch grows, both the duration of the batch and the passage time grow. Therefore, as in section 4.2.1 we introduce the normalised delay for a single packet defined as:†

$$\tau'_{1m}(b) = \frac{\tau_m(b)}{T_1 b} \quad . \tag{4.3.22}$$

The diagrams of $\tau'_{1m}(b)$ as a function of ν_m and b are shown in Fig. 4.16. Figure 4.16(a) represents the case when both test batch size and average batch size change. The value of $\nu'_{1m}(b)$ for $\nu = 0$ is the constant component in (4.3.21) which grows as b decreases. Figure 4.16(b) shows that the delay of the test batch size of the background traffic grows.

† In the notation $\tau'_{1m}(b)$ the prime reminds us that this is the delay normalised with respect to packet duration, and that it is normalised in respect to number of blocks and '$1m$' is the node number.

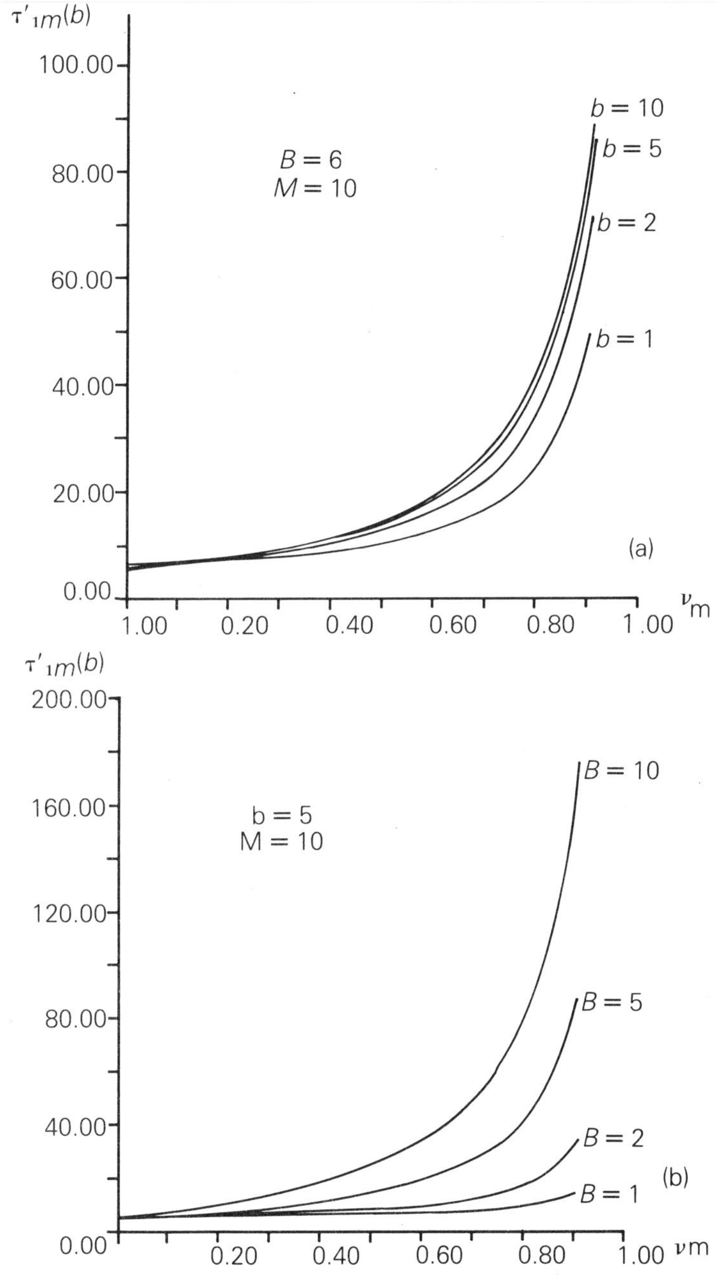

Fig. 4.16 – Dependence of the normalised delay $\tau'_{1m}(b)$ on the normalised intensity ν_m and on test batch size. b, fixed access rule. (a) $b = 3$, (b) $b = 5$, $\bar{B}$ variable; $\bar{B}$, average background batch size.

4.3.3 Flexible access rule

We next consider the flexible access rule, under which the packet waiting in the buffer is put into the first empty slot and travels in that slot to the central node. The jth slot arriving at the mth terminal, will be empty if no 'upstream' node inserted a packet. This occurs if, and only if, at the times $t_n(j), n=1,2,\ldots,m-1$, that the slot passed the upstream nodes all the terminal buffers were empty. Let

$l_m[t_m(j)]$ be the number of packets at instant $t_m(j) = 0$ on the mth terminal.

$\Lambda_m^{(1)}(j)$ be the number of packets put into the buffer of the mth terminal in the small slot $\langle t_m(j-1), t_m(j)\rangle$.

In the latter notation we use the subscript 1 since $\langle t_m(j-1), t_m(j)\rangle$ is the working interval of length T_1. From the description of flexible access rule it follows that:

$$l_1[t_1(j)] = \{l_1[t_1(j-1)]-1\}^+ + \Lambda_1^{(1)}(j) \tag{4.3.23a}$$

$$l_2[t_2(j)] = \{l_2[t_2(j-1)] - \{1-l_1[t_1(j-1)]\}^+\}^+ + \Lambda_2^{(1)}(j) \tag{4.3.23b}$$

$$\ldots\ldots$$

$$l_m[t_m(j)] = \left\{l_m[t_m(j-1)] - \left\{1 - \sum_{n=1}^{m-1} l_m[t_n(j-1)]\right\}^+\right\}^+ + \Lambda_m^{(1)}(j) \tag{4.3.23c}$$

and that

$$\sum_{n=1}^{m-1} l_n[t_n(j)] = \left\{\sum_{n=1}^{m-1} l_n[t_n(j-1)] - 1\right\}^+ + \sum_{n=1}^{m-1} \Lambda_m^{(1)}(j) \tag{4.3.24}$$

It is evident from these equations that the analysis of a set of m buffers can be reduced to the analysis of a set of two buffers: the mth and a second, virtual buffer containing all packets in nodes lying upstream the node considered. It is also evident that while the process $L_m[t_m(j)]$ representing the number of packets in the mth buffer is not a first order Markovian process, the two-dimensional process

$$L_m[t_m(j)] \equiv \left(\sum_{n=1}^{m-1} L_n[t_n(j)], L_m[t_m(j)]\right) \tag{4.3.25}$$

is a first order Markovian process. Appendix A.5 gives the detailed derivation of the generating function for the stationary joint probability distribution of the two-dimensional process $L_m(t_j)$. This derivation is the exact counterpart of the derivation of the generating function for the number of packets in a single buffer, which we gave in Appendix 1.

Knowing the generating function of the two-dimensional probability distribution, we can easily obtain the generating function of the probability distribution of the random variable $L_m[t_m(j)]$ as the marginal distribution, and (directly from the generating function) the mean value of $L_m[t_m(j)]$. The detailed calculation are given in Appendix A.4. The ultimately obtained mean value is:

$$\bar{L}_m[t_m(j)] = \frac{\text{var}\,[\Lambda_m^{(1)}(j)]}{2(1-\nu_{\Sigma m})} + \frac{E\Lambda_m^{(1)}(j) \sum_{n=1}^{m-1} \text{var}\,[\Lambda_m^{(1)}(j)]}{2(1-\nu_m^*)(1-\nu_{m-1}^*)} + \frac{1}{2}E\Lambda_m^{(1)}(j) \tag{4.3.26}$$

where

$$\nu_m^* \equiv \sum_{n=1}^{m} \nu_n \tag{4.3.27}$$

and

$$\nu_m \equiv E\Lambda_m^{(1)}(j) \ . \tag{4.3.28}$$

The parameter ν_m^* is the total intensity of packets delivered by all sources located upstream of the node m normalised with respect to the duration T_1 of the slot. The necessary condition for the average number of packets $\bar{L}_m[t_m(j)]$ at the mth node remaining finite is that:

$$\nu_m^* < 1 \ . \tag{4.3.29}$$

The average $\bar{L}_m[t_m(j)]$ given by (4.3.26) is the average number of packets in the buffer at the instant just prior to the new slot arrival. For single packet arrivals, we obtain the overall average by subtracting $[E\Lambda_m^{(1)}(j)]/2$. This gives us:

$$\bar{L}_m = \bar{L}_m[t_m(j)] - 1/2\,E\Lambda_m^{(1)}(j) \ . \tag{4.3.30}$$

If we further assume that the modal of the packet's arrival instants is a Poisson process, we obtain

$$\bar{L}_m = \frac{\nu_m}{2(1-\nu_m^*)(1-\nu_{m-1}^*)} \ . \tag{4.3.31}$$

Using Little's theorem, we obtain the average packet delay

$$\tau_{\text{wm}} = \frac{\bar{L}_m}{\lambda_m} \ . \tag{4.3.32}$$

From 4.3.31 we have ultimately:

$$\tau_m = T_1 \frac{1}{2(1-\nu_m^*)(1-\nu_{m-1}^*)} + T_1 \tag{4.3.33}$$

As we mentioned, formulae (4.3.26) and (4.3.33) are valid only if ν_m, given by (4.3.27) satisfies condition (4.3.29). The parameter $\nu_m^{(\Sigma)}$ can be interpreted as the total intensity of packets normalised with respect to the duration T_1 of the slot, delivered by all sources located upstream the node m inclusive. It is a non-decreasing function of m. When all sources deliver single packets with the same intensity $\nu_m = \nu_1 = \text{const.}$, then

$$\nu_m^* = m\nu_1 \ . \tag{4.3.34}$$

Since ν_m^* does not decrease with m, when the condition that $\nu_m^* < 1$ is satisfied for one value of m, it is also satisfied for all $n \leqslant m$. Then the average numbers of packets in the buffers at nodes $n = 1, 2, \ldots, m$ are finite and therefore all packets delivered by the sources at nodes $n = 1, 2, \ldots, m$ ultimately go through the channel. Thus the parameter ν_m^* can also be interpreted as the common channel utilisation factor in the section between the mth and the $(m+1)$th node.

The numbers of packets in all the buffers will be finite if

$$\nu_m^* < 1 \tag{4.3.35}$$

or equivalent if

$$\nu_m < \frac{m}{M} \ . \tag{4.3.36}$$

This means that in the initial segments of the channel the admissible utilisation factors are quite small and they change along the channel. This is obviously a disadvantage, but in view of systems topology is rather unavoidable. Figure 4.17 shows the dependence of the normalised delay τ_m' on ν_1 on the assumption that $\nu_m = \nu_1 = \text{const.}$ and (4.3.36) is satisfied. It is evident from this figure that the dependence of the delay is quite large but even in the worst case the delay is smaller than for the fixed access rule.

Hitherto we have assumed that the source delivers single packets, but we now briefly consider batch arrivals. As in the case of fixed access, we consider a batch consisting of b packets delivered by the mth source just before the jth slot. The sequence of packets in the block arriving at the destination is the same as the primary sequence at the source, but the time intervals between packets are different. The components of the batch transmission time $\bar{\tau}_m(b)$ are:

(1) the waiting time until the first slot arrives;
(2) the waiting time caused by packets delivered to the buffer at nodes $1, 2, \ldots, n-1$ during the time interval $\langle t', t'' \rangle$ where t'' is the instant the last packet in the batch is put into the common channel;
(3) the last packet's transmission time, T_1;
(4) the waiting time for the next slot.

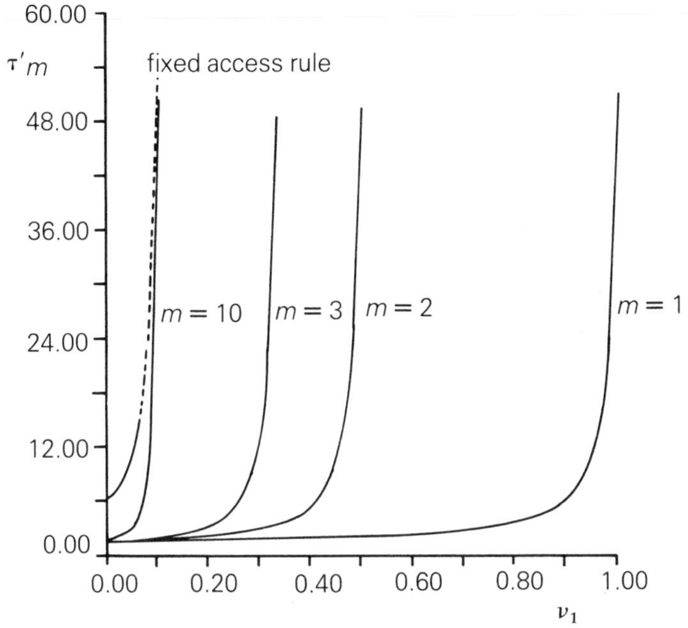

Fig. 4.17 – Dependence of the normalised delay τ'_m on the utilisation factor ν_1 of the channel in the segment behind the node $m = 1$. Normalised packet input intensities $\nu_m = \nu_1 = \text{const}$. Flexible *en route* access system, the source delivers single packets.

Taking these components into account, it can be shown that

$$\tau_m(b) = \left[\frac{\bar{L}_m^*(t_m) - \sum_{n=1}^{m} E\Lambda_m^{(1)} + b}{1 - \nu_{m-1}^*} + 1 \right] T_1 \tag{4.3.37}$$

where $\bar{L}_m^*(t_n)$ is the average total number of packets in buffers in the nodes $1, 2, \ldots, m$ at the instant just before the slot starts, and

$$\nu_m = \bar{B}\lambda_{mb}T_1 \tag{4.3.38}$$

is the normalised intensity of packets delivered by the mth node. The average $\bar{L}_m^{\Sigma}(t_m)$ entering in (4.3.37) is given by the formla

$$\bar{L}_m^*(t_m) = \frac{1}{2}(1 - \nu_m^*)^{-1} \sum_{n=1}^{m} \text{var}[\Lambda_m^{(1)}] + \frac{1}{2}\nu_m^* \ . \tag{4.3.39}$$

In particular, in the case when for each node the number of packets in the batch has the same geometric distribution we have

$$\bar{L}_m^*(t_m) = \frac{\nu_m^* \dfrac{1+P_1}{1-P_1}}{2(1-\nu_m^*)} + \frac{1}{2}\nu_m^* \ . \tag{4.3.40}$$

Hitherto we have considered the single node. To define the parameters characterising the whole system applying flexible access rule we have to take into account that even when statistical properties of all information sources and all rules according to which the nodes operate are the same the normalised intensity $\nu_{\Sigma m}$ of packets passing through the common channel behind the mth node and the packet time depend essentially on the number m of the node, thus the system in inherently non-homogeneous. Therefore, when defining the parameters characterising the system we have to introduce an operation removing the dependence on the node number m.

Let us start with the intensity of packets passing through the channel. Since we usually do not want to have channels with capacity varying along them we must take into account the largest possible packet intensity in the channel. Therefore to define the normalised intensity – characterising the whole channel we use the max dependence removing operation, see section 1.3, and we define

$$\nu \equiv \max_m \nu_m^* \tag{4.3.41}$$

where ν_m^* is the normalised intensity of total packets flow just behind the mth node, is given by formula (4.3.38). As we have indicated ν_m^* grows with m and therefore as the parameter characterising the whole channel is:

$$\nu = \nu_M^* \ . \tag{4.3.42}$$

Let us take for example a system with $M = 10$ nodes, and let us assume $\nu_m = \nu_1 =$ const. Figure 4.18 shows the dependence of the normalised single packet delay τ_m' given by (4.3.33) on the parameter ν given by (4.3.42) and the number m of the node. The important conclusion is that the dependence of the delay on node number is pronounced only for ν approaching 1. Hitherto we considered single nodes. For parameters characterising the whole system we take

$$\bar{\tau} = \frac{1}{M} \sum_{m=1}^{m} \tau_m \tag{4.3.43}$$

where $\bar{\tau}_m$ is the average delay of packets from mth node. We call $\bar{\tau}$ the doubly average packet passage time averaged over events in transmission and over

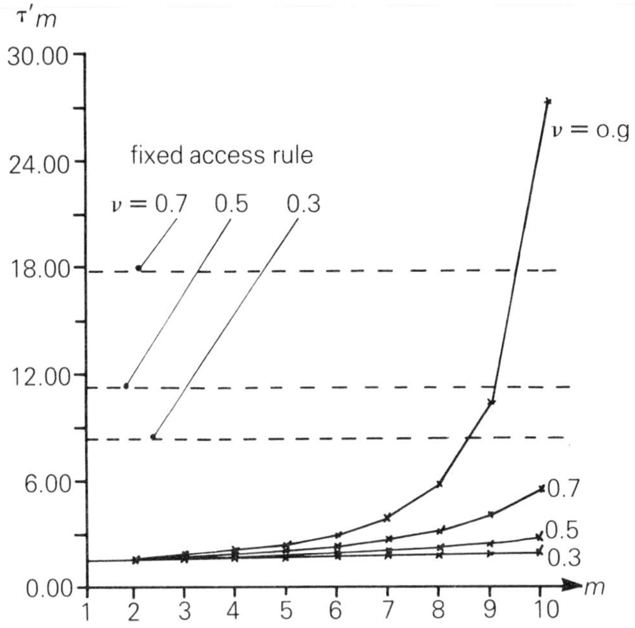

Fig. 4.18 – Dependence of the normalised delay τ'_m on the node number m. The parameter ν characterising the common channel utlisation is fixed. Flexible *en route* access system, the source delivers single packets.

node number. If batches are delivered, we similarly define the double average normalised passage time per single packet

$$\bar{\tau}'_1(b) = \frac{1}{M\tau_1} \sum_{m=1}^{M} \bar{\tau}_{1m}(b) = \frac{1}{M} \sum_{m=1}^{M} \frac{\tau_m(b)}{b} \quad . \tag{4.3.44}$$

The dependence of $\bar{\tau}'_1(b)$ on ν and b is shown in Fig. 4.19. The case $\bar{B} = b = 1$ corresponds to the single packet arrival. Growth of the delay with both sides can be explained in such a way that if we keep ν constant and increase $\bar{B}$, we have on average longer pauses between batches which compensates for clustering of packets inside the batch.

4.4 RULES FOR HANDLING SYSTEMS WITH ACCESS *EN ROUTE* WITH INTERRUPTIONS

We will now consider the packet handling rule with interruptions, i.e. the rule admitting the possibility of taking the packet out of the slot before it reaches its destination. For an inflow system with all information sources having the same

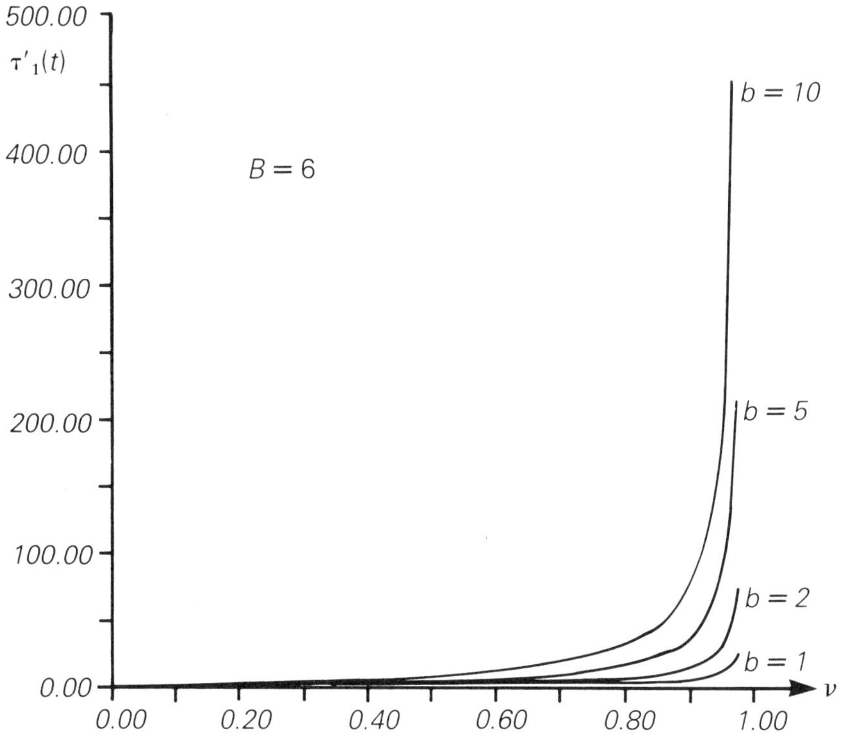

Fig. 4.19 – Dependence of the normalised doubly average delay $\bar{\tau}_1'(b)$ on the parameter ν characterising the common channel utilisation normalised source intensity $\nu_m = \nu_1 =$ const.; average batch size $B = b$, where b = test batch size.

properties, interrupting a packet's journey would be pointless. It is to be expected that, when sources located upstream deliver packets with higher intensities, than those downstream, the use of interruption may decrease the average packet passage time. This possibility was shown by Pawlikowski [4.7]. We may expect significant advantages from admitting interruptions in loop inflow–outflow systems with slot release. We are going to investigate such a system. As before, we assume that there are M local nodes numbered $m = 1, 2, \ldots, M$, and the central node which we designate 0. We call a packet directed from the central node to the mth local node type $0 \to m$, packet, and one directed from the mth local node to the central node an $m \to 0$ type packet. The system operates according to the rules:

1. An $m \to 0$ packet always has higher priority than $0 \to m$ packets.
2. An $m \to 0$ packet located in a slot always has higher priority than an $m \to 0$ packet in the buffer.

3. A $0 \to m$ packet directed to node m has first order priority, m.
4. Where two $0 \to m$ packets are directed to the same node, m, the packet which has spent more time in the system has higher priority.

The journey of a $0 \to m$ type packet directed to a node can be interrupted if either (1) an $m \to 0$ type packet or (2) a $0 \to n$ type packet which is directed to the node $n' > n$ is waiting in the buffer at the node the packet is just passing.

In view of subrule 1, subsystem $m \to 0$ does not depend on subsystem $0 \to m$. Contrary to it the subsystem $0 \to m$ depends heavily on subsystem $m \to 0$. The subsystem $m \to 0$ operates exactly as the flexible access system without interruptions considered previously.

We analyse the system in the same way as in the previous subsection. We first consider single packet arrivals and then batch arrivals. For each case we will first look at the subsystem for $m \to 0$ type and then that for $0 \to m$ type packet delivery.

4.4.1 The subsystem for transmission of packets from local nodes to the central node

The $m \to 0$ type packet delivery subsystem is identical to the flexible access inflow system discussed in the previous subsection, so we use the same formulae, but with new notation. Let

$l_{sr}(m,t)$ be the number of packets directed from node p to q stored in the mth node buffer at time t.

In our system only the combinations $p = 0, q = 1, 2, \ldots, M$ and $p = 1, 2, \ldots, M$, $q = 0$ are possible. Obviously:

$$l_{0m}(n,t) = 0 \tag{4.4.1}$$

for $n > m$. The journey of packets directed from node $m = 1, 2, \ldots, M$ to the central node is never interrupted, thus:

$$l_{m0}(n,t) = 0 \tag{4.4.2}$$

for $n \neq m$.

Let us look at the subsystem of $m \to 0$ packet transmission. Let

λ_{m0} be the intensity of $m \to 0$ type packet generated at node m;

$\Lambda_{m0}^{(1)} = \lambda_{m0} T_1$ be the number of $m \to 0$ type packets generated at node m during a slot;

$$\Lambda_{m0}^{*} \equiv \sum_{n=1}^{m} \Lambda_{n0}^{(1)} \tag{4.4.3}$$

be the local number of $m \to 0$ type packets generated by all local sources of nodes proceding node m without the central node and by node m itself during a slot.

$$\nu_{n0} \equiv E\Lambda_{n0}^{(1)} \tag{4.4.4}$$

$$\nu_{m0}^{*} = \sum_{n=1}^{m} \nu_{n0} \ . \tag{4.4.5}$$

The parameter ν_{n0} is the normalised intensity of $m \to 0$ type packets generated at the nth node normalised with respect to slot duration, and ν_{n0}^{*} is the total normalised intensity of packets generated by all local nodes preceding the nth node, and the nth node itself, directed to the control node. Obviously,

$$\nu_{n0} = \lambda_{n0}\bar{B}_{n0}T_1 \ . \tag{4.4.6}$$

On the assumption that

$$\nu_{n0}^{*} < 1 \tag{4.4.7}$$

the average $m \to 0$ type packet passage time, averaged over time, which we denote by $\bar{\tau}_{m0}$ is given by formula (4.3.33). In the notation of this section it has the form:

$$\tau_{m0} = \frac{1}{\nu_{m0}}(\bar{L}_{m0} - 1/2\nu_{m0})T_1 + T_1 \tag{4.4.8}$$

where

$$\bar{L}_{m0} = \frac{\text{var}\,(\Lambda_{m0}^{(1)})}{2(1-\nu_{m0}^{*})} + \frac{\nu_{m0}\ \text{var}(\Lambda_{m-1,0}^{*})}{2(1-\nu_{m0}^{*})(1-\nu_{m-1,0}^{*})} + 1/2\nu_{m0} \tag{4.4.9}$$

is the overall average number of packets directed from node m to the central node which, in view of the priorities assignment subrule are stored only at the mth node.

Let us now assume that all sources deliver single packets with the same intensity, i.e., we assume that

$$\lambda_{m0} = \lambda_{10} = \text{const.} \tag{4.4.10}$$

and that the packets starting instants are poissonian.
From (4.4.8), (4.4.9), we obtain:

$$\tau_{m0} = \frac{T_1}{2(1-m\nu_{10})[1-(m-1)\nu_{10}]} + T_1 \ . \tag{4.4.11}$$

Next we consider batch arrivals. The modified formula 4.3.37 takes the form

$$\tau_{m0}(b) = \left[\frac{\bar{L}^*_{m0}(t_n) - \sum_{n=1}^{m} \nu_{m0} + b}{1 - \nu^{\Sigma}_{m-1,0}} + 1\right] T_1 \tag{4.4.12}$$

where

$$\bar{L}^*_{m0}(t_n) = \frac{1}{2}(1 - \nu^*_{m0})^{-1} \sum_{n=1}^{m} \mathrm{var}[\Lambda^{(1)}_{n0}] + \frac{1}{2}\nu^*_{m0} \ . \tag{4.4.13}$$

4.4.2 The subsystem for transmission of packets from the central to the local nodes

We now consider the $0 \to m$ type packet transmission system, i.e. the outflow subsystem. The essential difference between this subsystem and the previously considered inflow subsystem is that faced with the priorities chosen, the journey of outflow packets can be interrupted by the inflow packets. Thus the operation of the outflow subsystem depends on the operation of the inflow subsystem. Let:

$$l_{0m}(t) = \sum_{n=0}^{m-1} l_{0m}(n,t) \tag{4.4.14}$$

be the total number of packets destined for node m which are waiting either at the central node or at an intermediate node where the packet's journey was interrupted. Taking into account both these reasons for interruptions we can write for $l_{0m}(t_j - 0)$ a recursive equation corresponding to (4.3.22), and evaluate the average $\bar{L}_{0m}(t_j - 0)$ in an analogous though much more complicated way, as in the case of the flexible inflow rule considered in the previous subsection. As shown by Pawlikowski [4.7], for single packets

$$\bar{L}^*_{0m}(t_j - 0) = \frac{\mathrm{var}\,\Lambda^{(1)}_{0m}}{2(1 - \nu^*_{0m} - \nu^*_{m-1,0})} +$$

$$+ \frac{\nu_{0m}[\mathrm{var}(\Lambda^*_{0,m+1}) + \mathrm{var}(\Lambda^*_{m-1,0})]}{2(1 - \nu^*_{0m} - \nu^*_{m-1,0})(1 - \nu^*_{0,m+1} - \nu^*_{m-1,0})} + \frac{1}{2}\nu_{0m} \tag{4.4.15}$$

where $\Lambda^{(1)}_{0m}$ is the random variable representing the number of packets directed from the central node to the mth local node during one slot;

$$\Lambda^*_{0m} \equiv \sum_{n=m}^{M} \Lambda^{(1)}_{0n} \tag{4.4.16}$$

denotes the random variable representing the total number of packets directed from the central node to the mth local node and all local nodes following it,

$$\nu_{0m} \equiv \sum_{n=m}^{M} \nu_{0n} \tag{4.4.17}$$

$$\nu_{0n} \equiv E\Lambda_{0n}^{(1)} \ . \tag{4.4.18}$$

As in the outflow subsystem, ν_{m0} and ν_{m0}^{*} can be interrupted as normalised intensities. However, Λ_{0m}^{*} and ν_{0m}^{*} are not direct counterparts of Λ_{m0}^{*} and ν_{m0}^{*}, since in the first case we include nodes following node m, while in the second, nodes preceding m.

Notice now that taking into account packets directed from the central node to the mth node, we can apply Little's theorem knowing the average number of these packets buffered at all nodes in the system at which their journey can be interrupted. Thus

$$\tau_{0m} = \left(\frac{\bar{L}_{0m}^{*}}{\lambda_{0m}} + 1\right) T_1 \tag{4.4.19}$$

where

$$\bar{L}_{0m}^{*} = \bar{L}_{0m}^{*}(t_j) - \frac{1}{2}\nu_{0m} \tag{4.4.20}$$

and $\bar{L}_{0m}^{*}(t_j - 0)$ is given by (4.4.14).

Formulae (4.4.15) and (4.4.19) show that, as we might expect, the average passage time of $0 \to m$ type packets depends essentially on the properties both of $0 \to m$ and of $m \to 0$ to the mth node. The average passage time of $0 \to m$ type packets depends essentially both on the properties of $0 \to m$ and of $m \to 0$ type packets. When all the intensities are the same:

$$\lambda_{0m} = \lambda_{01} = \lambda_{m0} = \lambda_{10} = \text{const.} \tag{4.4.21}$$

we get from (4.3.57) and (4.3.61)

$$\tau_{0m} = \frac{T_1}{2(1 - M\nu_1)[1 - (M-1)\nu_1]} + T_1 \tag{4.4.22}$$

where

$$\nu_1 = \lambda_1 T_1 \ . \tag{4.4.23}$$

We next consider the general case when packets both at the central and at the local nodes are delivered by the sources in batches, and the properties of the sequences of the packets are determined by assumptions A5 and A6. The system can be analysed as in the previous subsection, namely, we consider the average waiting time of a test batch consisting of 'a' packets.

Since, as indicated previously, the inflow subsystem is isolated from the outflow subsystem, and operates exactly as the inflow system, we obtain the average batch passage time of $m \to 0$ type packets which we write as:

$$\tau_{m0}(b) = \frac{\mathrm{var}(\Lambda^*_{m0})}{2(1-\nu^*_{m0})} - 1/2\nu^*_{m0} + b \; T_1(1-\nu^*_{m-1,0})^{-1} + T_1 \qquad (4.4.24)$$

where $\Lambda^*_{m0}, \nu^*_{m0}$ are defined as in formulae (4.4.3)–(4.4.5).

The evaluation of the average waiting time of $0 \to m$ type packets is more complex since the operation of the outflow system depends on the operation of the inflow system. As has been shown by Pawlikowski [4.7], we have

$$\bar{\tau}_{0m}(b) = \frac{\bar{L}^*_m - \nu^*_{0m} - \nu^*_{m-1,0} + b}{1 - \nu^*_{0,m+1} - \nu^*_{m-1,0}} \; T_1 + T_1 \qquad (4.4.25)$$

where $\bar{L}^*_m$ is the total average number of the packets buffered at the central node and the node $1, 2, \ldots, m-1$, destined for node $m, m+1, \ldots, M$ and to the central node, i.e.

$$\bar{L}^*_m = \sum_{n=m}^{M} \sum_{k=0}^{m-1} \& \; \bar{L}_{0n}(k, t_k) + \sum_{n=1}^{m-1} \bar{L}_{n0}(n, t_n) \; .$$

Finally,

$$\bar{L}^*_m = \frac{\mathrm{var}(\Lambda^*_{0m}) + \mathrm{var}(\Lambda^*_{m-1,0})}{2(1-\nu^*_{0m} - \nu^*_{m-1,0})} + 1/2(\nu^*_{0m} + \nu^*_{m-1,0}) \; . \qquad (4.4.26)$$

To illustrate the properties of the system with interruptions we take an example. We assume ten local nodes and Poisson sequences of packets or batches, with the same intensity from all sources. The dependence of the average delay $\bar{\tau}_{0m}(b)$ of batches consisting of $b = 2$ packets from the central to local nodes with intensity ν_{01} and on the node number are shown in Fig. 4.20(a). As could be expected the average delay decreases with m. This effect is illustrated in Fig. 4.20(b), which shows the dependence of $\tau_{0m}(b)$ on m for $\nu_{0m} = 0.5$. For comparison, the dependence of the delay $\bar{\tau}_{m0}$ of packets sent to local nodes from the central node by separate fixed assignment subchannels is also shown. We see that the system considered is much better than the system with fixed assignment. In the system considered packets flow both from the central to local nodes ($0 \to m$ type packets) and from local to central nodes ($m \to 0$ type packets). Thus the channel utilsiation is characterised by:

$$\nu_m = \nu^*_{0m} + \nu^*_{m0} \qquad (4.4.27)$$

where ν^*_{0m} and ν^*_{m0} were defined previously.

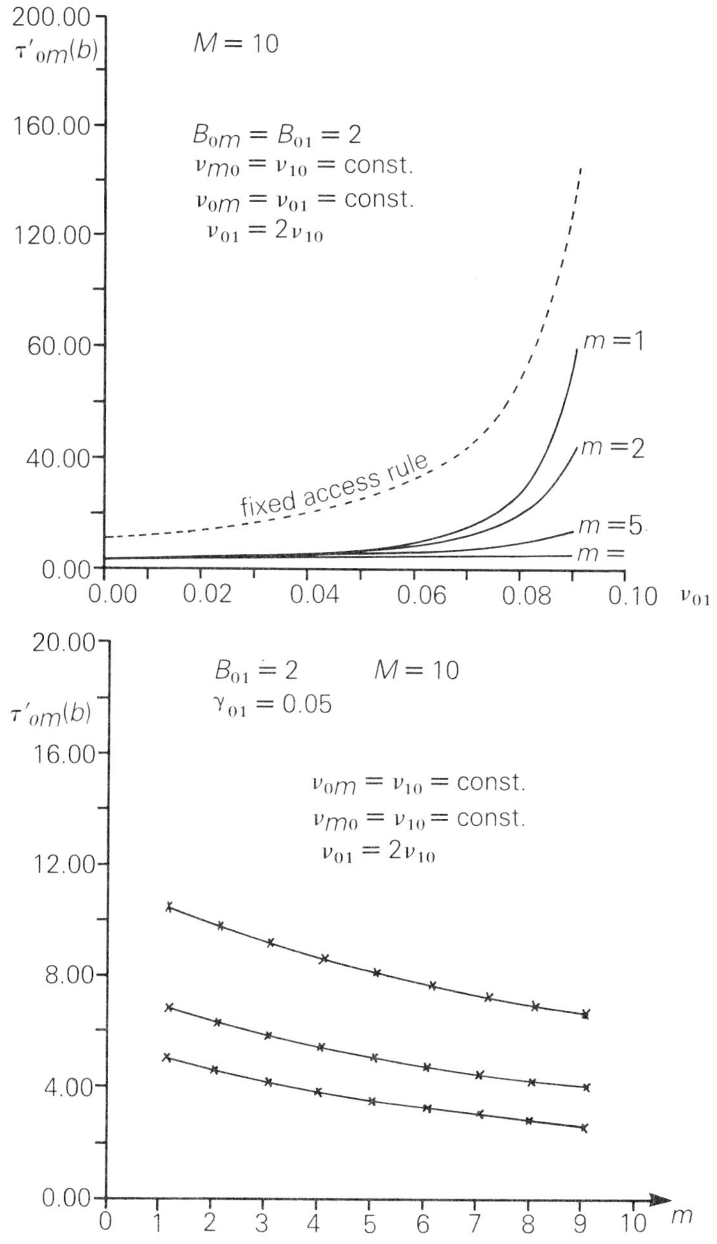

Fig. 4.20 — Dependence of the normalised delay $\tau'_{0m}(b)$ on: (a) normalised intensity ν_{01} of $(m \rightarrow 0)$-type packets delivered by the source; (b) on the node number m. Inflow/outflow system with the access rule with interruptions. $M = 10, B_{0m} = B_{01} = 2, \nu_{m0} = \nu_{10} = \ldots; \nu_{0m} = \nu_{01} = \ldots.$

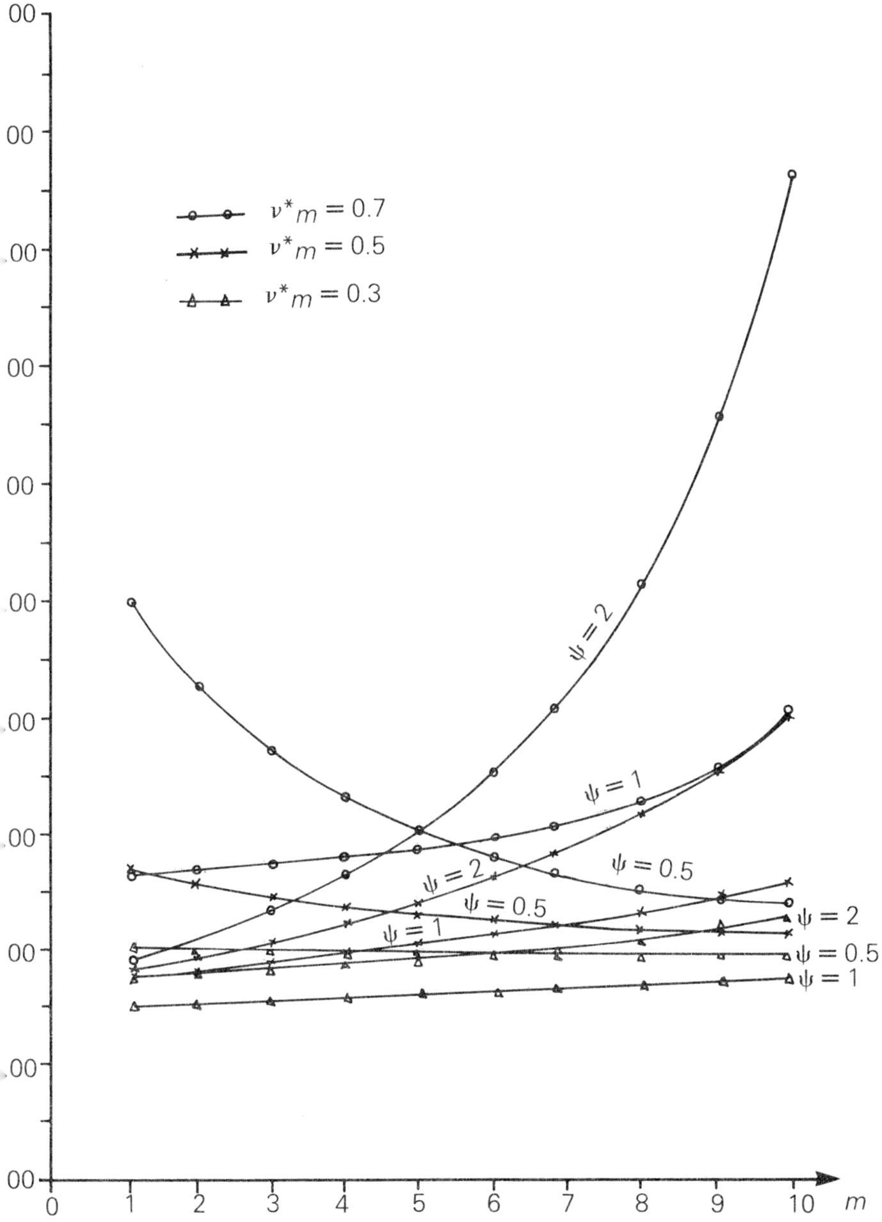

Fig. 4.21 – Dependence of the overall normalised delay τ'_m (request–answer time) on node number for the system with interruptions. ν^*_m, normalised total intensity of all upstream sources, ψ, request/answer batch size.

This parameter depends on the value of m. To obtain the utilisation for the whole system we have to remove the dependence on m. Thus:

$$\nu = \max_m \nu_m \tag{4.4.28}$$

which is an index of the cost of using the common channel capacity, on the assumption that the channel capacity in all channel segments between nodes is constant.

The quality of the systems operation is characterised by the overall time T_m elapsing from the instant of arrival of the batch of packets at the lcoal node destined for the central node, and the instant of arrival of the reply, defined by formula (4.3.7). The dependence of T'_m on ν^*_m, and m is shown in Fig. 4.21 for various ratios ψ of the task and answer batch lengths. The advantages offered by the rule of access, with interruptions, are evident from this figure. In particular the dependence of the average delay T'_m on the node number m is greatly reduced.

REFERENCES

[4.1] Hayes, J. F., and Sherman, D. N., (1972), A study of data multiplexing techniques and delay performance, *Bell System Technical Journal*, **51** No. 9, 1983–2011.

[4.2] Konheim, A. G., and Meister, B., (1974), Waiting lines and times in a system with polling, *Journal of the Association for Computing Machinery*, **21**, No. 3, 470–490.

[4.3] Roberts, L. G., (1973), Dynamic allocation of satellite capacity through packet reservation, *AFIPS Conf. Proc. 1973*, **42**, National Computer Conference, 711–716.

[4.4] Fratta, L., (1978), Improved random access techniques in computer communications, *Proc. URSI XIX, General Assembly, Helsinki, 1978.*

[4.5] Pierce, J. R., (1972), How for can data loops go?, *IEEE Trans. on Comm.*, **COM-20**, 527–530.

[4.6] Kobayashi, H., Konheim, A., (1977), 6 queueing models for computer communications system analysis, *IEEE Trans. on Comm.*, **COM-25**, 1–29.

[4.7] Pawlikowski, K., (1980), Message waiting time in a packet switching system, *J.A.C.M.*, **27**, No. 1, 30–42.

5

Fundamental problems of routing

In this chapter we shall consider routing rules. We introduced the fundamental concepts of routing in Chapter 1. We start this chapter with a comprehensive review of methods for finding shortest paths in oriented graphs. This is essential for solving a variety of routing analysis and optimisation problems which we will encounter in subsequent chapters.

In section 5.2 we will consider in more detail the primary parameters characterising the quality of routing, such as packet transit time through the network, and important secondary parameters, such as the number of channels the packet must pass in order to reach its destination. We try to obtain analytical relationships between these parameters by introducing quite restrictive simplifying assumptions. We must be aware that, in most practical networks, such assumptions are not strictly satisfied and therefore the results which we are going to derive are approximate. Our main purpose is to show the essential relationships between the parameters characterising the routing. These relationships can then be used as guidelines for designing a simulation of the real network, which can yield the exact quantitative relationships between the parameters we are interested in.

In section 5.3 we extend the problems of routing rule optimisation which we introduced in Chapter 1. We derive the solution to the optimisation problem for a network whose statistical properties are known completely. These properties are not usually known in practice; however, the structure of the optimum routing rule, combined with the general principle of adaptivity formulated in section 1.5, suggested good routing rules which can be implemented in practice. Such rules are considered in section 5.4. We first describe a general adaptive routing rule and then describe the rule used in the ARPA network. Finally, we consider composite routing rules including one combining centralised and decentralised routing.

In the last section we consider random routing rules. These rules are interesting for certain applications, and because we can derive general relationships between the various parameters characterising them. These relationships are also valid for a wide class of deterministic rules.

5.1 PROPERTIES OF SHORTEST PATHS AND ALGORITHMS USED TO FIND THEM

In this section we first formulate fundamental properties of the shortest paths and their lengths, then we give two algorithms for finding the shortest path between a pair of nodes. Later, we describe an algorithm for simultaneously finding the shortest paths between all pairs of nodes in a network. Because there are excellent monographs and review papers† on this topic we will not take the strict graph-theoretical approach, but we will give a simplified exposition of the problems orientated towards our applications.

5.1.1 General properties of shortest paths

The chain of channels $(w_0, v_0), (w_1, v_1), \ldots, (w_{I+1}, v_{I+1})$ i.e. $v_0 = w_1, v_1 = w_2, \ldots$ $v_{I-1} = w_I$, we call a **path**. We denote a path by $P(w_0, w_1, w_2, \ldots, w_I)$. We will also use an abbreviated notation indicating only the ends of the path, viz. P_{w_0, w_I}. We will also use mixed notation, specifying some channels directly and using the abbreviated notation for the other segments of the path. For example, the path $P(w_0, w_1, w_2, \ldots, w_I)$ can also be written as $P(w_0, w_1, P_{v_1}, w_I)$.

With each channel (u, v) we associate a non-negative number $d(u, v) > 0$ which we call channel length. We define the length of path:

$$d\,[P(w_0, w_1, \ldots, w_I)] = \sum_{i=0}^{I-1} d(w_i, w_{i+1}) \ldots \qquad (5.1.1)$$

The path from w_0 to w_I for which $d[P(w_0, w_1, \ldots, w_I)]$ takes the smallest possible value we call the shortest path. There can be several shortest paths from w_0 to w_I.

Let $P(w_0, w_1, \ldots, w_I)$ be the shortest path joining nodes w_0 and w_I.

The path $P(w_k, w_{k+1}, \ldots, w_l)$
where $0 \leqslant k < I$, $0 \leqslant l \leqslant I$ and $l > k$,
which is a part of path $P(w_0, w_1, \ldots, w_I)$,
is also the shortest path joining w_k and w_l. (5.1.2)

The proof is immediate. From (5.1.1) it follows that:

If $P^*(w_0, w_1, \ldots, w_I)$ is a shortest path,
then for any intermediate node w_k
the paths $P^*(w_0, w_1, \ldots, w_k)$ and $P^*(w_k, w_{k+1}, \ldots, w_I)$ (5.1.3)
will be the shortest paths
from w_0 to w_k and from w_k to w_I respectively.

† Among many monographs on graph theory we quote Christofides [5.1]. More application oriented is Frank and Frish [5.2]. Domschke [5.3] gives an advanced review of problems of finding shortest paths while Pierce [5.4] gives an extensive bibliography on the subject.

Suppose next that we have two shortest paths $P^*(w_0, w_1', \ldots, w_{I'}')$ and $P^*(w_0, w_1'', w_2'', \ldots, w_{I''}'')$, from node w_0 to nodes $w_{I'}'$ and $w_{I''}''$, and that these paths have one, and only one node in common as shown in Fig. 5.1. Suppose that this is node $w' = w_3' = w_3''$. From property (5.1.3) it follows that the path $P(w_0, w_1', w_2', w_3')$ and path $P^*(w_0, w_1'', w_2'', w_3'')$ must be the same length. Therefore the path $P(w_0, w_1', w_2', w_3', w_4'', w_5'', \ldots, w_{I''}'')$ is also a shortest path from w_0 to $w_{I''}''$.

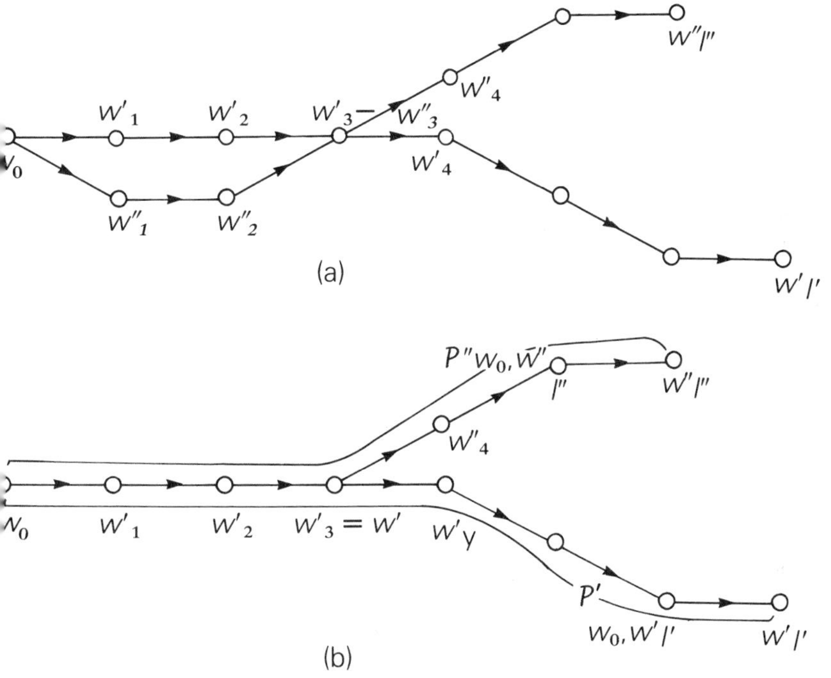

Fig. 5.1 – Illustration to the proof of property (5.1.3); (a) paths $P^{(0)}_{w_0, w_{I'}'}$, $P^{(0)}_{w_0, w_{I''}''}$, (b) paths $P'_{w_0, w_{I'}'}$, $P''_{w_0, w_{I''}''}$.

Thus if two shortest paths $P^*_{w_0, w_{I'}'}$ and $P^*_{w_0, w_{I''}''}$ from a node w_0 to two other nodes $w_{I'}'$ and $w_{I''}''$ have one node w' in common, we can always find two other paths $P'_{w_0, w_{I'}'}$ and $P''_{w_0, w_{I''}''}$ such that: (1) the length $d(P'_{w_0, w_{I'}'}) = d(P^*_{w_0, w_{I'}'})$ and $d(P''_{w_0, w_{I''}''}) = d(P^*_{w_0, w_{I''}''})$; (2) the paths $P'_{w_0, w_{I'}'}$ and $P''_{w_0, w_{I''}''}$ have the whole initial segment from w_0 to w' in common. It follows that:

$$\begin{array}{l}\text{we can always find a set of paths from a node } w_0\\ \text{to a set of nodes } w^{(m)}, m = 1, 2, \ldots, M\\ \text{which are the shortest paths and which form a tree.}\end{array} \qquad (5.1.4)$$

We now consider the properties of shortest paths. Let:

$$\delta(w,r) = d(P^*_{w,r}) \tag{5.1.5}$$

be the length of the shortest path from w to q, and let $N_{out}(w)$ be the set of nodes at the outputs of channels going out of node w. The definition of $N_{out}(w)$ is illustrated in Fig. 5.2. From the definition, if follows that $v \in N_{out}(w)$ that the channel (w, v) exists. We call the set $N_{out}(w)$ the **upper neighbourhood** of node w.

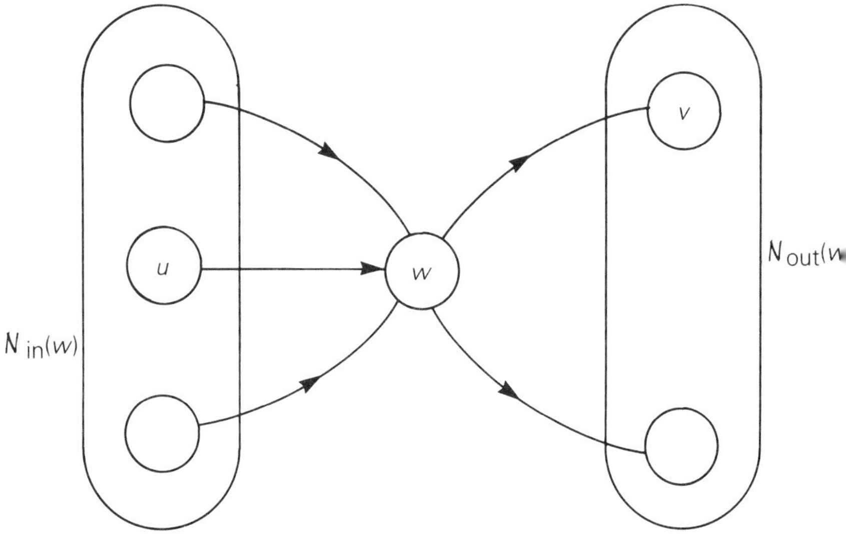

Fig. 5.2 – Illustration to the definition of upper neighbourhood $N_{out}(w)$ and lower neigbourhood $N_{in}(w)$.

Let us suppose that $v \in N_{out}(w)$ and let $\delta(w,r|v)$ be the length of the shortest path from w to q with the constraint that the first channel of this path is (w, v). This definition is illustrated in Fig. 5.3. Obviously we get:

$$\delta(w,r|v) = d[(w,v), P_{v,r}] = d(w,v) + \delta(v,r) \tag{5.1.6}$$

As the shortest path from w to q must pass through one of the nodes belonging to $N_{out}(w)$ we have:

$$\delta(w,r) = \min_{v \in N_{out}(w)} \delta(w,r|v) \tag{5.1.7}$$

Using (5.1.5), we get:

$$\delta(w,r) = \min_{v \in N_{out}(w)} [d(w,v) + \delta(v,r)] \tag{5.1.8}$$

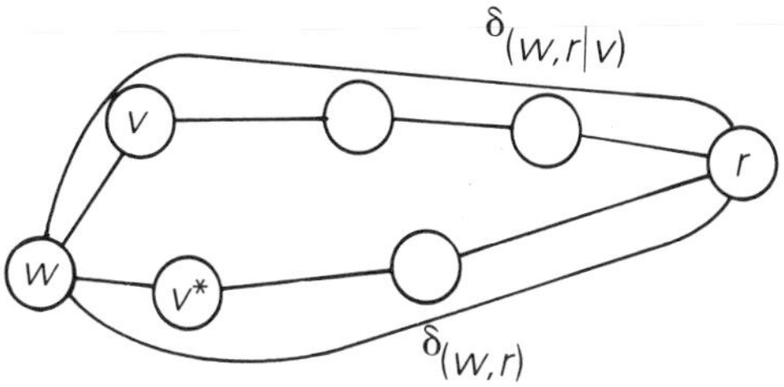

Fig. 5.3 – Illustration to the definition of functions $\delta(w,q)$ and $\delta(w,q\,|\,v)$.

Let $v^*(w)$ be the node from $N_{out}(w)$ for which the minimum in (5.1.8) is reached. We then have:

$$\delta(w,r) = d(w,v^*) + \delta(v^*,r) \tag{5.1.9}$$

If we know the values of $\delta(v,q)$ for all nodes $N_{out}(w)$, we can easily find $v^*(w)$. Thus we can guide the packet along the shortest path using the following rule:

R1 After the packet has arrived at the node w, we find the minimum value of $\delta(w,q\,|\,v)$ for all $v \in N_{out}(w)$ and put the packet into the channel (w,v^*), where v^* minimises $\delta(w,q\,|\,v)$.

Often the channels are symmetrical, i.e.

$$d(w,v) = d(v,w) \tag{5.1.10}$$

We will show now that we can guide a packet along the shortest path in a similar way to rule R1 but by using the function, introduced by Butrymenko [5.5], defined by the formula:

$$\Delta[(w,v);r] \equiv d(w,v) + \min\,[\delta(w,r);\delta(v,r)] \tag{5.1.11}$$

The advantage of using this function is that when channel lengths change it is easy to adjust locally the value of $\Delta[(w,v);q]$.

From (5.1.10), it follows that:

$$\delta(w,r\,|\,v) = d(w,v) + \delta(v,r) \tag{5.1.12}$$

$$\delta(v,r\,|\,w) = d(w,v) + \delta(w,r) \tag{5.1.13}$$

This equation $\Delta[(w,v);r]$ is illustrated in Fig. 5.4. Thus $\Delta[(w,v);r]$ can be interpreted as the length of the shortest path from either end of channel (w,v) going through the other end to q. We will now show how this function can be

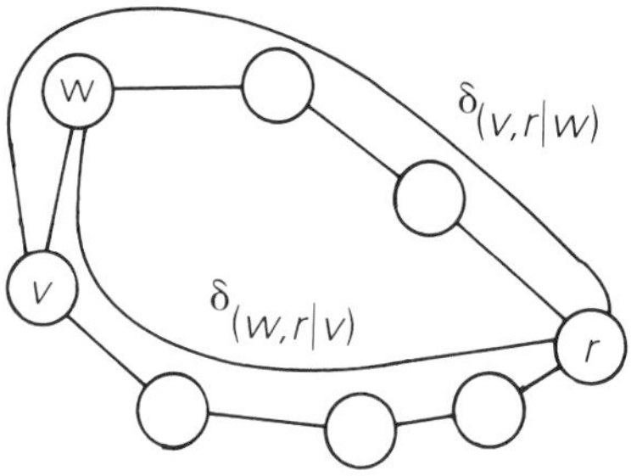

Fig. 5.4 – Illustration to the definition (5.1.13) of the Butrymenko function $\Delta[(w,v);q]$.

used to obtain $\delta(w,v)$. Let us denote by v^* the successor node to w on the shortest path from w to q. From (5.1.8) as $d(w,v^*) > 0$, we have:

$$\delta(w,r) > \delta(v^*,r) \tag{5.1.14}$$

Thus from definition (5.1.11), we have:

$$\Delta[(w,v^*);r] = d(w,v^*) + \delta(v^*,r) \tag{5.1.15}$$

and from (5.1.8), it follows that:

$$\Delta[(w,v^*);r] = \delta(w,r) \tag{5.1.16}$$

Let us now take a channel (w,v) such that:

$$\delta(w,r\,|\,v) > \delta(w,r\,|\,v^*) \tag{5.1.17}$$

From our definition of v^* it follows that:

$$\delta(w,r\,|\,v) > \delta(w,r) \tag{5.1.18}$$

From definition (5.1.6) it follows that:

$$\min[\delta(w,r\,|\,v), \delta(v,r\,|\,w)] = \min[\delta(w,r\,|\,v), d(v,w) + \delta(w,r)] > \delta(w,r) \tag{5.1.19}$$

Using (5.1.13) and (5.1.16) we can rewrite (5.1.19) thus:

$$\Delta\Delta[(w,v);r] > \Delta[(w,v^*);r] \tag{5.1.20}$$

Hence:

$$\min_{v \in N_{out}(w)} \Delta[(w,v);r] = \delta(w,r) \tag{5.1.21}$$

which we can use to evaluate $\delta(w,q)$ if we know the values of $\Delta[(w,v);q]$ for all nodes in $N_{out}(w)$.

We will next show that we can obtain $\Delta[(w,v);r]$ recursively, without using $\delta(w,q)$ or $\delta(w,q\,|v)$. From (5.1.11) and (5.1.21) we have:

$$\Delta[(w,v);r] = d(w,v) + \min[\delta(w,r), \delta(v,r)] =$$
$$= d(w,v) + \min_{\substack{v' \in N_{out}(w) \\ v'' \in N_{out}(w)}} \{\Delta[(w,v');r], \Delta[(v,v'');r]\} \qquad (5.1.22)$$

We start to evaluate (5.1.22) by calculating $\Delta[(w,v);r]$ for channels, one of whose ends is node q. For such channels $\Delta[(w,r);r] = d(w,q)$. These calculations also give us $\Delta[(w,v');r]$ and $\Delta[(v,v'');r]$ for some channels. Hence we can evaluate $\Delta[(w,v);r]$ for these channels. We can repeat this process to evaluate $\Delta[(w,v);r]$ for all channels in the network. The results of this procedure are illustrated by the following example.

Example 5.1.1

The values of $\Delta[(w,v);r]$ are given in Fig. 5.5(a). Figure 5.5(b) shows the values of the function $\delta(w,q\,|v)$. As might be expected, for some pairs, $\delta(w,q\,|v)$ and $\Delta[(w,v);q]$ take different values.

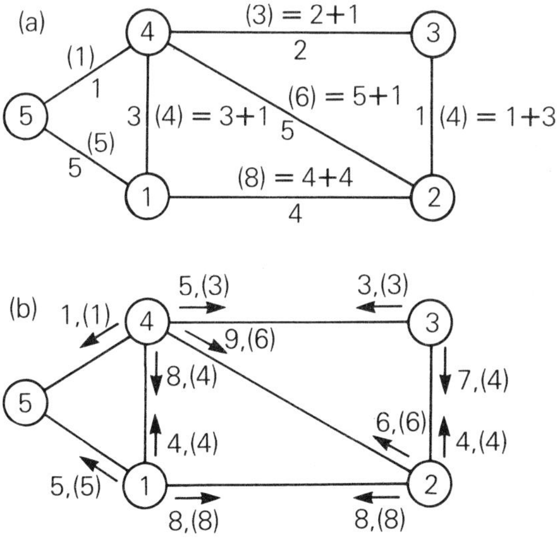

Fig. 5.5 – (a) Example of calculating the Butrymenko function; symmetrical channels (on one side of the channel is given its length, on the other, in brackets, the distance from pole q); (b) illustration of the equivalence of packet forwarding on the basis of function $\delta(w,q\,|v)$ and $\Delta[(w,v);q]$; values of $\delta(w,q\,|v)$ are given next to the arrow at node w pointing towards node v and values of $\Delta[(w,v);q]$ are given in brackets.

The following rule for forwarding packets is based on Butrymenko's function

After the packet has arrived at node w it is put into the channel, (w,v), for which $\Delta[(w,v);r]$ is minimum. (5.1.23)

From (5.1.20) it is evident that the packet's path is the same whether rule (5.1.23) or (5.1.9) is used; thus this is the shortest path.

Having described the fundamental properties of shortest paths we will now consider algorithms for finding them.

5.1.2 An algorithm for finding the shortest path by successive approximation

We wish to find the shortest path from node p to node w, and we start with some initial (longer) path. To make the computations easier, we associate with node w a label consisting of two elements: d_{pw} and ω_w. The second element ω_w, is the number of the immediate predecessor of w on the path found previously. The first element, d_{pw}, is the length of that path. This labelling defines the complete path $P_{s,w}$.

To find the shortest path between nodes p and w, we have, in general, to consider all the nodes in the network, thus we have to label them all. Consequently we obtain other shortest paths by this algorithm.

When describing the algorithm, we use the upper neighbourhood $N_{out}(w)$, and the set $N_{in}(w)$, illustrated in Fig. 5.2, called the **lower neighbourhood** of w. The statement $a \in N_{in}(w)$ implies that a channel (a,w) exists.

We start by labelling the nodes in $N_{out}(s)$ by $d(s,w)$ and s. The lengths of paths going to other nodes are considered to be infinite and the preceding node undetermined and denoted by x. The detailed algorithm is:

Algorithm 5.1.1

Step 1

The labelling rule is:

Type of node	Label	
	$\omega_w^{(1)}$	$d_{sw}^{(1)}$
$w \in N_{out}(s)$	s	$d(s,w)$
$w \notin N_{out}(s)$	x	∞

(5.1.24)

where x denotes the undetermined node.

Step n, $n \geqslant 2$

For each $w \neq p, u \in N_{in}(w)$, we find:

$$d_{sw|u}^{(n)} = d_{su}^{(n-1)} + d(u,w) \tag{5.1.25}$$

$$D_w^{(n)} \equiv \min_{u \in N_{out}(w)_s} d_{sw|u}^{(n)} \tag{5.1.26}$$

and denote by u_n^* the node for which the minimum is achieved, i.e.:

$$d_{su_n^*}^{(n-1)} + d(u_n^*, w) = D_w^{(n)} \tag{5.1.27}$$

The labelling rule is:

(5.1.28)

Type of node	Label	
	$\omega_w^{(n)}$	$d_{sw}^{(n)}$
$d_{sw}^{(n-1)} \geqslant D_w^{(n)}$	u_n^*	$D_w^{(n)}$
$d_{sw}^{(n-1)} \leqslant D_w^{(n)}$	$\omega_w^{(n-1)}$	$d_{sw}^{(n-1)}$

We stop the procedure when $d_{sw}^{(n)} = d_{sw}^{(n-1)}$ for all $w \neq s$.

For computational reasons, it is convenient to write the results of each step in the form of arrays:

$$\mathbf{d}^{(n)} = \{d_{sw}^{(n)},\ w = 1,2,\ldots,N,\ w \neq s\} \tag{5.1.29a}$$

$$\boldsymbol{\omega}^{(n)} = \{\omega_w^{(n)},\ w = 1,2,\ldots,N,\ w \neq s\} \tag{5.1.29b}$$

Operation (5.1.26) is illustrated in Fig. 5.6.

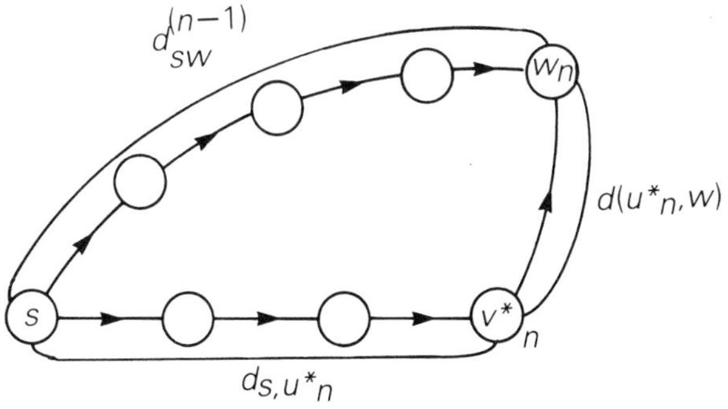

Fig. 5.6 – Illustration to the definition of $D_w^{(n)}$.

There are other possible formulations of successive approximation algorithms, but algorithm 5.1.1 is generally good computationally.

To simplify the description of the algorithm we formulated it in such a way that its nth step consists of $N-1$ substeps corresponding to the whole set of values $w = 1, 2, \ldots, N, w \neq p$. In all substeps in a step of the algorithm 5.1.1, we use the labels established in the previous step. An obvious improvement of the algorithm would be to use the new labels inside the step if they have already been changed in the present step.

We illustrate algorithms 5.1.1 with the following example.

Example 5.1.2

We assume the network shown in Fig. 5.7(a) and look for the shortest paths from p to all other nodes.

Step 1

From Fig. 5.7(a) we see that $N_{\text{out}}(s) = \{1, 4\}$. According to the labelling rule (5.1.24)

$$\mathbf{d}^{(1)} = (5, \infty, \infty, 1)$$
$$\boldsymbol{\omega}^{(1)} = (s, x, x, s)$$

Step 2

We take node $w = 1$. From Fig. 5.7(a) we see that $N_{\text{in}}(1) = \{s, 4\}$ and $d_{s1|s} = 5$, $d_{s1|4}^{(2)} = 1 + 3 = 4$. Thus $D_1^{(2)} = 4$ and $d_{s1}^{(2)} = 4$, $\omega_1^{(2)} = 4$. We next take $w = 2$. We get $N_{\text{in}}(2) = \{1, 4, 3\}$, $d_{s2|1} = 4 + 5 = 9$, $d_{s2|4} = 1 + 5 = 6$, $d_{s2|3} = \infty$.

Thus $D_2^{(2)} = 6$. Proceeding similarly with nodes 3, 4 we obtain the arrays:

$$\mathbf{d}^{(2)} = (4, 6, 3, 1)$$
$$\boldsymbol{\omega}^{(2)} = (4, 4, 4, s)$$

In step 3 we get

$$\mathbf{d}^{(3)} = (4, 4, 3, 1)$$
$$\boldsymbol{\omega}^{(3)} = (4, 3, 4, s)$$

and in step 4

$$\mathbf{d}^{(3)} = \mathbf{d}^{(4)}$$

and the procedure stops. The resulting shortest paths are shown in Fig. 5.7(c). As predicted by conclusion 5.1.3 they form a tree.

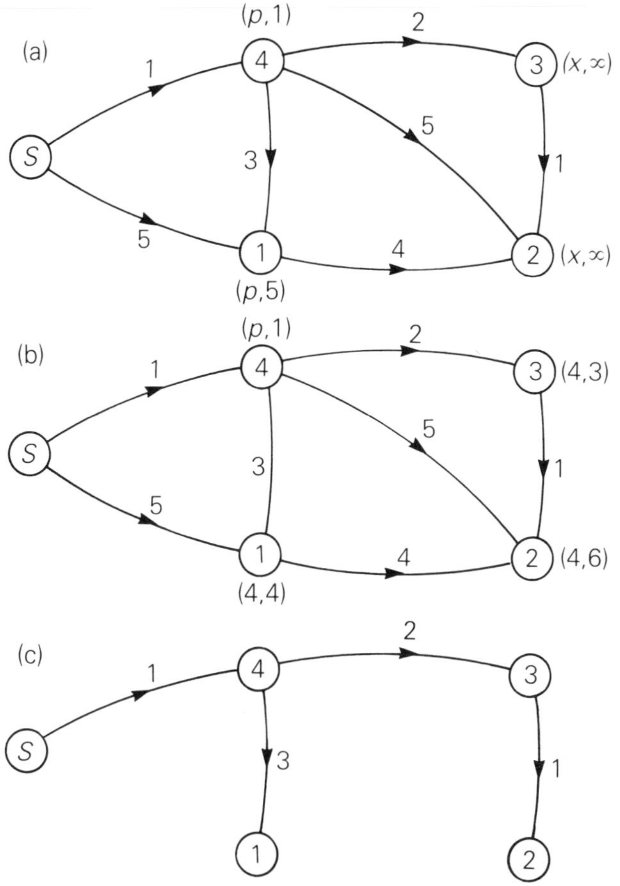

Fig. 5.7 – (a) Network assumed in Example 5.1.2 and labelling in step $n = 1$; (b) Labelling in step $n = 2$; (c) shortest paths. Numbers on arcs indicate channel lengths; numbers in brackets beside nodes denote labels.

5.1.3 The algorithm for searching the neighbourhood of the end nodes for shortest paths

In algorithm 5.1.1 we searched for the shortest path without taking into account the network topology. We now present an algorithm which uses the topology of the network, and which when we are starting the search for shortest paths from scratch, requires less computation than algorithm 5.1.1. However, when we want to correct the set of routes by taking into account the time dependency of the channel lengths, algorithm 5.1.1 may yield the shortest paths with less computational effort than the algorithm we are going to describe.

There are three basic ideas behind this algorithm. The first is that we find successively nodes $z_1^*, z_2^*, \ldots, z_n^*$ and paths, $P_{s,z_1^*}^*, P_{s,z_2^*}^*, \ldots, P_{s,z_n^*}^*$ such that $P_{s,z_n^*}^*$ is the shortest path from s to z_n^*, and

$$d(P_{s,z_1^*}) \leqslant d(P_{s,z_2^*}) \leqslant \ldots \leqslant d(P_{s,z_n^*}) \leqslant \ldots$$

We denote the first n nodes by

$$Z^{(n)} = \{z_m^*, m = 1, 2, \ldots, n\} \tag{5.1.30}$$

The second basic idea is that, in searching for a new node z_n^*, we analyse upper neighbourhoods of the nodes z_m^*, $m < n$. We denote the set of these nodes analysed before step n by $A^{(n)}$.

The third idea behind the algorithm is that when searching for z_n^* we change the set of channels, rejecting those which are obviously unfavourable. The modified set of channels which we use in the nth step are denoted by $K^{(n)}$. Thus the network considered at the nth step is $(N, K^{(n)})$, where N is the set of all the nodes. For computational reasons, we also use two labels $d_{sw}^{(n)}$ and $\omega_w^{(n)}$ in the nth step. The second is the number of the immediate predecessor to z on the path from s to w (found in previous steps) and $d_{sw}^{(n)}$ is the length of this path. The algorithm is:

Algorithm 5.1.2

Step 1

We take

$$K^{(1)} = K \tag{5.1.31}$$

where K is the set of all channels.

$$A^{(1)} = N_{\text{out}}(s) \tag{5.1.32}$$

and as z_1^* we take a node from $A^{(1)}$ for which

$$d_{s,z_1^*} = \min_{w \in A^{(1)}} d_{sw}^{(1)} \tag{5.1.33}$$

where:

$$d_{sw}^{(1)} = d(s, w) \tag{5.1.34}$$

The labelling rule is:

Type of node	Label	
	ω_w	$d_{sw}^{(1)}$
$w \in A^{(1)}$	s	$d(s, w)$
$w \notin A^{(1)}$	x	∞

(5.1.35)

Step n

We denote:

$$A_1^{(n)} \equiv A_{n-1}^{(n-1)} - z_{n-1}^* \tag{5.1.36a}$$

$$A_2^{(n)} \equiv N_{out}(z_{n-1}^*) - \bigcup_{k=1}^{n-1} z_k^* \tag{5.1.36b}$$

$$A^{(n)} \equiv A_1^{(n)} \cup A_2^{(n)} \tag{5.1.36c}$$

These set are illustrated in Fig. 5.8.

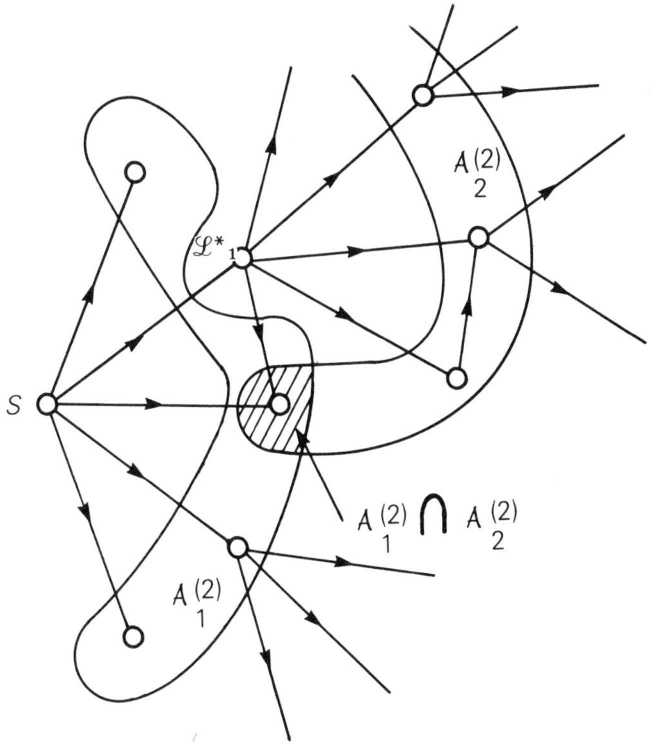

Fig. 5.8 – Illustration to the definition of sets $A_1^{(2)}$, $A_2^{(2)}$, occurring in algorithm 5.1.2.

We put set $A^{(n)}$ in the form:

$$A^{(n)} = (A_1^{(n)} - A_1^{(n)} \cap A_2^{(n)}) \cup (A_2^{(n)} - A_1^{(n)} \cap A_2^{(n)}) \cup (A_1^{(n)} \cap A_2^{(n)}) \tag{5.1.37}$$

The set $A_1^{(n)}$ is the set of nodes which were already analysed and which may belong to the shortest paths which are not an extension of the shortest path $P^*(s, z^*_{n-1})$. The set $A_2^{(n)}$ is the set of nodes which may belong to shortest paths, which are extensions of $P^*(s, z^*_{n-1})$. We also define:

$$D'_n(w) \equiv d^{(n-1)}_{s,z^*_{n-1}} + d(z^*_{n-1}, w) \tag{5.1.38a}$$

$$D''_n(w) \equiv d^{(n-1)}_{sw} \tag{5.1.38b}$$

The labelling rule is:

	Type of node	Label	
		$\omega_w^{(n)}$	$d_{s,w}^{(n)}$
$w \in A^{(n)}$	$w \in A_1^{(n)} - A_1^{(n)} \cap A_2^{(n)}$	$\omega_w^{(n-1)}$	$d_{sw}^{(n-1)}$
	$w \in A_2^{(n)} - A_1^{(n)} \cap A_2^{(n)}$	z^*_{n-1}	$D'_n(w)$
	$w \in A_1^{(n)} \cap A_2^{(n)}$, $D'_n(w) \leqslant D''_n(w)$	z^*_{n-1}	$D'_n(w)$
	$w \in A_1^{(n)} \cap A_2^{(n)}$, $D'_n(w) > D''_n(w)$	$\omega_w^{(n-1)}$	$d_{sw}^{(n-1)}$
	$w \notin A_n^{(n)}$	$\omega_w^{(n-1)}$	$d_{sw}^{(n-1)}$

(5.1.39)

We find the node $z^*_n \in A^{(n)}$ for the network $N, K^{(n)}$ such that:

$$d_{s,z^*_n} = \min_{w \in A^{(n)}} d_{sw}^{(n)} \tag{5.1.40}$$

and

$$Z^{(n)} = Z^{(n-1)} \cup z^*_n \tag{5.1.41}$$

The set of channels $K^{(n+1)}$ to be analysed in step $n+1$ is the set $K^{(n)}$ with channels (z^*_n, w), for which $D'_{n+1}(w) \geqslant D''_{n+1}(w)$ removed. The procedure stops when the destination pole p becomes an element of $Z^{(n)}$.

Example 5.1.3

The result of applying algorithm 5.1.2 to the network in Fig. 5.7 is presented in Table 5.1.1. The table gives the length of the path chosen in the nth step, linking node w with node p. The preceding node lying on the chosen path is indicated by an arrow.

Table 5.1.1

p		1	2	3	4	$A^{(n)}$	$Z^{(n)}$
Step 1	0	∞	∞	∞	1	{1, 4}	{4}
Step 2	0	∞	∞	0	1	{1, 2, 3}	{4, 3}
Step 3	0	4	∞	3	1	{1, 2}	{4, 3, 1}
Step 4	0	4	4	3	1	{2}	{4, 3, 1, 2}

In order to elucidate algorithm 5.1.2 we describe the component operators of step n of the algorithm as set out in (5.1.39). We consider each line of (5.1.39) in turn starting at the top. For nodes which have been previously analysed, and which are not in $N_{out}(z_{n-1}^*)$, we have not found a shorter route, so the labelling remains the same.

For nodes in $N_{out}(z_{n-1}^*)$ which have not been previously analysed we take as shortest path the existing shortest path to z_{n-1}^* and the direct channel (z_{n-1}^*, w). For nodes in $N_{out}(z_{n-1}^*)$ which have been analysed previously we take the shortest of the two paths described above. If $D_n'(w) \geqslant D_n''(w)$ then the channel (z_{n-1}^*, w) can be disregarded in subsequent searches because we can reach w by a path which is shorter than the shortest possible path passing through z_{n-1}^*. The final line refers to nodes which have not been considered in this step.

We can prove (by induction) that this algorithm yields shortest routes, but we do not present the proof here.

We will now give an example of the application of this algorithm. Algorithm 5.1.2 can be implemented using an analogue model suggested by Silk [5.6]. Channel (w, v) is modelled by means of a circuit introducing a delay proportional to the length of the corresponding channel; we call this circuit the **(w, v)-D-circuit.** At the output of each of these circuits there is an element which is called a **blockade-identification** circuit (or **(w, v)-b-i-circuit**). This circuit performs the following functions: (a) if an impulse appears at its output before an impulse appears at its input, the b-i-circuit does not let impulses propagate; (b) if an impulse appears at its input before an impulse at its output, the b-i-circuit permits all impulses arriving at its input to go through. An indicator shows which function has been performed. We now illustrate the use of the model by an example.

Example 5.1.4

The network shown in Fig. 5.7(a) is modelled by that shown in Fig. 5.9. To reproduce the effects of algorithm 5.1.2 we put an impulse into the circuit shown in Fig. 5.9, at node p. After unit time has elapsed, the impulse appears at the output of the $(p,4)$-D-circuit. Since the output of the $(p,4)$-b-i-circuit has not been reached by any other impulse, the impulse coming from the $(p,4)$-D-circuit passes through the $(p,4)$-b-i-circuit. The impulse now proceeds to channels $(4,1)$, $(4,2)$ and $(4,3)$. Consider next the $(4,1)$-b-i-circuit. It is connected to the outputs of the two D-circuits: one is the $(p,1)$-D-circuit, the other is the

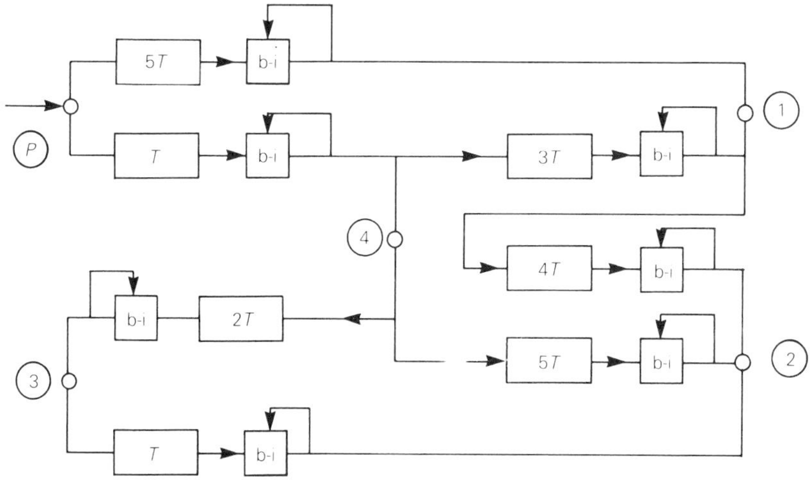

Fig. 5.9 – Circuit for modelling algorithm 5.1.2 for the network shown in Fig. 5.7(a); kT, $k = 1, 2, \ldots$, denotes D-circuit introducing delay kT; b-i indicates the blockade-identification circuit.

$(4,1)$-D-circuit. Because of the magnitude of the delays, the first impulse appears at the output of the $(4,1)$-D-circuit, and the impulse from the $(p,1)$-D-circuit will no longer have any effect in the network. One can easily see that the model described here corresponds to the algorithm 5.1.2. The b-i-circuits show which channels are unblocked and therefore indicate the shortest paths.

This technique is generally applicable.

5.1.4 The algorithm for finding a set of shortest paths between all pairs of nodes

We want to produce algorithms for finding the shortest paths between all pairs of nodes.† We could find these paths by repeatedly applying algorithms 5.1.1 or 5.1.2, but we shall see that other algorithms are more efficient.

† An analysis of such algorithms and their programming was given by de Mercado [5.7].

We can define any shortest path by giving the number of only 3 nodes: the two extreme nodes p,q, and any intermediate node u. We can find from the description of the paths $P_s u$ and $P u_{wr}$ two further nodes lying on the path P_{sr} and so on, until all the nodes on the path are identified. Combining this reasoning with the principle which led to the algorithm 5.1.1 we obtain the following algorithm:

Algorithm 5.1.3

Step 1

For each $s = 1, 2, \ldots, N$, $r = 1, 2, \ldots, N$, $s \neq r$, the labelling rule for node r is:

Type of node	Label	
	$\omega_{sr}^{(1)}$	$d_{sr}^{(1)}$
$r \in N_{out}(s)$	s	$d(s,r)$
$r \notin N_{out}(s)$	x	∞

(5.1.42)

Step n, $n = 2, 3, \ldots, N-1$

For each $s = 1, 2, \ldots, N$, $N = 1, 2, \ldots, N$, $s \neq r$, we find

$$d_{sr|u}^{(n)} \equiv d_{su}^{(n-1)} + d_{u,r}^{(n-1)} \tag{5.1.43}$$

$$D_{sr}^{(n)} \equiv \min_{u \in N - \{s,r\}} d_{sr|u}^{(n)} \tag{5.1.44}$$

and let u^* be the node u for which the minimum is achieved. The labelling rule for node r is:

Type of node	Label	
	$\omega^{(n)}$	$d^{(n)}$
$d_{sr}^{(n-1)} > D_{sr}^{(n)}$	u_n^*	$D^{(n)}$
$d_{sr}^{(n-1)} \leqslant D_{sr}^{(n)}$	$\omega_{sr}^{(n-1)}$	$d_{sr}^{(n-1)}$

(5.1.45)

As for algorithm 5.1.1 it is convenient to write down the results of each step in the form of two tables:

$$\mathbf{d}^{(n)} = \begin{matrix} - & d_{12}^{(n)} & d_{13}^{(n)}, & \ldots, & d_{1N}^{(n)} \\ d_{21}^{(n)} & - & d_{23}^{(n)}, & \ldots, & d_{2N}^{(n)} \\ d_{N1}^{(n)} & d_{N2}^{(n)} & & \ldots, & - \end{matrix} \qquad (5.1.46a)$$

$$\boldsymbol{\omega}_n = \begin{matrix} x & \omega_{12}^{(n)} & \omega_{13}^{(n)}, & \ldots, & \omega_{1N}^{(n)} \\ \omega_{21}^{(n)} & x & \omega_{23}^{(n)}, & \ldots, & \omega_{2N}^{(n)} \\ \omega_{N1}^{(n)} & \omega_{N2}^{(n)} & & \ldots, & x \end{matrix} \qquad (5.1.46b)$$

To illustrate the algorithm, we give the following example.

Example 5.1.5

We take the network with symmetrical channels shown in Fig. 5.10. The successive tables are:

Step 1

$$\mathbf{d}^{(1)} = \begin{bmatrix} - & 5 & 4 & \infty & \infty \\ 5 & - & 3 & 8 & \infty \\ 4 & 3 & - & 3 & 7 \\ \infty & 8 & 3 & - & 3 \\ \infty & \infty & 7 & 3 & - \end{bmatrix}$$

$$\boldsymbol{\omega}^{(1)} = \begin{bmatrix} - & 1 & 1 & x & x \\ 2 & - & 2 & 2 & x \\ 3 & 3 & - & 3 & 3 \\ x & 4 & 4 & - & 4 \\ x & x & 5 & 5 & - \end{bmatrix}$$

Step 2

$$\mathbf{d}^{(2)} = \begin{bmatrix} - & 5 & 4 & 7 & 11 \\ 5 & - & 3 & 6 & 10 \\ 4 & 3 & - & 3 & 6 \\ 7 & 6 & 3 & - & 3 \\ 11 & 10 & 6 & 3 & - \end{bmatrix}$$

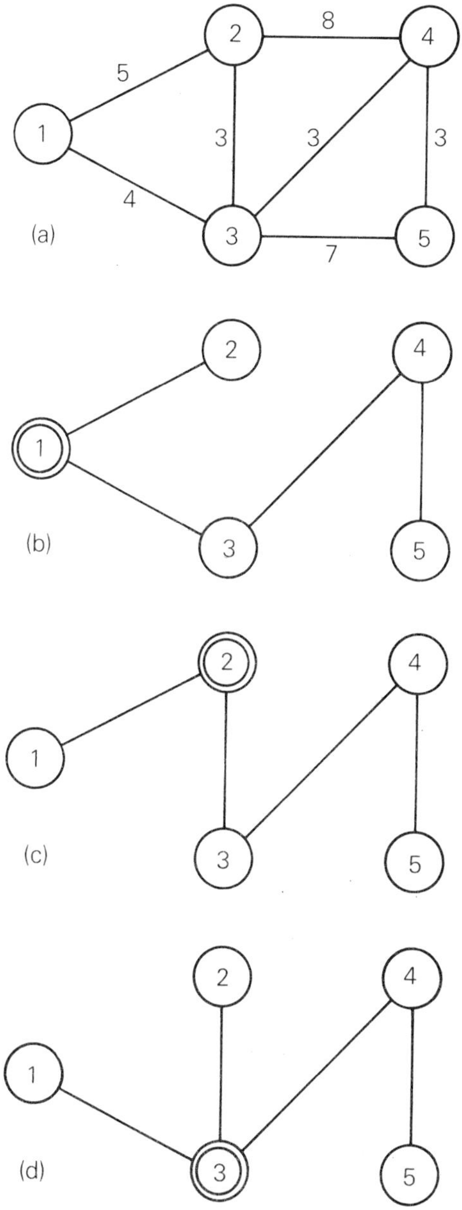

Fig. 5.10 – Network considered in example 5.1.5, (a), and the shortest paths, (b), (c), (d). Channels are symmetrical. Numbers denote channel capacities.

$$\omega^{(2)} = \begin{bmatrix} - & 1 & 1 & 3 & 3 \\ 2 & - & 2 & 3 & 3 \\ 3 & 3 & - & 3 & 4 \\ 3 & 3 & 4 & - & 4 \\ 3 & 3 & 4 & 5 & - \end{bmatrix}$$

Step 3

$$\mathbf{d}^{(3)} = \begin{bmatrix} - & 5 & 4 & 7 & 10 \\ 5 & - & 3 & 6 & 9 \\ 4 & 3 & - & 3 & 6 \\ 7 & 6 & 3 & - & 3 \\ 10 & 9 & 6 & 3 & - \end{bmatrix}$$

$$\omega^{(3)} = \begin{bmatrix} - & 1 & 1 & 3 & 4 \\ 2 & - & 2 & 3 & 4 \\ 3 & 3 & - & 3 & 4 \\ 3 & 3 & 4 & - & 4 \\ 4 & 4 & 4 & 3 & - \end{bmatrix}$$

In this agorithm step 1 is as in algorithm 5.1.1, except that we now take into account all pairs of nodes. In the nth step instead of searching for the better path among the paths passing through the lower neighbourhood, we now search among the paths going through any node, u, other than p or q. As in algorithm 5.1.1, instead of finding the minimum (5.1.26), we can search among all triples s,u,r for a new path passing through u which is shorter than the previous path $P_{sr}^{(n-1)}$. We use the labelling rule:

$$s = 1,2,\ldots,N, r = 1,2,\ldots,N, r \neq s, u = 1,2,\ldots,N, u \neq s, u \neq r.$$

Type of node	Label	
	$\omega_{sr}^{(n)}$	$d_{sr}^{(n)}$
$d_{sr}^{(n-1)} > d_{sr\|u}^{(n-1)}$	u	$d_{sr\|u}^{(n-1)}$
$d_{sr}^{(n-1)} \leqslant d_{sr\|u}^{(n-1)}$	$\omega_{sr}^{(n-1)}$	$d_{sr}^{(n-1)}$

(5.1.47)

where

$$d_{sr|u}^{(n-1)} = d_{su}^{(n-1)} + d_{ur}^{(n-1)} \quad . \tag{5.1.48}$$

Each step of algorithm 5.1.3 consists of $N(N-1)$ substeps corresponding to values $s = 1, 2, \ldots, N$, $r = 1, 2, \ldots, N$, $r \neq s$. We can, however, change $n \to n+1$, every time a change of labels occurs.

We now show that algorithm 5.1.3 enables all the shortest paths to be found. We divide the shortest paths consisting of more than one channel into subsets $\mathcal{Y}_u$, $u = 1, 2, \ldots, N$. Subset $\mathcal{Y}_u$ includes those paths in which the largest intermediate node number is equal to u. Thus $\mathcal{Y}_1$ includes shortest paths possessing only one intermediate node, namely node 1. Similarly, set $\mathcal{Y}_2$ comprises: (a) all shortest paths consisting of two channels with the intermediate node 2, (b) all shortest paths consisting of 3 channels with the intermediate nodes 1, 2. The set $\mathcal{Y}_u$ includes: (a) all shortest paths consisting of two channels with u as intermediate node, (b) all shortest paths consisiting of 3 channels with u and one of $1, 2, \ldots, u-1$ as intermediate nodes, and so on. Thus we have $\mathcal{Y}_1 \subset \mathcal{Y}_2 \subset \mathcal{Y}_3 \ldots \subset \mathcal{Y}_u$.

We work with a modification of algorithm 5.1.3. We fix the intermediate node u and search for $s = 1, 2, \ldots, N$, $s \neq u$ and $r = 1, 2, \ldots, N$, $r \neq u, r \neq s$. We call the group of operations with fixed u a step and the operations with fixed s and r a substep. Suppose that the set $\mathcal{Y}_1$ is not empty, i.e. there is at least one path $\mathcal{P}(s', 1, q')$ which is the shortest path from s' to r', and all other members of $\mathcal{Y}_1$. We will find this path in step 1. Since these are shortest paths, the algorithm will not change them in subsequent steps. Taking $u = 2$, we find all the shortest paths with two channels and intermediate node $u = 2$, and those consisting of 3 channels with the intermediate nodes 1 and 2. Suppose there exists a shortest path $\mathcal{P}_{sr}^*$. We can represent this path in the form $\mathcal{P}_{s2}$, $\mathcal{P}_{2r}$. Since $\mathcal{P}_{sr}^*$ is a shortest path, the path $\mathcal{P}_{s2}$ is shortest. However, node 1 is the only intermediate node on $\mathcal{P}_{s2}$, thus $\mathcal{P}_{s2}$ has been found previously for $u = 1$. Obviously this reasoning can be applied to subsequent steps and thus we will have found all the shortest paths in the set $\mathcal{Y}_k$ in steps corresponding to $u = 2, 3, \ldots, k$. As the set $\mathcal{Y}_N$ includes all the possible shortest paths and the index u covers all values from 1 to N, we shall find all the shortest paths.

5.2 PARAMETERS CHARACTERISING ROUTING RULES

A methodology for defining parameters characterising routing rules was introduced in Chapter 1. In this section we will discuss these parameters in more detail and derive their most important properties. First we consider the delay characterising the routing rule. Next we consider the average number of hops which a packet makes in traversing the network and derive a relationship between this parameter and the delay. Finally we introduce parameters characterising buffer overflow and routing reliability.

5.2.1 The parameters characterising delay

The method of defining these parameters was given in Example 1.4.2 in Chapter 1. Here we derive some general properties of the delay. We first derive an expression for the parameter $\tau[R_{sr}(\cdot)]$ given by 1.4.16, characterising the rule $R_{sr}(\cdot)$ for routing packets from source s to destination r. We introduce the incidence coefficient:

$$a[P_{sr}; (w,v)] \equiv \begin{cases} 1 & \text{if} \quad (w,v) \in P_{sr} \\ 0 & \text{if} \quad (w,v) \notin P_{sr} \end{cases} \tag{5.2.1}$$

so formula (1.4.15) can now be put into the form:

$$\tau[P_{sr}] = \sum_{(w,v)\in K} a[P_{sr}; (w,v)]\, \tau_1(w,v) \tag{5.2.2}$$

Both the incidence coefficient $a[P_{sr};(w,v)]$ and the delay are to be considered as random variables. These variables are in general statistically interdependent which greatly complicates the analysis of the average delay $\tau[P_{sr}(\cdot)]$. However, if we make the simplifiying assumption:

The random variables representing the incidence coefficient $a[P_{sr}.(w,v)]$ and the delay $\tau_1(w,v)$ are statistically independent (5.2.3)

then, from (5.2.2) we have:

$$\tau[R_{sr}(\cdot)] = \sum_{(w,v)\in K} \bar{a}[(s,r);(w,v)]\,\tau(w,v) \tag{5.2.4}$$

where $\tau(w,v)$ is the average delay introduced by the channel (w,v) and

$$\bar{a}[(s,r);(w,v)] = \underset{\Xi}{E}\, a[R_{sr}(\Xi);(w,v)] \tag{5.2.5a}$$

From (5.2.1) it follows that:

$$\bar{a}[(s,r);(w,v)] = P[(w,v) \in R_{sr}(\Xi)] \tag{5.2.5b}$$

where on the right-hand side we have the probability that the channel (w,v) belongs to the path $R_{sr}(\xi)$ chosen according to the routing rule considered.

We next consider the parameter $\bar{\tau}[\mathbf{R}(\cdot)]$ characterising the set $R(\cdot)$ of rules $R_{sr}(\cdot)$, $s,r \in (S,R)$, defined by formulae (1.4.19), (1.4.20). In the present notation (1.4.20) takes the form:

$$\tau[\mathbf{R}(\cdot)] \equiv \frac{1}{X} \sum_{(s,r)\in(S,R)} \tau[R_{sr}(\cdot)]X_{sr} \tag{5.2.6a}$$

where X_{sr} is the intensity of flow directed from s to r and

$$X \equiv \sum_{(s,r)\in(S,R)} X_{sr} \tag{5.2.6b}$$

is the total intensity put into the network. The sum appearing in (5.2.6) has an interesting interpretation. Consider a time interval $\langle t_a, t_b \rangle$ of length $T = t_b - t_a$ such that $T \gg \tau[R_{sr}(\cdot)]$. During the interval $\langle t_a, t_b \rangle$ the amount of information flowing from s to r is $X_{sr}T$. Thus the product $\tau[R_{sr}(\cdot)]X_{sr}T$ is the total time which packets flowing from s to r during time T spend in the network. Obviously TX is the total number of bits delivered to the network from external sources during time T. Thus:

The parameter $\bar{\tau}[\mathbf{R}(\cdot)]$ defined by (5.2.6) is the ratio of the total time spent by all packets delivered to the network during a given time interval to the number of packets delivered in that time. (5.2.7)

We will now derive an expression for $\bar{\tau}[\mathbf{R}(\cdot)]$ which will be useful later. From formulae (5.2.3) and (5.2.5) we obtain

$$\begin{aligned}\bar{\tau}[\mathbf{R}(\cdot)] &= \frac{1}{X} \sum_{(s,r)\in(S,R)} X_{sr} \sum_{(w,v)} \tau(w,v)\, P[(w,v)\in R_{sr}(\Xi)] \\ &= \frac{1}{X} \sum_{(w,v)\in K} \tau(w,v) \sum_{(s,r)\in(S,R)} X_{sr} P[(w,v)\in R_{sr}(\Xi)] \end{aligned} \tag{5.2.8}$$

The second sum is $F(w,v)$, the intensity of the flow through channel (w,v). Thus:

$$\bar{\tau}[\mathbf{R}(\cdot)] = \frac{1}{X} \sum_{(w,v)\in K} \tau(w,v)\, F(w,v) \tag{5.2.9}$$

This formula is quite important. It permits us to calculate $\bar{\tau}[\mathbf{R}(\cdot)]$ using channel parameter $\tau(w,v)$ instead of the path parameter $\tau[R_{sr}(\cdot)]$.

Our reasoning is based on assumption (5.2.3). It can be justified using the hypothesis proposed by Kleinrock see [2.1]).

If the sequences of packets delivered by the sources are independent Poisson-exponential sequences, then the sequences of packets put into a channel of the network can be accurately considered as independent Poisson-exponential sequences. (5.2.10)

by a Poisson-exponential sequence we mean here a sequence having the properties:

(1) the starting instants of the packets form a Poisson process;
(2) the packet durations are mutually independent random variables with exponential probability distributions;
(3) the starting instants of the packets and the packet durations are mutually independent sequences.

If we take Kleinrock's hypothesis, formula (5.2.10) simplifies greatly, since we obtain queueing time from the simple formula (A.2.16). Taking $\bar{T}_{as} = \bar{T}_{tr} = 0$ we obtain then from (2.1.3):

$$\bar{\tau}[\mathbf{R}(\cdot)] = \frac{1}{X} \sum_{(w,v)\in K} \left[\frac{1}{C(w,v) - F(w,v)} + T_{pr}(w,v)\right] F(w,v) \tag{5.2.11}$$

The strict proof of Kleinrock's hypothesis would be difficult, since after buffering and routing the primary Poisson-exponential sequences delivered by the source are no longer poissonian-exponential. However, we can expect that the superimposition of such several sequences in a channel partially restores the poissonian-exponential character. In view of the difficulties in strictly proving Kleinrock's hypothesis, several simulation experiments were made and they showed that results based on this hypothesis are usually quite accurate. Let us notice that the simplifying assumption A12 made in 3.1.2 about the sequence of all packets in the common channel which we used analysing remote access systems are special cases of Kleinrock's hypothesis.

5.2.2 The number of packet hops

The number of channels in a path taken by a packet is called the number of packet hops. Let us denote this by $H(P_{sr})$. From (5.2.1) we have:

$$H(P_{sr}) = \sum_{(w,v)} a(P_{sr}; w, v) \tag{5.2.12}$$

We now consider the routing rule $R_{sr}(\cdot)$. Proceeding as before we define the parameter:

$$H[R_{sr}(\cdot)] = \underset{\Xi}{\mathrm{E}} H[R_{sr}(\Xi)] \tag{5.2.13}$$

which characterises a single routing rule, and the parameter

$$\bar{H}[\mathbf{R}(\cdot)] = \bigcup_{(s,r)\in(S,R)} H[R_{sr}(\cdot)] \tag{5.2.14}$$

(where $\bigcup_{s,r}$ denotes the operation of removing the dependence on (s,r)) which characterises the set of all routing rules.

We will now show that, under certain simplifying assumptions, a simple relationship exists between the parameters $H[R_{sr}(\cdot)]$ and $\tau[R_{sr}(\cdot)]$. We assume:

A1 the same number of channels go out of each node; let this number be J;

A2 each node of the network produces new packets at rate $\lambda(0, w)$ with average length $\bar{T}$;

A3 the same node-to-node routing rule is applied at each node;

A4 no packets are lost on the network;
A5 the packet-delay, τ, is finite.

Examples of networks satisfying A1 are shown in Fig. 5.11.

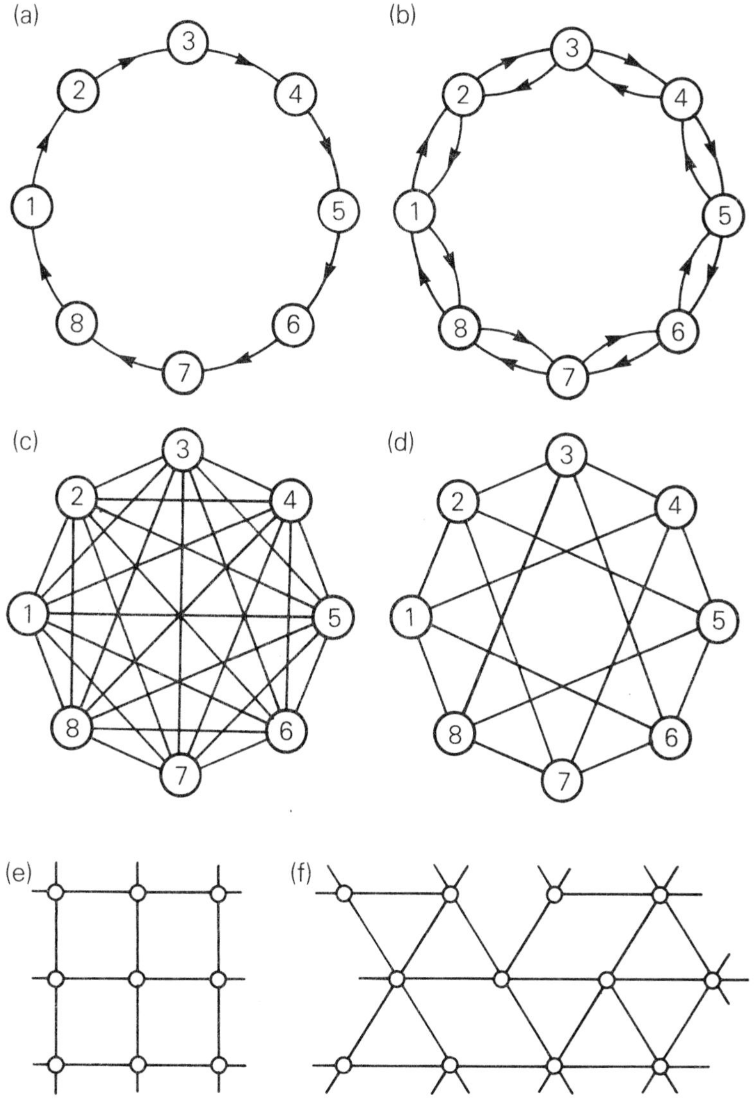

Fig. 5.11 – Examples of networks: (a) – (e), homogeneous; (f), almost homogeneous.

Consider the interval $\langle -T/2, T/2\rangle$ such that

$$T \geqslant \tau \ . \tag{5.2.15}$$

Let $L(T)$ be the number of packets which are generated by all nodes in the time interval $\langle -T/2, T/2\rangle$. In view of assumption A3 we get:

$$L(T) = T \sum_{w=1}^{N} \lambda(0, w) \tag{5.2.16}$$

Under assumptions A5–6, the number of packets which reach their destinations during the interval $\langle -T/2+\tau, T/2+\tau\rangle$ is approximately $L(T)$.

Each packet makes on average $\bar{H}[R(\cdot)]$ hops, therefore approximately $\bar{H}[R(\cdot)]L(T)$ packets must pass through all channels during the time interval $\langle -T/2+\tau, T/2+\tau\rangle$.

The intensity of packets leaving node w is denoted by $\lambda'(w)$, thus:

$$\bar{H}[\mathbf{R}(\cdot)]L(T) \cong T \sum_{w=1}^{N} \lambda'(w) \tag{5.2.17}$$

The approximation is better the greater the value of T. Taking $T \to \infty$, we obtain a fundamental relationship:

$$\bar{H}[\mathbf{R}(\cdot)] \sum_{w=1}^{W} \lambda(0, w) = \sum_{w=1}^{W} \lambda'(w) \tag{5.2.18}$$

If we further assume:

A6 the statistical properties of all information sources are the same,

then:

$$\lambda(0, w) = \lambda(0) = \text{const.} \tag{5.2.19}$$

In view of the homogeneity assumptions A1, A3 and A6, we have:

$$\lambda'(w) = \lambda'(1) = \text{const.} \tag{5.2.20}$$

From formulae (5.2.18–5.2.20) we get:

$$\lambda'(1) = \bar{H}[\mathbf{R}(\cdot)]\,\lambda(0) \tag{5.2.21}$$

The packet intensity in channel (w, v) is $\lambda(w, v)$. From our homogeneity assumptions

$$\lambda(w, v) = \frac{\lambda'(w)}{J}, \qquad v \in N_{\text{out}}(w) \tag{5.2.22}$$

From this formula and from (5.2.18) we ultimately obtain the duty ratio of signals in channel (w, v):

$$v = \frac{\lambda(0)\bar{H}[\mathbf{R}(\cdot)]}{J}\bar{T} \tag{5.2.23}$$

If a single source were connected to a single channel, the duty ratio would be $\lambda(0)\bar{T}$. We see from (5.2.23) that the packet flow is equally distributed over all the channels.

Let us assume in addition that:

A7 the information sources deliver Poisson-exponential sequences, with parameters $\lambda(0), \bar{T}$.

Using Kleinrock's hypothesis (5.2.10), we can use formula A.2.17 which gives us the delay introduced by a single channel:

$$\tau(w,v) = \bar{T}\frac{1}{1-v} + T_{\text{pr}} \tag{5.2.24}$$

where T_{pr} is propagation time. If we assume that:

A8 the delays introduced by the channels forming the packet's path are statistically independent,

we obtain the average packet passage time:

$$\bar{\tau}[\mathbf{R}(\cdot)] = \bar{H}[\mathbf{R}(\cdot)]\tau(w,v) \tag{5.2.25}$$

From formulae (5.2.23) and (5.2.24) it is evident that $\tau(w,v)$ depends essentially on $\bar{H}[\mathbf{R}(\cdot)]$. Thus the dependence between $\tau[\mathbf{R}(\cdot)]$ and $\bar{H}[\mathbf{R}(\cdot)]$ is non-linear even under the restrictive assumptions made here.

5.2.3 Other parameters characterising the quality of routing rules

As we mentioned in Chapter 1 and as we will show in detail in Chapter 7 an efficient method of counteracting congestion is to not admit packets into the node in some circumstances and to reject them from the network. Rejection may also occur since the capacities of buffers are finite. For a single channel the average intensity of the rejected flow (overflow), is:

$$F^{-}(w,v) = P^{-}(w,v)F(w,v) \tag{5.2.26}$$

where $P^{-}(w,v)$ is the probability of overflow and $F^{-}(w,v)$ is the intensity of flow offered to the channel. The probability of overflow can be interpreted as the relative intensity of lost flow which we denote by:

$$f^{-}(w,v) \equiv \frac{F^{-}(w,v)}{F(w,v)} \tag{5.2.27}$$

It is $\eta(w,v) = P^{-}(w,v)$. The relative intensity of flow lost on the path P_{sr} is given by:

$$f^{-}(P_{sr}) = 1 - \prod_{(w,v)\in P_{sr}} [1 - f^{-}(w,v)] \tag{5.2.28}$$

Assuming that, for all channels, $\eta(w,v) \ll 1$, we have

$$f^{-}(P_{sr}) \cong \sum_{(w,v)\in P_{sr}} f^{-}(w,v) \tag{5.2.29}$$

Let us next consider the effect of node and channel failures. Let $P^{+}(w,v)$ denote the probability that node w and channel (w,v) are operating correctly. Assuming that failures are statistically independent, the probability that all channels and nodes on a path are operating correctly is given by:

$$P^{+}[P_{sr}] = \prod_{(w,v)\in P_{sr}} P^{+}(w,v) \tag{5.2.30}$$

Thus:

$$\log P^{+}[P_{sr}] = \sum_{(w,v)\in P_{sr}} \log P^{+}(w,v) \tag{5.2.31}$$

In general if $\epsilon(P_{sr})$ characterises the quality of transmission along path P_{sr}, then:

$$Q_1(P_{sr}) = \sum_{(w,v)\in P_{sr}} Q_1(w,v) \tag{5.2.32}$$

where $Q_1(w,v)$ characterises the quality of transmission through a single channel (w,v). Thus the procedure described in Example 1.4.1 can be used directly to define parameters characterising the routing rules based on $Q_1(w,v)$. We define

$$Q[R_{sr}(\cdot)] \equiv \underset{\Sigma\times\Xi}{\mathrm{E}}\; Q[R_{sr}(\Xi), \Sigma] \tag{5.2.33}$$

as the characteristic routing rule for (s,r). Further, generalising definition (1.4.13) to:

$$\bar{Q}_\beta[\mathbf{R}(\cdot)] \equiv \left\{\sum_{(s,r)} \{\alpha(s,r)\; Q[R_{sr}(\cdot)]\}^{\beta}\right\}^{1/\beta} \tag{5.2.34}$$

with $\beta \geqslant 1$, we define the family of parameters characterising the set of routing rules for all pairs (s,r).

We now consider the cost of routing; the two main components are:

(1) cost of the equipment which executes the routing rule and

(2) cost of the sub-system for auxiliary information delivery. The ratio of these factors depends on the use of centralised or decentralised n.s.i. collection and evaluation. It is quite difficult to write down a general function describing the cost of implementing routing rules. In practice, we have to make more detailed designs, to enable all the economic factors to be taken into account.

The cost of transmission is also of interest. It depends primarily on the distance travelled through the network, and hence on the number of hops, if the channels are of comparable length. Thus we can offen take $\bar{H}[\mathbf{R}(\cdot)]$ as a parameter characterising the routing rule from the point of view both of quality of transmission and of cost.

5.2.4 The number of packets in the network

The average number of packets L in the network and the delay τ are related. If the system is stationary then

$$\bar{L} = \tau\lambda^{+} \tag{5.2.35}$$

where λ^{+} is the intensity of packets admitted into the network. Here, we will consider the average number of packets in a system without assuming that it is stationary.† This will enable us to formulate the conditions for stationarity. Let:

$\bar{L}(t)$ be the average number of packets in the network at instant t;
$\bar{L}_{tr}(t)$ be the average number of packets being transmitted;
$\bar{\Lambda}[0,\langle t,t+\Delta t\rangle]$ be the average number of packets fed into the network from external sources during the time interval $\langle t,t+\Delta t\rangle$;
$\bar{\Lambda}[1,\langle t,t+\Delta t\rangle]$ be the average number of packets removed from the network during the time interval $\langle t,t+\Delta t\rangle]$;

$$\lambda(i,k) \equiv \lim_{\Delta t\to 0} \frac{\bar{\Lambda}[i;\langle t,t+\Delta t\rangle]}{\Delta t} \tag{5.2.36}$$

$i=1,2$ be the corresponding intensity.

From the definitions it follows that

$$\frac{dL}{dt} - \lambda(0,t) - \lambda(1,t) = 0 \tag{5.2.37}$$

This equation is difficult to solve analytically as $\lambda(1,t)$ depends on $L(t)$. However, we will define an auxiliary parameter, which permits us to define the concept of heavy and light loading of the network and for these cases the solution of (5.2.37) simplifies. The parameter is

$$\chi = \frac{L_{tr}(t)}{L(t)} \tag{5.2.38}$$

† Our reasoning is based on the paper by Prosser [5.8].

i.e. the ratio of the number of packets being transmitted to the total number of packets in the network. This coefficient depends on the number of packets in the network and on the routing rule used.

We now assume that:

A11 the statistical properties of packets in each node of the network are the same.

Under such an assumption, the value of χ can be easily determined for two extreme cases. If the network is lightly loaded, then

$$\bar{L}(t) \ll N \tag{5.2.39}$$

on average less than one packet per node, thus all packets in the system are being transmitted. Therefore:

$$\bar{L}(t) \cong \bar{L}_{\mathrm{tr}}(t) \tag{5.2.40}$$

and

$$\chi = 1 \tag{5.2.41}$$

If there are many more packets than nodes

$$\bar{L}(t) \gg N \tag{5.2.42}$$

then, on average, there are many packets per node. Thus every transmitter is active and there are as many transmitted packets as there are nodes and

$$\chi = N/L(t) \tag{5.2.43}$$

Considering the solution of equation (5.2.37) it is convenient to introduce the ratio

$$\lambda'(1,t) \equiv \frac{\lambda(1,t)}{L_{\mathrm{tr}}(t)} \quad . \tag{5.2.44}$$

This is the intensity of packets leaving the network, normalised with respect to the number of packets being transmitted. Since only a packet being transmitted has a chance to reach its destination after the next hop, we can expect that to a good approximation

$$\lambda'(1,t) = \lambda'(1) = \text{const.} \tag{5.2.45}$$

We also will assume that the source are stationary. Then

$$\lambda(0,t) = \lambda(0) = \text{const.} \tag{5.2.46}$$

We consider first the solution of fundamental equation (5.2.37) when the load is light. Using (5.2.41), (5.2.38), and (5.2.44)–(5.2.46) we put equation (5.2.37) into the form:

$$\frac{\mathrm{d}L}{\mathrm{d}t} - \lambda'(1)L(t) + \lambda(0) = 0 \ . \tag{5.2.47}$$

We look for a solution to this equation in the form of $A\,\mathrm{e}^{-\alpha t} + B$. After substituting in (5.2.47) and comparing coefficients we obtain:

$$\bar{L}(t) = \frac{\lambda(0)}{\lambda'(1)} + \mathrm{e}^{-\alpha t}\left[l(0) - \frac{\lambda(0)}{\lambda'(1)}\right] \tag{5.2.48}$$

in which $l(0)$ is the initial number of packets in the network. So, as $t \to \infty$, the number of packets in the network

$$L(t) \to L(\infty) \tag{5.2.49}$$

where

$$L(\infty) \equiv \frac{\lambda(0)}{\lambda'(1)} \tag{5.2.50}$$

For consistency of our argument it must be:

$$L(\infty) \ll N \tag{5.2.51}$$

thus:

$$\frac{\lambda(0)}{\lambda'(1)} \ll N \ . \tag{5.2.52}$$

For the heavily loaded network, equation (5.2.37) takes the form

$$\frac{\mathrm{d}\bar{L}}{\mathrm{d}t} + \lambda(0) - N\lambda'(1) = 0 \tag{5.2.53}$$

the solution to this equation is

$$\bar{L}(t) = l(0) + [N\lambda'(1) - \lambda(0)]t \tag{5.2.54}$$

Since it is reasonable to assume that $N\lambda'(1) - \lambda(0) > 0$ we see that in a loaded network, the number of packets in the network increases with time and the system is unstable.

5.3 OPTIMISATION OF THE ROUTING RULE

In this section we formulate the problem of routing rule optimisation and illustrate it with two examples. In the first we assume that the parameters characterising the routing rule are fixed, then we use the general adaptivity principle formulated in section 1.5.3 to allow for changes in parameters. In the second we assume that we have full statistical information about the network. The solution depends on statistical averages, which are difficult to evaluate, but the solution suggests rules which may be applied in practice.

5.3.1 Formulation of the routing rule optimisation problem and an example of its solution

To simplify the terminology and notation we consider only deterministic rules. The extension of our reasoning to randomised routing rules is obvious. As before we denote the path on which a packet is routed (from s to r) with n.s.i., ξ, by $R_{sr}(\xi)$. $\mathbf{R}(\cdot)$ is the set of routing rules so $\mathbf{R}(\xi)$ is the corresponding set of paths. The above terminology corresponds to centralised routing. For decentralised routing, the routing at node w is designated $R^{w}_{sr}(\cdot)$ and the auxiliary information $\xi^{(w)}$.

We introduce first the optimisation of $R_{sr}(\cdot)$, with criterion $\bar{\epsilon}[R_{sr}(\cdot)]$, and constraint C, as discussed in section 1.5.

The optimisation problem can be formulated in the following way:

The network, its channels, information sources and their properties are given. We wish to find the routing rule $R^{*}_{sr}(\cdot)$ such that $\epsilon[R_{sr}(\cdot)]$ is minimum, under constraint C. (5.3.1)

We denote this problem briefly as $OP\,R_{sr}(\cdot), Q\,|\,C$. We omit other implicit constraints from the notation for the sake of clarity.

The optimisation of $\mathbf{R}(\cdot)$ is denoted by $OP\mathbf{R}(\cdot), Q\,|\,C$, where $Q[\mathbf{R}(\cdot)]$ is a criterion of interest and C are the constraints imposed.

We now give a simple example of $OP\,R_{sr}(\cdot), Q$ without constraints, assuming that:

A1 the quality criterion has the form given by (5.3.2) and (5.3.3) below;
A2 the quality $Q_1(w, v)$ of passing the packet through channel (w, v) is invariant;
A3 each node knows all $Q_1(w, v)$ precisely.

Assumption A2 is very restrictive, but it is approximately satisfied in a network with time-invariant background traffic which is much greater than that under consideration. If A2 is satisfied, and each node knows all $\epsilon_1(w, v)$ when the system starts, then A3 is also satisfied.

Having made assumption A2, we can consider only fixed routing rules. If P_{sr} is the fixed route then:

$$Q[R_{sr}(\cdot)] = Q(P_{sr}) \tag{5.3.2}$$

The solution of $OP\,R_{sr}(\cdot), Q$ is straightforward. Let us interpret $Q_1(w,v)$ as the length of the channel (w,v), so we have:

$$d(w,v) \equiv Q_1(w,v) \tag{5.3.3}$$

Then:

$$d(P_{sr}) \equiv \sum_{(w,v)\in P_{sr}} d(w,v) \tag{5.3.4}$$

is the length of the path P_{sr}. We minimise $Q[R_{sr}(\cdot)]$ if we use the shortest path. Thus the solution of $OP\,R_{sr}(\cdot), Q$ is the rule:

packets should be routed along the path P^*_{sr} which is the shortest under definitions (5.3.3) and (5.3.4) (5.3.5)

5.3.2 Solution of the optimisation problem for the model with complete statistical information

Let us now assume that:

A4 the states of the network can be considered as random events;
A5 the criterion has the form of (5.2.53).

The quality of transmission through a single channel depends on its state, which in turn is a component of the network state $\boldsymbol{\sigma}$; thus we will denote the quality index by $Q_1[(w,v);\boldsymbol{\sigma}]$.

Similarly we write

$$Q[P_{sr},\boldsymbol{\sigma}] = \sum_{(w,v)\in P_{sr}} Q_1[(w,v);\boldsymbol{\sigma}] \tag{5.3.6}$$

for the quality of transmission on P_{sr}. We can rewrite (5.2.21) as:

$$Q[R_{sr}(\cdot)] = \mathop{\mathrm{E}}_{\boldsymbol{\Sigma}\times\Xi} Q[R_{sr}(\Xi),\boldsymbol{\Sigma}] \tag{5.3.7}$$

where we average over all pairs Σ and Ξ (Ξ is the random variable representing the n.s.i., Σ the state). We next introduce:

$$Q(P|\xi) = \mathop{\mathrm{E}}_{\boldsymbol{\Sigma}|\xi} Q(P;\boldsymbol{\Sigma}) \tag{5.3.8}$$

which is the average over all states of the network $\boldsymbol{\Sigma}$ on condition that the auxiliary information is ξ. Using (5.3.6) we have

$$Q(P|\xi) = \sum_{(w,v)\in P} Q_1[(w,v)|\xi] \tag{5.3.9}$$

where

$$Q_1[(w,v)\,|\,\xi] \;\equiv\; \underset{\Sigma\,|\,\xi}{\mathrm{E}}\; Q_1[(w,v);\Sigma] \qquad (5.3.10)$$

is the average quality index on condition that the n.s.i. is ξ. Using the formula for conditional averages we write (5.3.7) in the form:

$$Q[R_{sr}(\cdot)] \;=\; \mathrm{E}\, Q[R_{sr}(\Xi)\,|\,\Xi] \qquad (5.3.11)$$

If the routing rule $R_{sr}(\cdot)$ is considered to be variable, then $R_{sr}(\xi)$ can vary. As before we define channel length as:

$$d(w,v) \;\equiv\; Q_1[(w,v)\,|\,\xi] \qquad (5.3.12)$$

hence the solution to $OP\; R_{sr}(\cdot), Q$ is† the rule:

the packet should be routed along path $P^*_{sr}(\xi)$, which is the shortest according to definition (5.3.12). (5.3.13)

To apply the optimum rule (5.3.13), we have to calculate the conditional averages $Q_1[(w,v)\,|\,\xi]$. Even if we had a complete statistical description of the network, which is an unrealistic assumption, the evaluation of $Q_1[(w,v)\,|\,\xi]$ would be difficult. However, from the structure of (5.3.13), we can conclude that efficient routing rules must be based on knowledge of the statistical relationships between the state of the network and the n.s.i. Again we have recourse to the general principle of adaptation explained in section 1.5.3. In our case this gives the following rule:

the packet should be routed along path P^*_{sr} which is the shortest according to the definition of channel length

$$d(w,v) \;=\; Q_1^*[(w,v);\xi] \qquad (5.3.14)$$

where $Q_1^*[(w,v);\xi]$ is an estimate of $Q_1(w,v)$ based on ξ.

The quality of the adaptive rule depends essentially on the auxiliary rules for making estimates of $Q_1^*(w,v;\xi)$, even when these rules are optimised, the adaptive rule may not be optimal. However, in practice, we can expect the adaptive rule (5.3.14) to be good, but the quality should be checked experimentally or by simulation.

Hitherto we considered $OP\; R_m(\cdot), \tau_m\,|\,C$ with the constraint C that the background traffic is fixed and without taking into account the effects of routing packets on the delay of other packets. Therefore the solution of $OP\; R_m(\cdot), \tau_m\,|\,C$

† A detailed justification of the rule can be found in Seidler [5.9].

may be called a selfish rule. However, we are in general interested in the $OP\,\mathbf{R}(\cdot),\bar{\tau}|C$ where $\mathbf{R}(\cdot) = R_m(\cdot)$, $m = 1, 2, \ldots,$ M is the set of all routing rules and $\bar{\tau}$ is the overall average delay. Often we assume that the system is homogeneous and all component rules $R_m(\cdot)$ are the same. We can expect that even with this simplifying assumption we cannot decompose $OP\,\mathbf{R}(\cdot),\bar{\tau}|C$ into the set of $OP\,R_m(\cdot),\tau_m|C$ and the selfish rules are not the solution of $OP\,R(\cdot),\bar{\tau}|C$. To explain the difficulties in solving the latter problem we assume: (1) exact, up-to-date n.s.i. is available for routing decisions; (2) after instant t_0 no new packets are delivered by sources; (3) all packets have the same duration T; (4) buffer capacities are infinite; (5) the buffer at the input of a channel operates according to FIFO discipline.

Let us denote

$\omega(l,t)$ – the node at which lth packet is at instant t;
$r(l)$ – the destination of the lth packet;
$\Pi(l)$ – the set of all loopless paths from $\omega(l,t_o)$ to $r(l)$ (i.e. of all paths along which the packet can move);
$P_j(l)$ – jth element of $\Pi(l)$ i.e. jth path along which lth packet can move;
$\tau[P_j(l)]$ – time taken to pass lth packet along $P_j(l)$;
$l(t)$ – the number of all packets in the network at instant t_o.

The overall average delay is

$$\bar{\tau} = \frac{1}{l(t_o)} \sum_{l=1}^{l(t_o)} \tau[P_{j(l)}(l)] \tag{5.3.15}$$

and we consider $OP\,\mathbf{R}(\cdot),\bar{\tau}$ | ideal network state information, no new influx, fixed topology. We call this the optimum discharge problem.

Let us denote

$l(w,t)$ – the number of packets at node w at instant t.

Since we assumed that packet duration is fixed we have

$$\tau[P_j(l)] = T_1 \sum_{w \in P_j(l)} l(w,t) \tag{5.3.16}$$

where t_w is the instant at which the lth packet arrived at a node belonging to the path $P_j(l)$. Since $L(w,t_w)$ depends on the paths $P_{j(l')}(l)$ along which packets $l' \neq L$ are routed, we see that $\tau[P_j(l)]$ depends strongly on paths $P_{j(l')}(l')$ along which packets other than the lth are routed. Thus we can not minimise $\bar{\tau}$ given by (5.3.15) by minimising $\tau[P_{j(l')}(l')]$ separately. To find the set of paths $P^*_{j(l)}(l)$, $l = 1, 2, \ldots, l(t_o)$ minimising $\bar{\tau}$ we could use integer programming, taking into account the relationships between $l(w,t_w)$ for all nodes w and the paths $P_j(l)$.

This would require very great computing power even for small networks. If we dropped the simplifying assumption that we have no new influx we would have to apply stochastic integer programming, which requires even more computing power.

In view of these difficulties there is a need for a simpler method giving at least some insight into the properties of the set $\mathbf{R}(\cdot)$ of routing rules which are favourable in the sense of the overall quality criterion $\bar{\tau}$. Such methods will be presented in Chapter 6. In particular we will show that shortest path rules are favourable, but the lengths of channels are no more than estimates of the quality index.

5.4 ADAPTIVE ROUTING RULES

In this section we consider routing rules of types (5.3.19) taking into account the subsystem of network state information (n.s.i.) acquistion and distribution. The general features of these subsystems were described in section 1.3.1.

In the case of a mesh network, the n.s.i. subsystem is also a mesh network. The channels of this network are usually subchannels obtained by dividing primary channels into subchannels for working information and n.s.i. transmission. The division may be fixed or flexible. Usually the n.s.i. is carried either by special packets or as a component of the large working packets (for examples see 4.2). The n.s.i. transmission subsystem may be separated from the system for working packet transmission, but they may be also inherently coupled, e.g. the n.s.i. may be obtained by watching the working packet traffic. An example is a network with backward learning which uses the delay of packets coming to node w from node r as an estimate of the delay of packets which can be sent from w to r. The delay of packets from r arriving at w can be obtained if the packet carries the time of its departure from r. The n.s.i. obtained by such a method is useful only in specific circumstances. In the first two subsections we consider the algorithm for making adaptive decentralised routing decisions and give an example. Then we deal with partially decentralised and hierarchic routing rules.

5.4.1 The adaptive routing rule based on shortest path length estimates

By length we mean the parameter linked with the quality index of the path, viz.:

$$d(P_{sr}) = \sum_{(w,v)\in P_{sr}} d(w,v) \tag{5.4.1}$$

which may well be measured in terms of time, not necessarily distance. We assume that channel lengths vary and are not known in advance. Consider a system, with n.s.i. for the immediate neighbourhood, such that:

node w is able to make an estimate $d^*(w,v)$ of the lengths of channels leaving that node; (5.4.2a)

the node possesses similar information about the length of paths going out of nodes belonging to the upper neighbourhood of w. (5.4.2b)

Describing the adaptive rule, we simplify the notation by assuming that destination nodes receive the first Q successive numbers. If there is a source at each node $Q = N$.

The application of the principle of adaptation to rule (5.3.5) described in the previous section leads us to the following algorithm for making routing decisions:

Routing algorithm 1

Step 0

Using the primary estimates of channel length $d_0^*(u,v), u,v = 1,2,\ldots,N$, the set of shortest paths P_{wr} $r = 1,2,\ldots,M$ is† determined, and estimates of their lengths:

$$d_0^*(P_{wr}) \equiv \sum_{(u,v)\in P_{wr}} d_0^*(u,v) \tag{5.4.3}$$

are made. Knowing these paths, we determine the routing tables in the set:

$$\mathbf{d}_1^*(w) = \{d_0^*(P_{wr}), \quad r = 1,2,\ldots,M\} \tag{5.4.4}$$

where

$$d_0^*(P_{wr}) = \sum_{(u,v)\in P_{wr}} d_0^*(u,v) \tag{5.4.5}$$

is sent to all nodes in the lower neighbourhood.

Step n, n $= 1,2,\ldots$

n.1. Using the information about its own state the node makes the estimates

$$d_{n-1}^*(w,v_\mu), \; v_\mu \in N_{\text{out}}(w)$$

n.2. Using the local n.s.i.

$$\mathbf{d}_{n-1}^*(v_\mu) = \{d_{n-1}^*(P_{v_\mu,r}^{(n-1)}), \quad r = 1,2,\ldots,M\} \tag{5.4.6}$$

† To simplify the notation we assume that the set of destination poles R is the set of nodes with numbers $1, 2, \ldots, M$.

the estimates

$$\delta_n^*(w,r\,|\,v_\mu) \;=\; d_n^*(w,v_\mu) + d_{n-1}^*(P_{v_\mu,r}^{(n-1)}) \tag{5.4.7}$$

are made for the length of the shortest path from w to r over v.

n.3. The node $v_{\mu*}^{(n)}(r) \in N_{out}(w)$ is found such that

$$d_n(w, v_{\mu*}^{(n)}(r), P_{v_{\mu*}^{(n)}(r),r}^{(n-1)}) \;=\; \min d_n(w, v_\mu, P_{v_\mu,r}^{(n-1)}) \tag{5.4.8}$$

n.4. The nodes $v_{\mu*}^{(n)}(r)$, $r = 1, 2, \ldots, M$ become elements of the new routing table; we define

$$d_n^*(w, P_{w,r}^{(n-1)}) \;=\; d_n[w, v_{\mu*}^{(n)}(r), P_{v_{\mu*}^{(n)}(r),r}^{(n-1)}] \tag{5.4.9}$$

The set

$$\mathbf{d}_n^*(w) \;=\; \{d_n[w, v_{\mu*}^{(n)}(r), P_{v_{\mu*}^{(n)}(r),r}^{(n-1)}), \quad r = 1,2,\ldots,M\} \tag{5.4.10}$$

is sent as the information about state of node w to all nodes from N_{in} (see Fig. 5.12).

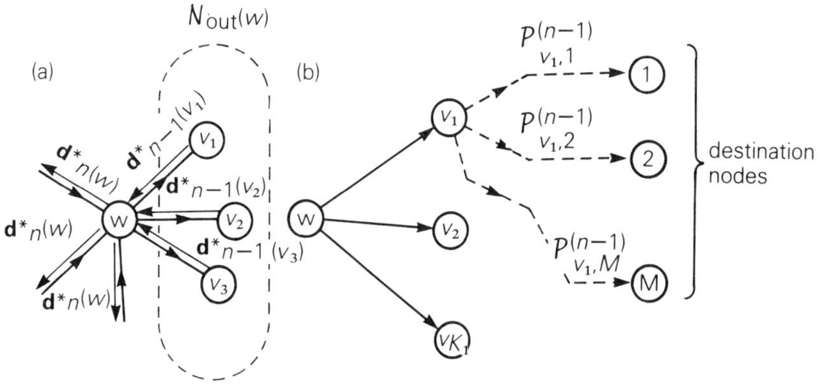

Fig. 5.12 – Illustration of notation used in the adaptive routing rule (5.4.1). (a) Transmission of sets of paths length estimates; (b) examples of paths $P(n-1)$; thin interrupted lines, channels for n.s.i. transmission.

To complete the description of the rule we must specify the subrule for stepping. This subrule must be closely coupled with the operation of the n.s.i. collection and distribution subnetwork. The fundamental types of the latter were described in section 1.5.2. Simplest is the rhythmical operation, with a fixed cycle. At the beginning of the cycle we execute steps n.1- n.4. Then we apply the routing table until a new one is determined at the beginning of the next cycle, as illustrated in Fig. 5.13. The essential parameter of the system operating rhythmically is the cycle duration T_{cy}. If the n.s.i. subsystem is separated from the working system, then increasing T_{cy} decreases the general system quality, e.g. we increase packet delay, since n.s.i. $\mathbf{d}^*_{n-1}(v_\mu)$, $v_\mu \in N_{out}(w)$ on which the routing table was based becomes outdated. However, if the n.s.i. subnetwork and the working network share the same channels, then if we decrease T_{cy} we increase the rate of n.s.i. transmission and less channel capacity remains for the working system. For small T_{cy} this may outweight the advantages of having up-to-date n.s.i., thus an optimum T^*_{cy} exists. An example of such behaviour of the system will be given in section 5.5.3.

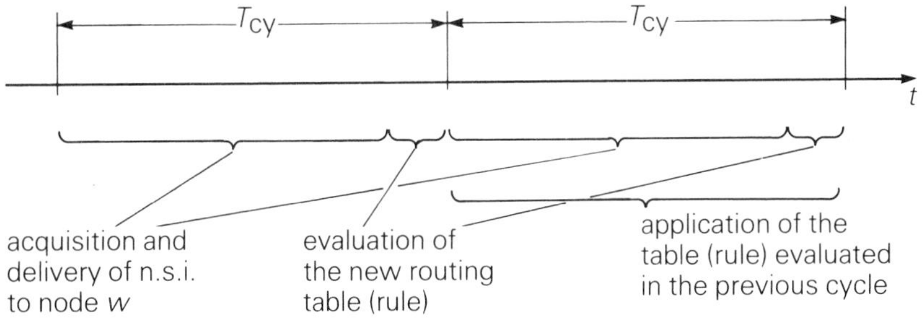

Fig. 5.13 – Timing in a network applying adaptive routing rule with periodic sampling.

The obvious way to reduce the channel capacity of the n.s.i. subnetwork without decreasing the quality of n.s.i. is to make the estimates of channel and path lengths continuously and apply the general principles of efficient sampling. We now describe in more detail the application of threshold sampling. Let us consider node w and let us denote by t^*_n the last instant when information about that node was sent to nodes in $N_{in}(w)$; this information is the set $\mathbf{d}^*_n(w) = \{d(P^{(t^*_n)}_{w,r}, t^*_n);\ r = 1,2,\ldots,M\}$ where $d(P^{(t)}_{wr}t)$ is the estimate made at instant t of the length of path $P^{(t)}_{wr}$, which at instant t is assumed to be the shortest path from w to r. We watch the increments

$$\Delta(w,r\,|\,v_\mu;t) \equiv \delta^*(w,r\,|\,v_\mu,t) - \delta^*(w,r\,|\,v_\mu,t^*_n) \qquad (5.4.11)$$

where

$$\delta^*(w,r\,|\,v_\mu;t) \equiv d(w,v_\mu;t) + d(P^{(t)}_{v_\mu,r};t) \qquad (5.4.12)$$

is the estimate of the length of the presumed shortest path from w to r over v and $d(w,v_\mu;t)$ is the currently updated length of channels going out of the considered node w. The new sample $\mathbf{d}^*_{n+1}(w)$ of the node state information is sent at instant t_{n+1}, when for the first time one of the increments surpasses a threshold, i.e. when for the first time since t_n^* we have:

$$\max_{v_\mu, r} \Delta(w, v \mid v_\mu; t) \geqslant \Delta_{\text{th}} \tag{5.4.13}$$

We make the estimate $\delta(w,r \mid v_\mu;t)$ by making the estimates on the right-hand side of (5.4.12). The length $d(w,v_\mu;t)$ we obtain by continuously monitoring the state of the node, in particular the lengths of the queues. There is a variety of methods for making the current estimate $d^*(P^{(t)}_{v_\mu, r};t)$. In the simplest case we use only the state information delivered by the node v_μ. Then $d^*(P^{(t)}_{v_\mu, r};t)$ changes stepwise as this information arrives. However, using *a priori* information and samples obtained in the past, we can use the well known methods of prediction. Node w can also apply feedback, as in Δ-modulation, requesting node v_μ to send a signal correcting the estimate of the state of mode v_μ made by node w. This would be a system with n.s.i. delivery on request by the user (see section 1.4.3).

In general sending a new sample of node state information must not change the routing table used in that node. However, these operations can be coupled in such a way that instead of checking the increment $\Delta(w,r \mid v_\mu;t)$ occurring in (5.4.13) we constantly evaluate the routing table, and when is changes we send a new sample of node state information.

5.4.2 Examples of adaptive routing rule based on estimates of packet delay

As an example of the general adaptive rule consider a system where the channel length is defined as the packet delay, τ. We can present the estimate of packet delay caused by a channel in the form:

$$\tau_n^*(w,v_\mu) = T_{\text{qu}}(w,v_\mu;n) + T_{\text{ch}}(w,v_\mu) \tag{5.4.14}$$

The first component is the estimated waiting time in the queue, and the subscript, n, is the sequence number of the estimate. The second component is the time to send the packet through the channel, which is assumed to be constant. If the network is lightly loaded

$$T_{\text{qu}}(w,v_\mu;n) \ll T(w,v_\mu) \tag{5.4.15}$$

and therefore:

$$\tau_n^*(w,v_\mu) \approx T(w,v_\mu) \tag{5.4.16}$$

The time to send the packet through the channel

$$T_{\text{ch}}(w,v_\mu) = T(w,v_\mu) + T_{\text{pr}}(w,v_\mu) \tag{5.4.17}$$

where $T_{pr}(w,v_\mu)$ is the propagation time and $T(w,v_\mu)$ is the duration of the packet passing through channel (w,v_μ).

Usually

$$T_{pr}(w,v_\mu) \ll T(w,v_\mu) \tag{5.4.18}$$

$$T(w,v_\mu) \approx T = \text{const.} \tag{5.4.19}$$

and so:

$$\tau_n^*(w,v) = T \ . \tag{5.4.20}$$

Thus the estimate of delay along a path, is TH_{wr}, where H_{wr} is the number of hops necessary to carry the packet from w to r. The routing rule 5.3.14 becomes the rule to send the packet along paths minimising the number of hops. Assuming that the network does not alter this rule could be applied statically. If the state of the channels changes because of a breakdown, then the paths change so that, in the new situation, the paths are again optimal.

For networks in which the queueing time in buffers is much greater than the transmission time, adaptive rule 5.3.14 sets up paths in which the total expected queuing time in buffers is as small as possible. The expected, rather than actual, waiting time is minimised, since the packet may not take the expected path. For example, if node w recognises path P_{wr} as optimal, but the first node $v_{\mu*}$ on the path P_{wr} regards path P_{vr}, not a segment of path P_{wr}, as optimal then the packet does not travel as w predicted. As a result of this, information may start to circulate in closed loops.

These properties bring us to the heuristic estimate of the delay along the path $P_{wr} = (w, v_\mu, P_{v_\mu,r})$

$$\tau_n^*(P_{wr}) \equiv T_A + T_{qu}(w,v_\mu;n) + \tau_{n-1}^* P_{v_\mu,r}) \tag{5.4.21}$$

where $T_{qu}(w,v_\mu;n)$ is the actual queueing time in the buffer at the input of (w,v_μ) channel; we treat T_A not as the transmission time of the signal through channel (w,v_μ) but as a variable parameter. If T_A is small in comparison with the average queueing times, the delays introduced by the buffer dominate. If T_A is too big, the delays introduced by the buffer play a small part and information may be directed to a node in whose buffer it has to wait a long time. One can therefore expect there to be an optimum value of the parameter T, which has been confirmed by the simulation.

Typical relationships between the normalised delay $\tau' = \tau/T$ and the normalised constant $T_A' = T_A/T$ are shown in Fig. 5.14 both for rhythmical and threshold sampling. These relationships also illustrate our general conclusions about the choice of sampling period T_{cy} and the threshold Δ_{th}.

The system considered is a typical system with decentralised evaluation. The other possibility is to evaluate routing decisions in a central control unit (CCU)

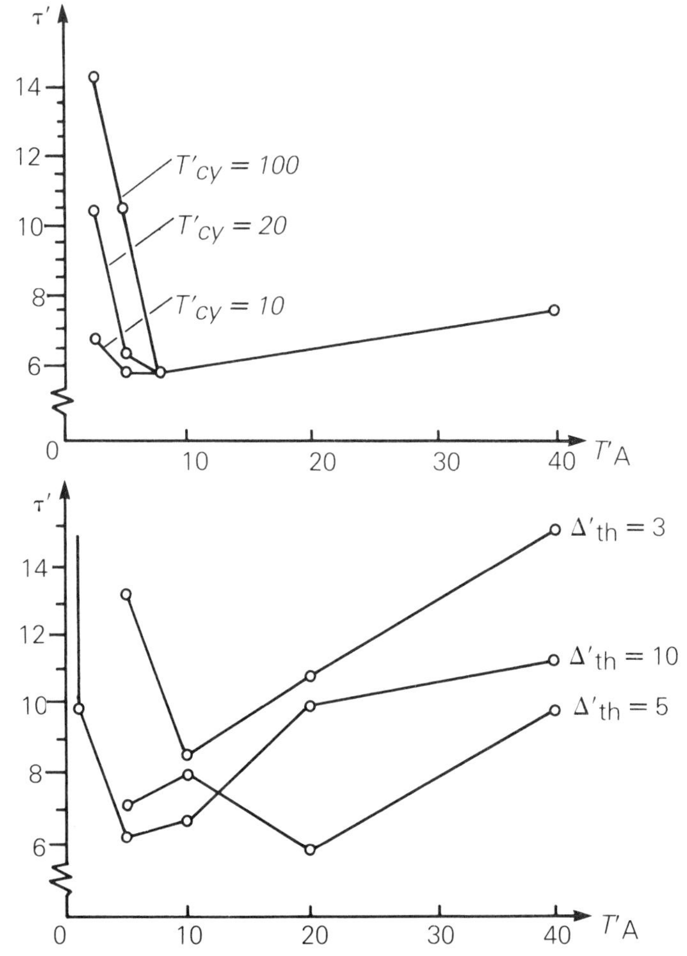

Fig. 5.14 – Example of the dependence of the normalised delay τ' on the normalised constant T'_A in the critical function: (a) rhythmical sampling; (b) threshold sampling. $T'_{cy} = T_{cy}/T$ normalised sampling period; Δ'_{th}, normalised threshold based on Fultz and Kleinrock [5.10].

which has at its disposal information about the state of all nodes. Obviously decentralised routing based only on local n.s.i. cannot be better than optimised centralised routing based on timely and accurate n.s.i. However, the n.s.i. subsystem delivering such information would be very costly. If the quality of n.s.i. available at the CCU is low (great delay, inaccurate) then centralised routing may introduce larger working packet delays than decentralised routing. We can diminish these disadvantages by combining the centralised and decentralised routing principles. A typical example is a system in which we have a CCU, a rather simple subsystem delivering n.s.i. to CCU and a subsystem delivering local n.s.i. to all nodes. The CCU, using the available n.s.i., makes binary decisions about the type of operation: centralised (C) or decentralised (D). If C decision is taken the system operates as a centralised one and the CCU works out and delivers the routing tables to all nodes. If D decision is taken, the nodes, using local n.s.i. operate as in a decentralised system. There are a variety of criteria for making decisions about the type of operation. One was proposed by Rudin [5.11] for a routing rule called Δ-routing. The CCU evaluates for each node two paths: the best with the least delay τ^* and second best with delay τ'. The rule for choosing the type of operations:

$$\begin{array}{ll} \text{C} & \text{if} \quad \Delta\tau \geqslant \Delta_{th} \\ \text{D} & \text{if} \quad \Delta\tau < \Delta_{th} \end{array} \tag{5.4.22}$$

where $\Delta\tau = \tau' - \tau^*$, and Δ_{th} is a threshold. The idea behind the system described is evident. When the best path is markedly better than any other, there is no need to look for any other path. If, however, the difference in quality between the best path and the next-best paths is small, we may expect that, owing to poor quality of n.s.i. available at the network control centre, the decision to route the packets along the path, which according to the estimates of the network control centre is the best, may in fact not be the best. Therefore, in such a situation we permit the nodes to do what according to their estimates is the best. In Rudin's paper [5.11] mentioned above, for a few simple networks, Δ-routing was compared by simulation with centralised and decentralised routing. It was found that for these networks Δ-routing is definitely superior to decentralised routing.

5.4.3 Hierarchical routing

The idea of hierarchical routing is to describe network topology with varying accuracy, decreasing with the distance of an area of the network from the node considered. We achieve this by introducing a hierarchy of clusters of primary nodes and considering the cluster as a single aggregated node. We base routing of the packet on information about the state of the aggregated nodes, which can be considered as reduced information about the states of the primary nodes included in the aggregate node. Introducing the less detailed network description and the correspondingly reduced n.s.i. we can greatly reduce the requirements for n.s.i. transmission. Because of this the routing corresponding to the higher levels of aggregation can be made similar to a centralised system with an effective n.s.i. subsystem. The hierarchical routing is based on the division of the set of all nodes into a hierarchy of clusters which are disjoint at any one level.†

† Such types of hierarchical routing were analysed in detail by Kleinrock and Kamoun [5.12].

The set of all nodes is divided into a hierarchy of clusters which are disjoint at any one level. Let $C_j^{(i)}$ be the jth, $j=1,2,\ldots,J(i)$, cluster of level i, $i=1,2,\ldots,I$. We assume that there is only one cluster of the highest level I and that this is the set of all nodes

$$C_1^{(I)} = N \tag{5.4.23}$$

where:

$$C_1^{(I)} = \bigcup_{j=1}^{J(I-1)} C_j^{(I-1)} \tag{5.4.24a}$$

and:

$$C_j^{(I-1)} \cap C_{j'}^{(I-1)} = \emptyset \tag{5.4.24b}$$

and so on.

Each cluster $C_j^{(i)}$ is distinguished by the **cluster centre node**, w, therefore we denote it by $C_{j(w)}^{(i)}$. Let $C_{j_\mu(w)}^{(1)}$, $\mu = 1,2,\ldots,M$, be all level 1 clusters which are components of the same level 2 cluster as $C_{j(w)}^{(1)}$. We denote this cluster by $C_{k(w)}^{(2)}$. From the point of view of node w, each cluster $C_{j_\mu(w)}^{(1)}$ is treated as the cluster central node, and routing is performed accordingly.

To illustrate this type of routing we take an example with $I=4$. We assume that: (1) the packet is put into the network at node $w \in C_{j(w)}^{(1)} \subset C_{k(w)}^{(2)} \subset C_{l(w)}^{(3)} \subset C^{(4)} = N$; (2) the destination $q \in C_{j(q)}^{(1)} \subset C_{k(q)}^{(2)} \subset C_{l(q)}^{(3)}$ and $j(w) \neq j(q)$, $k(w) \neq k(q)$ but $l(w) = l(q)$. Inside the cluster $C_{j(w)}^{(1)}$ the packet is routed node-to-node. When it enters $C_{j'}^{(1)}$, $j' \neq j(w)$, two approaches are possible: (a) we treat our packet as originating in $C_{j'}^{(1)}$, and we again forward it node-to-node inside that cluster; or, (b) we give the packet the status of an external packet which is to be forwarded along a path going through the cluster central nodes. We call the first approach **uniform hierarchical routing**, and the second, **routing through the central nodes.** Typical of the latter type of rule are those which try to reach the destination node by moving only through lowest level clusters, but if this is inefficient, move to higher level clusters and then go to the destination through clusters of decreasing level. This type of rule requires that packets carry a record of their route, hence they are not simple to implement. The uniform hierarchical routing rules are easier to implement. For these rules it is sufficient to deliver to each node w only the n.s.i. concerning the cluster centre nodes in the network seen by w. We can do this by transmitting the routing table for node w to nodes from $N_{in}(w)$. In these routing tables we have only entries for the cluster centre nodes, hence the reduction in n.s.i.

The fundamental criterion for grouping the nodes is minimising the size of the routing table at each node, i.e. minimising the sum:

$$J \equiv (J^{(1)}(w) - 1) + (J^{(2)}(w) - 1) + \ldots + (J^{(I-1)} - 1) \tag{5.4.25}$$

where $J^{(k)}(w)$ is the number of clusters at level k forming the cluster of level $k+1$. The problem of finding the optimum cluster sizes $J^{(k)}$ minimising J_Σ was solved by Kleinrock and Kamoun [5.12]. Under several simplifying assumptions Kleinrock and Kamoun [5.12] showed that for large networks the decrease of routing quality is very small, while the volume of the routing tables is greatly reduced. Thus hierarchical routing is very efficient for some networks.

5.5 RANDOM ROUTING RULES

Random routing rules are important for a number of reasons. For example, a given average flow pattern can be easily realised by means of a random routing rule as we shall show in section 6.5.2. These rules also are of interest in congestion control systems in which we distribute the entrance tickets uniformly over the whole network. Finally, approximate, closed form formulae relating the fundamental parameters of the rules have been found for random routing rules but not for any other type. So these rules are interesting from the analytic viewpoint.†

We start this section with a description of random routing rules, then concentrate on the so-called Δ-neighbourhood identification rules. We derive an approximate expression for the average number of hops made in traversing the network, then use it to find the packet delay. We show that, if we take into account the channel capacity needed for transmission of the n.s.i., there is an optimal level of n.s.i. We give approximate formulae for the number of packets waiting at the nodes in the network, and conclude by briefly comparing some of the random routing rules and the deterministic rules considered in section 5.3.

5.5.1 Description of random routing rules

In this section, we concentrate on node-to-node routing rules combined with decentralised n.s.i. evaluation and routing. The routing depends on the network state information $\xi_n(w)$ and information about the packet's history $\xi_s(w)$. The probability that a packet destined for π, which has arrived at node w, will be forwarded to node $v \in N_{out}(w)$ can be written as:

$$P_r[v \mid w; \xi_n(w), \xi_p(w)]$$

We will call this the **forwarding probability**. If there is no dependence on $\xi_n(w)$, then the routing is **fixed**, and if there is no dependence on $\xi_p(w)$ the rule is **memoryless**. A fixed, memoryless, rule is described by the set $P_q(v \mid w), v \in N_{out}(w)$, $w = 1, 2, \ldots, N$. We shall devote the largest part of this section to the analysis of the fixed, memoryless, routing rule; but first consider an example of flexible routing.

† The random routing rules were analysed in detail in the monograph by Kleinrock [2.1].

To simplify the description, we assume that only two channels leave the node under consideration and we denote them $(w, v_1), (w, v_2)$. We assume that the n.s.i. is delivered periodically, with period of T_{cy}. The rule is:

Routing rule 1

1.1 Estimate, $\tau_{wr}^{(n)}(v_k)$, $k = 1, 2$, of the time taken to forward the packet from w to q along a path whose first channel is (w, v_k), is valid until the $(n+1)$th update.

1.2 After obtaining the nth update we evaluate the ratio

$$\alpha_n \equiv \frac{\tau_{wr}^{(n)}(v_1)}{\tau_{wr}^{(n)}(v_2)} \quad . \tag{5.5.1}$$

1.3 Let $\Delta_1, \Delta_2 < \Delta_1$ be two constants < 1. During the $(n+1)$th updating interval we obtain the forwarding probabilities from the following recurrence formulae.

$$P_r^{(n+1)}(v_1 | w, \tau_{w_r}^{(n)}) = \begin{cases} [P_r^{(n)}(v_1 | w, \tau_{wr}^{(n-1)}) - \Delta_1]^+ & \text{if } \alpha_n < 0.5 \quad (5.5.2a) \\ [P_r^{(n)}(v_1 | w, \tau_{wr}^{(n-1)}) - \Delta_2]^+ & \text{if } 0.5 \leqslant \alpha_n < 1 \quad (5.5.2b) \\ P_r^{(n)}(v_1 | w, \tau_{wr}^{(n-1)}) & \text{if } \alpha_n = 1 \quad (5.5.2c) \end{cases}$$

$$P_r^{(n+1)}(v_2 | w, \tau_{wr}^{(n)}) = \begin{cases} P_r^{(n)}(v_2 | w, \tau_{wr}^{(n-1)}) & \text{if } \alpha_n = 1 \quad (5.5.3a) \\ [P_r^{(n)}(v_2 | w, \tau_{wr}^{(n-1)}) - \Delta_2]^+ & \text{if } 1 < \alpha_n < 2 \quad (5.5.3b) \\ [P_r^{(n)}(v_2 | w, \tau_{wr}^{(n-1)}) - \Delta_1]^+ & \text{if } \alpha_n > 2 \quad (5.5.3c) \end{cases}$$

where we denote $\tau_{wr}^{(n)} \equiv (\tau_w^{(n)}(v_1), \tau_w^{(n)}(v_2))$ and

$$U^+ \equiv \begin{cases} u & \text{for } Q\ u \geqslant 0 \\ 0 & \text{for } Q\ u < 0 \end{cases}$$

For all β_n we obtain the probability for the next node from the relationship:

$$P_r^{(n+1)}(v_1 | w, \tau_{wr}^{(n)}) + P_r^{(n+1)}(v_2 | \tau_{wr}^{(n)}) = 1 \ . \tag{5.5.4}$$

There now follows a justification of formulae (5.5.2). We prefer to direct packets along the path with the smallest estimated passage time. We expect that the state of the network will change therefore, if we find that the delay along the path passing through v_1 is at least twice that for the path through v_2, we decrease the probability of forwarding the packet to node v_1 used during the previous period. The forwarding probability must not be negative, therefore we introduce $[\cdot]^+$ to the function. When the difference between the estimated delays for the path passing through node v_1 is not large ($0.5 < \alpha_m < 1$) but still not favourable to the path passing through v_2, we decrease the probability of forwarding the packet to v_1 by a smaller amount $\Delta_2 P$ (5.5.2b). When both estimated delays are the same, we do not change the forwarding probability. When the path passing through node v_2 is less favourable, we reverse the procedure.

Routing rule 1 is called **the proportional routing rule.** It was analysed by Rudin [5.11]. As will be seen in section 6.5.2, this rule can be considered as a quantised version of the steepest descent rule with three admissible correction rules $(0, \Delta_1, \Delta_2)$.

If more channels go out of the nodes we can generalise our rule in a number of different ways. One example is algorithm 6.4.2.

It is often advantageous to use a deterministic routing rule in the vicinity of the destination, giving a hybrid random/deterministic rule. We say that:

the **order of the neighbourhood** of node w relative to node v is the minimum number of channels which we must pass along to get from w to v. (5.5.5)

We shall now look at the following randomised routing rule.†

Routing rule 2

1.1 If pole r to which the packet is being directed is an upper neighbour of the order Δ or lower of the node w which the packet has already reached, we send the packet to that pole according to the auxiliary deterministic rule $R_d(\cdot)$.

1.2 In the opposite case (q is an upper neighbour of an order greater than Δ) the next node $v \in N_{out}(w)$ to which we direct the packet is chosen from among the nodes v in the set $N_{out}(w)$ according to an auxiliary random rule $R_r(\cdot)$.

We wil call the rule 2 the randomised rule with Δ-order neighbourhood identification (abbreviated, Δ-NIR) the number Δ being the critical neighbourhood order.

The auxiliary rule $R_d(\cdot)$ for forwarding the packet determinisitically will be called briefly the **determinisitic component rule** (DR), the rule $R_{id}(\cdot)$ of random routing will be the **indeterministic component rule** (IDR). Accordingly, on splitting the Δ-neighbourhood rules, the segment of the packet's path from source to destination determined by the randomisation component rule will be called the **random segment**, while the segment determined by the deterministic is the **deterministic segment.**

† The rule considered was proposed and analysed by Seidler and Konorski [5.13].

We will first consider the indeterministic component rules $R_{id}(\cdot)$. We can classify these rules in the same way as we previously classified the random routing rules. Because here we introduce the Δ-NIR to simplify the network's identification information subsystem, we will now assume that:

A.1 the random component rule $R_r(\cdot)$ is a memoryless fixed routing rule described by the forwarding probabilities $P(v|w), v \in N_{out}(w), w = 1, 2, \ldots, N$.

The simplest case of such a random component rule is the one for which for every $v \in N_{out}(w)$ the probabilities $P(v|w)$ are the same, i.e. for which

$$P(v|w) = \frac{1}{L[N_{out}(w)]} \qquad v \in N_{out}(w) \tag{5.5.6}$$

where by $L(A)$ we denote the number of elements of a discrete set A.

We shall call the indeterministic routing component rule with forwarding probabilities given by (5.5.6) the **uniformly distributing component rule** (URC). From (5.5.6) it follows that the probabilities $P(v|w)$ are, in the case of the URC rule, completely determined by the network topology; knowing it, we can immediately find the numbers $L[N_{out}(w)]$. For example, for the network shown in Fig. 5.11(c) we can present the probabilities $P(v|w)$ as the elements of the matrix

$$P = \begin{matrix} 0 & 0.25 & 0 & 0.25 & 0 & 0.25 & 0 & 0.25 \\ 0.25 & 0 & 0.25 & 0 & 0.25 & 0 & 0.25 & 0 \\ \cdots & \cdots & \cdots & \cdots & \cdots & \cdots & \cdots & \cdots \\ \cdots & \cdots & \cdots & \cdots & \cdots & \cdots & \cdots & \cdots \\ 0.25 & 0 & 0.25 & 0 & 0.25 & 0 & 0.25 & 0 \end{matrix} \tag{5.5.7}$$

Hitherto, we have considered the random component rule of the Δ-order neighbourhood identification rule. When $\Delta = 0$, the random component rule describes it completely. Thus the analysis of Δ-NIR which we will give applies in particular to the memoryless fixed random routing rules.

The deterministic component rule of the Δ-NIR can again he classified according to the principles explained in section 1.6.1; it can be either fixed or flexible. An example of the fixed deterministic component rule is the following:

Routing rule 3

Having reached node w which is a Δ- or lower-order neighbour of the destination pole r, the packet is forwarded towards the pole along path $P(w,r)$ fixed in advance.

An example of the **flexible deterministic component rule** is based on the adaptive routing rule considered in section 5.3:

Routing rule 4

Having reached node w which is a Δ- or lower-order neighbour of the destination node r, the packet is forwarded on towards the destination node along the path for which the delay is estimated on the basis of: (a) delay, introduced by channels leaving the node, and (b) estimates of delays along the paths leaving upper neighbourhood nodes, is minimal.

Notice that the Δ-NIR with the component rules described previously can be interpreted as a hierarchical two-level routing rule. The difference between this rule and the hierarchical rule described in section 5.4.3 is that in the Δ-NIR, the first order cluster, corresponding to nodes whose neighbourhood order is not larger than Δ, moves together with the packet, while in the hierarchical rules described in section 5.4.3 the clusters are fixed.

To implement flexible routing rules we must have suitable n.s.i. at our disposal. We will assume the following n.s.i. collection and delivery subrules:

NSI subrule 1

Network identification information is rhythmically sent from upper neighbourhood nodes;

i.e. the rhythmic updating rule is applied (see section 5.4.1). For n.s.i. delivery we assume the n.s.i. is sent either along separate channels, i.e.

NSI subrule 2a

The forwarding of n.s.i. does not affect the capacity of the channels carrying the working packets;

or along the same channels as the packets themselves, i.e.

NSI subrule 2b

The channels must bear the burden of carrying the n.s.i.

The randomised rule, characterised by the IDR and DR can be implemented in the following way: having identified the destination pole of the packet, the neighbourhood order of the node w at which the packet arrived with respect to the destination pole r, is found. If this order is greater than the critical order Δ, the next channel is chosen with equal probability among the channels going out of w and the packet is fed into the buffer at the chosen channel input. If, however, the neighbourhood order is equal to or lower than the critical order Δ, the next channel is read from the routing table realising the deterministic component rule and the packet is fed into the buffer at the input of that channel. If we apply the fixed DR, the routing table is fixed. If we apply the flexible DR, it is modified on the basis of n.s.i. Figure 5.15 shows the block diagram of a node implementing flexible DR.

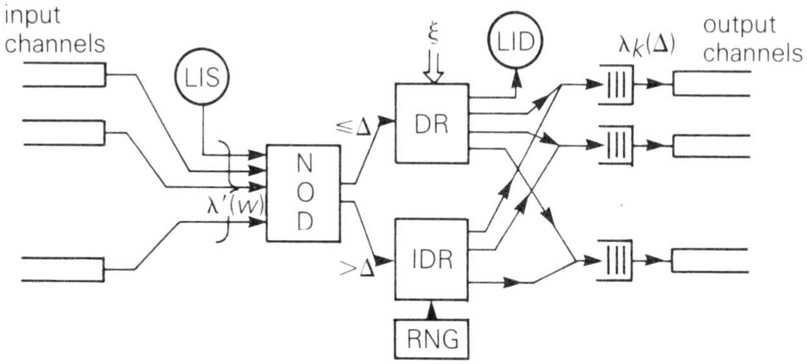

Fig. 5.15 – Model of a node in a network realising the randomised Δ-NIR rule. IS, local information source; NOD neighbourhood order determining facility; LID, local information destination; DCR, facility realising deterministic component rule. IDR, facility realising indeterministic component rule; RNG, random number generator.

5.5.2 Approximate evaluation of the average number of packet hops

The fundamental parameter characterising the quality of routing rules is the average packet delay which depends on the number of hops which the packet has to make to reach its destination, see section 5.2.3.

For a limited set of problems we can find the average number of hops by application of the theory of Markovian chains (see, for example, section 5.2.2). In order to achieve generality we derive formulae for the average number of hops, $\bar{H}$, which can be used for order 0 neighbourhood identification.

We introduce the following simplifying assumptions:

A2 The topology of the network is homogeneous and J channels leave each node.

A3 We have an information source at each node.

A4 All information sources deliver independent Poisson-exponential sequences of packets with the same statistical properties.

A5 The capacities of the buffers are infinite but the packets average waiting time is finite.

Notice, that assumptions A3–A6, satisfy assumptions introduced in section 5.2.3. Thus, knowing the average number of hops, we can easily evaluate the average packet delay from 5.2.45. Let:

$\mathcal{D}(r)$ be the set of nodes such that, for w, r is a Δ- or lower-order upper neighbour;

$H_{su}^{(id)}$ be the number of hops which the packet directed from s to r makes in the indeterministic part of the path, i.e. on the path $\mathcal{P}_{su}$ from p to the first node $u \in \mathcal{D}(r)$;

$H_{ur}^{(d)}$ be the number of hops which the packet makes in the deterministic part of the path, i.e. on the path $\mathcal{P}_{ur}$;

$P(w)$ be the probability that a packet sent from s to r reaches a given node w for the first time.

The set $\mathcal{D}(r)$ is the set of nodes from which the packet is deterministically sent to the destination node. Since reaching a node of the set $\mathcal{D}(r)$ is tantamount to reaching the destination, we call $\mathcal{D}(r)$ the **destination set**. The average number of hops, $\bar{H}_{sr}$ which a packet sent from s, to r makes is:

$$\bar{H}_{sr} = \sum_{u \in \mathcal{D}(r)} \bar{H}_{su}^{(id)} + H_{ur}^{(d)} P(u) \tag{5.5.8}$$

where:

$$\bar{H}_{su}^{(id)} \equiv E\mathrm{H}_{su}^{(id)}$$

and: (5.5.9)

$$\bar{H}_{ur}^{(d)} \equiv E\mathrm{H}_{ur}^{\mathrm{d}}$$

Since we can go from $u \in \mathcal{D}(q)$ to q through at most Δ channels, we assume that:

$$\bar{H}_{ur}^{(\mathrm{d})} \cong \Delta\ . \tag{5.5.10}$$

We now develop an estimation of $\bar{H}_{ur}^{(\mathrm{id})}$. From our homogeneity assumptions we know that:

$$\bar{H}_{su}^{(\mathrm{id})} \text{ is independent of both } s \text{ and } r. \tag{5.5.11}$$

Thus we may write $\bar{H}^{(\mathrm{id})}$ instead of $\bar{H}_{su}^{(\mathrm{id})}$.

We evaluate $\bar{H}^{(\mathrm{id})}$ using an approximate expression for the probability that, in the next step, a packet will be sent from a given node to the destination set. We must first introduce some additional symbols. Let:

$\mathsf{N}[\mathcal{D}(r)]$ be the set of lower neighbours of nodes in $\mathcal{D}(r)$, which are not themselves in $\mathcal{D}(r)$;

$\mathsf{N}_i(r)$ be the set of nodes for which r is an upper neighbour of order i;

$P(\mathcal{D}|w)$ be the probability that a packet in node $w \in \mathsf{N}[\mathcal{D}(r)]$ is directed to one of the nodes in $\mathcal{D}(r)$.

Figure 5.16 illustrates these definitions. Obviously:

$$\mathcal{D}(r) = \bigcup_{i=0}^{\Delta} \mathsf{N}_i(r) \tag{5.5.12}$$

and

$$\mathsf{N}[\mathcal{D}(r)] = \mathsf{N}_{\Delta+1}(r) \tag{5.5.13}$$

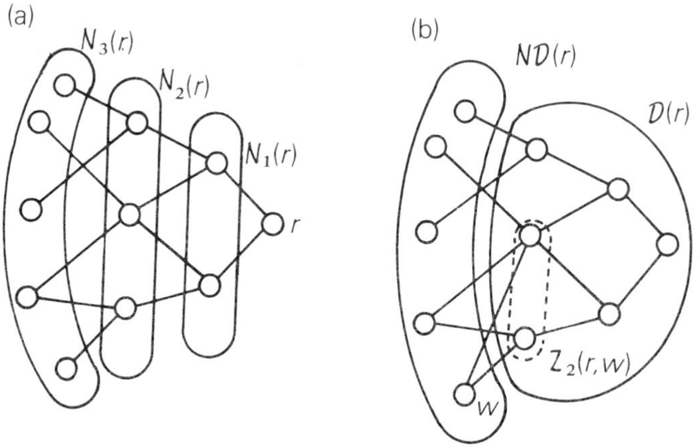

Fig. 5.16 – Illustration to the definition of sets:
(a) $N_i(r)$. (b) $\mathcal{D}(r)$, $N[\mathcal{D}(r)]$, $Z_i(r, w)$, $\Delta = 2$.

Finally let:

P_D be the probability that a packet in node $w \in \mathcal{D}(r)$ will be directed into a channel whose output belongs to the set $\mathcal{D}(r)$.

From the definition of the set $N[\mathcal{D}(r)]$ it follows, that the event mentioned in the definition of δ is possible only if $v \in N[\mathcal{D}(r)]$. We thus have:

$$P_D = \sum_{w \in N[\mathcal{D}(r)]} P(\mathcal{D}|w)P(w) \tag{5.5.14}$$

where $P(w)$ is the previously introduced probability of a packet from node s reaching a given node w. Assuming that $w \notin \mathcal{D}(r)$, i.e. that the travel of the packet was governed by the fixed, memoryless, randomised, component rule, this probability can be calculated on the basis of the results of the Markovian chain theory. In general the probability $P_D w$ depends on both p and w. Because of the complexity of the formulae for δ, we shall not use them here. Taking into account the homogeneity assumptions A2 and A5 and introducing the additional assumption that the average number of packets hops $\bar{H}$ is large, we shall make the simplifying hypothesis that for $w \notin \mathcal{D}(r)$ the probability $P_D w$ depends only to a small degree on Δ and w. Or, to a good approximation

$$P(w) = \text{const.} \tag{5.5.15}$$

for nodes $w \notin \mathcal{D}(r)$. Let $L(A)$ be the number of nodes in a subset A of the set of all nodes N. Using (5.5.15) for $w \notin \mathcal{D}(r)$ we have:

$$P(w) = \frac{1}{N - L[\mathcal{D}(r)]} \tag{5.5.16}$$

where N is the number of nodes in the network. $\mathcal{D}(r)$ is dependent on v and r, but under the homogeneity assumptions we have:

$$P(\mathcal{D}|w) \cong \text{const.} \tag{5.5.17}$$

for all $w \in N[\mathcal{D}(r)]$.

Let $Z_i(r,w)$ be a subset of $N_i(r)$, such that its elements are lower neighbours of a node, w say, in the set $N_{i+1}(r)$ – see Fig. 5.16. $Z_i(r,w)$ can thus be called the rim of set $N_i(r)$ in contact with w. If J is the number of channels leaving each node then:

$$P(\mathcal{D}|w) = \frac{L\,[Z_\Delta(r,w)]}{J} \tag{5.5.18}$$

Because of the homogeneity assumption, $L\,[Z_\Delta(r,w)]$ depends neither on q nor on w, hence from (5.5.13), (5.5.17) and (5.5.18)

$$P_\mathrm{D} = \frac{L\{N[\mathcal{D}(r)]\}}{N - L[\mathcal{D}(r)]} \cdot \frac{L[Z_\Delta(r,w)]}{J} \tag{5.5.19}$$

where $\mathcal{D}(r)$ and $N[\mathcal{D}(r)]$ are expressible in terms of the sets $N_i(r)$ alone.

Consider an example network with zero-order identification. For this network, $\mathcal{D}(r) = \{r\}$, and q has J immediate neighbours. Thus $L\{N[\mathcal{D}(r)]\} = J$ and $L[Z_\Delta(r,w)] = 1$. From (5.5.18) we have:

$$P_\mathrm{D} = \frac{1}{N-1}\ . \tag{5.5.20}$$

Now let us take a network with first order identification. We assume structure is such that:

A6 none of the immediate neighbours of q are themselves immediate neighbours.

$\mathcal{D}(r)$ consists of $J+1$ nodes, i.e. q and its lower neighbours. Assuming network homogeneity, each of these last nodes again has J lower neighbours, and one of them is node q (see Fig. 5.2). Each neighbour of node q has $J-1$ neighbours not belonging to $\mathcal{D}(q)$, therefore:

$$L\{N[\mathcal{D}(r)]\} = J(J-1) \tag{5.5.21}$$

If the network has a structure such that only one channel leading to set $\mathcal{D}(r)$ leaves a node from set $N[\mathcal{D}(r)]$ we get $L[Z_\Delta(r,w)] = 1$. Under the assumptions made, we get from (5.5.19)

$$P_\mathrm{D} = \frac{J-1}{N-J-1}\ . \tag{5.5.22}$$

We shall now return to the calculation of $\bar{H}$. To reach the destination set in h hops, a packet must have failed to do so in the first $h-1$ hops, so if $\mathrm{H}^{(r)}$ is the random variable representing the number of hops in the random component of the path, we get

$$P(\mathrm{H}^{(\mathrm{id})} = h) = (1-P_{\mathrm{D}})^{h-1} P_{\mathrm{D}} \; . \tag{5.5.23}$$

Knowing the distribution of the random variable $\mathrm{H}^{(r)}$ we can find its average value and dispersion. Using equation (5.5.23) and the well-known occurrence formulae for the sums we get:

$$\bar{H}^{(\mathrm{id})} = \sum_{h=1}^{\infty} hP(\mathrm{H}^{(\mathrm{id})} = h) = \frac{1}{P_{\mathrm{D}}} \tag{5.5.24}$$

and

$$\sigma^2(\mathrm{H}^{(\mathrm{id})}) = \sum_{h=1}^{\infty} h^2 P(\mathrm{H}^{(\mathrm{id})} = h) - [\bar{H}^{(\mathrm{id})}]^2 = \frac{1-P_{\mathrm{D}}}{P_{\mathrm{D}}^2} \; . \tag{5.5.25}$$

From these equations we can see that the dispersion of the number of hops in the random segment of the path is very large, so we expect that some packets will circulate for a long time. From (5.5.2), (5.5.8), (5.5.10) and (5.5.19), (5.5.24) we get the final estimate of the number of hops averaged over all poles.

$$\bar{H} = \bar{H}^{(\mathrm{id})} + \bar{H}^{(\mathrm{d})} = \frac{N - L\left[\bigcup_{i=0}^{\infty} N_i(r)\right]}{L\{N[\mathcal{D}(r)]\}} \quad \frac{J}{L[Z_{\Delta}(r,w)]} \; . \tag{5.5.26}$$

In calculating $\bar{H}$ we did not take into account the number of packets in the overall flow whose path does not contain a random segment, i.e., for which the source node is a member of $\mathcal{D}(r)$. The proportion of such packets is:

$$\beta = \frac{L\left[\bigcup_{i=1}^{\Delta} N_i(s)\right]}{N} = \frac{\sum_{i=1}^{\Delta} L[N_i(s)]}{N} \tag{5.5.27}$$

The average number of hops for this kind of packet is:

$$\bar{H}_{s \in \mathcal{D}(r)} = \frac{1}{\sum_{i=1}^{\Delta} L[N_i(s)]} \sum_{i=1}^{\Delta} iL[N_i(s)] \tag{5.5.28}$$

Assuming homogeneity the above quantities do not depend on p. Thus the corrected average number of hops is:

$$\bar{H}' = (1-\beta)\bar{H} + \beta \bar{H}_{s \in \mathcal{D}(r)} \qquad (5.5.29)$$

where $\bar{H}$ is the number of hops given by (5.5.26).

From (5.5.26) and (5.5.29) we find that the calculation of the average number of hops is reduced to the determination of sets $\mathcal{N}_i(r)$ and $\mathcal{Z}_i(r,w)$. Approximate relationships obtained by Seidler and Konorski [5.13] are shown in Fig. 5.17. These show rapid fall in the number of hops as Δ increases.

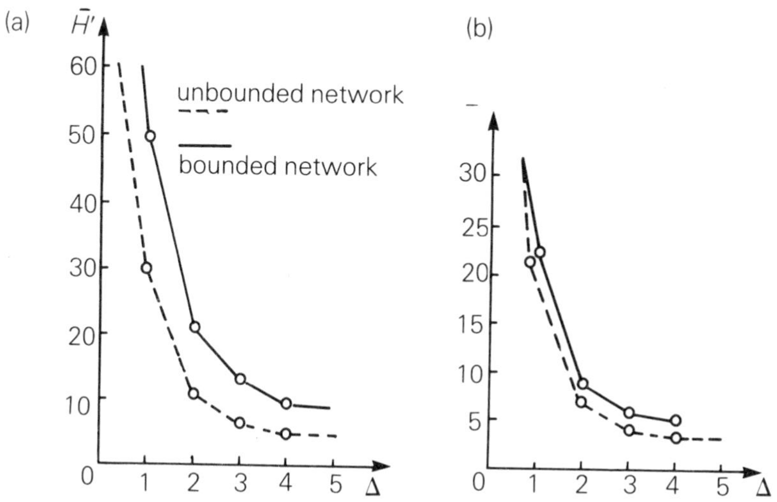

Fig. 5.17 – Example of the dependence of the average number of hops $\bar{H}$, on the neighbourhood identification order Δ. Homogeneous network, number of nodes $N = 100$, number of channels leaving the node: (a) $J = 4$, (b) $J = 6$. Broken lines, network edge effects not considered; continuous lines, network edge effects considered.

We have been assuming network homogeneity and therefore we have not considered edge effects. Konorski [5.14] gives a method for including edge effects in the calculations and the results are illustrated in Fig. 5.17.

In section 5.2.4 we considered the fundamental properties of the number of packets in the network, i.e. either waiting in a buffer for transmission or being transmitted. We showed that these properties depend essentially on the auxiliary parameter ψ. We show now that for the Δ-NIR rule, this parameter is directly related to the parameters introduced previously. Let:

$\mathcal{OU}$ denote the event that the removal of a packet from the network is completed within the time interval $\langle t, t+\mathrm{d}t\rangle$;

PC denote the event that a transmitted packet has been routed into the correct channel, i.e. the channel at whose output is located the destination node;
TR denote the event that a packet is being transmitted;
dC denote the event that the transmission of a packet which was being transmitted at instant t will be completed within the time interval $\langle t, t+\mathrm{d}t \rangle$.

From definition (5.5.14) we get:

$$\lambda'(1) = P(\mathrm{d}OU|TR)/\mathrm{d}t \qquad (5.5.30)$$

The previously considered probability P_D can be written as

$$P_\mathrm{D} = P(OU|TR)$$

From the definitions above, we also get:

$$P(\mathrm{d}OU|TR) = P(PC \cap \mathrm{d}C|TR) = P(\mathrm{d}C|PC,TR)\,P(PC|TR) \; . \qquad (5.5.31)$$

Since, according to the definition, $\mathrm{d}C$ is an event taking place under the condition that at instant t the packet was being transmitted, the condition that TR occurs is intrinsic in the defintion of $\mathrm{d}C$, whereas, according to the routing rule being considered here, $\mathrm{d}C$ does not depend on PC. We thus have:

$$P(\mathrm{d}C|PC,TR) = P(\mathrm{d}C) \qquad (5.5.32)$$

Let:

$$\gamma \equiv \frac{P(\mathrm{d}C)}{\mathrm{d}t} \; . \qquad (5.5.33)$$

Using this definition we can write equation (5.5.30) in the form

$$\lambda'(1) = \gamma P_\mathrm{D} \; . \qquad (5.5.34)$$

We previously gave the approximate method for the evaluation of probability P_D. The second parameter γ depends on the statistical properties of the packet length. When the length of the block has an exponential distribution,

$$\gamma = \bar{T}^{-1} \; . \qquad (5.5.35)$$

5.5.3 Approximate evaluation of the delay

In this section we will consider the average transit time of a packet routed according to the Δ-NIR rule. When the rule is fixed and memoryless, and has only a random component, the nodes through which the packet passes form a Markovian chain. Methods of finding the average time after which a Markovian chain, starting from a given state, will pass to another given state for the first time, are well-known, i.e. the so-called first passage time problem. We will give an approximate formula for the average passage time for the Δ-NIR rule with a deterministic component, using the general relationship between that time and the average number of hops, which we discussed in section 5.2.3.

We will assume that the packet carrying the working information with addresses consists on average of N_p bits and that the n.s.i. is not transmitted on the channels through which the packets transmitted. Thus the average duration of the packets is:

$$T = \frac{N_p}{C^1} \tag{5.5.36}$$

where C is the channel capacity and N_p is the number of bits the packet consists of.

The duty ratio ν of packets passing through a single channel can be obtained from formula (5.2.43). Thus:

$$\nu = \bar{H}\nu(0) \tag{5.5.37}$$

where $\bar{H}$ is the average number of hops, which we previously evaluated, and

$$\nu(0) = T\lambda(0) \tag{5.5.38}$$

is an auxiliary parameter which can be interpreted as the duty ratio of packets when channels leaving a given node are used only for transmission of packets delivered by the external source at that node.

By introducing the Kleinrock hypothesis we obtain from A.2.37 the average delay caused by the single channel:

$$\bar{\tau}_1 = T\frac{1}{1-\nu(0)\bar{H}} \ . \tag{5.5.39}$$

Because the packet makes an average of $\bar{H}$ hops, the average delay on the path from source to destination is

$$\tau = \bar{H}\tau_1 = \frac{\bar{H}}{1-\nu(0)\bar{H}} \ . \tag{5.5.40}$$

We will now consider the case when the channels are used for transmitting both working packets and n.s.i. Let T_{cy} be the cycle of delivery of network state information, and let N_ξ be the average number of bits making up that information. From the description of the Δ-NIR rule, it follows that $N_\xi \sum_{i=1}^{\Delta} L[N_i(w)]$ bits of updating information must be delivered along a single channel to node w. Transmission of this information requires a capacity of

$$C_\xi = \frac{N_\xi \sum_{i=1}^{\Delta} L[N_i(w)]}{T_{cy}} \ . \tag{5.5.41}$$

The capacity

$$C' = C - C_\xi \ . \tag{5.5.42}$$

remains for transmitting working packets. The parameter

$$\zeta_c \equiv 1 - \frac{C_\xi}{C} \ . \tag{5.5.43}$$

is the channel capacity utilisation factor. We can increase it by decreasing C_ξ From (5.5.41) it is evident that this can be achieved by either increasing T_{cy} or decreasing N_ξ. In both cases, the quality n.s.i. of deteriorates. This degrades the quality of the working packet transmission. In some cases this decrease will balance the gains due to the increase in the channel capacity C' available for working packets transmission. To obtain the packets delay we can use formula (5.5.40), but we have to substitute C' for C.

To illustrate the properties of the delay of packets forwarded according to Δ-NIR we again take the homogeneous network with 100 nodes, from each of which radiate J channels; Fig. 5.18(a) shows the dependence of the normalised delay τ' on the order of neighbourhood Δ for the Δ-NIR rule, on the assumption that the working channel is not loaded with n.s.i. transmission. Both fixed and flexible deterministic component routing rules are considered. Analogously, it can be seen from the graphs in Fig. 5.18(a) how increasing the deterministic part which in turn diminishes the random path shortens the delay. Figure. 5.18(b) shows some interesting graphs of the case when n.s.i. is sent along the same channels as the packets themselves. The occurence of a minimum can be explained as follows. If the critical neighbourhood order is small, we have little information about the state of the network, so the routing quality is low. If on the other hand Δ is too large, the n.s.i. occupies too great a part of the channel capacities, hence waiting time in buffers are extended, all of which again tends to reduce the quality of the routing rule.

REFERENCES

[5.1] Christofides, N., (1975), *Graph Theory: An Algorithmic Approach*, Academic Press, London.

[5.2] Frank. H., and Frisch, J., (1972), *Communication, Transmission and Transportation Networks*, Addison-Wesley, Reading, Mass.

[5.3] Domschke, W., (1972), *Kürzeste Wege in Graphen: Algorithmen, Verfahrensvergleiche*, Verlag Anton Hain, Meisenheim am Glan.

[5.4] Pierce, A. R., (1975), Bibliography on algorithm for shortest path, shortest spanning tree and related circuit routing problems 1956–1971, *Networks*, **5**, 129–149.

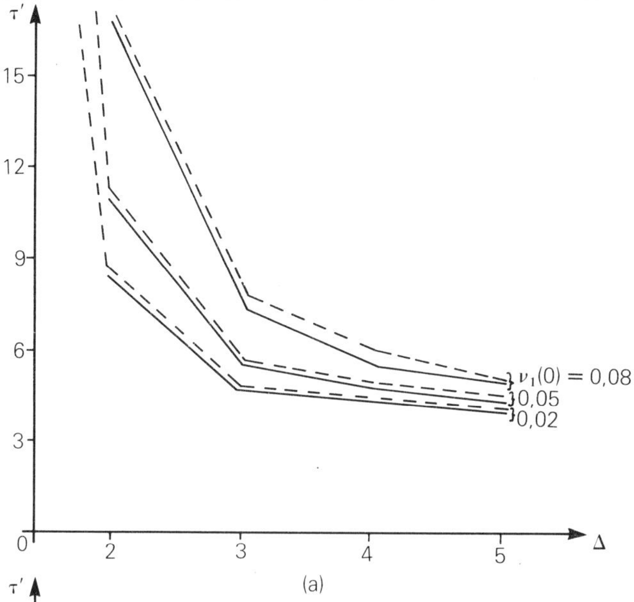

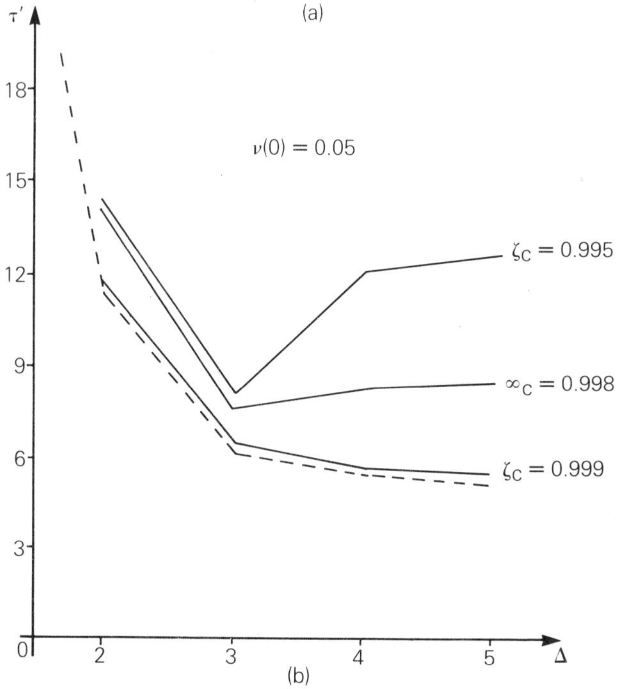

Fig. 5.18 – Dependence of the normalised delay τ' on the neighbourhood order Δ for Δ-NIR. The network contains $N = 100$ nodes, $J = 6$ channels leave each node; $\nu(0)$, normalised intensity of packets put into the network; ζ_c, channel capacity utilisation factor; broken lines, deterministic component, flexible rule: (a) Separate channels for n.s.i. transmission; (b) n.s.i. and working information transmitted through the same channels. Based on Konorski [5.14].

[5.5] Butrymenko, A. B., (1964), English translation, 3–28 (in Russian).

[5.6] Silk, D. J. (1969), Routing doctrines and their implementation in message switching networks, *Proc. IEE Eng.*, **116**, 1631–1638.

[5.7] De Mercado, J., and Teth, K., (1972), *The Synthesis of Computer Communication Networks*, Dept. of Communications of Government of Canada, Ottawa.

[5.8] Prosser, R. J., (1962), Routing procedures in communications networks, Part I: Random procedures, *IRE Trans. on Comm. Systems*, **CS-10**, 322–329; Part II: Directory procedures, *IRE Trans. on Comm. Systems*, **CS-10**, 329–335.

[5.9] Seidler, J., (1979), Relationships between the performance and organisation of a computer communication network, *System Science*, **5**, 33–48.

[5.10] Fultz, G., and Kleinrock, L., (1971), Adaptive routing techniques for store and forward computer communication network, in *Computer Networks, Infotech State of the Art Report 6*, Infotech, Maidenhead.

[5.11] Rudin, H., (1976), On routing and 'delta routing': A taxonomy and performance comparison of techniques for packet-switched networks, *IEEE Trans. of Comm.*, **COM-24**, 43–59.

[5.12] Kleinrock, L., and Kamoun, F., (1977), Hierarchical routing for large networks, Performance evaluation and optimisation, *Computer Networks*, **1**, 155–174.

[5.13] Seidler, J., and Konorski, J., (1979), Average length of packet route in a network with mixed deterministic random routing, *Bul. de L'Academie Polonaise des Sciences*, **XXVII**, No. 3, 1–8.

[5.14] Konorski, J., (1979), Average packet delay in a network with mixed deterministic–random routing, *Bull. Ac. Pol. Sci., Ser, Sc. Techn.*, **27**, 295–306.

6

Routing rules based on optimum flows

In the previous chapter we introduced fundamental concepts of packet routing. We showed how the problem of routing rule optimisation could be analysed also indicating that the systematic solution of such problems are very complicated. In this chapter, we will concentrate on the methods of determining 'good' routing rules which are suggested by the solution of optimisation problems corresponding to the models of information flow, and network states less accurate than the previously used model, taking into account individual packets. These less accurate models are based on statistical averages of flow intensities. The first, which we call the **time variant** model, is based on short time averages, the second, called **static**, is based on long-term averages. The individual packet, time variant and static models can be considered as a hierarchy of models of decreasing accuracy, since with a model of greater accuracy we can determine exactly models of lower accuracy but not vice versa. The basic idea of this chapter is to solve the optimisation problems corresponding to the less accurate models, mostly to the simplest static models and then to try to find individual packet routing rules yielding the optimum static flow. Since the passage from less to more accurate models is not unique, the last step is partially heuristic.

We first discuss the models mentioned more exactly and next we present methods for describing the set of flow intensities in the network, and formulate their fundamental properties. The third section studies the problem of finding the largest static flow intensities which can be sustained by the network. In the fourth section we will formulate the optimality conditions for the static flow intensities. In section 6.5 we present algorithms for finding the optimal flow intensities. In all these sections we systematically set out three approaches to network flow description and analysis viz. the channel-, path- and node-oriented approaches. They are essentially equivalent but some of them are more suitable for certain aspects of networks analysis. Also when we are looking for efficient routing rules, the channel- and path-orientated approaches seem to be better suited to centralised network control systems, while the node-oriented approach is better for decentralised network control.

Although obtaining closed solutions of the time varying flow optimisation problem seems to be pretty difficult the analysis of this model permits us to understand some important features of 'good' individual packet routing rules not suggested by the static model. In particular it gives insight into inherently non-stationary routing problems, such as the discharging of overloaded nodes, which cannot be tackled at all if we apply the static model. In the last section we discuss the general methodology for finding efficient routing rules using optimum flow intensities. As explained, the routing rule presents a much more detailed description of network operation than does the set of channel intensities. As the transformation from flow intensities to routing rules cannot be systematic, our considerations in this section will to a great extent be heuristic.

6.1 MODELS OF FLOWS AND NETWORK STATES

The most accurate model of the flow of information which we call the **individual packet model** is the sequence of packets, as shown in Fig. 1.2. Defining the corresponding model of the state of the network we introduce I disjoint classes of packets and we do not distinguish between packets belonging to the same class. Often we only take the source and destination of the packet as the class membership criterion. The individual packet model of network state at instant t is the set

$$l(t) = \{l(k;t), \quad k = 1, 2, \ldots, K\} \tag{6.1.1}$$

where K is number of channels.

$$l(k;t) = \{l_i(k;t) \quad i = 1, 2, \ldots, I\} \tag{6.1.2}$$

and $l_i(k;t)$ is the number of packets of ith class waiting at the input of kth channel. We call $l(k;t)$ **the state of the kth channel.** As explained in Appendix A.6, for some purposes we introduce a more accurate channel state description taking into account the sequencing of packets in the buffer at channel inputs, but in most cases we use the state $l(k,t)$ defined by (6.1.2).

The number of components of $l(t)$ is $K \times I$, hence it is large even for small networks, and the components $l(k,i;t)$ are time variable. The delivery of information about $l(t)$ to the place where routing decisions are taken would require an extremely elaborate and costly n.s.i. subsystem. One way to avoid this difficulty is only to use samples, or only to use the states of neighbouring nodes, as we described in the previous chapter. The other way is to introduce less accurate models of flow and network state. We do this by taking into account the fact that packets are blocks of bits which, like packets, are characterised by their class membership. Let us denote by $\bar{N}_i(k; < t, t + \Delta t)$ the average number of bits belonging to class i passing to channel output during the time interval $\langle t, t + \Delta t\rangle$. We call

$$F_i(k;t) = \lim_{\Delta t \to 0} \frac{\bar{N}_i(k;t,t+\Delta t)}{\Delta t} \tag{6.1.3}$$

the instantaneous intensity of i-class information flow through the kth channel.

The set

$$\mathbf{F}(t) = \{F_i(k;t),\quad i=1,2,\ldots,I,\quad k=1,\ldots,K\} \tag{6.1.4}$$

is called the **time variable** model of the average flow in the network. The corresponding model of the state of the network is the set

$$\mathbf{L}(t) \equiv \{\bar{L}_i(k;t);\quad i=1,\ldots,I,\quad k=1,\ldots,K\} \tag{6.1.5}$$

where

$$\bar{L}_i(k;t) \equiv \mathrm{E}\,\mathrm{L}_i(k;t) \tag{6.1.6}$$

is the average number of packets of ith class at the input of the kth node; $\mathrm{L}_i(k;t)$ is the random process representing the number of packets of instant t.

Although $L(t)$ has the same number of components as the state defined by (6.1.1), the rate of change of averages $\bar{L}_i(k;t)$ is usually much smaller than that of instantaneous values $l_i(k;t)$.

Finally let us observe the network for a long time period $\langle -T,T \rangle$. The static model of the average flow is the set

$$\mathbf{F} = \{F_i(k),\quad i=1,2,\ldots,I,\quad k=1,2,\ldots,K\} \tag{6.1.7}$$

where

$$F_i(k) \equiv \frac{1}{2T}\int_{-T}^{T} F_i(k,t)\,\mathrm{d}z \tag{6.1.8}$$

is the long-term average of ith class information intensity at kth channel. The corresponding model of network state would be set $\mathbf{L}$ of long time averages $\bar{L}_i(k)$ defined similarly to (6.1.8). Since they are constant, we usually do not take them into account.

To the three models of flow and network states correspond various rules for handling the flow. To the individual packet model correspond the rules for routing individual packets considered in the previous chapter. For average models the rules for dividing flow intensities apply. Again the rule corresponding to more accurate models determines the rules corresponding to the less accurate model, but not vice verse. The same can be stated about the criteria characterising these rules. The general idea behind the methods presented in this chapter is to solve the optimisation problems corresponding to the less accurate models and then to try to determine the corresponding routing rule for individual packets, for which we hope to induce the optimum average flow.

For the static model we can derive in closed form several results which give us important suggestion for the choice of good individual packet routing rules. In particular it suggests a modification to rule 5.3.14, which reduces its drawbacks. Therefore in the subsequent sections we will concentrate on the static model. Nevertheless, being a time-class model, it is inadequate from the point of view of features of routing rules related to inherently non-stationary situations. Therefore we will also consider some aspects of the time variable model.

6.2 FUNDAMENTAL PROPERTIES OF FLOWS

In this section we introduce the three fundamental methods for describing flows, namely: channel-, path- and node-orientated descriptions, and formulate the constraints which the flows must satisfy. We concentrate initially on time invariant flows.

6.2.1 Channel-oriented flow description

We shall assume that we are given:

A1 the topology of the network described by the graph $\{\mathcal{N}, \mathcal{K}\}$ where $\mathcal{N}$ is the set of nodes and $\mathcal{K}$ is the set of channels; we denote a directed channel joining nodes w, v by (w, v);

A2 the channel capacities; the capacity of channel (w, v) we denote by $C(w, v)$;

and that:

A3 the flow originates at a pole $s \in \mathcal{S}$ where $\mathcal{S} \subset \mathcal{N}$ is the set of source poles and it is directed to pole $r \in \mathcal{R}$ where $\mathcal{R} \subset \mathcal{N}$ is the set of destination poles; we denote† the intensity of this flow by X_{sr} and call it **external flow intensity**:

A4 no flow is lost in the network.

The set of pairs s, r form a set $\{\mathcal{S}, \mathcal{R}\}$ and the number of elements in the set is denoted by M. If $M = 1$ we have a **one commodity flow**; if $M \geqslant 2$ we have a **multicommodity flow**.

The intensity X_{sr} can be interpreted as the throughput for the commodity forwarded from pole s to pole r.

We assume next

A5 the packet classes introduced previously are identical to classes of packets generated at a given source and directed to a given destination.

† Here and later lower-case indices are used to denote parameters related to pairs of nodes which are not necessarily connected by a direct channel.

It should be noticed that the set $(\mathcal{S}, \mathcal{R})$ is the set of such pairs that $s \in \mathcal{S}$ is a source pole and $r \in \mathcal{R}$ is the destination pole to which flow is forwarded from s to r. Thus in general $(\mathcal{S}, \mathcal{R})$ is not the cartesian product $\mathcal{S} \times \mathcal{R}$.

In view of this assumption the number of classes $I = M$. To follow the general rule of denoting packets coming from s and directed to r by subscript s,r, in place of the previously used notation $F(i,k)$ for intensity of packets directed from s to r and passing through channel (w,v) we write now $F_{sr}(u,v)$ or equivalently $F_m(u,v)$.

We call the set

$$\mathbf{F}_{sr} \equiv \{F_{sr}(w,v);\ (w,v) \in \mathcal{K}\};$$

the **flow pattern from pole** s to pole r. The set of sets $\mathbf{F}_{sr}$ we denote

$$\mathbf{F} \equiv \{\mathbf{F}_{sr};\ s,r \in \{\mathcal{P},\mathcal{Q}\}\}$$

and we call it **total flow pattern**.

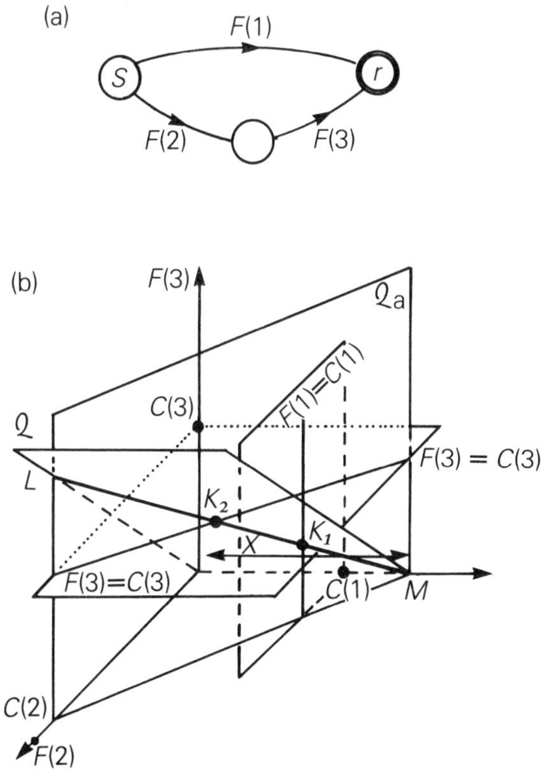

Fig. 6.1 – Geometrical interpretation of constraints $\mathcal{A}(\mathbf{X}), \mathcal{B}, \mathcal{D}$. (a) The network considered; (b) structure of sets: $\mathcal{F}_{\mathbf{AB}}$, line LM; $\mathcal{F}^{+}_{\mathbf{AB}}$, interval $\langle K_1, K_2 \rangle$.

We now formulate three relationships which hold for the components $F_{sr}(w,v)$ of a flow pattern satisfying assumptions A1–A4. We use $N_{in}(\cdot)$ and $N_{out}(\cdot)$ as defined in Chapter 5. See Fig. 6.1. The sum:

$$F_{sr}^{in}(w) \equiv \sum_{u \in N_{in}(w)} F_{sr}(u,w) \tag{6.2.1a}$$

is the flow intensity from s to r going into mode w intermediate between s and r, while

$$F_{sr}^{out}(w) \equiv \sum_{v \in N_{out}(w)} F_{sr}(w,v) \tag{6.2.1b}$$

is the flow intensity leaving node w. If w is neither the source nor the destination then:

$$F_{sr}^{in}(w) = F_{sr}^{out}(w) \tag{6.2.2}$$

For the source pole p:

$$F_{sr}^{out}(s) - F_{sr}^{in}(s) = X_{sr} \tag{6.2.3a}$$

Similarly, for the destination pole:

$$F_{sr}^{in}(r) - F_{sr}^{out}(r) = X_{sr} \tag{6.2.3b}$$

We can write formulae (6.1.3) in the form:

$$\sum_{u \in N_{in}(w)} F_{sr}(u,w) - \sum_{v \in N_{out}(w)} F(u,v) = \begin{cases} 0 & \text{if } w \neq s,\ w \neq r \\ X_{sr} & \text{if } w = s \\ -X_{sr} & \text{if } w = r \end{cases} \tag{6.2.4}$$

We call the above equations the **flow conservation** or **flow preservation constraints.** We denote this set of constraints by $A(R_{sr})$. The set of sets $A(X_{sr})\,(s,r) \in (S,R)$ we denote $A(\mathbf{X})$ where $\mathbf{X} \equiv \{X_{sr};\,(s,r) \in (S,R)\}$.

The flow intensity in channel (w,v) is:

$$F(w,v) = \sum_{(s,r) \in (S,R)} F_{sr}(w,v) \tag{6.2.5}$$

The intensity cannot exceed the channel capacity, hence:

$$F(w,v) \leqslant C(w,v) \tag{6.2.6}$$

We call this set of inequalities for all $(w,v) \in K$ the **capacity constraints** and denote them by $\mathcal{B}(\mathbf{C})$ where $\mathbf{C} \equiv \{C(w,v);\ w,v \in \mathcal{K}\}$. Finally, the intensities must be non-negative, thus for $(w,v) \in \mathcal{K}$,

$$F_{sr}(w,v) \geqslant 0 \ . \tag{6.2.7}$$

This set of inequalities is denoted by $\mathcal{F}^+$ the **non-negativity constraints.** The flow pattern F satisfying the constraints $\mathcal{A}(\mathbf{X})$, $\mathcal{B}(\mathbf{C})$ and $\mathcal{F}^+$ is called the **admissible flow pattern.**

We will now investigate admissible flow patterns. To simplify the considerations we assume that in our network there is only a single source-destination pair s,r thus the sets $\mathcal{S}$ and $\mathcal{R}$ consist of single elements, and we will therefore write $F(w,v)$ instead of $F_{sr}(w,v)$;

We number the channels by an index k, hence we denote the capacity of the kth channel by $C(k)$ and the flow intensity in the kth channel by $F(k)$. Thus

$$\mathbf{F} = \{F(1), F(2), \ldots, F(K)\}$$

If we interpret the flow pattern as a vector in K-dimensional space $\mathcal{E}_K$ then the channel flow intensities $F(k)$ can be interpreted as components of this vector. The set of vectors satisfying an equation of type (6.2.5) is a hyperplane in the space $\mathcal{E}_K$. The set of vectors satisfying all the equations (6.2.5), and thus the set of constraints $\mathcal{A}(X_{sr})$, is a cross-section of such hyperplanes. This cross-section is a linear subspace of $\mathcal{E}_K$ which we denote by $\mathcal{F}_A$. The set of vectors satisfying the constraint $F(k) \leqslant C(k)$ is the half-space of $\mathcal{E}_K$ under the hyperplane $F(k) = C(k)$. Thus the set $\mathcal{F}_B$ of vectors satisfying the set of constraints $\mathcal{B}(\mathbf{C})$ is the octahedron bounded by the hyperplanes $F(k) = C(k)$, $k = 1, 2, \ldots, K$. Similarly, the set of vectors satisfying the set of constraints $\mathcal{F}^+$ is the octahedron bounded by the hyperplanes $F(k) = 0$, $k = 1, 2, \ldots, K$. We denote it also $\mathcal{F}^+$ the set $\mathcal{F}_{adm}$ of vectors representing the admissible flow patterns (i.e. satisfying the constraints $\mathcal{A}(X)$, $\mathcal{B}(\mathbf{C})$, $\mathcal{F}^+$ is the product:

$$\mathcal{F}_{adm} = \mathcal{F}_A \cap \mathcal{F}_B \cap \mathcal{F}^+ \ . \tag{6.2.8}$$

As the faces of the sets, $\mathcal{F}_B$, $\mathcal{F}^+$ are hyperplanes, and the set $\mathcal{F}_A$ is a cross-section of hyperplanes, we come to the conclusion that:

> the set $\mathcal{F}_{adm}$ of points corresponding to the vectors representing the admissible flow patterns is a polyhedron whose faces are hyperplanes. (6.2.9)

To illustrate this important conclusion, let us consider the following example.

Example 6.2.1

We take the network shown in Fig. 6.1(a). The constraints $\mathcal{A}$ for this network take the form:

$$F(1)+F(2) = X \tag{6.2.10a}$$
$$F(2)-F(3) = 0 \tag{6.2.10b}$$
$$F(1)+F(3) = X\ . \tag{6.2.10c}$$

We restrict ourselves to the linearly independent equations (6.1.10a, b). Equation (6.2.10a) corresponds to the plane $\mathcal{Q}_a$, and equation (6.2.10b) corresponds to the plane $\mathcal{Q}_b$ shown in Fig. 6.1(b). Thus the subspace $\mathcal{F}_A$ is a straight line LM (shown by a thick line).

The set $\mathcal{F}_{AB}$ of vectors satisfying constraints $A(R)$ and $B(C)$ is a part of the subspace $\mathcal{F}_A$ cut out by the planes $F(1) = 0$, $F(2) = 0$, $F(3) = 0$. We see that Fig. 6.1(b) that this is the interval $\langle K,M \rangle$. Lastly, we obtain the set $\mathcal{F}_{adm}$ as the part of this section cut off by the plane $F(k) = C(k)$. This is the interval $\langle K_1,K_2 \rangle$. Let us return to general considerations. If $\mathbf{F}_1 \in \mathcal{F}_{adm}$ and $\mathbf{F}_2 \in \mathcal{F}_{adm}$ are two admissible flow patterns then it is evident that for an α such that $0 \leqslant \alpha \leqslant 1$ the numbers

$$F(k) \equiv \alpha F_1(k) + (1-\alpha)\,F_2(k) \tag{6.2.11}$$

satisfy the constraints $\mathcal{A}(X_{sr})$, $\mathcal{B}(C)$ and $\mathcal{F}^+$. We can formulate this conclusion as the following theorem:

If $\mathbf{F}_1$ and $\mathbf{F}_2$ are two flow patterns satisfying the constraints $\mathcal{A}(X_{sr})$, $\mathcal{B}(C)$ and $\mathcal{F}^+$ then the flow pattern $\mathbf{F} \equiv F(k); k = 1, \ldots, K$ with $F(k)$ given by (6.2.11) is another admissible flow pattern (6.2.12)

Geometrically we can interpret equation (6.2.11) as a condition that a point with coordinates $F(k)$ lies inside the interval with ends $F_1(k)$ and $F_2(k)$. Thus using (6.2.9) and (6.2.12) we can state that

the polyhedron representing the set of admissible flow patterns satisfying constraints $\mathcal{A}(X_{sr})$, $\mathcal{B}(C)$ and $\mathcal{F}^+$ is a convex one. (6.2.13)

Geometrical interpretations can also be used when we have a multicommodity flow and (6.2.12) and (6.2.13) still held; we merely have to replace the constraints $\mathcal{A}(X)$ by the set $\mathcal{A}(\mathbf{X})$ of constraints $\mathcal{A}(X_{sr}), sr \in (\mathcal{S}, \mathcal{R})$.

So far we have assumed that packets coming from different sources but going to the same destination pole are treated differently. However, it is often the case that:

A5 after reaching node w the transmission of packets depends only on the destination pole.

This is known as **memoryless flow**. For memoryless flow, it is convenient to introduce the flow intensity F_{wr}^{in} which flow from the network into node w and is forwarded to node r, and the flow intensity F_{wr}^{out} forwarded from node w to node r. For $w \neq s$, $w \neq r$ we have:

$$F_{wr}^{\text{in}} = \sum_{s \in S, s \neq w} F_{sr}^{\text{in}}(w) \tag{6.2.14a}$$

$$F_{wr}^{\text{out}} = \sum_{s \in S, s \neq w} F_{sr}^{\text{out}}(w) \tag{6.2.14b}$$

where $F_{sr}^{\text{in}}(w)$ and $F_{sr}^{\text{out}}(w)$ are given by (6.2.1). For memoryless flow, the flow preservation constraints (6.2.5) can be written in the homogeneous form

$$F_{wr}^{\text{out}} = X_{wr} + F_{wr}^{\text{in}} \tag{6.2.15}$$

Returning to the two index notation for the channel, we denote by

$$F_r(w, v) \equiv \sum_{s \in S} F_{sr}(w, v) \tag{6.2.16}$$

the total flow intensity passing through channel w, v to destination node q. Obviously, for the node output and input flow intensities we have:

$$F_{wr}^{\text{out}} = \sum_{v \in N_{\text{out}}(w)} F_r(w, v) \tag{6.2.17a}$$

and

$$F_{wr}^{(\text{in})} = \sum_{v \in N_{\text{in}}(w)} F_r(u, w) \tag{6.2.17b}$$

The flow preservation constraint (6.2.15) can thus be written in the form

$$\sum_{v \in N_{\text{out}}(w)} F_r(w, v) = X_r + \sum_{u \in N_{\text{in}}(w)} F_r(u, w) \tag{6.2.18a}$$

for $u \neq r$, and for $u = r$

$$\sum_{u \in N_{\text{in}}(r)} F_r(u, r) - \sum_{w \in N_{\text{out}}(r)} F_r(r, w) = X_r \tag{6.2.18b}$$

where

$$X_r \equiv \sum_{s \in S, s \neq r} X_{sr} \tag{6.2.19}$$

is the total flow intensity to node s from all sources. We can frequently assume that:

A6 Packets directed to pole q, having reached that pole, do not leave it.

This is called **non-return flow**. Assumption A6 may be written:

$$F_r(r, w) = 0 \tag{6.2.20}$$

for $w \in \mathcal{N}_{out}(r)$.

6.2.2 Path-orientated flow description

We now consider path-oriented flow description. Let $\mathcal{P}_{sr}(j), j = 1, 2, \ldots, J(p,q)$ be the paths from pole s to r. Also let the coefficients

$$a_{sr}(j; w, v) = \begin{cases} 1 \text{ if the channel } (w,v) \in \mathcal{P}_{sr}(j) \\ 0 \text{ if the channels } (w,v) \notin \mathcal{P}_{sr}(j) \end{cases} \tag{6.2.21}$$

These are **channel-path incidence coefficients.** Let $G_{sr}(j)$ be the branchless flow intensity along the jth path. The set of all $G_{sr}(j)$ we denote

$$\mathbf{G}_{sr} \equiv \{G_{sr}(j),\ j = 1, 2, \ldots, J_{sr}\}$$

and we call it the path flow pattern.

The intensity of flow from s to r through channel w, v is:

$$F_{sr}(w, v) = \sum_{j=1}^{J_{sr}} a_{sr}(j; w, v)\, G_{sr}(j) \tag{6.2.22}$$

Therefore, knowing the path flow pattern $\mathbf{G}_{sr}$ we can calculate the channel flow pattern $\mathbf{F}_{sr}$. The number of paths J_{sr} is usually much greater than the number of channels K, so if we know the intensity in the channels, the intensity in the paths is not normally stated explicitly. However, we can describe the flow using the set of intensities:

$$\mathbf{G} \equiv \{G_{sr};\ (s,r) \in (\mathcal{S}, \mathcal{R})\}$$

We shall call this set the total path flow pattern.

We now deal with the constraints on the total path flow pattern $\mathbf{G}$. Notice that if the node is not a pole, the constraints for flow preservation are automatically fulfilled. Thus the equivalent of the constraints $\mathcal{A}(X_{sr})$ for path intensities is

$$\sum_{j=1}^{J_{sr}} G_{sr}(j) = X_{sr} \ . \tag{6.2.23}$$

The equivalent of the non-negativity constraints $\mathcal{D}$ are

$$G_{sr}(j) \geqslant 0 \tag{6.2.24}$$

for $j = 1,2, \ldots, J$. Lastly, the constraints $\mathcal{B}(\mathbf{C})$ take the form

$$\sum_{(s,r)\in(S,R)} \sum_{j=1}^{J_{sr}} a_{sr}(j;w,r)\, G_{sr}(j) \leqslant C(w,v) \tag{6.2.25}$$

We shall denote 6.2.23–6.2.25 constraints $\mathcal{A}(X_{sr})$, $\mathcal{B}(\mathbf{C})$ and $\mathcal{F}^+$ respectively. Comparing these constraints with their equivalents $\mathcal{A}(X_{sr})$, $\mathcal{B}(\mathbf{C})$ and $\mathcal{F}^+$ we can see that the path oriented description yields a simple continuity constraint than the channel-orientated description but capacity constraints are much more complicated.

6.2.3 Node-orientated flow description

Our final method of description is **node-orientated**. We assume that the flow is memoryless (A5, see p. 268) and that it is a non-return flow (A6, see p. 270). The basis of the node-orientated description of flow is the relative flow through channel (w,v) forwarded to pole q defined by the equation:

$$f_r(w,v) \equiv \frac{F_r(w,v)}{F_{wr}} \tag{6.2.26}$$

where $F_q(w,v)$ is defined by (6.2.16) and where

$$F_{wr} \equiv \sum_{v\in \mathcal{N}_{\text{out}}(w)} F_r(w,v) \tag{6.2.27}$$

From (6.2.26) and (6.2.27) if follows that

$$\sum_{v\in \mathcal{N}_{\text{out}}(w)} f_r(w,v) = 1 \;. \tag{6.2.28}$$

Using (6.2.26), we can write the flow preservation constraint (6.2.18a) in the form

$$F_{wr} = X_{wr} + \sum_{u\in \mathcal{N}_{\text{out}}(w)} f_r(u,w)\, F_{ur} \tag{6.2.29}$$

for $w \neq r$. Notice that, if we know that intensities of the external input X_{wr} and the intensities $F_r(w,v)$, we can calculate the relative intensity $f_r(w,v)$ from equations (6.2.26) and (6.2.27). The inverse problem is to find the intensities F_{ur} when the set of external flow intensities X_{wr} and the set of relative intensities

$f_r(w,v)$ are known. This task is equivalent to the solution of the set of equations (6.2.29) for $w = 1, 2, \ldots, N$, $w \neq q$, where N is the number of nodes in the network, in which F_{wr}, $w \neq r$, is unknown, and R_{wr} and $f_r(w,v)$ are given.

Example 6.2.2

To illustrate the nature of such a set of equations, let us take network shown in Fig. 6.2. The relative intensity $f_r(w,v)$ is indicated by the side of the arcs (which represent channels). Taking successive nodes, we get the set of equations:

$$F_{14} = 1 + 0.1F_{34}$$
$$F_{24} = 0.1F_{14}$$
$$F_{34} = 0.2F_{14} + 0.3F_{24}\ .$$

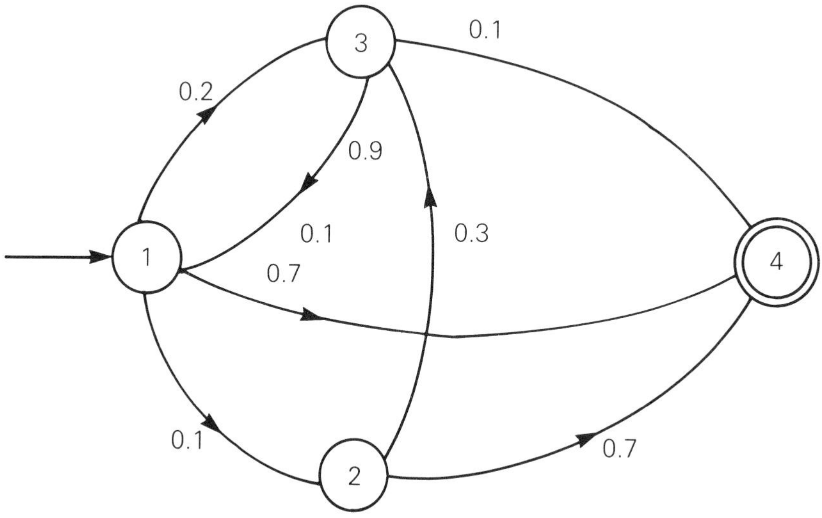

Fig. 6.2 – Illustration to the definition of the product $V \times \bar{V}$.

It is easy to check that the solution of this set is the set $F_{14} = 1.023$, $F_{24} = 0.0102$, $F_{34} = 0.235$.†

Let us go back to general considerations. Let $\mathbf{F}_r \equiv (F_{wr},\ w = 1, 2, \ldots, N)$, $\mathbf{X}_r \equiv (X_{wr},\ w = 1, 2, \ldots, N)$ be column vectors with elements F_{wr} and X_{wr}; let $\mathfrak{f}'_q$ be a matrix of elements

$$f'_r(u,w) \equiv \begin{cases} f(u,w) & \text{if} \quad u \in N_{\text{in}}(w) \\ 0 & \text{if} \quad u \notin N_{\text{in}}(w) \end{cases} . \qquad (6.2.30)$$

† In Fig. 6.2 we denote the destination pole by a double circle; this notation will be used in subsequent figures.

The set of equations (6.1.29) can be written in the form

$$\mathbf{F}_r \equiv \mathbf{X}_r + \mathbf{f}_r'\mathbf{F}_r \tag{6.2.31}$$

or, in the equivalent form,

$$(1 - \mathbf{f}_r')\mathbf{F}_r = \mathbf{X}_r \tag{6.2.32}$$

A solution exists if there is an inverse for the matrix $(1 - \mathbf{f}_q')$. In trying to show the existence of a solution to the set of equations, we introduce the concept of an **unclogged** path for flow forwarded to pole q. The path $P_{u0,u_L} = P(u_0, u_1, \ldots, u_L)$ is unclogged if $f_r(u_{\mu-1}, u_\mu) > 0$ for $\mu = 1, 2, \ldots, L$.

In Gallagher's paper [6.1] the following theorem has been proved:

> If the set of numbers $\{f_r(u,w); q,w,v = 1,2,\ldots,N\}$ fulfils the conditions: (a) $f_q'(u,w) \geqslant 0$; (b) the normalisation condition (6.2.26); (c) for each pair of nodes, u,w, $u \neq w$, there is an unclogged path for flow forwarded to pole q, then the set of equations (6.2.29) for fixed sets $\mathbf{R}_r$ and $\mathbf{f}_r'$ has a unique solution. (6.2.33)

Condition (c) is important for if an external flow is fed into a node for which there is no unclogged path, the set of equations (6.2.29) has no solution. In Example 6.1.2, condition (c) is fulfilled from theorem (6.2.33), so knowing $\mathbf{R}_r'$ and $\mathbf{f}_r'$, we can uniquely determine the set $\{F_{wr}; (w,r) = 1,2,\ldots,N\}$.

6.2.4 Time-varying flows

We previously considered the least accurate, static, timeless model. We now deal with the time-varying model described in section 6.1. Using similar notation as for the static model we denote by:

- $X_{sr}(t)$ the flow intensity fed into source pole s from outside the network and forwarded to destination pole r; at time t, defined similarly to (6.1.2)
- $F_r(w,v;t)$ be the flow intensity in channel (w,v) going to pole r, at time t;
- $L_r(w,v;t)$ be the number of packets in the buffer and transmitter at the channel input (w,v) destined for pole r at time t;
- $L_r(w;t)$ be the number of packets at node w, destined for pole r, at time t.

We assume that $t \in \langle t_a, t_b \rangle$, where $\langle t_a, t_b \rangle$ is the observation interval.

We have

$$L_r(w;t) = \sum_{v \in N_{\text{out}}(w)} L_r(w,v;t) \tag{6.2.34}$$

As the flow is time-varying the following equation corresponds to the flow preservation constraint (6.2.15)

$$\frac{\mathrm{d}L_r(w;t)}{\mathrm{d}t} = X_{wr}(t) + \sum_{u \in N_{\text{in}}(w)} F_r(u,w;t) - \sum_{v \in N_{\text{out}}(w)} F_r(w,v;t) \tag{6.2.35}$$

Usually the initial values $L_r(w, t_a)$ at the beginning of the observation interval are given. In order to write down the continuity constraint for the destination pole q, we assume that the removal is instantaneous, then $L_r(r;t) = 0$ and (6.2.25) simplifies suitably. These constraints we denote $\mathcal{A}[\mathbf{X}(\cdot)]$ where $\mathbf{X}(\cdot) \equiv \{X_{sr}(t);\ s,r = 1, 2, \ldots, R, s \neq r, t \in \langle t_a, t_b \rangle\}$. If the number of waiting packets and intensities are independent of the time then we have **stationary flow**. For stationary flow, the flow preservation constraint (6.2.35) becomes equation (6.2.18).

For time varying flows, the capacity constraints take the form

$$\sum_r F_r(u,w;t) \leqslant C(u,w) \tag{6.2.36}$$

whereas the non-negativity constraints take the form

$$F_r(u,w;t) \geqslant 0 \tag{6.2.37}$$

We call these constraints $\mathcal{B}(\mathbf{C})$ and $\mathcal{F}^+$ respectively as before.

Although constraints (6.2.35)–(6.2.37) correspond to the constraints for the static flow model there are differences between these cases. Most important is that considering the stationary flow we do not need to consider the average numbers of packets at nodes at all, since they are constant and do not enter in the relationships between flow components. In the case of time-varying flows we have to consider both the flow intensities $F_r(u,w;t)$ and the numbers of packets $L_r(w;t)$. The latter depend on: (a) statistical properties of the input flow, (b) the packet processing discipline. Only in special cases we can expect that the average number of packets at a node $L_r(w,t)$ will depend only on the intensity $F_r^{(\text{in})}(w,\tau)$, $\tau \leqslant t$, since in general $L_q(w,t)$ may depend on statistical properties of the input flow other than the average $F_r(w,v;t)$. If we can assume that all input flows have the same character, for example they are Poisson (in general, time-varying) sequences of packets, we may assume that $L_r(w,t)$ depends only $F_r^{(\text{in})}(w,\tau)$, $\tau \leqslant t$, the dependence being of the type

$$\frac{\mathrm{d}L_r(w,t)}{\mathrm{d}t} = \Psi[\mathbf{L}_r(t),\ F_r^{(\text{in})}(w,t)] \ \ldots \tag{6.2.38}$$

where $\Psi(\cdot)$ is a non-linear function of the arguments indicated and $\mathbf{L}_r(t) \equiv \{L_r(w,t);\ w \in N\}$. Analysis of a single buffer with FIFO discipline into which a time varying flow is put in supports such a hypothesis (see [6.2]). If in the time interval considered the flow intensities and the numbers of packets change slightly it is convenient to introduce the deviations

$$\delta L_r(t,w) \equiv L_r(w,t) - \tilde{L}_r(w)$$

$$\delta L_r(t,w) \equiv F_r(w,t) - \tilde{F}_r(w) \qquad (6.2.39)$$

$$\delta \dot{L}_r(t,w) \equiv \frac{\mathrm{d}L_r(w,t)}{\mathrm{d}t} - \frac{\widetilde{\mathrm{d}L_r(w)}}{\mathrm{d}t}$$

where the symbols with the tildes indicates long period time independent averages.

Let us denote by $\delta\,\mathbf{L}_r(t)$, $\delta\,\dot{L}_r(t)$ and $\delta\,\mathbf{F}(t)$ the sets of the corresponding deviations for all nodes $w \in N$. Assuming that (6.2.38) holds and linearing (6.2.39) we obtain

$$\delta \dot{L}(t) = \mathbf{A}\delta\mathbf{L}(t) + \mathbf{B}\delta F(t) + \mathbf{C}\delta\mathbf{X}(t) \ldots \qquad (6.2.40)$$

where $\mathbf{A}$, $\mathbf{B}$, $\mathbf{C}$ are matrices of coefficients determined by networks topology, the functions $\Psi(\cdot)$ and $\delta X(t)$ is the set of deviations $X_r(w,t) - \tilde{X}_r$ where $X_r(w,t)$ are the intensities of packets put in at node w by the external source. The differential equation is exactly the same as equations describing multidimensional linear dynamic systems. We can therefore directly use the results of the well developed theory of these systems. Examples of such an approach can be found in Filipiak [6.3].

Let us notice that, given a routing rule, knowing, the intensities $F_r(w,t)$ for $\tau < t$ and the initial numbers $L_r(w,t_a)$ we can determine the number of packets $L_r(w,t)$ at nodes. We can, however, consider $F_r(w,t)$ and $L_r(w,t)$ as independent functions, except we require that they satisfy the continuity constraints (6.2.35), and the non-negativity constraints (6.2.37). The mechanical analogue would be a network of non-permeable but flexible containers corresponding to the buffer and storages. The dynamic properties of the outflow of the containers are not specified; we require only that the continuity constraint is satisfied. To the assumption that the routing rule is deterministic corresponds the assumption that the dynamic properties of the outflow are determinisitic. The analysis and optimisation of such a system would be of course different to that of a container network in which the dynamic properties of the outflow from the containers is not specified in advance. Analysing the network in which flows are time varying we have thus two types of problems. The first is when we consider both flow intensities and numbers of packets as variable and introduce only continuity and non-negativity constraints, the other, when we introduce relationships between $L_r(w,t)$ and $F_r(w,t)$, as for example (6.2.38), and we consider only one of the sets of these functions as variable.

6.3 THE MAXIMUM POSSIBLE THROUGHPUT

We showed in the previous section that it is possible to find an admissible flow pattern for a network only if the intensities X_{sr} of the input flows are not large. In this section we consider what 'not too large' means. We start with single commodity flow and then we pass on to multicommodity flow.†

For single commodity flow the formal approach would be to consider X_{sr} as variable and to look for the solution of OP $\mathbf{F}_{sr}, X_{sr} | A, B(\mathbf{C}), F^{+}$. Since all the constraints are linear, this is simply a linear programming problem. We present an alternative approach which is related to the primary flow pattern problem. We first define the capacity of a cut of the network relative to a pair of nodes and, hence the capacity C_{sr} of the network between the pair of nodes s, r. Next we give an algorithm for finding an admissible flow pattern yielding $X_{sr} = C_{sr}$. If X_{sr}, C_{sr}, it is not possible to find an admissible flow, thus C_{sr} is an accessible upper limit for the single commodity throughput. The latter statement is the essence of the famous Ford–Fulkerson theorem.

6.3.1 Cut of the network

To define the network capacity C we have to introduce several new concepts. N denotes a set of nodes in the network $\{N, K\}$ where K is the set of channels and we consider a subset of the nodes $V \subset N$. We denote by $\bar{V}$ the complement of this set:

$$\bar{V} \equiv N - V \ . \tag{6.3.1}$$

The Cartesian product $V \times \bar{V}$ is a set of ordered pairs $(u, v)'$, such that $u \in V, v \in \bar{V}$. These pairs can be regarded as potential channels, not necessarily existing in the network considered. In order to distinguish such potential channels from actual ones, we add a prime (') to the notation, as above. By way of example, Fig. 6.3 shows a set of potential channels corresponding to the product $V \times \bar{V}$. The product

$$C(V) \equiv K \cap (V \times \bar{V}) \tag{6.3.2}$$

is a set of real channels between nodes in V and $\bar{V}$. Removing channels in the set $C(V)$ from the network breaks all the connections going out of V to the rest of the network. For this reason $C(V)$ is called **the cut of the network** generated by the set V. The channels directed from set V to $\bar{V}$ make up the set

$$C(\bar{V}) \equiv K \cap (\bar{V} \times V) \ . \tag{6.3.3}$$

We call the sum of the sets

$$C_t(V) \equiv C(V) \cup C(\bar{V}) \tag{6.3.4}$$

† The problem can be equivalently formulated as the problem of evaluating network capacity. The latter is a classical one which is considered in most monographs on graphs and networks, see Christofides [5.1], Frank and Frisch [5.2] De Mercado [5.7].

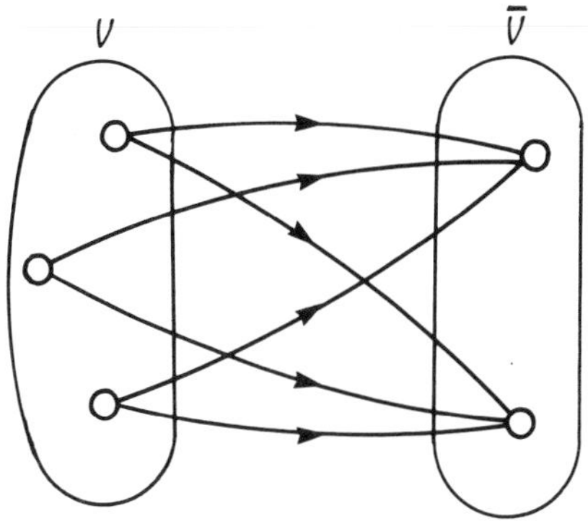

Fig. 6.3 – Network assumed in section 6.3.1.

the **total cut of the network.** Removing $C_t(V)$ from the network isolates V from the rest of the network.

6.3.2 Minimum cut capacity

Let us now assume that each of the channels (u,v) has capacity $C(u,v)$. The sum of the capacities of the channels making up the cut is called the **cut capacity**, and we will denote it by $C[C(V)]$. So:

$$C[C(V)] = \sum_{(w,v)\in(CV)} C(w,v) \;. \tag{6.3.5}$$

Consider a pair of nodes p,q and the set V^* such that $s \in V$, $r \in \bar{V}^*$. Obviously, removing the channels in $C(V)$ separates node p from q. We shall be interested in the cut $C(V^*)$ such that $C[C(V^*)]$ is minimum. We shall call the cut $C(V^*)$ the **minimum cut** separating nodes s and r, and denote its capacity by C_{sr}. This definition of minimum cut capacity can be written in the form

$$C_{sr} = \min_{v\in U_{sr}} C[C(V)] \tag{6.3.6}$$

where U_{sr} is the set of sets V such that $p \in V$ and $q \in \bar{V}$.

Example 6.3.1

We take the network shown in Fig. 6.4. As can be seen, the first line of Table 6.3.1 gives the elements of the set U_{sr}. The second line of the table gives the capacities of the cuts. We see that the minimum cut is $C(V_7) = \{(p,1),(2,1),(2,4)\}$ having the capacity 12. Thus for the network considered $C = 12$.

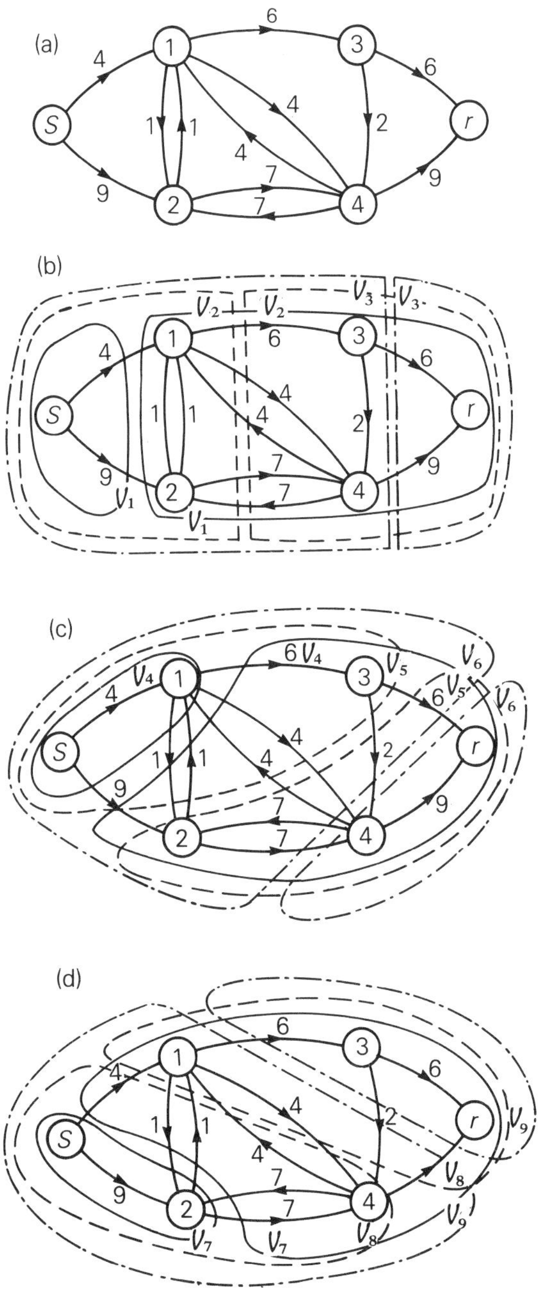

Fig. 6.4 – Examples of network cuts: (a) network, (b), (c), (d) the sets V_μ.

Table 6.3.1

μ	1	2	3	4	5	6	7	8	9
V_μ	p	$p,1,2$	$p,1,2,4$	$p,1$	$p,1,3$	$p,1,2,3$	$p,2$	$p,2,4$	$p,1,2,4$
$C[C(V_\mu)]$	13	17	15	20	22	19	12	18	15

μ	10	11	12	13	14	15	16
V_μ	$p,3$	$p,4$	$p,1,4$	$p,2,3$	$p,3,4$	$p,1,3,4$	$p,2,3,4$
$C[C(V_\mu)]$	21	33	32	20	29	32	24

6.3.3 Throughput maximisation for single commodity flow

So far we have introduced only graph-theoretical concepts. We will now show that the concept of minimum cut capacity plays a crucial role in solving the throughput maximisation problem: OP $\mathbf{F}, X_{sr} | \mathcal{A}, \mathcal{B}(\mathbf{C}), \mathcal{F}^+$, where $\mathbf{C} \equiv \{C(w,v), (w,v) \in \mathcal{K}\}$ is the set of channel capacities. This follows from the well-known Ford–Fulkerson theorem:

> The maximum throughput $(X_{sr})_0$ is equal to the minimum cut capacity C_{sr} separating pole s from r. (6.3.7)

Thus we may call the minimum cut capacity C_{sr} the **network capacity from pole** s **to** r; or more briefly the s–r **network capacity.** We shall now give an algorithm which shows that $R_{pq} = C_{pq}$, and also permits us to determine the flow pattern $\mathcal{F}^{(0)}$ which is the solution to OP $\mathcal{F}_{sr}, X_{sr} | \mathcal{A}, \mathcal{B}(\mathbf{C}), \mathcal{F}^+$. The algorithm is iterative, and proceeds by deducing potential flow increments through each node. First each node receives a label which gives: (1) the magnitude of the potential increase of flow intensity through the node from pole s to r and at the same time traverse the given node (denoted by δF), (2) the number of the node at which this increase may be obtained, (3) information as to whether this increase is achieved by increasing flow on existing paths, or changing paths. The node numbers given in the second part of the label indicate the path along which an additional flow can be sent.

The algorithm consists of the interleaved application of two procedures: (1) labelling, and (2) flow augmentation. We perform both operations moving from the source pole towards the destination pole. We proceed until all potential increments are zero.

Algorithm 6.3.1

Labelling procedure.

Step 1

We start by taking the throughput and intensities of all flows to be equal to zero. We give the source pole p the label $(\delta F, s) = [\alpha, s, a]$, and we call it a **labelled** but **unscanned node**.

Step n

Lab. 1 For each labelled but unscanned node, e.g. node w_n, we consider channels entering and leaving that node. There are two possibilities:

(a) There is a channel (w_n, v_n) where v_n is unlabelled, whose capacity is not being utilised to the full;

(b) There is a flow from an unlabelled node u_n entering node w_n which may be transferred to another channel so as to direct it to the destination pole.

Lab. 2.1 If in place of situation (a) we give the node v_n the label $[\delta F(v_n), w_n, a]$ where

$$\delta F(v_n) = \min [\delta F(w_n), C(w_n, v_n) - F_{sr}(w_n, v_n)] \tag{6.3.8}$$

$F_{pq}(w_n, v_n)$ is the flow intensity along the channel (w_n, v_n) assumed at the start of labelling. We then call node v_n a labelled but unscanned node.

Lab. 2.2 If we have situation (b), we give node u_n the label $[\delta F(u_n), w_n, b]$ where

$$\delta F(u_n) = \min [F(u_n, w_n), \delta F(w_n)] \tag{6.3.9}$$

Node u_n is called a labelled, unscanned node.

Lab. 2.3 After having given labels to all the neighbours of node w_n, it becomes a scanned node, which we indicate by underlining the label w_n.

Lab. 3 Process Lab. 2 is applied until:

Lab. 3.1 we give the destination pole a label, or

Lab. 3.2 there are no more nodes to be labelled.

In the case of Lab. 3.2 we end the algorithm, but in case of Lab. 3.1 we move on to the process of flow augmentation described below.

The justification for step 2.1 is as follows: $\delta F(w_n)$ is the potential flow increment which we can bring to node w_n; we try to bring the whole of this increment to node v_n, but we are limited by the capacity of channel (w_n, v_n).

Therefore if $\delta F(w_n) > C(w_n, v_n) - F_{sr}(w_n - v_n)$, we can only bring to node v_n an additional flow of $C(w_n, v_n) - F_{sr}(w_n - v_n)$. Fig. 6.5 illustrates this.

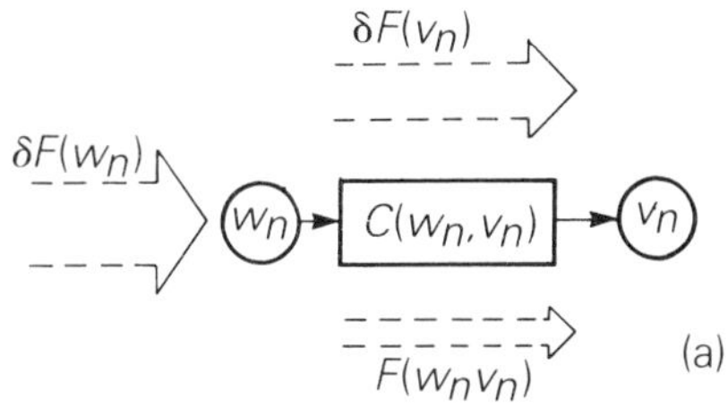

Fig. 6.5 – Illustration of the situation occurring during labelling. When the channel capacity is not fully used. The width of the arrow indicating the flow is proportional to its intensity; on the same scale, the thickness of the channel is proportional to its capacity.

Step 2.2 is justified because: if a flow $F_{sr}(w_n, u_n)$ reaches node w_n, we attempt to compensate part of this flow in channel (w_n, u_n) by sending the excess we have in node w_n towards node u_n. Since, however, we can only have a flow from node u_n to node w_n going through channel (u_n, w_n), this excess cannot be greater than the flow intensity $F_{sr}(u_n, v_n)$. The appropriate flow transfer corresponds to the formal subtraction of the flow intensity between w_n and v_n from the flow intensity between v_n and w_n. As an example, let us examine the situation illustrated in Fig. 6.6(a), which uses the same symbol convention as Fig. 6.5. We assume that $\delta F(w_n) < F(u, w_n)$, so $\delta F(w_n)$ is equal to the intensity of part of the flow coming into node w_n, along channel k''''. If, as shown in Fig. 6.6(b), we direct a flow of intensity $\delta F(w_n)$ into k'''' we obtain an excess flow of intensity $\delta F(w_n)$ at node u_n.

The situation mentioned in 3.2 occurs at nodes which have completely saturated channels leaving them. A set of channels leaving all such nodes forms a minimum capacity cut interrupting all paths from s to r. The cut capacity is the sum of the capacities of all these channels.

If the situation described in 3.1 occurs we move on to the process of flow augmentation, which operates as follows: on moving backwards from the destination pole to the source pole along the path indicated by the labels, we increase the flow by the increment which can be brought to the destination pole.

Flow augmentation procedure

Aug. 1.1 If the destination pole r received the label $(\delta F(r), w_\mu, a)$, we augment the flow intensity entering through channel (w_μ, r) by $\delta F(r)$.

Aug. 1.2 If pole q received the label $(\delta F(r), w_\mu, b)$, the flow intensity leaving through channel (r, w_μ) is diminished by $\delta F(r)$.

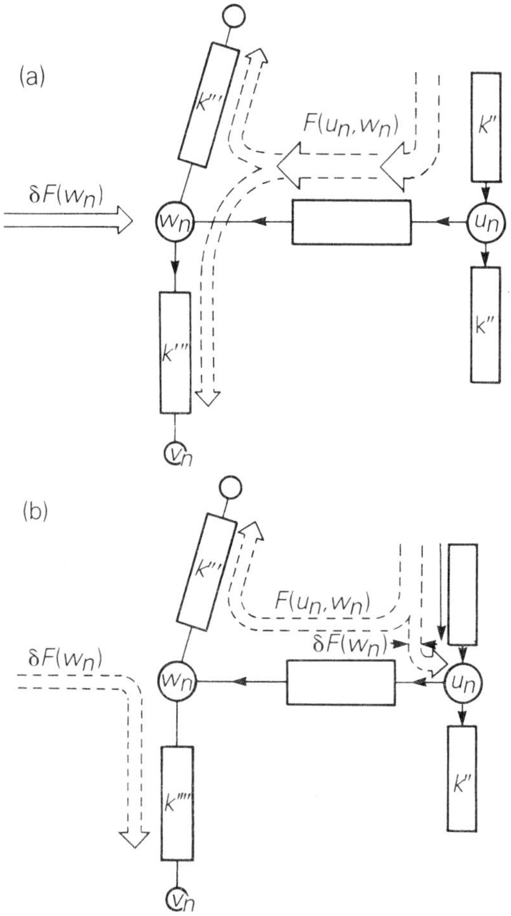

Fig. 6.6 – Illustration to situation (b) occurring during labelling when a flow approaches a node. (a) State from the previous step, (b) state after flow change (notational convention as on Fig. 6.5).

Aug. 2.1 If, using the augmentation procedure, we have arrived at node w_n which has the label $(\delta F(w), w_1, a)$, we augment the flow intensity in channel (w_1, w_n) by $\delta F(q)$ and say that the flow augmentation procedure has reached node w_1.

Aug. 2.2 If, using the augmentation procedure, we have arrived at node w_n' which has the label $(\delta F(w_n'), w_1', b)$, we diminish the flow leaving the node in channel (w_1', w_n') by $\delta F(r)$, and we say the flow augmentation procedure has reached node w_n'.

Aug. 2.3 If the procedure reaches the source pole we remove all labels and restart the labelling procedure from the beginning for the new flow pattern.

There now follows an example of the application of Algorithm 6.2.1.

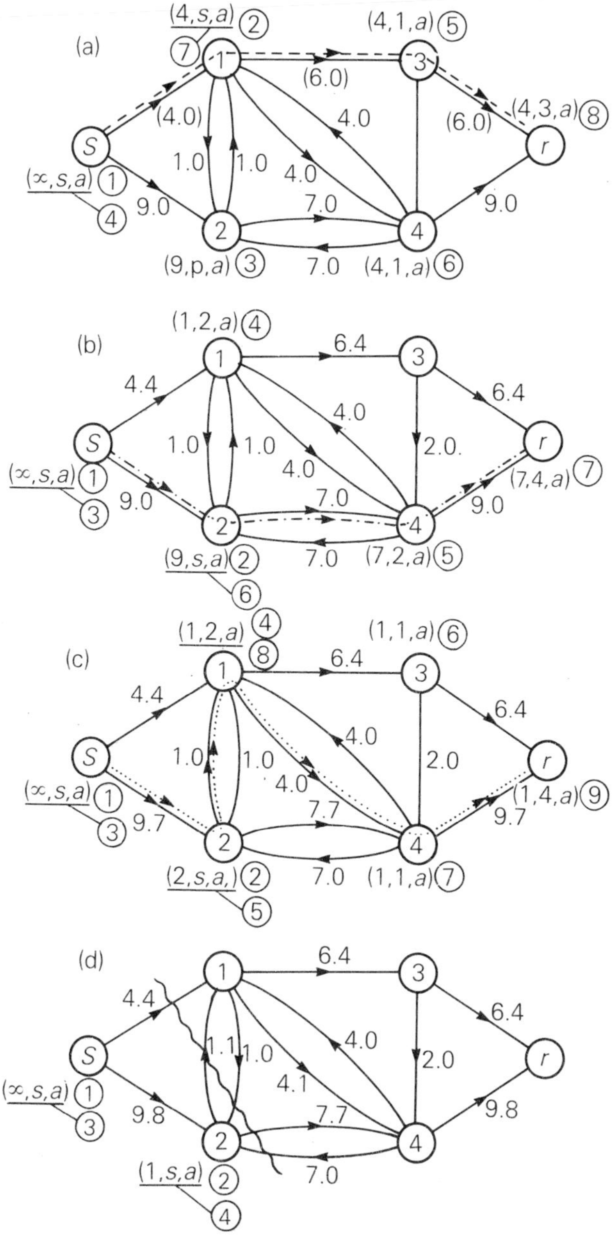

Fig. 6.7 – Network assumed in example 6.3.2. (a) Network, (b), (c), (d) successive stages in the labelling and flow augmentation procedures. The first figure next to the arrow denotes the capacity, the second, the flow. Numbers in circles give the order of introducing labels; broken and dotten lines indicate paths along which an additional flow can be sent; the wavy line in (d) traces the minimal cut.

Example 6.3.2

Consider the network shown in Fig. 6.7. The numbers next to the channel are the capacity and the flow intensity respectively. We assume the starting flow to be zero, and use principle (a) during labelling. The order in which labels are given and nodes are accepted is shown. Lastly, a broken line indicates the path along which a flow of intensity 4 can be taken from s to r. The network and flow intensity after applying the flow augmentation procedure is shown in Fig. 6.7(b). Labels given during the second stage of labelling, according to rule 3.1, are shown in this figure. Node 3 is not given a label since the destination pole r has clearly already received one. As in Fig. 6.7(a), a dot-dash line traces the path along which it would be possible to send an additional flow of intensity 7. The third stage of labelling is shown in Fig. 6.7(c). According to the accepted order of labelling, node 1 receives a label of type 'a'. A dotted line indicates the path along which one could send an additional flow of intensity 1. Finally, in Fig. 6.7(d) we are given the flow intensity obtained after completion of the flow augmentation procedure. This figure also shows the result of labelling for the fourth time. Having got to node 2, the procedure breaks off, because the second channel leaving node p and the channels (2,4) and (2,1) leaving node 2 are saturated, whereas channels (1,2) and (4,2) arriving at node 2 are not used. Hence the intensity flow of $8 + 4 = 12$ obtained is the maximum flow which can be sent in this network from pole s to r. The cut separating the nodes p, q which has minimum capacity is the set of channels leaving the nodes to which labels were given, i.e. channels $(p,1)$, $(2,1)$, $(2,4)$. Since this network is the same as the one assumed in Example 6.3.1 and shown in Fig. 6.4, it follows from the Ford–Fulkerson theorem that the minimum cut found here is the same as the minimum cut found in Example 6.3.1 by means of searching all the separating cuts.

6.3.4 Throughput maximisation for multicommodity flow

So far we have considered throughput maximisation for single commodity flow. If we have multicommodity flow, but a central controller which permits only a single source–destination pair to use the whole network at a given instant, we can directly apply the conclusions derived for single commodity flow. The problem then arises of analysing the relationships between the set of network capacities C_{sr}, for all $(s,r) \in (S,R)$. Such an analysis is called **multiterminal** analysis and there is a vast literature pertaining to it, see for example, Frank and Frisch [5.2]. In computer communication networks, this situation is atypical. We will therefore not go into the details of multiterminal analysis here.

In most computer communication networks we have several source–destination pairs which use the network simultaneously; we have therefore to take into account the set of $M \geqslant 2$ external flow intensities X_{sr}, $(s,r) \in (S,R)$. Thus the situation is the same as the optimisation of a system described multiple quality indeces, which we considered in section 1.5.2. As we explained there, three approaches are possible. In describing them briefly, we will apply the abbreviated notation, numbering the source–destination pair (s,r) by a single index $m, m = 1,2,\ldots,M$, and so writing the single index m instead of the double index sr, e.g. writing X_m for X_{sr}, C_m for C_{sr} etc.

The first approach in formulating throughput optimisation for a multi-commodity flow is to introduce a synthetic index for the quality of the set $\mathbf{X} = \{X_1, X_2, \ldots, X_M\}$ throughputs, for example taking:

$$Q_{\text{synt}} = \sum_{m=1}^{M} \alpha_m X_m \qquad (6.3.10)$$

where α_m are weighting coefficients. If we take $\alpha_m = m, m = 1, 2, \ldots, M$, we obtain the quality index

$$X = \sum_{m=1}^{M} X_m \; . \qquad (6.3.11)$$

Thus the sum of all external flow intensities entering the network can be considered as the special case of the synthetic index defined by (6.3.10). The optimisation problem is to find an admissible flow pattern with the largest possible synthetic index, i.e. OP $\mathbf{F}, Q_{\text{synt}} | \mathcal{A}, \mathcal{B}(\mathbf{C}), \mathcal{D}$. Let F_0 be the solution of OP F, $\mathrm{X} | \mathcal{A}, \mathcal{B}(C), \mathcal{D}$ and let X_0 be the corresponding maximum value of the sum of external flow intensities. The condition which the set of external flow intensities must satisfy in order that the total flow pattern is feasible is:

$$\sum_{m=1}^{M} X_m \leqslant X_0 \; . \qquad (6.3.12)$$

Obviously, this condition is not sufficient because the optimum flow pattern F_0 determines not only X_0 but also all the external flow intensities, which we denote by X_{m0}, $m = 1, 2, \ldots, M$. If for some reason we get $X_m \neq X_{m0}$, it may not be possible to find a total flow pattern having prescribed $\hat{X}_m$s and satisfying the constraints $\mathcal{A}$, $\mathcal{B}(\mathbf{C})$, $\mathcal{D}$. Examples of such a case can be found in Frank and Frisch [5.2].

The second approach to throughput maximisation for multicommodity flow is to take one of the external flows, e.g. X_1 as the criterion, and to require that the other external flow intensities are constant: $X_m = \hat{X}_m, m = 2, 3, \ldots, M$. The corresponding optimisation problem is OP $\mathbf{F}$, $X_1 | \mathcal{A}$, $\mathcal{B}(\mathbf{C})$, $\mathcal{D}$, $X_m = \hat{X}_m$, $m = 2,3,\ldots,M$. Finally, the third approach would be polyoptimisation.

The three approaches mentioned are generalisations of single commodity external flow intensity maximisation considered in the preceding two sections. It is questionable whether there exists a direct relationship between the maximum flow intensities R_0 or R_{m0} which correspond to the solutions of OP$\mathbf{F}$, $X|\mathcal{A}, \mathcal{B}(\mathbf{C}), \mathcal{D}$ or OP$\mathbf{F}_1 R_1|\mathcal{A}, \mathcal{B}(\mathbf{C}), \mathcal{D}$, $R_m = \hat{R}_m$, $m = 2, 3, \ldots, M$, and a suitable generalisation of the network capacity C_{sr} for multicommodity flows. Let us introduce a generalisation for the case where we have several source–destination pairs s_m, r_m, $m = 1, 2, \ldots, M$, $m \geqslant 2$. The generalisation of the definition (6.1.7) of the network capacity between the source s and destination r, is the following definition of network capacity $C_{s_1, s_2, \ldots, s_M; r_1, r_2, \ldots, r_M}$ between the set of source poles $s_1, \ldots, s_M$ and destination poles $r_1, \ldots, r_M$:

$$C_{s_1, s_2, \ldots, s_M; r_1, r_2, \ldots, r_M} = \min_{\mathcal{U}} \sum_{(w,v) \in \mathcal{U}} C(w, v) \tag{6.3.13}$$

where $\mathcal{U}$ is a set of sets of channels such that removing these channels separates each source pole from its associated destination pole. From definition (6.3.13), it follows that

$$R_{\Sigma 0} \leqslant C_{s_1, s_2, \ldots, s_M; r_1, r_2, \ldots, r_M} \; . \tag{6.3.14}$$

Unlike single commodity flow, it is possible for some networks that the strict inequality holds. We will now give such an example.

Example 6.3.3

Consider the network shown in Fig. 6.8 with all channel capacities equal to 2. It can be easily checked that for this network

$$C_{s_1, s_2, s_3; r_1, r_2, r_3} = 8$$

Figs. 6.8(b), (c), (d) show three possible flows of three components, and gives the characteristics of these flows.

The maximum total intensity for the network can be estimated. Notice that each of the paths $\mathcal{P}_{s_m, r_m}$, $m = 1, 2, 3$, must consist of at least three channels, so the threefold total flow intensity cannot exceed the total throughput of all the channels. As there are 10 such channels, and each has a throughput of 2, we have

$$X \leqslant \frac{20}{3} < 8$$

thus the total flow intensity X cannot be equal to the network capacity.

An obstacle in the way of using the network capacity even only as an upper limit are the difficulties in calculating this parameter, since for networks comprising a large number of branches, finding all the sets of branches separating the poles is very time-consuming. It is simpler to find the optimum flow and the corresponding X_0 by using linear programming without introducing the network capacity concept.

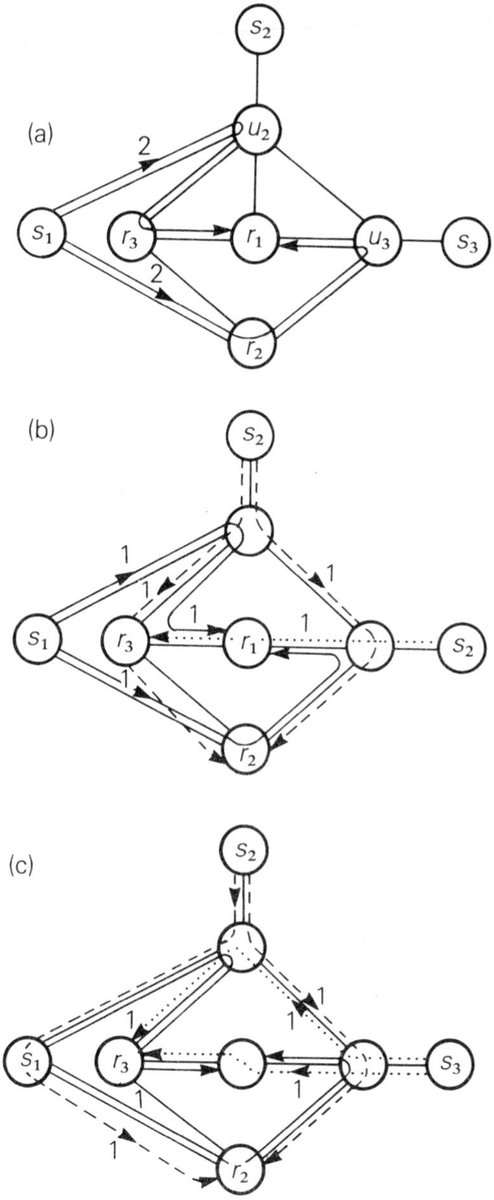

Fig. 6.8 – Example of mutual blocking of flows of different components, (a), (b), (c) flow patterns $\mathbf{F}_A$, $\mathbf{F}_B$, $\mathbf{F}_C$ described in Table 6.4.1. Flows in channels satisfy conditions (6.4.4), symmetrical channels, each channel has a capacity of $C(v, w) = 2$; paths are denoted by thin lines, the number by the arrow on the path indicates the flow intensity along the path; continuous thin lines, component s_1,r_1; broken lines, s_2,r_2; dotted lines, s_3,r_3.

Table 6.3.2

Flow path	Path	Component	Intensity
$\mathbf{F}_a$	s_1, u_2, r_3, r_1	1	2
	s_1, r_2, u_3, r_1	1	2
$\mathbf{F}_b$	s_1, u_2, r_3, r_1	1	1
	s_1, r_2, u_3, r_1	1	1
	s_2, u_2, r_3, r_2	2	1
	s_2, u_2, u_3, r_2	2	1
	s_3, u_3, r_1, r_3	3	1
$\mathbf{F}_c$	s_1, u_2, r_3, r_1	1	1
	s_1, r_2, u_2, r_1	1	1
	s_2, u_2, s_1, r_2	2	1
	s_2, u_2, u_3, r_2	2	1
	s_3, u_3, r_1, r_3	3	1
	s_3, u_3, u_2, r_3	3	1

So far, we have considered the properties of the maximum sum of external flow intensities R_Σ corresponding to the solution of OP $\mathbf{F}, X \mid \mathcal{A}, \mathcal{B}(\mathbf{C}), \mathcal{F}^+$. It can be shown, that there is also no direct relationship between the maximum throughput R_{M0} which corresponds to the solution of OP $\mathbf{F}, X_1 \mid \mathcal{A}, \mathcal{B}(\mathbf{C}), \mathcal{F}^+, X_m = \hat{X}_m$, $m = 2, 3, \ldots, M$ and a parameter defined like C_{sr} or $C_{s_1, s_2, \ldots, s_M; r_1, r_2, \ldots, r_M}$. For these reasons, we shall here not go into details of the properties of network capacity for multicommodity flows. This is justified, the more so because the procedures for finding the optimum flow which we are going to describe later reject sets of external flow intensities R which are 'too large'. An analysis of the degree of channel capacity usage by an optimum flows does indicate which R_m can be augmented, and thus permits sets of 'large' X_m's to be found.

6.4 FUNDAMENTAL PROPERTIES OF THE OPTIMUM SINGLE-COMMODITY FLOW

We are considering here the average flow optimisation problem as a step towards finding efficient rules for individual packet routing. We may draw conclusions about efficient packet routing rules from considerations on the optimum flow pattern if there is a relationship between the indices of routing rules and flow pattern quality. Let us first consider the special case when both indices coincide. As we have shown in section 2.2.1 under quite general assumptions, the fundamental index of routing rule quality is the weighted delay given by the formula:

$$\tau = A_1 \sum_{k=1}^{K} \left[\frac{1}{C(k) - F(k)} + A_2(k) \right] F(k) \qquad (6.4.1)$$

where

$$F(k) = \sum_{s,r \in (S,R)} F_{sr}(k)$$

is the total flow intensity in the kth channel, $F_{sr}(k)$ is the intensity of flow forwarded from s to r and A_1 and $A_2(k) = T_{\text{pr}}(k)$ propagation time. In formula (6.4.1) and subsequently we use single index channel numbering introduced on page 181.

From (6.4.1) we see that the average delay depends only on the flow pattern $\mathbf{F}' = \{F(k), k = 1, 2, \ldots, K\}$. This flow pattern is distinct from the total flow pattern $\mathbf{F} = \{F_{sr}(k);\ s,r = 1, 2, \ldots, N,\ k = 1, 2, \ldots, K\}$ which we considered previously. In cases when confusion arises we will call $\mathbf{F}'$ the **reduced** flow pattern and $\mathbf{F}$ the **complete** flow pattern. Obviously the reduced flow pattern can be deduced from the complete, and therefore Q can be considered as a quality index for the complete flow pattern. In cases when (6.4.1) is valid for the delay of packets routed by a given routing rule, the parameter τ can serve as the quality index both of the routing rule and the flow pattern resulting from applying that rule.

The average flow pattern is a less detailed description of the passage of a packet than the routing rule, thus we can derive the first from the second but not always vice versa. Therefore, when defining the parameters characterising flow pattern, we may have to operate on the primary parameters characterising the routing rule, using a suitably chosen dependence-removing operation.

It is essential that the parameter characterising the average flow pattern corresponds to the primary parameter chracterising the individual packet routing rule. We require that the flow quality becomes very poor when one or more channels become saturated. If $Q(\mathbf{F})$ is the parameter characterising the quality of the flow, we can formulate the above requirement in the form:

$$\text{if for a channel } F(k) \to C(k) \text{ then } Q(\mathbf{F}) \to \infty \qquad (6.4.2)$$

An example of a parameter satisfying this requirement is the parameter $\bar{\tau}$ given by (6.4.1). It is evident that if the throughput $X_{sr} = C_{sr}$, at least some channels are saturated. Therefore to guarantee that $Q(\mathbf{F})$ remains finite, we will assume in this section that

$$X_{sr} < C_{sr} \quad . \tag{6.4.3}$$

In this section we consider the conditions necessary to optimise $Q(\mathbf{F})$ while achieving a given throughput R_{sr}. To simplify the terminology we first consider one commodity flow, but all the procedures which we will present here are directly applicable for multicommodity flows. We simplify the notation by omitting everywhere the subscripts s, r, writing for example, X for X_{sr}, $\mathbf{F}$ for $\mathbf{F}_{sr}$ etc. The existence and properties of optimum flow depend on the properties of the quality index $Q(\mathbf{F})$. We assume here that

A1 The quality index $Q(\mathbf{F})$ depends only on the total channel flow intensities $F(k)$ and it has property (6 4.2).

A2 The function $Q(\mathbf{F})$ is differentiable in respect to all $F(k)$, and the derivatives are contiguous.

The optimisation problem which we now deal with can be written as OP $\mathbf{F}, Q \mid \mathcal{A}(X), \mathcal{B}(\mathbf{C})\, \mathcal{F}^+$. On the assumption that the quality index $\mathcal{A}(X)$ has property (6.4.2) the problem becomes simpler. It can be seen that if there is a solution to the optimisation problem OP $\mathbf{F}, Q \mid \mathcal{A}(X), \mathcal{B}(\mathbf{C}), \mathcal{F}^+$, then among the flow patterns minimising the function $Q(\mathbf{F})$, under conditions $\mathcal{A}(R), \mathcal{D}$, there is a flow pattern coresponding to the optimum solution under constraints $\mathcal{A}(X), \mathcal{B}(\mathbf{C}), \mathcal{F}^+$. This is so, because at the set boundary $\mathcal{F}_{\mathrm{adm}}$, which is limited by the planes corresponding to the constraints $F(k) = C(k)$, the criterial function if infinite, therefore the minimum cannot lie there, i.e. the criterial function satisfying (6.4.2) plays the role of a penalty function with respect to the constraints $\mathcal{B}(\mathbf{C})$. Therefore instead of OP $\mathbf{F}, Q \mid \mathcal{A}(X), \mathcal{B}(\mathbf{C}), \mathcal{F}^+$ we may consider the simpler OP $F, Q \mid \mathcal{A}(X), \mathcal{F}^+$. We shall give two derivations of the conditions which must be satisfied by the solution to this problem. The first derivation corresponds to the channel-oriented flow description, the second to the path-oriented description. Each of these proofs leads to different iterative algorithms for finding the optimum flow, which we shall give later.

6.4.1 Derivation of the fundamental property of the optimum flow based on the channel-orientated flow description

If we take into account only constraints $\mathcal{A}(X)$ and $\mathcal{F}^+$, then the conclusion of theorem (6.2.12) holds true. If we introduce a set of vectors satisfying these conditions, which we denote by $\mathcal{F}_A^+$, we can state that $\mathcal{F}_A^+$ is a convex polyhedron. The derivation of the necessary conditions for the optimum flow pattern, which we give here, is based on the conclusion. We consider two flow patterns, $\mathbf{F}, \mathbf{V} \in \mathcal{F}_A^+$, and the infinitesimally small parameter $\delta\alpha > 0$. The flow pattern

$$\mathbf{F}_\delta \equiv (1 - \delta\alpha)\, \mathbf{F} + \delta\alpha \mathbf{V} \tag{6.4.4}$$

may be called the infinitesimally small deviation of flow pattern **F**. According to the above modification of theorem (6.2.12), $\mathbf{F}'_\delta \in \mathbf{F}^+_A$. Let us denote by:

$$q(k,\mathbf{F}) = \frac{\partial Q}{\partial [F(k)]}_F \tag{6.4.5}$$

the partial derivative; its existence and continuity follow from A2. The increment of the criterial function corresponding to the infinitesimally small deviation flow pattern amounts to:

$$\delta Q(\mathbf{F}) = \sum_{k=1}^{K} q(k,\mathbf{F})[V(k)-F(k)]\delta Q \ . \tag{6.4.6}$$

A necessary condition for the flow pattern $\mathbf{F}_0$ to be optimal in respect of criterial function Q under constraints $A(R)(\mathbf{D})$ is that it should be a stationary point, i.e. that the increment δQ with each infinitesimally small deviation is non-negative. The condition

$$\delta Q(F_0) \geqslant 0 \tag{6.4.7}$$

must therefore be satisfied. Substituting (6.4.6) in (6.4.7) we obtain:

$$\sum_{k=1}^{K} q(k,\mathbf{F}_0)V(k) \geqslant \sum_{k=1}^{K} q(k,\mathbf{F}_0)F_0(k) \tag{6.4.8}$$

for all $\mathbf{V} \in F^+_A$. Assuming that the minimum is attainable, we can write the dependence (6.4.8) as the equation:

$$\min_{\mathbf{V}\in F_A} \sum_{k=1}^{K} q(k,\mathbf{F}_0)V(k) = \sum_{k=1}^{K} q(k,\mathbf{F}_0)F_0(k) \tag{6.4.9}$$

We denote by $P(j)$, $j = 1, 2, \ldots, J$, all paths leading from pole s to pole r and by U the unbranching flow of unit intensity attainable along path $P(j)$, i.e. $U_j(k) = 1$ for $k \in P(j)$ and $U_j(k) = 0$ for $k \notin P(j)$. Using equation (6.2.24) we can represent the flow pattern **V** in the form

$$\mathbf{V} = X\sum_{j=1}^{J} \alpha_j \mathbf{U}_j \tag{6.4.10}$$

where

$$\alpha_j \equiv \frac{G(j)}{X} \tag{6.4.11}$$

and $G(j)$ is the intensity along the path $P(j)$; obviously, α_j can be interpreted as the relative intensity. Constraints $A'(X)$ (formula (6.2.25)) and the non-negativity constraints $\mathcal{F}^+$ take the form:

$$\sum_{j=1}^{J} \alpha_j = 1 \tag{6.4.12}$$

$$\alpha_j \geqslant 0 \ . \tag{6.4.13}$$

If we introduce the incidence coefficients $a_{pq}(j,k)$ as defined by formula (6.2.23)[†] we can rewrite formula (6.4.10) as the set of equations:

$$V(k) = \sum_{j=1}^{J} \alpha_j a(j,k) X \tag{6.4.14}$$

$k = 1, 2, \ldots, K$

Substituting this equation in (6.4.8) we get:

$$\sum_{k=1}^{K} q(k, \mathbf{F}_0) V(k) = \sum_{k=1}^{K} q(k, \mathbf{F}_0) \sum_{j=1}^{J} \alpha_j a(j,k) X =$$

$$= X \sum_{j=1}^{J} \alpha_j \sum_{k=1}^{K} a(j,k) q(k, \mathbf{F}_0) = X \sum_{j=1}^{J} \alpha_j q[P(j), \mathbf{F}_0] \tag{6.4.15}$$

where

$$q(P, \mathbf{F}) \equiv \sum_{k \in P} q(k, \mathbf{F}) \tag{6.4.16}$$

whereby we sum over the channels which make up part of the path $P(j)$. The index $\mathbf{F}$ indicates that the derivatives depend on the point for which they are evaluated. In cases where there is no doubt about that, we shall omit index $\mathbf{F}$.

Since the partial derivative $q(k, \mathbf{F})$ can be interpreted as the rate of change of the criterial function with intensity changes in the kth channel, the function $q[P(j), \mathbf{F}_0]$ can be interpreted as the rate of change of the criterial function with change of intensity of the branchless flow along the path $P(j)$. It is convenient to interpret the coefficient $q(k, \mathbf{F}_0)$ as the channel length; $q[P(j), \mathbf{F}_0]$ can then be interpreted as the length of paths $P(j)$.

We assume the paths $P(j)$ are arranged in order of increasing length, i.e.

$$q[P(1), \mathbf{F}_0] \leqslant q[P(2), \mathbf{F}_0] \leqslant \ldots \leqslant q[P(J), \mathbf{F}_0] \tag{6.4.17}$$

† With the modification taking into account the fact that in formula (6.4.14) we used double index channel numbering, while here we are using-single index numbering.

Let I denote the number of shortest paths, i.e. paths which have the same length but are shorter than the other paths, thus:

$$q[\mathcal{P}(1),\mathbf{F}_0] = q[\mathcal{P}(2),\mathbf{F}_0] = q[\mathcal{P}(I),\mathbf{F}_0] \qquad (6.4.18a)$$

$$q[\mathcal{P}(I),\mathbf{F}_0] < q[\mathcal{P}(I+1),\mathbf{F}_0] \leqslant q[\mathcal{P}(I+2),\mathbf{F}_0] \leqslant \ldots \leqslant Q[\mathcal{P}(J,\mathbf{F}_0] \qquad (6.4.18b)$$

Let $\mathcal{H}(I)$ be the set of paths $\mathcal{P}(1), \ldots, \mathcal{P}(I)$; we call set $\mathcal{H}(I)$ the **set of shortest paths.** Using (6.4.15), we can rewrite formula (6.3.8) in the form:

$$\min \sum_{j=1}^{J} \alpha_j(\mathbf{V})\, Q[\mathcal{P}(j),\mathbf{F}_0] = \sum_{k=1}^{K} q(k,\mathbf{F}_0)F_0(k) \qquad (6.4.19)$$

in which we indicate the dependence, resulting from (6.4.14) of the coefficient α_j on the flow pattern $\mathbf{V}$. From formula (6.4.18), it follows directly that we obtain the minimum of the left-hand side of (6.4.19) by choosing any number $I' \leqslant I$ paths from the set $\mathcal{H}(I)$ and taking $\alpha_j > 0$ for these paths, while taking $\alpha_j = 0$ for all other paths. So we come to the conclusion that the optimum flow pattern must possess the following property:

The optimum flow pattern can be represented as the superposition of branchless flows along a set of shortest paths when taking the length to be $q(\mathcal{P},\mathbf{F}_0)$. (6.4.20)

A fundamental difficulty using this property for optimising flow effectively is that, except when the criterial function is a linear function of intensities $F(k)$, the path length, as defined by (6.4.16), depends on the assumed flow pattern, which defines the point at which we calculate the partial derivatives. Since we determine the optimal flow pattern $\mathbf{F}_0$ in this way, it is necessary to use iterative algorithms, which we shall consider in the next section.

Our reasoning so far has been concerned with the optimum under constraints $\mathcal{A}(\mathbf{X})$, $\mathcal{F}^+$. We concluded that if the criterial function fulfils condition (6.4.2), the optimum flow also possesses the property (6.4.20) under constraints $\mathcal{A}(\mathbf{X})$, $\mathcal{B}(\mathbf{C})$, $\mathcal{F}^+$. In this case it is essential that condition (6.4.3) is fulfilled, if it is not, and the occurrence of a minimum at the boundary of the set $\mathcal{F}_{adm}$ corresponding to the planes $F(k) = C(k)$, became possible, the shortest paths could not be utilised because of saturation of their constituent channels. The conclusion (6.3.20) would then be incorrect.

6.4.2 Derivation of the fundamental property of optimum flow based on the path-orientated flow description

The derivation of property (6.4.20) of optimum flow was based on the channel-orientated flow description.

The previously introduced definition of flow pattern deviation was formulated in such a way that constraints $\mathcal{A}(\mathbf{X})$, $\mathcal{F}^+$ were automatically fulfilled. We shall now show, that if we employ the path-orientated flow description we have a much simpler constraint $\mathcal{A}(\mathbf{X})$ (formula (6.2.25)). We can derive the fundamental property (6.4.20) almost directly by applying the method of the Lagrange multipliers. As in the previous section we will consider only single commodity flow therefore we will omit indices s,r of source and destination poles. Let us consider the path flow pattern

$$G \equiv \{G(j),\ j = 1, 2, \ldots, J\}$$

introduced on page 270. By formulae (6.2.27) we can express the components of channel flow pattern $\mathbf{F} \equiv \{F(w, v);\ w, v = 1, 2, \ldots, N\}$ as linear functions of the components of the path flow pattern. We can express the quality index $Q(\mathbf{F})$ as a function of the path flow $\mathbf{G}$; denote $Q(\mathbf{G})$. We shall consider here the optimisation problem OP $\mathbf{G}, Q \mid \mathcal{A}'(\mathbf{X}), \mathcal{F}^+$ where $\mathcal{A}'(\mathbf{X})$ are the constraints (6.1.25) and $\mathcal{F}^+$ are the non-negativity constraints (6.2.26). In view of assumption (6.4.2) we do not take directly into account capacity constraints $\mathcal{B}'(\mathbf{C})$ (6.2.27).

In order to find the necessary conditions the minimum point of $Q(\mathbf{G})$ under constraints $\mathcal{A}'(\mathbf{X}), \mathcal{F}^+$ must satisfy, we introduce the Lagrange auxiliary functions:

$$Q(\mathbf{G}, A) \equiv Q(G) - A\left[\sum_{j=1}^{J} G(j) - X\right] \tag{6.4.21}$$

where A is a Lagrange multiplier. The conditions which the minimum point of this function must fulfil, together with the non-negativity constraints $\mathcal{D}'$, called the Kuhn–Tucker conditions (see [6.4], [6.5]) are of the form:

$$\frac{\partial Q}{\partial A} = 0 \tag{6.4.22}$$

$$\frac{\partial Q}{\partial G(j)} G(j) = 0, \quad j = 1, 2, \ldots, J \tag{6.4.23}$$

$$\frac{\partial Q}{\partial G(j)} \geqslant 0, \quad j = 1, 2, \ldots, J \tag{6.4.24}$$

Condition (6.4.22) is equivalent to constraints $\mathcal{A}'(\mathbf{X})$. Conditions (6.4.23) are called slackness conditions. We may see from conditions (6.4.23), (6.2.24) that if a flow of non-zero intensity traverse the jth path, we must get:

$$\frac{\partial Q}{\partial G(j)} = 0\ . \tag{6.4.25}$$

From formula (6.4.21) we have:

$$\frac{\partial \psi}{\partial G(j)} = \frac{\partial Q}{\partial G(j)} - A \ . \tag{6.4.26}$$

From definition (6.4.16), it is apparent that:

$$\frac{\partial Q}{\partial G(j)} = q\,[P(j), \mathbf{F}] \tag{6.4.27}$$

thus the derivative $\partial Q/\partial G(j)$ can be interpreted as the rate of change of critical function with changing flow intensity along the path $P(j)$.

A consequence of (6.4.24) is that for all values of j

$$\frac{\partial Q}{\partial G(j)} \geqslant A \ . \tag{6.4.28}$$

Let us introduce a path numbering system, in order to arrange the rates of changes $\partial Q/\partial G(j)$ in order of their magnitudes, i.e.

$$\frac{\partial Q}{\partial G(1)} \leqslant \frac{\partial Q}{\partial G(2)} \leqslant \frac{\partial Q}{\partial G(3)} \leqslant \ldots \leqslant \frac{\partial Q}{\partial G(J)} \ . \tag{6.4.29}$$

From formulae (6.4.26) and (6.4.28) it follows, however, that if for a path P_{sr} having the smallest rate of change we get

$$\frac{\partial Q}{\partial G(1)} = A \tag{6.4.30}$$

for paths with numbers $j \geqslant 2$ we must get

$$\frac{\partial Q}{\partial G(j)} = A \tag{6.4.31}$$

or

$$\frac{\partial Q}{\partial G(j)} > A \ . \tag{6.4.32}$$

If we get the equality (6.4.30), in accordance with (6.4.23) we must have $G(j) = 0$. This is equivalent to the fact that the optimum flow must possess property (6.4.20). If we apply the flow description using the path flow vector, property (6.4.20) can be derived as an almost direct consequence of the Kuhn–Tucker conditions.

6.4.3 Derivation of the fundamental properties of optimum flow based on the node-oriented flow description

We shall apply here the node-oriented flow description introduced in section 6.4.1. Therefore we return to the two index numbering of channels and use the single index only for numbering the nodes. We will also, contrary to the two previous sections, write the source-destination indices. In place of the general assumptions A1 and A2 we shall assume that:

A2′ the flow quality index has the form

$$Q(\mathbf{F}) = \sum_{(w,v)\in K} Q_1[F(w,v);(w,v)] \tag{6.4.33}$$

whereby we sum for all channels, and $F(w,v)$ denotes the total flow intensity in the channel (w,v). The function $Q_1[F(w,v); w,v]$ represents the quality of flow in channel (w,v). An example of function $Q(\mathbf{F})$ having the form (6.4.33) is the quantity function given by (6.3.1). We further assume that:

A3′ the channel quality function $Q_1[F;(w,v)]$ is the convex, twice differentiable function of total intensity F in the channel and

$$Q_1[0;(w,v)] = 0 \tag{6.4.34}$$

In addition, we shall assume that:

A4 the flow is memoryless and a non-return flow (see A5, p. 000, A6, p. 000).

As in section 6.2.3, let

$\mathrm{f} \equiv \{f_r(w,v), r,w,v = 1,2,\ldots,N\}$ be the set of all relative intensities,
A_f be the set of continuity constraints (6.2.30),
$\mathbf{X} = \{X_{wr}; w,r = 1,2,\ldots,N\}$ be the set of given intensities fed into the network from outside,
C be the set of conditions a,b,c mentioned in theorem 6.2.35 which are imposed upon the set of relative intensities f.

Notice that according to definition (6.4.35), the criterial function Q depends on the total flow intensities $F(u,w)$, and that these in accordance with (6.2.5) and (6.2.28) depend on the intensities F_{wr} and the relative intensities $f_r(u,w)$. As previously mentioned the intensities F_{wr} can be calculated from the set of equations (6.2.31) as a function of f and X. We can therefore present Q as a function of the sets f and X. We will use various forms of implicit dependence of Q on f and X.

We deal here with $\mathrm{OP}\,\mathbf{f},Q\,|\,C,A_f;\mathbf{X}$ where C is the set of assumptions introduced in theorem (6.2.35). Before we determine the necessary conditions which the solution of this optimisation problem must satisfy, we deal with the properties of the derivatives $\partial Q/\partial f_r(w,v)$. We introduce an infinitely small increment of the relative intensity $f_r(w,v)$ which we shall denote by δ_f. This increment brings about:

a) a rise of $\delta_f F_{wr}$ in the intensity flowing through the channel (w,v); the change in quality index as a result of this rule is:

$$\delta_f F_{wr} Q_1[F(w,v); w,v]$$

where we denote briefly:

$$Q_1[F;(w,v)] = \left(\frac{\partial Q_1[F;(w,v)]}{\partial F}\right)_F$$

b) a rise of $\delta_f F_{wr}$ in the intensity of the flow fed into node v and forwarded to pole r; according the assumption A4, the flow in memoryless and the effect of this rise on the quality Q is the same as for changes in the intensity of a flow introduced from the outside; thus the change of value of the quality index is

$$\delta Q_2 = \delta_f F_{wr} \frac{\partial Q}{\partial X_{vr}}$$

We finally get:

$$\frac{\partial Q}{\partial f_r(w,v)} = \frac{\delta_1 Q + \delta_2 Q}{\delta_f} = F_{wr}\left\{Q_1[F(w,v);(w,v)] + \frac{\partial Q}{\partial X_{vr}}\right\} \quad (6.4.35)$$

We now consider the derivative $\partial Q/\partial X_{vr}$ which appears above. Suppose we increment δ_X the intensity X_{wr} of flow fed into node u from the outside and forwarded to pole r. This causes an increase δ_X in the total intensity F_{wr}, which can change the flow intensity being forwarded from node u to channel v by $_R F(w,v)$. The total change in the quality index is

$$\delta_X f_r(w,v)\, Q_1[F(w,v);(w,v)] + \delta_X f_r(w,v) \cdot \frac{\partial Q}{\partial X_{vr}} .$$

Such changes occur by flow changes in all the channels issuing from node w. We thus have

$$\frac{\partial Q}{\partial X_{vr}} = \sum_{v \in N_{out}(w)} f(w,v)\left\{Q_1[F(w,v);(w,v)] + \frac{\partial Q}{\partial X_{vr}}\right\} \quad (6.4.36)$$

From this equation, we see that the change in flow quality caused by the change in flow intensity from outside a given node w, is the sum of the changes in the quality index caused by bringing an additional flow into the nodes from these channels.

Equation (6.4.36) is valid for all nodes $w = 1, 2, \ldots, N$, $w \neq r$. If the relative intensity $f_r(w, v)$ and the derivative $Q_1[F(w, v); (w, v)]$ are fixed, the equation (6.4.37) can be treated as a set of equations linking the derivative $\partial Q/\partial X_{vr}$ with them. The following theorem has been proved in Gallager's paper [6.1]:

$$\text{If the set of relative intensities fulfils assumptions } a, b, c \text{ mentioned in theorem (6.2.35), the set of equations (6.4.36) for } w, r = 1, 2, \ldots, N \text{ has a unique solution for } \partial Q/\partial X_{vr} \tag{6.4.37}$$

We now discuss the conditions which a solution of OP $\mathbf{f}, Q \mid C, A_f, \mathbf{X}$ must satisfy. Let:

$f_q(w)$ be the set of relative intensities $f_r(w, v)$, $v \in N_{\text{out}}(w)$ for fixed w and r,
$C(w,r)$ be the set of conditions concerning set $\mathbf{f}_r(w)$ mentioned in theorem (6.2.35).

We can treat OP $\mathbf{f}, Q \mid C, A_f, \mathbf{X}$ as a set of interconnected OP $f_r(w), Q \mid C(w,r), A_f, \mathbf{X}$, $r, w = 1, 2, \ldots, N$, $r \neq w$. The problems for various w, q are interconnected, since both the criterial function Q and the continuity constraints A_f depend on all $f_r(w, v)$. The necessary conditions which the solution of OP $f_r(w)$, $Q \mid C_r(w, r)$, $C(w,r)$, $A_f, \mathbf{X}$ must fulfil are immediately obvious from the Kuhn–Tucker theorem. For fixed w, q, these conditions take the form:

$$\frac{\partial Q}{\partial f_r(w, v)} \begin{cases} = A_{wr} & \text{if } f_r(w, v) > 0 \\ \geqslant A_{wr} & \text{if } f_r(w, v) = 0 \end{cases} \tag{6.4.38}$$

for all $v \in N_{\text{out}}(w)$, whereby A_{wr} is a Lagrangian multiplier corresponding to the constraints. The above conditions are necessary for the set $\mathbf{f}(w)$ to be a solution of OP $f_r(w), Q \mid C(w,r), C_r(w,r), A_f, \mathbf{X}$. We now illustrate the point of conditions (6.4.38), and show that they are necessary but not sufficient conditions. We shall use the previously given equations (6.4.35), (6.4.37) which enable us to calculate the derivatives occurring in these conditions.

Example 6.4.1

Consider the network shown in Fig. 6.9. In this figure are given values of the derivatives $Q_1[F(w, v); (w, v)]$. These derivatives will be briefly denoted by $Q_1(w, v)$. From (6.4.36), (6.4.37) and Fig. 6.9 we get:

$$\frac{\partial Q}{\partial f_4(1,4)} = F_{14} Q(1,4), \frac{\partial Q}{\partial f_4(1,2)} = F_{14}\, Q(1,2) + \frac{\partial Q}{\partial X_{24}} .$$

$$\frac{\partial Q}{\partial f_4(2,4)} = F_{24}Q(2,4), \frac{\partial Q}{\partial f_4(2,3)} = F_{24}\ Q(2,3) + \frac{\partial Q}{\partial X_{34}}$$

$$\frac{\partial Q}{\partial f_4(3,4)} = F_{34}Q(3,4)$$

$$\frac{\partial Q}{\partial X_{24}} = f_{24}Q_{24} + f_{23}\left(Q(2,3) + \frac{\partial Q}{\partial X_{34}}\right) \frac{\partial Q}{\partial X_{34}} = f_{34}Q(3,4)$$

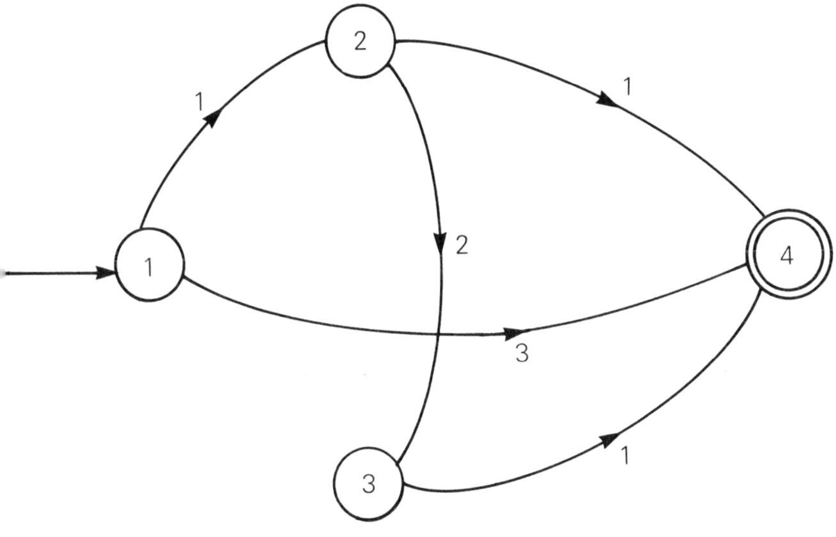

Fig. 6.9 – Network assumed to Example 6.4.1. The number by the arc denotes the derivative $Q_1[F(w,v),(w,v)]$.

Table 6.4.1 gives the values of the derivatives $\partial Q/\partial f_4(w,v)$ for a few sets

$$\mathbf{f} = \{f_4(1,4), f_4(1,2), f_4(2,4), f_4(2,3), f_4(3,4)\}, \ X_{14} = 1$$

The flow pattern corresponding to these sets are devoted by $\mathbf{F}_A$, $\mathbf{F}_B$, ..., $\mathbf{F}_E$. From Table 6.4.1 it is evident that the flow pattern $\mathbf{F}_A$ fulfils conditions (6.4.38), whereby $A_{14} = 3$, $A_{24} = 0$. Similarly, flow pattern $\mathbf{F}_E$ fulfils conditions (6.4.38) whereby $A_{14} = 2, A_{24} = 1$. The flow passes along channels with $Q = 1$ in the case of flow pattern $\mathbf{F}_E$, and along channels with $Q = 3$ for flow pattern $\mathbf{F}_A$. Flow pattern $\mathbf{F}_E$ is therefore better than flow pattern $\mathbf{F}_A$. As can be checked, flow pattern $\mathbf{F}_A$ corresponds to the inflexion of function $Q(f)$. Flow patterns $\mathbf{F}_B, \mathbf{F}_C$, $\mathbf{F}_D$ do not satisfy conditions (6.4.38).

Table 6.4.1

	Flow pattern	$\mathbf{F}_A$	$\mathbf{F}_B$	$\mathbf{F}_C$	$\mathbf{F}_D$	$\mathbf{F}_E$
relative intensities	$f_4(1,2)$	0	0	0	1	1
	$f_4(1,4)$	1	1	1	0	0
	$f_4(2,3)$	1	0.5	0.25	0.25	0
	$f_4(2,4)$	0	0.5	0.75	0.75	1
	$f_4(3,4)$	1	1	1	1	1
derivatives $\dfrac{\partial Q}{\partial f_4(w,v)}$	$\dfrac{\partial Q}{\partial f_4(1,2)}$	4	3	2.5	2.5	2
	$\dfrac{\partial Q}{\partial f_4(1,4)}$	3	3	3	3	3
	$\dfrac{\partial Q}{\partial f_4(2,3)}$	0	0	0	3	3
	$\dfrac{\partial Q}{\partial f_4(2,4)}$	0	0	0	1	1
	$\dfrac{\partial Q}{\partial f_4(3,4)}$	1	1	1	1	1
	$\dfrac{\partial Q}{\partial X_{24}}$	3	2	1.5	1.5	1

It is apparent from Table 6.4.1 why these conditions are only necessary conditions. As can be seen from (6.3.35), if a flow is not fed into a given node, i.e. taking $F_{wr} = 0$, $\partial Q/\partial f_r(w,v) = 0$ for all $v \in N_{\text{out}}(w)$ so for such a node, conditions (6.4.38) are fulfilled automatically. Hence if we only consider conditions (6.4.38) we do not take into account more advantageous paths, an example of which for flow pattern $\mathbf{F}_A$, is the path 1, 2, 4 (for the network in Fig. 6.9). This suggests that, when checking the optimality of a flow, we should take only the expression

$$q_r(w,v) \equiv Q_1[F(w,v);(w,v)] + \frac{\partial Q}{\partial X_{vr}} \tag{6.4.39}$$

occurring in equation (6.4.35). From equations (6.4.35) and (6.4.39) we see that

$$\frac{\partial Q}{\partial f_r(w,v)} = F_{wr}Q_r(w,v) \tag{6.4.40}$$

and so, if $F_w > 0$, we have

$$q_r(w,v) = \frac{\partial Q}{\partial f_r(w,v)} \; F_{wr} \; . \tag{6.4.41}$$

The function $q_r(w,v)$ introduced is called the **normalised** (with respect to the intensity F_{wr}) **rate of change of criterial function.**

The conditions corresponding to conditions (6.4.39) are

$$q_r(w,v) \begin{cases} = A'_{wr} & \text{if} \quad f_r(w,r) > 0 \\ \geqslant A'_{wr} & \text{if} \quad f_r(w,r) = 0 \end{cases} \tag{6.4.42}$$

for $v \in N_{out}(u)$.

It is apparent from equation (6.4.40) that if conditions (6.4.42) are fulfilled, conditions (6.4.38) are also satisfied, whereas the converse does not hold.

We now determine the constant A'_{wr} occurring in (6.4.42). By multiplying both sides of the upper part of equation (6.4.42) by $f_q(w,v)$ and summing for $v \in N_{out}(w)$. We get

$$\sum_{v \in N_{out}(w)} \left\{ Q[(w,v)] + \frac{\partial Q}{\partial X_{vr}} \right\} f_r(w,v) = A'_{wr} \sum_{v \in N_{out}(w)} f_r(w,v) \; . \tag{6.4.43}$$

According to equation (6.2.30), the sum appearing on the right-hand side is equal to 1, whereas according to equation (6.4.36), the sum on the left-hand side is equal to $\partial Q / \partial X_{wr}$. So from equation (6.4.43) we find that

$$A'_{wr} = \frac{\partial Q}{\partial X_{wr}} \; . \tag{6.4.44}$$

Conditions (6.4.42) can be interpreted such that the minimum (with respect to the nodes v to which channels come directly from the node w) is A''_{wr}. Conditions (6.4.42) can thus be written down in the form

$$q_r(w,v) - \min_{v \in N_{out}(w)} q_r(w,v) \begin{cases} = 0 & \text{if} \quad f_r(w,v) > 0 \\ \geqslant 0 & \text{if} \quad f_r(w,v) = 0 \end{cases} \tag{6.4.45}$$

The following theorem was proved by Gallager [6.1]:

> Let f be a set of relative intensities fulfilling conditions a, b, c defined in 6.2.35. The condition sufficient for such a set to be a solution of OP$\mathbf{f}, Q \,|\, A_f(\mathbf{X}), F^+$ is that conditions (6.4.42) are satisfied for $w,r = 1, 2, \ldots, W$. (6.4.46)

From theorem (6.4.46) we see that for optimum flow, the flow from node w is forwarded only to channels whose normalised rate of change of quality index is equal, and at the same time less than the normalised rate of change of the remaining channels.

Example 6.4.2

We consider the network discussed in Example 6.4.1. Table 6.4.2 gives values of the normalised rate of change of $q_4(w, v)$ for flow patterns $\mathbf{F}_A$, $\mathbf{F}_C$, $\mathbf{F}_E$ defined in Table 6.4.1. It is evident from Table 6.4.2 that flow pattern $\mathbf{F}_A$, while fulfilling the conditions (6.4.39) does not satisfy conditions (6.4.43), whereas flow pattern $\mathbf{F}_E$ does fulfil conditions (6.4.43) and thus automatically, also conditions (6.4.39). As we have already emphasised, flow pattern $\mathbf{F}_A$ is not optimal whereas flow pattern $\mathbf{F}_E$ is.

Table 6.4.2

	$\mathbf{F}_A$	$\mathbf{F}_C$	$\mathbf{F}_E$
$q_4(1,4)$	3	3	3
$q_4(1,2)$	4	2.5	2
$q_4(2,3)$	3	3	1
$q_4(2,4)$	1	1	3

6.4.4 Fundamental properties of optimum time-varying flow

In this section we consider optimisation when external flow intensities entering the network are time-varying. As a result the optimised intensities of the flow in the channels may also be time-varying. We assume, as in section 6.2.4, that the flow is memoryless and also:

A1 we know in advance the intensities of the external flow put into the network during the observation time interval $\langle t_a, t_b \rangle$; we denote them by $X_{sr}(t)$, $t \in \langle t_a, t_b \rangle$, $s, r = 1, 2, \ldots, N$, $s \neq r$.

Thus the model of the network is, as in the static models, assumed to be deterministic.

For time-varying flow, we will use the notation introduced in section 6.2.4, where we formulated the constraints which such a flow must satisfy. Let $L_r(w;t)$ be the number of packets at node v (in buffers and transmitters) which are to be forwarded to destination node r. Notice that the integral

$$\int_{t_a}^{t_b} L_r(w;t)\,dt$$

is the total time which packets observed during the time interval $\langle t_a, t_b \rangle$ spend at the node. As we mentioned in section 5.2.3, for static flow the waiting time $F(w,v)\,\tau(w,v)$ of weighted packets can be interpreted in the same way. Thus, as the characteristic delay of packets for the time-varying case, we take

$$Q[\mathbf{L}(\cdot)] = A\int_{t_a}^{t_b} \sum_{w,r=1,2,\ldots,N,\, w \neq r} L_r(w;t)\,dt \tag{6.4.47}$$

where A is a scaling factor. In this notation, we emphasise that the flow quality index is a function of the set of time functions

$$\mathbf{L}(t) = \{L_r(w;t)\; w,r = 1,2,\ldots,N,\, w \neq r\} \quad t \in \langle t_a, t_b \rangle \tag{6.4.48}$$

Evidently to evaluate the numbers of packets waiting in nodes for a time $t \in \langle t_a, t_b \rangle$, we have to know the initial numbers of these packets at time t_a. Therefore we assume:

A2 the initial numbers of packets in nodes at the instant t_a are given.

i.e. we assume that

$$L_r(w;t_a) = L_r(w) \quad w,r = 1,2,\ldots,N,\, w \neq r \tag{6.4.49}$$

where $L_r(w)$ are given numbers. We call the set of conditions (6.4.49) **initial conditions** and we denote them by $\mathcal{IC}(\mathbf{L})$, where

$$\mathbf{L} = \{L_r(w);\, w,r = 1,2,\ldots,N,\, w \neq r\}\ .$$

As explained in section 6.2.4, the numbers $L_r(w;t)$ are related to the time-variable channel flow pattern

$$\mathbf{F}(t) = \{F_r(w,v),\, r,\, w,v = 1,2,\ldots,N,\, w \neq v,\, r \neq w\} \quad t \in \langle t_a, t_b \rangle$$

by the continuity constraints (6.2.37). We also assume that both $L_r(w,t)$ and $F_r(w,v)$ are non-negative. Introducing only these constraints we will consider both the flows going into the node and the flows going out as variables. As we explained on page 275 this implies that in finding the optimum flows we also determine some features of the routing rules.

The constraints can be considered as a set of differential equations. If we know the flow pattern for $t \in \langle t_a, t_b \rangle$, these equations together with the initial conditions $\mathcal{IC}(\mathbf{L})$ permit us in general to find the set of functions $\mathbf{L}(t)$. In other words, we can write

$$\mathbf{L}(t) = \Psi_t[\mathbf{F}(\cdot)] \quad t_a \leqslant t \leqslant t_b \tag{6.4.50}$$

where $\psi_t(\cdot)$ is an operator determined by the set of differential equations (6.2.37) and $\mathcal{IC}(\Psi)$. Knowing the set of functions $\Psi(t)$ we can evalutate the quality index from (6.4.47). Thus (6.4.48) and (6.4.50) define a quality index for the flow pattern. Denoting this by $Q'[\mathbf{F}(\cdot)]$, we have

$$Q'[\mathbf{F}(\cdot)] = Q\{\Psi_{(\cdot)}[\mathbf{F}(\cdot)]\} \tag{6.4.51}$$

Having defined the quality index for the time-variable flow pattern, we can formulate the optimisation problem. Knowing the set of external flow intensities put into the network

$$X(t) = X_{sr}(t),\ s,r = 1,2,\ldots,N,\ s \neq r,\ \ t \in \langle t_a, t_b\rangle$$

we have to find the set of time functions $F(t)$, $t \in \langle t_a, t_b\rangle$ satisfying the continuity constraint $\mathcal{A}[\mathbf{X}(\cdot)]$, the capacity constraint $\mathcal{B}(\mathbf{C})$ and the non-negativity constraints, which we denote by $\mathcal{F}^+$, for minimum $\varphi'[\mathbf{F}(\cdot)]$. In our shorthand notation this problem can be written as

$$\mathrm{OP}\,\mathbf{F}(\cdot), Q'[\mathbf{F}(\cdot)] \,|\, \mathcal{A}[\mathbf{X}(\cdot)], \mathcal{B}(\mathbf{C}), \mathcal{D}_F$$

Obviously, this procedure, based on the quality index $Q'[\mathbf{F}(\cdot)]$, which depends on the operator $\Psi_t[\mathbf{F}(\cdot)]$, would be quite inpracticable. Remembering the meaning of the functions $\Psi(t)$, we have to add the non-negativity constraints $L_{vr}(t) \geqslant 0$, $t \in \langle t_a, t_b\rangle$ which we denote by L^+. The previously considered optimisation problems can be formulated as

$$\mathrm{OP}\,\mathbf{F}(\cdot), \mathbf{L}(\cdot); Q[\mathbf{L}(\cdot)] \,|\, \mathcal{A}[\mathbf{X}(\cdot)], \mathcal{B}(\mathbf{C}), \mathcal{F}_F^+, \mathcal{L}_I^+, \mathcal{IC}(\mathbf{L})$$

As mentioned we now interpret the constraints $\mathcal{A}[\mathbf{R}(\cdot)]$ (given by 6.2.37) as the set of differential equations relating $\mathbf{L}(\cdot)$ and $\mathbf{F}(\cdot)$.

An additional advantage of this formulation of the flow pattern optimisation problem is that we can expect the solution, i.e. the optimum flow pattern $\mathbf{F}_0(t)$ to be expressed as a function of the external flow intensities $\mathbf{X}(\tau)$, $\tau \in \langle t_a, t_b\rangle$ and the numbers of packets $\mathbf{L}(\tau)$, $\tau \in \langle t_a, t\rangle$. In a control system, such a solution can be implemented as a controller using the feedback signal (state $L(\tau), \tau \in \langle t_a, t\rangle$) and this solution is also called a **feedback solution**. The structure of such a solution is frequently much simpler than that of the equivalent $\mathrm{OP}\,\mathbf{F}(\cdot)$, $Q'[\mathbf{F}(\cdot)] \,|$ $\mathcal{A}[\mathbf{X}(\cdot)]$, $\mathcal{B}(\mathbf{C})$, $\mathcal{F}_F^+$ which depends only on $\mathbf{X}(\tau)$, $\tau \in \langle t_a, t_b\rangle$ and which is called the **open solution**. To formulate the necessary conditions which the solution of $\mathrm{OP}\,\mathbf{F}(\cdot)$, $\mathbf{L}(\cdot)$, $Q[\mathbf{L}(\cdot)] \,|\, \mathcal{A}[\mathbf{X}(\cdot)]$, $\mathcal{B}(\mathbf{C})$, $\mathcal{F}_F^+$, $\mathcal{L}_L^+$, $\mathcal{IC}(\mathbf{L})$ must satisfy, we can use Portryagin's minimum (maximum) principle.† Taking into account the constraints $\mathcal{A}[\mathbf{X}(\cdot)]$, $\mathcal{L}_L^+$, $\mathcal{IC}(\mathbf{L})$, we have to calculate the Hamiltonian for the system being

† For details of this approach see monographs on control optimisation, e.g. Athans and Falb in [6.6].

considered and then look for a flow pattern satisfying the constraints $\mathcal{B}(\mathbf{C}), \mathcal{D}_F$ which maximise it. The Hamiltonian is

$$H(\mathbf{L},\mathbf{F},A,A';t) \equiv A\sum_{w,q}\sum_{v\neq q} L_{vr}(w;t) +$$

$$+\sum_{w,q}\sum_{w\neq q} A_{wr}(t)\frac{\mathrm{d}L}{\mathrm{d}t}q^{(w;t)} + \sum_{w,r}\sum_{w\neq r} A'_{wr}(w;t)\,L_{wr}(w;t) \qquad (6.4.52)$$

where the first sum corresponds to the criterion (6.4.47), $A_{wr}(t)$, $w,r = 1,2,\ldots,N$, $w \neq r$ is the set of functions called costates, while $A'_{wr}(t)$, $w,r = 1, 2, \ldots, N$, $w \neq r$ is the set of Lagrangian multipliers which take constraints $\mathcal{L}_L^+$ into account. The costates satisfy the differential equation

$$A_{wr}(t) = \frac{\partial H}{\partial L_{wr}} = A + A'_{wr}(t) \qquad (6.4.53a)$$

$$t \in \langle t_\mathrm{a}, t_\mathrm{b}\rangle \qquad (6.4.53b)$$

with the end value constraint

$$A_{wr}(t_\mathrm{b}) = 0\ . \qquad (6.4.53c)$$

The multipliers $A'_{wr}(t)$ satisfy the so-called slackness conditions:

$$A'_{wr}(t)L_{wr}(t) = 0 \qquad (6.4.54a)$$

$$t \in \langle t_\mathrm{a}, t_\mathrm{b}\rangle \qquad (6.4.54b)$$

$$A'_{wr}(t) \leqslant 0\ . \qquad (6.4.54c)$$

The slackness conditions reflect the non-negativity constraints $\mathcal{L}_L^+$, they correspond to slackness constraints (6.4.23) in the stationary cases. The Portryagin minimum principle states that the necessary condition for a flow pattern $\mathbf{F}_0(t)$ to be a solution of OP $\mathbf{F}(\cdot), \mathbf{L}(\cdot), \mathcal{Q}[\mathbf{L}(\cdot)]\,|\,A\,[\mathbf{X}(\cdot)], \mathcal{B}(\mathbf{C}), \mathcal{F}_F^+, \mathcal{L}_L^+, \mathcal{IC}(\mathbf{L})$ is that

$$H(\mathbf{L},\mathbf{F}_0,\mathbf{A},\mathbf{A}';t) = \min_{\mathbf{F}\in F[\mathcal{B}(\mathbf{C}),\mathcal{F}_F^+]} H(\mathbf{L},\mathbf{F},A,A';t) \qquad (6.4.55)$$

where $F[\mathcal{B}(\mathbf{C}),\mathcal{F}_F^+]$ is the set of flow patterns satisfying constraints $\mathcal{B}(\mathbf{C})$ and $\mathcal{F}_F^+$. In view of the linearity of the criterial function, condition (6.4.55) is also a sufficient condition for optimality.

We have assumed that the time interval during which we observe the system is fixed. We can also formulate the optimisation problem for an unlimited time interval instead requiring the network to be brought to a desired state, e.g. we discharge packets which have accumulated at some node: this problem was considered by Segall [6.7]. The necessary conditions which the solution of an optimisation problem involving movement of the upper end of the time interval must satisfy can be formulated similarly. Instead of constraints (6.4.53c) we introduce constraints imposed on the desired end states of the network. The techniques for effectively finding solutions of such problems are different in some respects from finding the solutions of the fixed ends optimisation problem.

We now give an example of the application of the minimum principle for determining optimum flow pattern for fixed ends. We show that the time-varying flow model permits us to tackle important problems which cannot be considered in the stationary flow scheme.

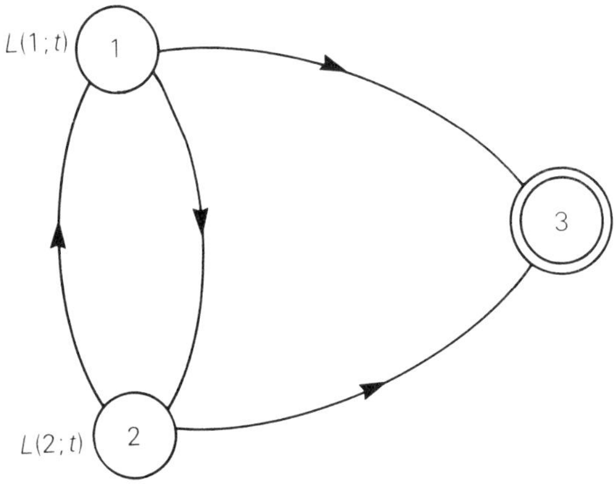

Fig. 6.10 – Network assumed in Example 6.4.3.

Example 6.4.3 – Optimum discharging of buffers

We take the network shown in Fig. 6.10 and assume that:

(1) the flow is memoryless and non-return (see page 269–270),

(2) no external flows are put into the network, thus $X_{w,r}(t) = 0$, $t \in \langle t_a, t_b \rangle$

(3) at the instant t_a that observation begins we have packets which should be forwarded to node 3 only in one or both of the nodes 1 and 2,

(4) we take the integral (6.4.47) with $A = 1$ as flow quality index.

The problem considered is the time-variable average flow model of the individual packet routing problem OP$\mathbf{R}(\cdot)$, $\bar{\tau}\,|\,C$ discussed at the end of section 5.3.2. In view of assumption (3), we consider only the flow of packets destined for node 3 and omit the indices q, numbering the destination pole by writing briefly $F(w,v;t)$ for $F_r(w,v;t)$, $\Psi(w;t), w = 1, 2$, for the number $\Psi_r(w,t)$ of packets destined for node 3 and waiting at node w etc. Using the abbreviated notation the quality index

$$Q(L) = \int_{t_a}^{t_b} [L(1;t) + L(2;t)]\,dt \ . \tag{6.4.56}$$

The continuity equations (6.2.27) take the form

$$\frac{\mathrm{d}L(1;t)}{\mathrm{d}t} = F(2,1;t) - F(1,2;t) - F(1,3;t) \tag{6.4.57a}$$

$$\frac{\mathrm{d}L(2;t)}{\mathrm{d}t} = F(1,2;t) - F(2,1;t) - F(2,3;t) \tag{6.4.57b}$$

Let us notice that the first component in 6.4.52 does not depend on Fs. Therefore we consider only the second and third terms. We denote them H_1. We have:

$$H_1(t) = A(1,t)\frac{\mathrm{d}L(1;t)}{\mathrm{d}t} + A(2,t)\frac{\mathrm{d}L(2;t)}{\mathrm{d}t}. \tag{6.4.58}$$

Using (6.4.57) we express $H(t)$ as the function of the flow pattern $F(t) = \{F(1,2;t), F(2,1;t), F(1,3;t), F(2,3;t)\}$ and the set of costates $A(t) = \{A(1,t) + A(2,t)\}$. To use the optimality principle we have to understand the properties of the costates $A(w,t)$. They satisfy the differential equations (6.4.53) with fixed end values

$$A(w,t_b) = 0, \; w = 1,2, \; . \tag{6.4.59}$$

In order to conclude from these differential equations values of $A(w,t)$ needed for the minimisation of the Hamiltonian, we must obtain insight into the properties of functions $A'(w,t)$, which satisfy the slackness conditions:

$$A'_w(w,t)L(w,t) = 0 \tag{6.4.60}$$

$$t \in \langle t_a, t_b \rangle$$

$$A(w,t) \leqslant 0, \; w = 1,2, \; . \tag{6.4.61}$$

The difficulty in using these conditions to determine the functions $A(w,t)$ is that we do not know in advance the functions $L(w,t)$. In control theory, methods of overcoming this difficulty and making effective use of the minimum principle are known. However, some form of guesswork is usually involved. Instead, we shall apply elements of heuristic reasoning, taking into account the fact that the functions considered are flow intensities.

We introduce the assumption that during the whole observation interval we have packets at both nodes, i.e. that

$$L(w,t) > 0 \tag{6.4.62a}$$

$w = 1,2, t \in \langle t_a, t_b \rangle$. We term this case I. From (6.4.60) it follows that

$$A'(w,t) = 0 \tag{6.4.62b}$$

$w = 1,2, t \in \langle t_a, t_b \rangle$. Thus the differential equations (6.4.57) take the form

$$\frac{dA(1,t)}{dt} = -1 \tag{6.4.63a}$$

$$\frac{dA(2,t)}{dt} = -1 \tag{6.4.63b}$$

with the end conditions (6.4.59). The solution of these equation is

$$A^*(1,t) = A^*(2,t) = t_b - t \tag{6.4.64}$$

substituting (6.4.57) and (6.4.64) in (6.4.54), we obtain the Hamiltonian

$$H(t) = -(t_b - t)[F(1,3;t) + F(2,3;t)] \tag{6.4.65}$$

Now we have to find $F(1,3;t)$ and $F(2,3;t)$ for each $t (t \in \langle t_a, t_b \rangle)$, minimising H($t$). At the same time we have to respect the capacity and non-negativity constraints

$$F(w,3;t) \leqslant C(w,3) \tag{6.4.66}$$

$$F(w,3;t) \geqslant 0 \tag{6.4.67}$$

$w = 1, 2$. Because the factor ahead of the square bracket in (6.4.65) is always negative, we have to make $F(1,3;t)$ and $F(2,3;t)$ as large as possible. In view of (6.4.66), we obtain the optimum flow intensities

$$F^*(w,3;t) = C(w,3) \tag{6.4.68}$$

$w = 1, 2$. Thus the optimum flow discharging the nodes is the flow in which direct channels from these nodes to the destination are fully used. Notice that the Hamiltonian does not depend on the intensities in channels joining nodes 1 and 2 in this case. We can therefore choose these intensities arbitrarily, with the restriction that we do not violate the continuity, capacity and non-negativity constraints. The capacity constraints are

$$F(1,2;t) \leqslant C(1,2) \tag{6.4.69a}$$

$$F(2,1;t) \leqslant C(2,1) \tag{6.4.69b}$$

From (6.4.69b), it follows that by taking $F(1,2;t)$ $F(2,1;t)$ we can transfer packets from node 1 to node 2 or vice versa without changing the quality index. However, we must satisfy the condition assumed when defining case A, that neither $L(1,t)$ nor $L(2,t)$ drops to zero. This is so because our quality index does not account for transportation costs and as long as we have some extra packets in the system, it does not matter whether we retain some packets at a node or circulate them around a loop. In particular, we satisfy all the constraints mentioned, taking

$$F^*(1,2;t) = F^*(2,1;t) = 0 \quad t \in \langle t_a, t_b \rangle \tag{6.4.70}$$

Substituting (6.4.58) and (6.4.60) in (6.4.57), integrating, and noting that the initial values $L(w, t_a)$, $w = 1, 2$, are given, we obtain the numbers of packets for optimum flow

$$L(w,t) = L(w,t_a) - (t - t_a)\, C(w,3) \tag{6.4.71}$$

$w = 1, 2$. The diagrams of the numbers of packets given by this formula are shown in Fig. 6.11(a). Eliminating the time t from these equations, we obtain on the plane with coordinates $L(1,t)$ and $L(2,t)$ the trajectories shown in Fig. 6.11(b).

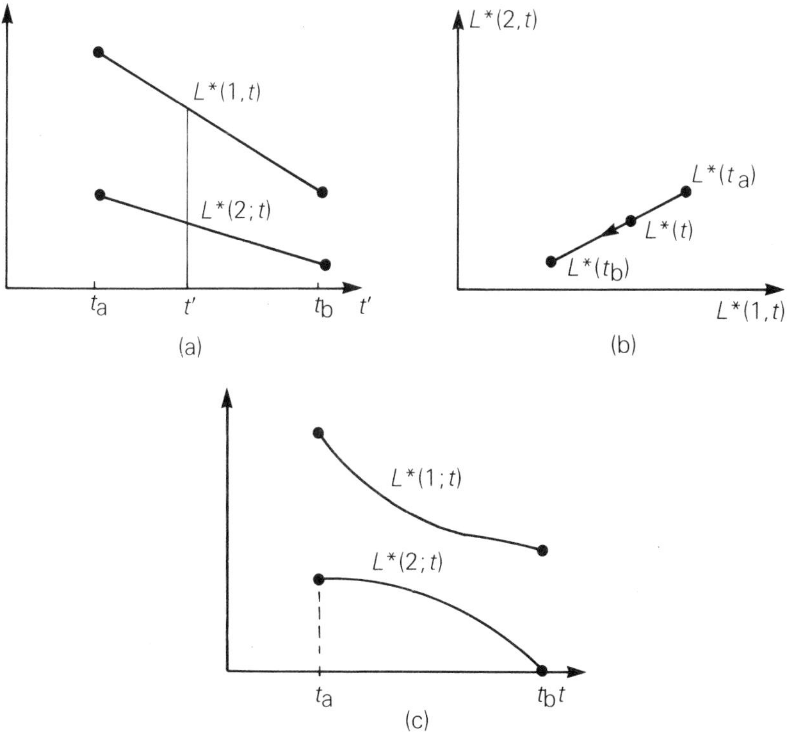

Fig. 6.11 – The numbers of packets $L^*(1,t)$, $L^*(2,t)$ at nodes in the network shown in Fig. 6.10 during optimum discharge; (a) time dependence when no flow is circulating between nodes 1, 2; (b) trajectory corresponding to the time dependency shown in (a); (c) example of $L^*(1,t)$ and $L^*(2,t)$ when flow circulation between nodes 1 and 2.

Notice, that it is essential to our reasoning that during the whole observation interval the buffers do not become empty. Because in the criterion (6.4.47) we do not take into account the transportation costs, it is evident that all flow patterns satisfying (6.4.58) yield the same value of the quality index (6.4.56) as the flow determined by (6.4.58) and (6.4.60) and are optimum, provided that no value of $F(1,2;t)$ or $F(2,1;t)$ violates the continuity, capacity and non-negativity constraints for F and the positivity constraint for $L(t)$. Examples of trajectories for such flow are shown in Fig. 6.11(c). The characteristic of these flows is, that for all the total number of packets in the system

$$L(1,t) + L(2,t) = L^*(1,t) + L^*(2,t) \ .$$

By suitably choosing $F(1,2;t)$ and $F(2,1;t)$ we can change $L(1,t_a)$ and $L(2,t_b)$. This possibility is crucial when considering the general case, not requiring that the number of packets at nodes never falls to zero.

Next we consider case II in which we have packets only at node 1.

$$L(1;t) > 0 \tag{6.4.72a}$$

$$L(2;t) = 0 \tag{6.4.72b}$$

Here:

$$\frac{dL(2,t)}{dt} = 0 \tag{6.4.73}$$

$t \in \langle t_a, t_b \rangle$ and the Hamilton takes the form:

$$H(F,L,\lambda,t) = A_1(t)[F(2,1;t) - F(1,2;t) - F(1,3;t)] \tag{6.4.74}$$

As in case A, the costate is given by (6.4.69) and thus $A_1(t) < 0$ for $t \in \langle t_a, t_b \rangle$. We minimise the Hamiltonian by maximising the expression in the square bracket, taking into account the capacity and non-negativity constraints for values of F. Notice also that (6.4.74) combined with (6.4.57b) implies the constraint:

$$F(1,2,t) - F(2,1;t) + F(2,3;t) = 0 \tag{6.4.75}$$

Evidently the minimum of Hamiltonian H_B is achieved for

$$F^*(2,1;t) = 0 \tag{6.4.76a}$$

$$F^*(1,3;t) = C(1,3) \tag{6.4.76b}$$

$$F^*(2,3;t) = C_{123} \tag{6.4.76c}$$

$$F^*(1,2;t) = F^*(1,2;t) \tag{6.4.76d}$$

where

$$C_{123} = \min\{C(1,2), C(2,3)\} \tag{6.4.77}$$

is the capacity of the path 1, 2, 3. The interpretation of this flow pattern is obvious. We discharge node 1 most effectively when we use both the direct channel (1,3) and the other possible path 1, 2, 3 at all available times. It is apparent that in the general case when we assume only $L(1,t_a) > 0$ but do not require (6.4.72b) to be satisfied during the whole observation interval, the flow pattern is optimal if (6.4.76b, c, d) are satisfied, and as long as $L(1,t)+L(2,t)>0$, i.e. if we use both possible paths most efficiently so long as there are still packets at any one of the nodes 1, 2. The condition (6.4.76a) is in general not necessary, because as in case A we can circulate some packets around the loop (1, 2), (2, 1) without influencing the quality index.

The third case III is when we have packets at node 2 only. It is similar to case II and the optimum flow pattern is:

$$F^*(2,1) = F^*(1,3) \tag{6.4.78a}$$

$$F^*(1,3) = C_{213} \tag{6.4.78b}$$

$$F^*(2,3) = C(2,3) \tag{6.4.78c}$$

$$F^*(1,2) = 0 \tag{6.4.78d}$$

where

$$C_{213} = \min\{C(2,1), C(1,3)\} \tag{6.4.79}$$

The important point here is that if the number of packets at node 1 in case II is the same as the number of packets at node 2 in case III, and we use flow patterns optimum for each case, the numbers of packets left in the network at instant t_b or at the time the network is emptied are different if the total maximum removal rates are different, i.e. if $[F^*(1,3;t) + F^*(2,3)]_{\text{case II}} \neq [F^*(1,3;t) + F^*(2,3)]_{\text{case III}}$.

When we are looking for the optimum flow pattern in the general case, and are only assuming that $L(1,t_a) > 0$, $L(2,t_a) \geqslant 0$, we note that while $L(1,t)>0$ and $L(2,t) > 0$ we can transfer packets between nodes 1 and 2 and at the same time get the most efficient removal of packets. We must do this in such a way that when one of the nodes is emptied, the rest of the packets stay at node 1 or 2, depending on which of the nodes packets can be most quickly removed from. Fig. 6.12 shows trajectories for the optimum flow pattern obtained using heuristic arguments similar to those we used for cases I, II, III. The trajectories are optimum assuming that the observation interval is large enough to remove all packets from the network when using the optimum flow pattern. In sectors S1 and S2, the best flow pattern is such that we first completely empty one node and leave packets at the other. In sector S3 the flow is such that we empty both nodes simultaneously. The lines dividing the sectors are determined by the capacities of the channels. Notice that the trajectories shown in Fig. 6.12 are also optimal when moving the upper end t_b.

From this very simple example, we can draw the following conclusions: (1) the model of time-varying flows indicates the important possibilities of temporarily

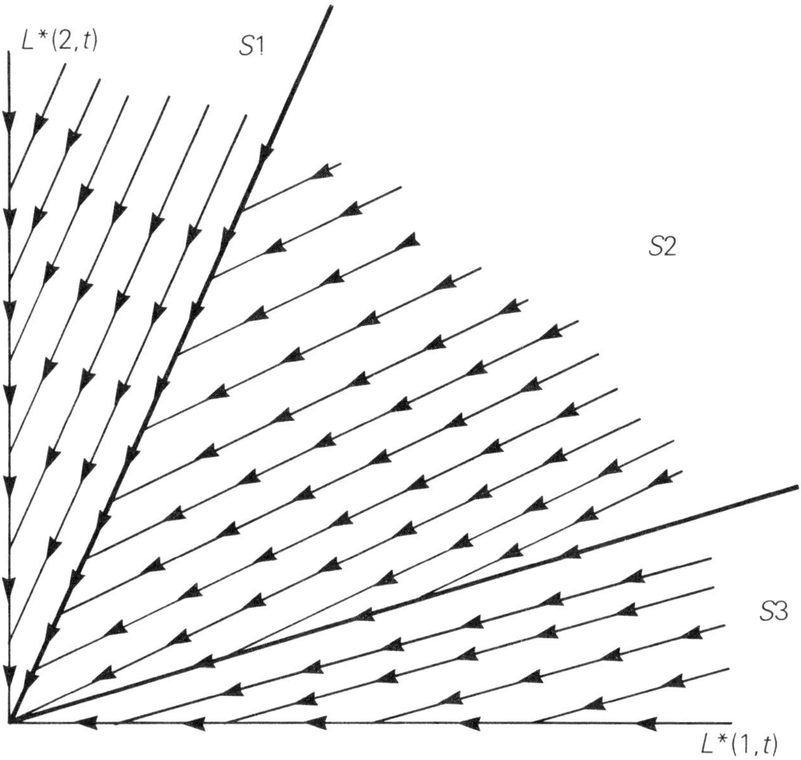

Fig. 6.12 – Trajectories corresponding to the optimum discharge of packets at nodes 1 and 2 in the network shown in Fig. 6.9.

transferring packets between nodes of the network in order to use the capacity of bottlenecks to the full, (2) the systematic use of the maximum principle is very cumbersome and for more complex networks we have to introduce heuristic methods to find optimum time-varying flows.

6.5 ITERATIVE PROCEDURES FOR FINDING OPTIMUM FLOW

Previously, we derived the necessary conditions which the flow pattern must satisfy in order to be optimal. These conditions allow us to check if a given flow pattern is optimal but do not direct us to the optimum flow pattern. In this section we shall give four iterative procedures for flow pattern optimisation.

It is typical of iterative methods of optimisation that the algorithm is easily formulated, but that it is hard to prove that it yields a sequence which converges to the optimum. We shall therefore concentrate on the algorithms and their physical justification. We formulate only briefly the condition for the convergence of sequences generated by the algorithms, and refer the reader to specialised publications on the subject. As in section 6.3, we first consider the optimisation of single-commodity flow, and later indicate how the algorithms can be used in the case of multicommodity flow.

6.5.1 Procedures based on the flow deviation concept†

We shall first consider the single-commodity flow entering at pole p and directed towards pole q. Let us introduce the operation Ψ of ordering flow pattern $Q_{\mathbf{F}} \in \mathcal{F}_{\mathrm{A}}^{+}$ to the flow pattern $\mathbf{F} \in \mathcal{F}_{\mathrm{A}}^{+}$. This operation, related to the criterial function $Q(\mathbf{F})$, is defined in the following way:

$$\psi\mathbf{F} = (1-\alpha^*)\mathbf{F} + \alpha^*\mathbf{V}^*(\mathbf{F}) \tag{6.5.1}$$

where $\mathbf{V}^*(\mathbf{F})$ is a flow pattern for a branchless flow along the path $\mathcal{P}_{sr}^*$, with shortest channel length given by formula (6.4.16), in which we calculate partial derivatives at the point which corresponds to the flow pattern $\mathbf{F}$. The coefficient α^* appearing in (6.5.1) is the value of the variable α for which the auxiliary function:

$$h(\alpha) = Q[(1-\alpha)\mathbf{F} + \alpha\mathbf{V}^*] \tag{6.5.2}$$

reaches its minimum, under the constraint $0 \leqslant \alpha \leqslant 1$. By this definition, the flow pattern $\mathbf{V}^*$ depends only on the flow pattern $\mathbf{F}$, thus α^* depends only on $\mathbf{F}$. The operator ψ will be called the **flow deviation operator.**

As we have said, Assumption A4 that the criterial function grows to infinity as we approach the boundary of the area $\mathcal{F}_{\mathrm{A},\mathcal{B},\mathcal{D}}^{+}$, corresponding to the planes determined by the capacity constraints, enables us to search for the minimum under constraints $\mathcal{A}(\mathbf{X})$, $\mathcal{B}(\mathbf{C})$ and $\mathcal{F}^+$ only among the minimal under constraints $\mathcal{A}^{(R)}$ and $\mathcal{F}^+$. To apply the iterative algorithm, we have to start with the flow pattern which lies inside the set $\mathcal{F}_{\mathrm{A}.\mathcal{B}}^{+}$ and take sucessive steps so as not to go beyond any of the planes determined by the capacity constraints. The following algorithm is of this type.

Algorithm 6.5.1

Step 1

We take $\mathbf{F}_1 = \mathbf{F}_{st}$ where F_{st} is the starting flow pattern fulfilling constraints $\mathcal{A}(\mathbf{X})$, $\mathcal{B}(\mathbf{C})$, $\mathcal{F}^+$ and thus belonging to the set $F_{\mathrm{A},\mathcal{B}}^{+}$.

Step n

We take

$$\mathbf{F}_{n+1} = \psi\mathbf{F}_n \tag{6.5.3}$$

† The method, which is a modification of the constrained variation method was given by Fratta *et al.* [6.8].

and let:

$$\delta Q \equiv |Q(\mathbf{F}_{n+1}) - Q(\mathbf{F}_n)| \tag{6.8.4}$$

$\delta\hat{Q}$ is the required tolerance of the solution.

If $\delta Q > \delta\hat{Q}$, we go on to step $n + 1$, otherwise we take $\mathbf{F}_{n+1}$ to be the optimal solution.

In accordance with property (6.4.20), the optimum flow is the superposition of branchless flows along shortest paths. Since an approximation of such a flow is the flow corresponding to the pattern $\mathbf{V}^*(\mathbf{F}_n)$, instead of δQ given by (6.5.4) we can take

$$\delta Q = \left| \sum_{k=1}^{K} q(k, \mathbf{F}_n)[F(k) - V^*(k, \mathbf{F}_n)] \right| \tag{6.5.5}$$

where $V^*(k, \mathbf{F}_n)$ is a member of the set of intensities $\mathbf{V}^*(\mathbf{F}_n)$ flowing through the kth channel (here and subsequently we use the single index numbering of channels introduced on page 181).

Algorithm 6.5.1 can be used in a virtually unchanged form for multicommodity flows. The definition of operation ψ (acting on the full flow pattern $\mathbf{F} = \mathbf{F}_{sr}, s,r \in (S,R))$ can be generalised by defining the flow $\mathbf{V}^*(\mathbf{F})$ as the flow pattern along the set of sets of shortest paths for all components flowing from s to r, $(s,r) \in (S,R)$, the definition of $\alpha^*(\mathbf{F})$ remains the same. With this definition, Algorithm 6.5.1 can be used unchanged.

For multicommodity flows, finding the starting flow pattern $\mathbf{F}_{st}$ satisfying constraints $\mathcal{A}(R)\ \mathcal{B}(\mathbf{C})$ and $\mathcal{F}^+$ is a difficult problem, as is checking whether the defining constraints $\mathcal{A}(\mathbf{X})$ (required external flow intensities R_m) have been realised. We now give an algorithm which enables us in an iterative way, to find the flow fulfilling constraints $\mathcal{A}(\mathbf{X})\ \mathcal{B}(\mathbf{C})$ and $\mathcal{F}^+$ or to state that the required external flow intensities $\mathbf{R}$ are not realisable. In this algorithm we change the set of external intensities $\mathbf{X}$ introduced from outside. We begin the algorithm with the flow pattern $\mathbf{F}_1$ which fulfils constraints $\mathcal{A}(\mathbf{R})$ and $\mathcal{F}^+$, we do not require constraints $\mathcal{B}(\mathbf{C})$ to be satisfied (the restrictions resulting from the given capacities). We can check that constraints $\mathcal{B}(\mathbf{C})$ are fulfilled by using the parameter

$$\varphi \equiv \max_k \frac{F(k)}{C(k)} \tag{6.5.6}$$

and taking $F(k) = F_1(k)$. If constraints $\mathcal{B}(\mathbf{C})$ are not fulfilled, $\varphi > 1$, we then proportionally decrease all the intensities, and consider the flow pattern

$$\mathbf{F}_2 = \alpha \mathbf{F}_1 \ . \tag{6.5.7}$$

Such a flow transformation is called a **proportionality transformation.** The flow pattern $\alpha \mathbf{F}_1$ fulfils constraints $\mathcal{A}(\alpha \mathbf{X})$, $\mathcal{F}^+$. If we make α sufficiently small, we can fulfil constraints $\mathcal{B}(\mathbf{C})$. We then attempt to increase the external flow intensities. Remembering the property (6.4.20), we transfer part of the flow on to shortest length paths as defined by

$$d(k) \equiv \left(\frac{\partial Q}{\partial F(k)}\right)_{\mathbf{F}} \tag{6.5.8}$$

in which $\mathbf{F} = \mathbf{F}_1$. We check if the flow pattern satisfies constraints $\mathcal{A}(\mathbf{X})$ and $\mathcal{B}(\mathbf{C})$, we either take the decision that the external flow intensities $\mathcal{X}$ cannot be realised, or repeat the procedure in an attempt to get $\alpha = 1$.

When formulating the algorithm we use single-index description of source–destination pairs, and thus of commodities, similar to the single-index description of channels. We will number the pairs (p,q) with the index $m, m = 1,2,\ldots,M$. The algorithm is as follows:

Algorithm 6.5.2

Step 1

For $m = 1,2,\ldots,M$, we find the shortest length paths:

$$d(k) = \left(\frac{\partial Q}{\partial F(k)}\right)_{\mathbf{F}=0} \tag{6.5.9}$$

Let $\mathbf{Y}_1$ be the flow pattern which corresponds to branchless flows along such paths, having intensity X. Thus flow pattern $\mathbf{Y}_1$ realises the set of external flow intensities $\mathbf{X}$, therefore $\alpha_1 = 1$. Thus it satifies constraints $\mathcal{A}(\mathbf{X})$, $\mathcal{F}^+$, but it may not fulfil constraints $\mathcal{B}(\mathbf{C})$. We calculate φ_1 from (6.5.6).

$$\begin{array}{lll} \text{If} & \varphi_1 \leqslant 1 & \mathbf{Y}_1 \text{ is solution} \\ \text{else} & \varphi_1 > 1 & \text{then step 2} \end{array} \tag{6.5.10}$$

Step n

n1

If

$$\beta_n < 1 \ , \tag{6.5.11}$$

where

$$\beta_n \equiv \frac{\varphi_{n-1}}{\alpha_{n-1}} \tag{6.5.12}$$

we complete the procedure and take as the solution flow pattern

$$\mathbf{Y}_n \equiv \frac{1}{\alpha_{n-1}} \mathbf{Y}_{n-1} \tag{6.5.13}$$

$n2$

If

$$\beta_n > 1 \ , \tag{6.5.14}$$

we introduce an auxiliary flow pattern

$$\mathbf{Z}_n \equiv \gamma_{n-1}\mathbf{Y}_{n-1} \tag{6.5.15}$$

in which

$$\gamma_{n-1} \equiv \frac{1-\eta_1}{\varphi_{n-1}} \tag{6.5.16}$$

and η_1 can be interpreted as the permitted magnitude of the unused part of the channel capacities. We take

$$\mathbf{Y}_n \equiv \psi \mathbf{Z}_n \tag{6.5.17}$$

where ψ is the flow deviation operator which is a generalisation for the use of M-commodity flow defined by (6.5.1). If

$$\sum_{k=1}^{K} q(k, \mathbf{Y}_n) | U_n(k) - Y_n(k) | < \epsilon_1 \tag{6.5.18}$$

where $U_n(k)$ is the flow intensity along the shortest path mentioned in the definition of the operator ψ, and

$$|\alpha_{n-1} - \gamma_{n-1}\alpha_n| < \epsilon_2 \tag{6.5.19}$$

in which ϵ_1 and ϵ_2 are two small fixed numbers defining the tolerance of the approximation, then we complete the procedure taking the decision that the given set of external flow intensities cannot be realised, otherwise go to step $n+1$.

To justify the individual steps, we introduce two simple properties of the changes in proportional flow transformations. Let **F** be the initial flow pattern which realises the set of external intensities $\alpha\mathbf{X}$. The appropriate parameters of the flow pattern

$$\mathbf{F}_a = a\mathbf{F} \tag{6.5.20}$$

which arises from the proportionality transformation, will be denoted by a. From the definition it is obvious that:

$$\alpha_a = \alpha a \tag{6.5.21}$$

and

$$\varphi_a = \varphi a \tag{6.5.22}$$

We start by justifying Step $n1$. From definition (6.5.12) we find that if $\gamma_n < 1$, then $\varphi_{n-1} < \alpha_{n-1}$, we can find a proportionality transformation such that $\varphi'_{n-1} \leqslant 1$, and $\alpha'_{n-1} \geqslant 1$. To get this, we may take

$$\gamma_{n-1} = \frac{1}{\alpha_{n-1}} . \tag{6.5.23}$$

From equations (6.5.21) and (6.5.22) we then get

$$\varphi'_n = \frac{\varphi_{n-1}}{\alpha_{n-1}} \tag{6.5.24}$$

and

$$\alpha_n = 1 . \tag{6.5.25}$$

Therefore the flow $\mathbf{Y}_n$ fulfils constraints F^+ and realises the set of external intensities **R**.

We now justify Step $n2$. If $\gamma_n \geqslant 1$, then we cannot by proportionality transformation simultaneously get $\varphi'_n \leqslant 1$ and $\alpha'_n \geqslant 1$. We therefore have to make another flow change. We change the flow to transfer part of the flow to the shortest path. However, so as to satisfy constraints F^+ we must first proportionately reduce the flow pattern $\mathbf{F}_{n-1}$. We could take, for example.

$$\gamma_n = \frac{1-\epsilon_1}{\varphi_{n-1}} \tag{6.5.26}$$

where ϵ_1 is the assumed tolerance (see 6.5.16). As γ_{n-1} approaches unity we should change the tolerance, allowing an ever greater approach to unity. We can do this by taking:

$$\epsilon_1 = \epsilon_1 |1-\varphi_{n-1}| . \tag{6.5.27}$$

The justification for terminating is fairly obvious. Since we are carrying out Step $n2$, we get $\gamma_n = 1$, and by scaling, we cannot obtain a flow pattern realising the external flow intensities X. If constraint (6.5.18) is fulfilled, the flow pattern $\mathbf{Z}_n$ has approached the optimum. If (6.5.19) is satisfied, the scaling coefficient has ceased to change. Thus, iterating the procedure cannot yield $\varphi < 1$ and $\alpha = 1$.

In general we may have a number of paths $P_m(j)$ of equal, minimum length in the sense of definition (6.5.8). The optimal flow of the mth component is then a branching flow. If: (1) the number of commodities M is large, (2) the network contains a large number of nodes, (3) the scattering of the required interpolar flow intensities is small, we can expect that, for the majority of channels, the intensity of the mth commodity flowing along the kth channel will be much smaller then the total flow intensity in the kth channel, and each commodity of the branchless flow will approach the optimum value. This flow will then be along the path corresponding to the minimum rate of change of quality with the mth commodity intensity change. To find such a flow we use a similar algorithm to 6.5.2. In the first stage, using an auxiliary algorithm analogous to 6.4.2, we find the initial branchless flow fulfilling conditions $\mathcal{A}(\mathbf{X})$, $\mathcal{B}(\mathbf{C})$ and $\mathcal{F}^+$. Then, in the nth step, we take as the channel length

$$d(k) = \left(\frac{\partial Q}{\partial F(k)}\right)_{\mathbf{F}_{n-1}} \qquad (6.5.28)$$

where $\mathbf{F}_{n-1}$ is the flow pattern obtained in the previous step; for each m we find the shortest path and transfer the whole flow of the mth commodity to it. The algorithm terminates when each of the commodities is flowing along its shortest path. An algorithm so modified is described in greater detail by Fratta *et al.* [6.8]. In this paper, the authors quote the results of applying the algorithm to an early model of the ARPA network with 21 nodes. Function (6.4.1) is chosen as the criterial function. In the first stage, a flow such as the initial flow $\mathbf{F}_1$ was chosen so that each component of the intensity X_m flows along the shortest path calculated according to (6.4.35) if $\mathbf{F} = 0$. Notice that instead of checking the fulfilment of constraints $\mathcal{B}(\mathbf{C})$ using parameter φ_1, we can make use of the property of the criterial function (6.3.1) by which $\bar{\bar{\tau}}(F) \to \infty$ if $F(k) \to C(k)$ for any of the channels. So if $\bar{\bar{\tau}}(F) < \infty$, constraints $\mathcal{B}(\mathbf{C})$ are fulfilled. Figure 6.13 shows typical dependence of the delay $\bar{\bar{\tau}}(\alpha F_1)$ for the flow pattern αF_1 as a function of α. The figure shows, $\bar{\bar{\tau}} \to \infty$ for $\alpha \to 0.85$. Therefore we cannot get a flow fulfilling constraints $\mathcal{A}(\mathbf{X})$, $\mathcal{B}(\mathbf{C})$ and $\mathcal{F}^+$ from the flow pattern $\mathbf{F}_1$ by

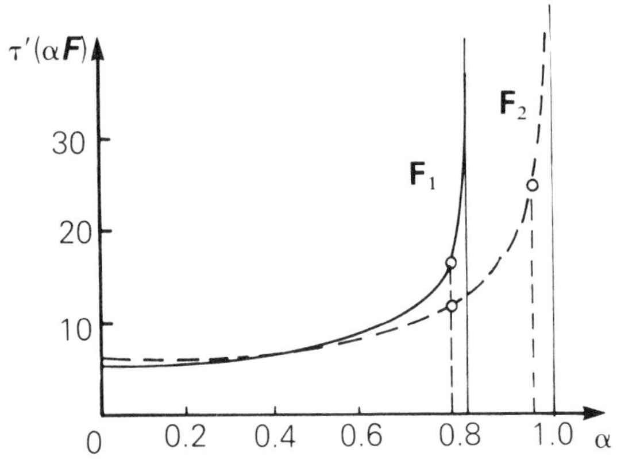

Fig. 6.13 – An example of the dependence of normalised delay τ' on the scaling factor α used in the algorithm 6.5.2 (based on Fratta [6.8]); $\mathbf{F}_1$, $\mathbf{F}_2$, two flow patterns.

proportionality transformation. Let the flow pattern $\mathbf{F}_2$ be the pattern of branchless flows of intensities X along the shortest length paths:

$$d_2(k) = \left(\frac{\partial Q}{\partial F(k)}\right)_{\mathbf{F}=0.8\mathbf{F}_1} \tag{6.5.29}$$

The graph of $\tau(\alpha \mathbf{F}_2)$ as a function of α is shown in Fig. 6.13 as interrupted line. From the graph we can obtain $\tau(\alpha\mathbf{F}_2) \to \infty$ for $\alpha \to 1.05$. Thus the flow pattern $\mathbf{F}_2$ satisfies constraints $\mathcal{A}(\mathbf{X})$, $\mathcal{B}(\mathbf{C})$ and $\mathcal{F}^+$. This can be used as an initial flow pattern for Algorithm 6.5.1 in which we do not constrain the optimal flow to only one branchless path. This algorithm leads to the optimal flow pattern $\mathbf{F}^*$ such that $|Q(\mathbf{F}_2) - Q(\mathbf{F}_0)|/Q(\mathbf{F}_2) \approx 5 \times 10^{-2}$. Therefore the flow $\mathbf{F}_2$ along branchless paths is reckoned to be very good.

6.5.2 A procedure based on the projected gradient algorithm and channel-orientated flow description†

To find the optimum flow path under constraints $\mathcal{A}$, $\mathcal{B}$ and $\mathcal{F}^+$, we can use the projected gradient algorithm described in detail in Appendix A.5. The projected gradient algorithm as applied to the single-commodity flow pattern described by channel flow intensities takes the following form.

Algorithm 6.5.3

Step 1

We take

$$\mathbf{F}_1 = \mathbf{F}_0 \tag{6.5.30}$$

where F is the starting flow fulfilling constraints $\mathcal{A}$, $\mathcal{B}$ and $\mathcal{F}^+$.

Step n

We take

$$\mathbf{F}_{n+1} = \mathbf{F}_n - \alpha_n \Pi_n [\operatorname{grad} Q(F)]_{\mathbf{F}_n} \tag{6.5.31}$$

where Π_n is the projection operator, and α_n is a coefficient. The method of calculating Π_n and α_n is discussed in Appendix A.6.

We finish the step or the whole procedure depending on the absolute value of the correction

$$\Pi_n [\operatorname{grad} Q(F)]_{F_n} \; .$$

This algorithm is illustrated by an example from Schwartz and Cheung [6.9].

† The procedure considered was proposed for flow optimisation by Schwartz and Cheung [6.9]. Its mathematical background is explained in Appendix A.6.

Example 6.5.1

We take a network consisting of $K = 6$ channels shown in Fig. 6.14 and the criterial function defined by (6.4.1). We take the following values of the parameters:

k	1	2	3	4	5	6
$C(k)$	3	2.5	3	2	2	2.5
$A_2(k)$	0	0.5	0	0.5	0.5	0.5

(6.5.32)

$$X = 2 \tag{6.5.33}$$

To simplify the solution, we have used non-dimensional parameters which may be treated as numbers of fixed units, e.g. kbit/s.

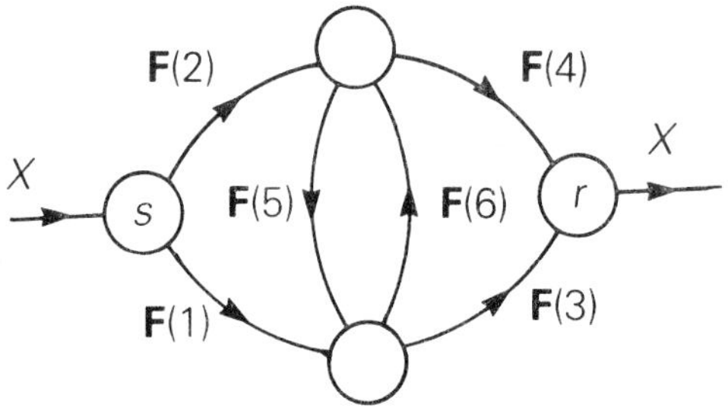

Fig. 6.14 – Network assumed in Example 6.5.1.

From Fig. 6.14, we see that constraints $A(X)$ (equations (6.2.4)) take the form:

$$\begin{aligned} F(1) + F(2) &= X \\ F(1) + F(5) - F(3) - F(6) &= 0, \\ F(2) + F(6) - F(4) - F(5) &= 0, \\ F(3) + F(4) &= X \end{aligned}$$

Only three of these four equations are independent. From now on we shall consider only the first three equations. The matrix $\mathbf{B}_1$, defined by formula (A.6.11), therefore takes the form:

$$\mathbf{B}_1 = \begin{bmatrix} 1 & 1 & 0 & 0 & 0 & 0 \\ 1 & 0 & -1 & 0 & 1 & -1 \\ 0 & 1 & 0 & -1 & -1 & 0 \end{bmatrix}$$

After substituting this matrix in formula (A.6.10), we get the projection matrix:

$$\Pi_1 = \frac{1}{12}\begin{bmatrix} 5 & -5 & 1 & -1 & -2 & 2 \\ -5 & 5 & -1 & 1 & 2 & -2 \\ 1 & -1 & 5 & -5 & 2 & -2 \\ -1 & 1 & -5 & 5 & -2 & 2 \\ -2 & 2 & 2 & -2 & 8 & 4 \\ 2 & -2 & -2 & 2 & 4 & 8 \end{bmatrix}$$

We now choose the starting flow vector $\mathbf{F}_0$. As can be checked, the constraints $A(\mathbf{X}_{sr})$, $B(\mathbf{C})$ and F^+ are fulfilled by the vector:

$$\mathbf{F}_0 = (1 \;\; 1 \;\; 1 \;\; 1 \;\; 0.5 \;\; 0.5)$$

We calculate $(\text{grad}\, Q)_F$, and obtain the components of this vector from formula (6.3.1):

$$[(\text{grad}\, Q)_\mathbf{F}]_k = \frac{C(k)}{[C(k) - F(k)]^2} + A_2(k)$$

The components are calculated by substituting values from (6.5.32). After some elementary matrix transformations we find the auxiliary column vector defined in A.6.18.

$$\mathbf{h}_1 = \Pi_1 (\text{grad}\, Q)_\mathbf{F} = \begin{bmatrix} -0.2743 \\ 0.2743 \\ -0.3785 \\ 0.3785 \\ 0.5764 \\ 0.6806 \end{bmatrix}$$

From formula (A.6.20) we find $k^* = 6$, $\alpha(6) = 0.7347$ and so $\alpha_0 = 0.7347$. Thus the vector corresponding to the point where the straight line (A.6.16) cuts the plane $Q_6 \equiv \{\mathbf{F}; F(6) = 0\}$:

$$\mathbf{C}_6 = F(1) - \alpha_0 h_1 = \begin{bmatrix} 1.2015 \\ 0.7985 \\ 1.2780 \\ 0.7219 \\ 0.0765 \\ 0.0000 \end{bmatrix}$$

The sixth component of vector $\mathbf{C}_6$ is, as it should be, zero. Furthermore, we get the inequality (A.6.23). Thus, we take:

$$\alpha_1 = \alpha_0$$

And according to (6.5.30),

$$\mathbf{F}_2 = \mathbf{F}_1 - \alpha_1 \mathbf{h}_1 = \mathbf{C}_6 \ .$$

Notice that we have arrived at plane Q_6. The condition of remaining on the plane $F(6) = 0$ is added to the set $A(X)$ constraints. Thus we obtain matrix $\mathbf{B}_2$ from matrix $\mathbf{B}_1$ by adding the line 0, 0, 0, 0, 0, 1:

$$\mathbf{B}_2 = \left[\begin{array}{cccccc} & & \mathbf{B}_1 & & & \\ \hline 0 & 0 & 0 & 0 & 0 & 1 \end{array}\right]$$

Proceeding further, after the eighth step, all components of the vector $(\Pi_6 \operatorname{grad} Q)_{\mathbf{F}(8)}$ are zero, therefore the intensities obtained in this step are the optimal solution. The individual flow vectors and the average time delays $\bar{\bar{\tau}}(F_n)$ corresponding to them are given in Table 6.5.1.

Table 6.5.1 – Flow patterns given by Algorithm 6.5.3.

	$F_n(1)$	$F_n(2)$	$F_n(3)$	$F_n(4)$	$F_n(5)$	$F_n(6)$	Q
$\mathbf{F}_1$	1.0	1.0	1.0	1.0	0.5	0.5	2.375
$\mathbf{F}_2$	1.202	0.799	1.278	0.722	0.077	0.000	1.641
$\mathbf{F}_3$	1.289	0.712	1.289	0.712	0.000	0.000	1.584
$\mathbf{F}_4$	1.421	0.579	1.421	0.579	0.000	0.000	1.544
$\mathbf{F}_5$	1.456	0.544	1.456	0.544	0.000	0.000	1.541
$\mathbf{F}_6$	1.466	0.534	1.466	0.535	0.000	0.000	1.541
$\mathbf{F}_7$	1.470	0.530	1.470	0.530	0.000	0.000	1.541
$\mathbf{F}_8$	1.471	0.529	1.471	0.529	0.000	0.000	1.541

If we use the flow pattern **F** based on the channel-orientated flow description, the projected gradient Algorithm (6.5.2) can be used unchanged with multi-commodity flow. However, the structure of the matrix of coefficients does change. As can be seen from the flow continuity equations, only flows of the same component are linked to each other. Thus matrix **B** for a full flow vector always takes the form of a block matrix

$$\mathbf{B} = \begin{bmatrix} \mathbf{B}_1 & \mathbf{0} & \mathbf{0} \\ \mathbf{0} & \mathbf{B}_2 & \\ \mathbf{0} & & \mathbf{B}_M \end{bmatrix} \qquad (6.5.34)$$

where **0** denotes submatrices consisting only of zeros, while **B** is the matrix corresponding to the flow conservation equations of the mth commodity. We can show that the projection matrix Π_1 defined by equation (A.6.11) has a similar form, that is, it can be broken down into submatrices such that the submatrices lying off the main diagonal consist solely of zeros. This considerably simplifies the calculation.

The algorithm based on the flow deviation described in the previous section and the algorithm being considered now both perform this task. There is also the problem of comparing the computational efficiency of these two algorithms. It would seem that for the general case such a comparison is not possible. We therefore compare them for particular networks. In Table 6.5.2, taken from Schwartz and Cheung [6.9], the times in seconds to determine the optimum flow using Algorithms 6.5.1 and 6.5.3 for selected networks with various numbers M of commodities and various numbers N of network nodes using an IBM 370/155 computer are given. The number of nodes and commodities in network W are given in the first two columns. The times of both algorithms are of a similar order, but for most of the selected networks, the projected gradient algorithm is slightly more efficient.

Table 6.5.2 – Times (in seconds) of execution of Algorithms 6.5.1 and 6.5.3. (N, number of network nodes; M, number of commodities).

N	M	Algorithm 6.5.1	Algorithm 6.5.3
4	1	0.78	0.39
4	2	2.65	1.04
10	4	41.4	39.8
10	2	45	53

6.5.3 A procedure based on the steepest descent principle and path-orientated flow description†

According to the steepest descent principle, we redirect the flow from paths which are not the shortest to the shortest one such that the flow continuity principle is maintained. We start with one-commodity flow.

Algorithm 6.5.4

Step 1

We take

$$\mathbf{G}_1 = \mathbf{G}_0 \tag{6.5.35}$$

† The procedure considered, which is also a modification of the constant variations method was given by Harris [6.10].

where $\mathbf{G}_1$ is the path intensity set, and $\mathbf{G}_0$ is a starting set chosen to fulfil constraints $\mathcal{A}(\mathbf{X}), \mathcal{B}(\mathbf{C}), \mathcal{F}^+$.

Step n

*n*1

We find the number of the path $\mathcal{P}(j^*)$ which corresponds to the smallest rate of increase of the criterial function so that:

$$\left[\frac{\partial Q}{\partial G(j^*)}\right]_{G_{n-1}} \leqslant \left[\frac{\partial Q}{\partial G(j)}\right]_{G_{n-1}} \tag{6.5.36}$$

for $j = 1, 2, \ldots, J(p,q)$.

*n*2

For flow intensities along paths $\mathcal{P}(j), j \neq j^*$, we introduce the primary corrections:

$$\Delta_n G(j) \triangleq \begin{cases} \left[\frac{\partial Q}{\partial G(j^*)}\right]_{G_{n-1}} - \left[\frac{\partial Q}{\partial G(j)}\right]_{G_{n-1}} & \text{if} \quad G_{n-1}(j) > 0 \quad \text{(a)} \\ 0 \quad \text{if} \quad \left[\frac{\partial Q}{\partial G(j')}\right]_{G_{n-1}} - \left[\frac{\partial Q}{\partial G(j)}\right]_{G_{n-1}} > 0 & \\ \quad \text{and} \quad G_{n-1}(j) = 0 & \text{(b)} \end{cases} \tag{6.5.37}$$

while for the intensity $G(j^*)$ we introduce the primary correction

$$\Delta'_n G(j^*) = -\sum_{j \neq j'} \Delta'_n G(j) \tag{6.5.38}$$

*n*3

We check the signs of the differences

$$G'_n(j) \triangleq G_{n-1}(j) - \Delta'_{n-1} G(j) \tag{6.5.39}$$

If we have $G_{n+1}(j) \geqslant 0$ for $j = 1, 2, \ldots, J$, we take

$$G_n(j) = G'_n(j) \tag{6.5.40}$$

If we have $G'_{n+1}(j'') < 0$ even for one j'', we go on to *n*4.

*n*4

We introduce secondary corrections

$$\Delta_n G(j) \triangleq \alpha_n \Delta_n G(j) . \tag{6.5.41}$$

whereby the auxiliary parameter α_n is selected such that for all j we get

$$G_{n-1}(j) - \alpha_n \Delta'_n G(j) \geqslant 0 \ . \tag{6.5.42}$$

We obtain this by taking, for example,

$$\alpha_n = \max_{j \neq j'} \frac{-\Delta_n G(j)}{G_{n-1}(j)} \tag{6.5.43}$$

Lastly, we take

$$G_n(j) = G_n(j) - \Delta'_n G(j) \tag{6.5.44}$$

We shall explain the reasons for the operations introduced here, beginning with operation $n2$. If a flow travels along one of the paths not corresponding to the smallest rate of cost increase (and hence the flow does not possess property (6.4.20)), we reduce the intensity of flow by as much as the difference between the rate of cost increase for a given path and the minimum rate of increase; this corresponds to the dependence (6.5.37a). In order to fulfil constraints $A'(\mathbf{X})$ (6.5.25), all these flow differences are directed to the path of smallest rate of increase; this corresponds to equation (6.4.38). The change (loss) of flow intensity $\Delta'_n G(j)$, calculated from (6.5.38), may be greater than the intensity of the flow $G_{n-1}(j)$ flowing along the path $P_{sr}(j)$. As the flow cannot be negative, we have to reduce $\Delta'_n G(j)$ accordingly. The easiest way of doing this is to reduce all the increments proportionately; hence (6.5.43).

An improvement to the algorithm is possible. We apply the increment $\Delta''_n G(j) = \alpha' \Delta'_n G(j)$, where the parameter $0 < \alpha'_n \leqslant 1$, is chosen such that the auxiliary function

$$\delta Q = Q'[G_n(j) - \alpha'_n \Delta'_n G] - Q'[G_{n-1}] \tag{6.5.45}$$

where the column vector $\Delta'_n G$ having components $\Delta'_n G(j)$ has reached a minimum. It can be shown (see Harris, [6.10]) that Algorithm 6.5.3 ensures the diminishing of the function in every step.

6.5.4 An algorithm for finding the optimal flow based on the node-orientated flow description†

We shall now deal with an algorithm suggested by the optimality conditions based on node-orientated flow description, derived in section 6.4.3. The algorithm has a structure similar to that of Algorithm 6.5.3. For a flow not satisfying conditions (6.4.42), we introduce primary corrections (cf. (6.4.17)):

$$\Delta'_r(w, v) \equiv q_r(w, v) - \min_{v \in N_{\mathrm{out}}(w)} q_r(w, v) \tag{6.5.46}$$

† The procedure considered was given by Gallager [6.1].

and a secondary correction:

$$\Delta_r''(w,v) = \alpha(r,w)\Delta_r'(w) \tag{6.5.47}$$

where $\alpha(r,w)$ is a weighting coefficient which we shall consider in detail later. Lastly, we introduce correction $\Delta_r(w,v)$, chosen so that, having subtracted it, the modified relative intensity is not negative. We can get this by taking:

$$\Delta_r(w,v) = \min\left[f_r(w,v);\ \Delta_r''(w,v)\right] \tag{6.5.48}$$

Let v^* be the node for which $\beta_r(w,v)$ is minimum, so the primary correction is $\Delta_r'(w,v^*) = 0$. The essence of the algorithm is that we decrease the relative intensity by the final correction in all channels except channel (w,v), in which we increase the relative intensity, such that for the modified relative intensities the normalisation condition (6.2.30) is again satisfied. Therefore the modification takes the form:

$$f_{r,n+1}(w,v) = \begin{cases} f_{rn}(w,v) - \Delta_{rn}(w,v) & \text{for } v \neq v^* \\ f_{rn}(w,v^*) + \sum\limits_{v \neq v^*} \Delta_{rn}(w,v) \end{cases} \tag{6.5.49}$$

A fundamental shortcoming of this equation is that it does not prevent us from introducing a flow which circulates in a loop. We therefore examine a modification of the recurrence equation (6.5.49) which eliminates this possibility. We start by introducing some helpful concepts.

First, we introduce the concept of **mutual position** of nodes. If a path P_{wv} exists form node w to v, so that for each channel $(u',v') \in P_{w,v}$ we have $f_r(u',v') > 0$, we say that with respect to the flow towards the destination pole r, the node **lies below** node w. In this case, we also say that node v lies above node w. It is possible that apart from path $P_{w,v}$ there is a path $P_{v,w}$ with channels for which $f_e(w'',u'') > 0$. The set of paths $P_{w,v}$ and $P_{v,w}$ will be called a loop, and we shall say that the flow contains **circulation.** If circulation takes place, node v lies both above and below node w. If circulation does not occur, the concept of mutual position of nodes introduces semi-order into the set of nodes.

We next introduce the concept of **improper flow.** We say that the flow forwarded by channel (w,v) to pole q is improper if: (a) the relative intensity $f_r(w,v) > 0$, and (b) the quality increment in node v to which we are forwarding the flow is not smaller than in the node from which the flow originates, i.e. $\partial Q/\partial R_{wr} \leqslant \partial Q/\partial R_{vr}$. If improper flow does not occur, we can order the nodes according to the values of the derivative $\partial Q/\partial X_{wq}$. Such ordering is equivalent to ordering according to the concept of mutual position in the sense that if $\partial Q/\partial X_{wr} < \partial Q/\partial X_{vr}$, node w lies below node v. It is possible to get a situation where we do not have circulation, but where we have an improper flow in one or more channels, an example of such flow is shown in Fig. 6.15. Suppose we had a flow described by the set of relative intensities f_w in which there was no circulation. It is possible to introduce a circulation in the next step if: (1) we have introduced a flow into a channel in which there was no flow, (2) there was a channel with improper flow, (3) after introducing the changes this flow was not reduced to zero. Often possibility (3) does not arise, since the algorithm has a tendency to reduce improper flows.

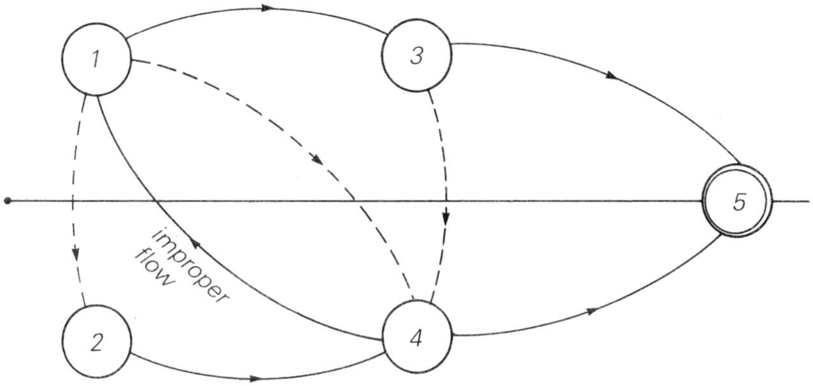

Fig. 6.15 – Example of a network in which circulation around loops may arise after applying flow modifications. Dotted lines denote channels in which initially there is no flow.

This conclusion suggests two countermeasures to prevent us from introducing circulations. The first is to increase the correction of improper flows so that they are reduced to zero. This would be quite complicated, however. The other method of avoiding circular flows, which we consider in more detail, is to reject nodes which start paths with improper flows.

This is achieved by not introducing a modified flow into channel (w', v') in which $f_r(w', v') = 0$, and where there is a path $P_{v',r}$ from v' to q so that there is an improper flow along at least one of the channels e.g. u'', v'', and that after modification the relative intensity of that flow does not fall to zero.

We now closely examine the condition, whose fulfilment ensures that the flow intensity along a channel does not fall to zero after modification. From (6.4.37) we have:

$$\frac{\partial Q}{\partial X_{w''r}} = \sum_{v \in N_{\text{out}}(w'')} f_r(w'', v) q(w'', v) \geqslant$$

$$\min_{v \in N_{\text{out}}(w'')} q(w'', v) \sum_{v \in N_{\text{out}}(w'')} f_r(w'', v) = \min_{v \in N_{\text{out}}(w'')} q(w'', v) \tag{6.5.50}$$

The primary flow correction

$$\Delta'_r(w'',v'') = q_r(w'',v) - \min_{v \in N_{out}(w'')} q_r(w'',v) \tag{6.5.51}$$

Taking (6.5.30) into account

$$\Delta'_r(w'',v'') \leqslant \Delta_1 \tag{6.5.52}$$

where

$$\Delta_1 \equiv q_r(w'',v'') - \frac{\partial Q}{\partial X_{w''r}} \tag{6.5.53}$$

From equations (6.5.44) and (6.5.48) defining the final correction, we find that the relative flow intensity after modification $f_{r,n+1}(w'',v'') > 0$ if

$$f_{r,n}(w'',v'') > \frac{\Delta_1}{\alpha(r,w'')} \tag{6.5.54}$$

where $\alpha(r,w)$ is the coefficient appearing in the definition of the secondary correction.

Remembering conclusion (6.5.50), we introduce the set of nodes $B_r(w) \subset N_{out}(w)$ such that: (I) $f_r(w,v) = 0$, and (II) a path P_{vr} leading to the destination pole r exists containing a channel in which there is improper flow. Set $B_r(w)$ is called a **set of blocked nodes.** From 6.5.50 we find that if the original flow was circulation free, we do not create circulation as long as we do not increase the relative flow intensities along the channels (w,v), $v \in B_r(w)$. So if in equation (6.5.52) we take the set

$$N^*_{out}(w) = N_{out}(w) - B_r(w) \tag{6.5.55}$$

in place of the set $N_{out}(w)$, and do not increase the flow in channels (w,v), $v \in N^*_{out}(w)$, we ensure that if the original flow was circulation free, the modified flow also is. The algorithm finally takes the form:

Algorithm 6.5.5

Step 1

We choose the original flow described by the set of relative intensities $f_{rv}(w)$, $r,v,u = 1,2,\ldots,N$, not having circulation.

Step n

We take

$$f_{r,n+1}(w,v) = 0 \quad \text{for} \quad v \neq N^*_{out}(w) \tag{6.5.56a}$$

$$f_{r,n+1}(w,v) \begin{cases} f_{r,n}(w,v) - \Delta_r(w,v) & \text{for } v \in N^*_{\text{out}}(w), v \neq v^* \\ f_{r,n}(w,v) + \sum\limits_{v \in N^*_{\text{out}}(w)} \Delta_{rn}(w,v) \end{cases} \qquad (6.5.56b)$$

in which we calculate the primary correction from the equation

$$\Delta'_r(w,v) = q_r(w,v) - \min_{v \in N_{\text{out}}(w)} q_r(w,v) \qquad (6.5.57)$$

and v^* is the node for which a minimum is obtained.

We have still to calculate the secondary correction, which is equivalent to the definition of the function $A(w,r)$ in equation (6.5.51). This correction is a correction of the relative intensity, therefore, if the total intensity F_{wq} forwarded from node w is small, even a large correction of the relative intensity will not affect a large change in the flow intensity forwarded into the channel. To accelerate the algorithm, we take

$$\alpha(w,r) = \frac{\alpha_0}{F_{wr}} \qquad (6.5.58)$$

where α_0 is a constant. If we assume that function $\alpha(w,r)$ is given by (6.5.58), we must choose a value for the constant α_0. In Gallager's paper [6.1], it was shown that if α_0 is small, the algorithm is convergent, albeit slowly. If α_0 is increased, Algorithm 6.5.5 becomes convergent more quickly, but if too large, it may cease to be convergent.

For the application of Algorithm 6.5.5 it is necessary to choose a certain initial flow which fulfils the continuity constraint $\mathcal{A}_f(\mathbf{X})$, the non-negativity constraints and constraints $\mathcal{B}(\mathbf{C})$, and does not have circulation. One of the possibilities is based on the application of the methods used in Algorithm 6.5.2.

6.6 METHODOLOGY FOR FINDING ROUTING RULES BASED ON THE PROPERTIES OF OPTIMUM FLOWS

In this section we will discuss methods of using the previously described properties of optimum flows to find routes for individual packets. The first part is devoted to experimental methods for estimating the rate of change of quality index $\partial Q[(w,v),F]/\partial F$ in a single channel, which, as we have shown is important in all procedures connected with the optimisation of flow. In the second part we formulate general heuristic principles for defining optimum routing rules.

6.6.1 Methods for the experimental determination of the rate of change of operating quality index for a single channel

In this section we discuss two experimental methods to estimate the rate of change of quality index for a single channel. The first, given by Agnew [6.11], is suitable where the flow introduced into a buffer located ahead of the channel can, to a good approximation, be treated as a Poisson exponential sequence. As we explained in section 5.4.3, this is the case in most networks. The second, given by Segall [6.7], does not require any assumptions about the statistical properties of the flow, but is more difficult to put into practice.

We assume:

A1 the quality of the flow takes the form

$$Q(\mathbf{F}) = \sum_{(w,v)\in K} Q[F(w,v),(w,v)] \tag{6.6.1}$$

and

A2 the channel quality is the weighted delay

$$Q[w,v;F(w,v)] = \frac{1}{F} F(w,v)\,\tau(w,v) \tag{6.6.2}$$

where

$$F = \sum_{(w,v)} F(w,v), \quad \text{and} \quad \tau(w,v)$$

is the delay introduced by the channel. The quality index defined by (6.6.1) and (6.6.2) is equal to the quality index (6.2.1). We now deal with the index

$$Q_1[F(w,v),(w,v)] = F(w,v)\,\tau(w,v) \tag{6.6.3}$$

As we indicated earlier, parameter Q_1 can be interpreted as the total time which the packets passing each second spend in the buffer and transmitter.

In the first method we try to find a function of the number L_t of all packets in the buffer and transmitter with an average value equal to the desired rate of change of quality index. Because we are considering a fixed channel (w,v), we omit the channel indices w,v and write F, τ, $Q_1(F)$ instead of $F(w,v)$, $\tau(w,v)$, $Q_1[F(w,v),(w,v)]$ etc.

We show in Appendix A.2 (formula A.2.17) that assuming (1) the packet flow is a Poisson exponential sequence, and (2) the buffer capacity is unlimited, the average time spent by the packet in the transmitter and buffer

$$\tau = \bar{T}\frac{1}{1-\nu} \tag{6.6.4}$$

where $\bar{T}$ is the average packet duration, and ν is the duty ratio of the channel (w,v). We have:

$$\nu = \frac{F}{C} \tag{6.6.5}$$

where F is the intensity of the flow forwarded to the channel (w, v), and C is the capacity. The quality index defined by (6.6.3) is:

$$Q_1(F) = \bar{T}\frac{\nu}{1-\nu} \tag{6.6.6}$$

Thus

$$\frac{\partial Q_1}{\partial F} = \bar{T}\frac{1}{(1-\nu)^2} \quad . \tag{6.6.7}$$

So estimating $\partial Q_1/\partial F$ can be reduced to estimating $(1-\nu)^{-2}$. Let us begin by estimating $(1-\nu)^{-1}$. Let L be a random variable representing the total number of packets in the buffer and channel (w, v), and λ the intensity of packet delivery. From Little's theorem we get

$$E\mathrm{L} = \lambda\tau = \frac{\lambda\bar{T}}{1-\nu} = \frac{\nu}{1-\nu} \tag{6.6.8}$$

because, $\lambda\bar{T} = \nu$. We can write equation (6.6.8) in the form

$$\frac{1}{1-\nu} = E(\mathrm{L}+1) \tag{6.6.9}$$

So $(1-\nu)^{-1}$ equals the average value of the random variable $L+1$. Now, analogously, we present $(1-\nu)^{-2}$ as the average value of a function of Ψ. Let P_1 indicate the probability of finding l packets in the buffer and transmitter. Hence:

$$E\mathrm{L}^2 = \sum_{n=1}^{\infty} l^2 P_1 \tag{6.6.10}$$

Substituting P_1 from equation (A.2.11), we get:

$$E\mathrm{L}^2 = \sum_{n=1}^{\infty} (1-\nu)\, l^2 r^1 = 1 - \frac{3}{1-\nu} + \frac{2}{(1-\nu)^2} \tag{6.6.11}$$

in which we make use of the well-known expression for the sum

$$\sum_{n=1}^{\infty} l^2 \nu^1 \ .$$

Taking (6.6.9) into consideration we obtain:

$$\frac{1}{(1-\nu)^2} = \frac{1}{2}(E\mathrm{L}^2 + 3E\mathrm{L} + 2) \tag{6.6.12}$$

Finally, considering (6.6.7), we have:

$$\frac{\partial Q_1}{\partial F} = \bar{T}E(\mathrm{L}^2/2 + 3/2\mathrm{L} + 1) \tag{6.6.13}$$

This suggests that we should take the averaged expression as the estimator of $\partial Q_1/\partial F$; such an estimator will then be the unbiased estimator. Thus equations (6.6.4) and (6.6.13) give the estimator:

$$\left(\frac{\partial Q_1}{\partial F}\right)_1^* = \bar{T}(1/2l^2 + 3/2l + 1) \tag{6.6.14}$$

where l is the actually observed number of packets at the B–Tr unit. The implementation of this estimator is very simple: to estimate the rate of change of quality index, it is enough to know the number of packets l in the buffer and transmitter. Strictly, this estimator should only be used when the packet flow is a Poisson exponential sequence. We shall now give a fairly universal estimator of the increment ratio $\partial Q/\partial F$ based on a specific procedure corresponding to the 'jack-knife' procedure used for estimating the variance of a random variable (Müller [6.12]). This estimator analyses the effect which the hypothetical removal of one packet would have on the waiting time of the other packets. Suppose that, with a probability of $\epsilon \ll 1$, we remove a packet from the sequence. Let T be the observation period during which we make our estimation, and let $l(T)$ be the number of packets arriving during this period. The change of flow intensity of information in bits is:

$$\delta F = \frac{\bar{N}_b l(t)\epsilon}{T} \tag{6.6.15}$$

where N_b is the average amount of binary information per packet. We assume that the packets are numbered according to their arrival time. When calculating the waiting time change as a result of the hypothetical removal of some packets, we introduce the time

$\vartheta(i\,|\,j)$ – the reduction of waiting time in a buffer of the ith packet if the jth packet were removed. (6.6.16)

Let $\vartheta_{\mathrm{arr}}(i)$ be the arrival time of the ith packet, and $\vartheta_{\mathrm{dep}}(i)$ the time the packet leaves the system. We now give recurrence equations for calculating $\vartheta(i\,|\,j)$. Obviously, if packet j arrives after the arrival of packet i, removal of packet j does not affect the waiting time of the ith packet. Thus:

$$\vartheta(i\,|\,j) = 0 \quad \text{for} \quad j > i\,. \tag{6.6.17}$$

We assume that the reduction in the waiting time of a packet as a result of its hypothetical removal is equal to the time really spent by that packet in the system, so

$$\vartheta(i\,|\,i) = \vartheta_{\text{dep}}(i) - \vartheta_{\text{arr}}(i) \tag{6.6.18}$$

Consider the effect of removing packet i on the time spent by packet $(i+1)$ in the system. Since $\vartheta_{\text{arr}}(i+1) > \vartheta_{\text{arr}}(i)$, three possibilities can arise, as shown in Fig. 6.16(a), (b) and (c).

(a) Where

$$\vartheta_{\text{dep}}(j-1) \leqslant \vartheta_{\text{arr}}(j+1) \leqslant \vartheta_{\text{dep}}(j)$$

we have

$$\vartheta(j+1\,|\,j) = \vartheta_{\text{dep}}(j) - \vartheta_{\text{arr}}(j+1)\ .$$

(b) Where

$$\vartheta_{\text{arr}}(j) \leqslant \vartheta_{\text{dep}}(j-1) \quad \text{and} \quad \vartheta_{\text{arr}}(j+1) < \vartheta_{\text{dep}}(j-1)$$

we have

$$\begin{aligned}\vartheta(j+1\,|\,j) &= \vartheta_{\text{dep}}(j) - \vartheta_{\text{arr}}(j+1) - [\vartheta_{\text{dep}}(j-1) - \vartheta_{\text{arr}}(j+1)] \\ &= \vartheta_{\text{dep}}(j) - \vartheta_{\text{dep}}(j-1)\ .\end{aligned}$$

(c) Where

$$\vartheta_{\text{arr}}(j+1) > \vartheta_{\text{dep}}(j)$$

we have

$$\vartheta(j+j\,|\,i) = 0$$

These equations can be written in the form

$$\vartheta(j+1\,|\,j) = \begin{cases} \vartheta_{\text{dep}}(j) - \max\,[\vartheta_{\text{arr}}(j+1), \vartheta_{\text{dep}}(j-1)] \\ \qquad\qquad \text{for} \quad \vartheta_{\text{arr}}(j+1) \leqslant \vartheta_{\text{dep}}(j) \\ 0 \quad \text{for} \quad \vartheta_{\text{arr}}(j+1) > \vartheta_{\text{dep}} \end{cases} \tag{6.6.19}$$

In the case in which $j < i+1$, the three situations shown in Fig. 6.16(d), (e) and (f) occur, in which $\vartheta^*_{\text{dep}}(j-1)$ is the time at which the $(i-1)$th packet leaves the system when the jth packet is removed. By the definition

$$\vartheta_{\text{dep}}(j-1) - \vartheta^*_{\text{dep}}(j-1) = \vartheta(j-1\,|\,j)$$

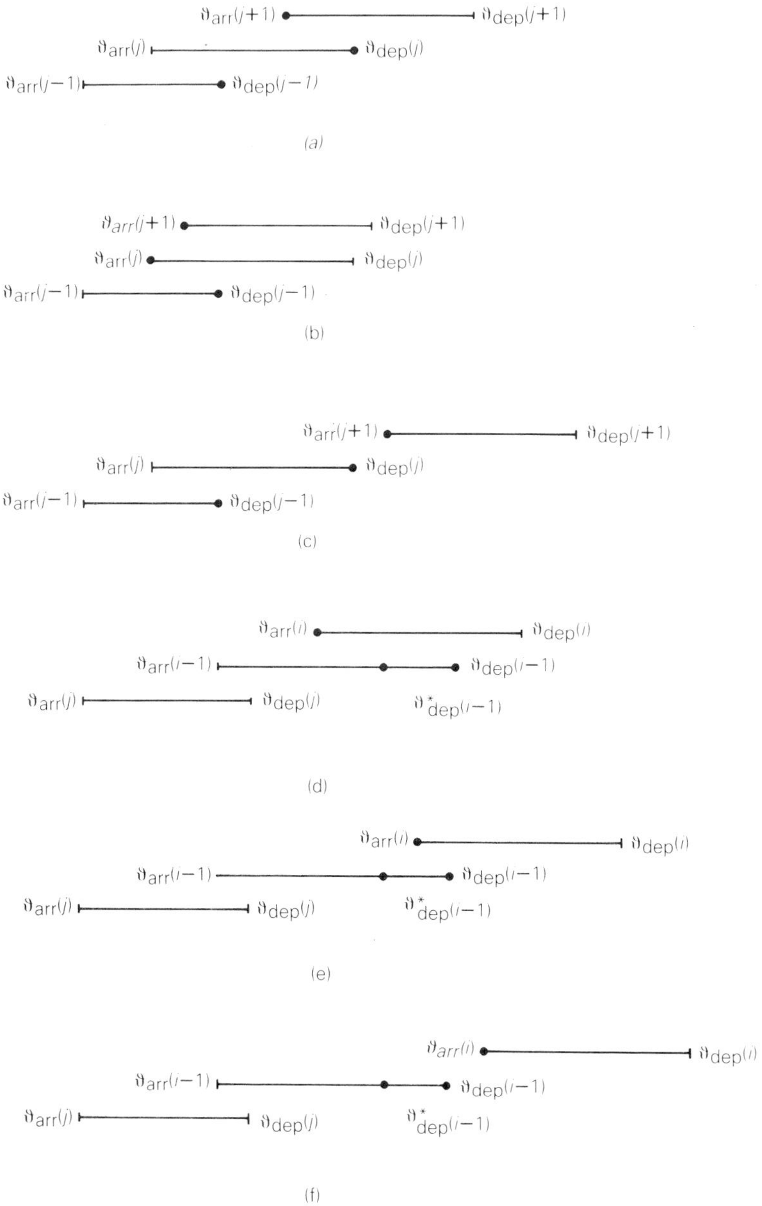

Fig. 6.16 – Possible mutual positions between arrival (ϑ_{arr}) and departure (ϑ_{dep}) instants of successive packets.

(d) Where

$$\vartheta_{\mathrm{arr}}(i) \leqslant \vartheta^*_{\mathrm{dep}}(i-1)$$

the gain as a result of removing the jth packet is

$$\vartheta_{\mathrm{dep}}(i-1) - \vartheta_{\mathrm{arr}}(i) - [\vartheta^*_{\mathrm{dep}}(i-1) - \vartheta_{\mathrm{arr}}(i)] =$$

$$= \vartheta_{\mathrm{dep}}(i-1) - \vartheta^*_{\mathrm{dep}}(i-1) = \vartheta(i-1|j) \; .$$

(e) Where

$$\vartheta^*_{\mathrm{dep}}(i-1) \leqslant \vartheta_{\mathrm{arr}}(i) \leqslant \vartheta_{\mathrm{dep}}(i-1)$$

the gain is equal to

$$\vartheta_{\mathrm{dep}}(i-1) - \vartheta_{\mathrm{arr}}(i)$$

(f) As in case (c), the gain is equal to 0.

Thus in general:

$$\vartheta(i|j) \begin{cases} \min\,[\vartheta(i-1|j), \vartheta_{\mathrm{dep}}(i-1) - \vartheta_{\mathrm{arr}}(i)] & \text{for } \vartheta_{\mathrm{arr}}(i) \leqslant \vartheta_{\mathrm{dep}}(i-1) \\ 0 & \text{for } \vartheta_{\mathrm{arr}}(i) \geqslant \vartheta_{\mathrm{dep}}(i-1) \end{cases} \tag{6.6.20}$$

We now show that knowing $\vartheta(i|j)$, we can calculate the change of average flow intensity. From the interpretation of the index Q_1 given after equation (6.6.3), and the definition $Q(i|j)$, it is immediately evident that the change in total time spent in the buffer and transmitter of a packet flowing through during one second is

$$\delta Q_1 = \frac{N_b}{XT} \sum_{i=1}^{l(T)} \sum_{j=1}^{i} \epsilon\nu(i|j) \tag{6.6.21}$$

whereby in the second sum we sum over only $j \geqslant i$ because of (6.6.17). Taking (6.6.15) into account we get the estimator for $\partial Q_1/\partial F$:

$$\left(\frac{\partial Q_1}{\partial F}\right)^*_2 = \frac{1}{Xl(T)} \sum_{i=1}^{l(T)} \sum_{j=1}^{j} \vartheta(i|j) \tag{6.6.22}$$

The implementation of this estimator is reduced to recording times $\vartheta_{\mathrm{arr}}(i)$ and $\vartheta_{\mathrm{dep}}(i)$ and calculating $\vartheta(i|j)$ recurrently on the basis of equations (6.6.18–6.6.20). This requires far more computation and memory than the calculation of the estimator $(\partial Q_1/\partial F)^*_1$ given by (6.6.14), but the estimator $(\partial Q_1/\partial F)^*_2$ can be applied without the restricting assumption being satisfied, as in the case when using the estimator $(\partial Q_1/\partial F)^*_1$. A modification of the estimator $(\partial Q_1/\partial F)^*_2$ is possible by analysing the results of introducing an additional packet instead of removing a packet; this kind of estimator is analysed by Segall [6.7].

6.6.2 Routing rules based on optimum flows

We will now show how the previously derived properties of optimum flow patterns and the algorithm for their determination can be applied to find good quality routing rules. As the method is essentially heuristic, we give here general hints and not precise rules of procedure.

When applying the conclusions concerning the optimum time-invariant flow pattern, we must remember that flow in a real network changes, and that a time-invariant flow can be a reasonably good model of the actual flow only during a finite time-interval. This suggests that the routing rules should operate in a similar way to the adaptive network described in section 5.3.2, i.e. that the time axis should be divided into adjacent intervals which we will call **updating intervals.** At the end of each interval, the state of the network is estimated and a suitable routing rule applied which is valid only until the end of the next updating interval. The state is again estimated and a routing rule, perhaps differing from the one before, is used during the next updating interval. There are two basic ways of choosing the updating interval: (a) fixed, (b) flexible. In fixed choice, the updating intervals are predetermined and usually have the same duration as shown in Fig. 5.13. In flexible choice, we take a time-dependent parameter characterising the state of the network, for example, the amount by which some of its quality indices change, and we start a new updating interval when this parameter exceeds a threshold value, also called **threshold-conditional choice.** These two methods of choosing the updating intervals correspond obviously to the methods of choosing instants for sampling the states of nodes, described in section 1.3.2.

We now discuss how our previous considerations on optimum stationary flow can be applied to the determination of the routing rule which is to be used during the next updating interval. Two approaches are possible: (a) at the end of the updating interval we determine the optimum flow pattern and try to route individual packets such that this flow pattern is realised during the next updating interval; (b) we use only the general conclusions about the properties of the optimum flow pattern and we try to guess the routing rule which would yield an average flow pattern similar to the optimum. We call the first approach the **direct application** of flow pattern optimisation, the second the **indirect application** approach. It is evident that for the direct application, the optimisation algorithms presented in section 6.5 will be needed, while for the indirect applications, a few of the general properties derived in 6.4 will suffice. In the direct application approach it is essential to determine a routing rule yielding a desired average flow pattern. When we have the whole flow along a single path only, the problem is trivial. We simply have to send each packet along that path. Usually, however, the flow has branches. Suppose that the flow is memoryless and a branch occurs at node w. We then take a randomised Markovian routing rule characterised by the conditional probabilities $P_r(v|w)$, where $v \in N_{out}(w)$, are the probabilities of directing a packet destined for q into channel (w, v).

If $F_{wr}^{(out)}$ is the intensity of total flow directed from w to destination q (see definition 6.2.15), the average flow intensity along channel (w, v) will be

$$F_r(w, v) = P_r(v|w)\, F_{wr}^{(out)} \tag{6.6.23}$$

Thus we obtain the desired flow pattern if we apply the randomised Markovian routing rule with

$$P_r(v|w) = \frac{F_r(w, v)}{F_{wr}^{(out)}} \quad . \tag{6.6.24}$$

The question arises whether the external flow intensities X_{wr} and the probabilities $P_r(v|w)$ determine the flow pattern uniquely. Using (6.2.15) and (6.6.23) we have for $w \neq r$

$$F_{wr} = X_{wr} + \sum_{u \in N_{in}(w)} P_r(w|u) F_{ur} \quad . \tag{6.6.25}$$

This set of equations is equivalent to the set (6.2.31) if we take $P_r(w|u)$ for $f_r(u, w)$ where the normalisation requirement for probabilities $P_r(v|w)$ corresponds to equation (6.2.30). We can directly use theorem (6.2.35) and conclude that assuming the path is not clogged (i.e. $P_r(w|v) > 0$), the probabilities $P_r(v|w)$ and external flow intensities X_{wr} determine the flow pattern uniquely.

The general direct application of the results of average flow optimisation for determining individual packet routing consists of two stages: (a) during the present updating interval we collect data needed to carry out one of the algorithms for finding the optimum flow pattern; (b) having determined this flow pattern, we apply the randomised Markovian routing rule determined by probabilities given by (6.6.24) during the next updating interval.

Let us consider stage (a) in more detail. Algorithms 6.5.1, 6.5.2 and 6.5.3 are suitable for application in systems with centralised network identification and centralised routing rule evaluation (see section 1.5.3). In such systems, each node delivers the estimates $(\partial Q/\partial F(k))^*$ of the derivatives $\partial Q/\partial F(k)$ (6.6.1) to the network control centre. The control centre also retains the values of the intensities $F(k)$ in its memory. With this data, one step of the algorithms can be performed. For the corrected flow pattern, the probabilities $P_r(v|w)$ can be evaluated and suitable corrections to the values of these probabilities for the previous updating interval are delivered to the nodes. The obvious problem is the choice of the length of the updating interval. If it is too short, not only do we have to pay a lot for frequently sending updating information, but the deviations of the mean values of intensities from their statistical averages may be large, thus the flow intensities resulting from the random choices of routes will not be optimal. If the updating interval is too large, the properties of the network may change, the optimum flow pattern will also change and the modification of flow intensities given by the algorithms will be outdated. In view of the many factors influencing the choice of updating interval, a procedure for its adaptive adjustment may be helpful.

The algorithm described in section 6.5.4 based on the node-orientated network description is suitable for decentralised n.s.i. collection and routing rule evaluation. The operation of such a system is similar to that of the system described to section 5.4.2. The nodes from the set $N_{\text{in}}(r)$ of nodes connected by direct channels to the destination node q estimate the increment ratios $(\partial Q/\partial F(k))^*$. These estimates are then sent backwards to nodes connected by direct channels to the nodes from the set $N_{\text{in}}(r)$. Taking the estimates obtained as the real incremental ratios and using (6.4.37), and if necessary, the conclusion (6.4.38), the estimates $(\partial Q/\partial X_{wr})^*$ can be evaluated and sent backwards again. As a result of such a procedure, each node w has an estimate of $(\partial Q/\partial X_{vr})^*$ for nodes $v \in N_{\text{out}}(w)$ and it can evaluate its own estimate $(\partial Q/\partial F(w, v))^*$. These estimates are sufficient for evaluating the corrections given by algorithm 6.5.4. The estimates can also determine the blocked nodes $B_r(w)$ which must be avoided to prevent flow circulation. At each node we can check if any of the outgoing flows is improper. If it is, the node adds a tag to its estimate $(\partial Q/\partial X_{wr})^*$ saying that an improper flow exists at node w, and this is forwarded to the nodes from set $N_{\text{in}}(w)$. After obtaining such a tag, each node $v^* \in N_{\text{in}}(w)$ adds it to its estimate of $(\partial Q/\partial X_{wr})^*$. When introducing modifications according to Algorithm 6.5.4 based on these estimates, we do not take into account nodes which delivered their $(\partial Q/\partial X_{vr})^*$ estimates with a tag.

It is evident that the two-stage procedure in which we first find the optimum or a 'good' average flow pattern and then apply the randomised Markovian routing rule governed by probabilities determined by the flow intensities is unnecessarily complicated. We cannot say that it gives us value for money. Therefore it is worth analysing heuristic routing rules based on the indirect application of the optimum flow patterns mentioned on page 336. We only look for paths which are shortest in the sense suggested by optimum flow analysis and forward packets along these paths. For the conclusions based on the channel- or path-orientated flow description (derived in sections 6.4.1, 6.4.2) we take the partial derivatives $\partial Q/\partial F(k)$ as the length. The procedure is as described in section 5.4.1, with one difference: instead of estimates of the delay, we propagate the estimates $(\partial Q/\partial F(k))^*$ through the network. In optimum flow analysis based on the node-orientated description, we use the previously discussed estimates $(\partial Q/\partial X_{wr})$. A rule primarily using the estimate $(\partial Q_1/\partial F(k))_1^*$ described in section 6.6.1 was suggested by Agnew [6.11]. In this paper the quality of this rule obtained by simulation was compared with quality of the rule described in section 5.3.1 (ARPA-type rule based on estimates of τ), and it was shown that for the simple network considered in the example, the rule based on $(\partial Q/\partial F(k))_1^*$ is better by some 10%.

Our discussion in section 6.5.3 suggests that the rule can be improved by adding a tag to the estimates of $\partial Q/\partial R_{wq}$, from node w if it contains an outgoing improper flow. The local routing decisions would be based on the available estimates of $\beta_r(w, v)$ defined by (6.5.40) with suitable estimates instead of real values, with nodes which sent an estimate with the tag, excluded. Such a rule was suggested by Gallager [6.1].

The application of the optimum time-varying flows is similar. Again we divide the time axis into updating intervals. At the end T_n of the present updating interval we estimate the next time-varying external flow intensities $R_{wr}^*(t)$, $t \in \langle T_n, T_{n+1}\rangle$ valid for the next updating interval $\langle T_n, T_{n+1}\rangle$. Thus we face a prediction problem. Knowing the estimates $X_{wr}^*(t)$ we can next find the optimum time-varying flow intensities $F_{wr}(t)$, $w,r = 1, 2, \ldots, N$, $w \neq r$, $t \in T_{n+1}$. Then taking the direct approach mentioned on page 336, we use the Markovian randomised rule, with time-dependent passage probabilities $P_r(v|w;t)$.

Obviously, the application of this procedure would be complicated. However, in most cases we may expect the network state to change slowly. Then we can present the external flow intensities in the form

$$X_{wr}(t) = X_{wr}^{(st)} + \delta X_{wr}(t)$$

where $X_{wr}^{(st)}$ is the large component, constant within the updating interval, and $\delta X_{wr}(t)$ is a slowly varying, linear function. The optimum flow pattern may then be presented as a stationary optimum flow pattern determined by

$$X^{(st)} = \{X_{w,r}^{(st)}, w,r = 1,2,\ldots,N\}$$

with a time-varying correction determined by the time-varying change

$$\delta X(t) = \{\delta X_{w,r}(t), w,r = 1,2,\ldots,N\}$$

Well-known methods of control theory of optimising can be used for the correction. Similarly, we can present the corresponding routing rule as a combination of two rules: the static rule inside the updating interval, and the time-varying rule. Such a routing rule was analysed by Filipiak [6.3].

REFERENCES

[6.1] Gallager, R., (1977), A minimum delay routing algorithm using distributed computation, *IEEE Trans. on Comm.*, **COM-25**, 73–85.

[6.2] Rider, K. L., (1975), A simple approximation of the average queue size in the time-dependent MM1 queue, *Journ. Ass. Comp. Mach.*, **23**, 361–367.

[6.3] Filipiak, J., (1981), Unloading of congestion in deterministic queueing networks, *Optimum Control Applications and Methods*, **2**, 35–45.

[6.4] Luenberger, D. G., (1972), *Introduction to Linear and Nonlinear Programming*, Academic Press, New York.

[6.5] Wilde, D. J., and Beightler, C. S., (1967), *Foundations of Optimization*, Prentice-Hall, Englewood Cliffs, N.J.

[6.6] Pontryagin, L. S., Boltyanski, V. G., and Gamkrelidze, R. V., (1962), *The Mathematical Theory of Optimal Processes*, Wiley–Interscience, New York.

[6.7] Segall, A., (1977), The modeling of adaptive routing in data-communication networks, *IEEE Trans. on Comm.*, **COM-25**, 85–95.

[6.8] Fratta, L., Gerla, N., and Kleinrock, L., (1973), The flow deviation method. An approach to store-and-forward communication network design, *Networks*, **3**, 97–133.

[6.9] Schwartz, and Cheung, C. K., (1976), The gradient projection algorithm for multiple routing in message-switched networks, *IEEE Trans. on Comm.*, **COM-24**, 449–456.

[6.10] Harris, R. J., (1974), Concepts of optimality in alternate routing networks, Doctoral Dissertation, University of Adelaide.

[6.11] Agnew, C. E., (1976), On quadratic adaptive routing algorithms, *Comm. of the ACM*, **19**, No. 1, 18–22.

[6.12] Müller, R. G., (1974), The jack knife; a review, *Biometrica*, **61**, No. 1, 1–15.

7

Congestion and methods of counteracting it

We previously assumed the intensities of external flows into the network to be fixed. We are often interested in network behaviour when the intensities increase. We may expect a deterioration in the quality of packet transmission, small for light loads but becoming rapidly worse for heavier loads. The rapid decrease of transmission quality is called **congestion**. This effect is well-known in other multiserver systems.

Congestion is usually caused by either or both of two mechanisms: (1) mutual blocking of access to the channels by various users (deadlocks), (2) unjustified seizure of channels or buffers by some users. Typical examples of (1) are the saturation effects on feedback systems, and of (2) are the unnecessary circulation of packets around loops.

The primary cause of congestion is insufficient accuracy or too great a delay of system state information on which packet-handling decisions are based. The improvement for heavy loads which can be achieved by supplying more s.s.i. in multiaccess systems with a common channel was discussed in Chapters 3 and 4 (see in particular Fig. 4.12).

The general method of counteracting congestion is not to admit new packets to the network when we already have too many packets in the network. Similarly, a packet may not be admitted to certain areas of the network or to certain channels. The non-admitted packets may be destroyed or may be stored outside the network.

In the first section of this chapter we introduce the fundamental concepts and the classification of methods of counteracting congestion. This classification is based on the type of network state information on which the admission decision is based. It can be information about various types of packets either in the whole network or in the nodes adjacent to the node at which the packet has just arrived. We call the first type of information **global information**, the other type **local information**. In the second section of this chapter we will deal with admission rules based on global information, while the last section is concerned with rules based on local information.

The analytic evaluation of characteristics of methods for counteracting congestion is possible only after making certain simplifying assumptions. This is because as a result of applying an admission control rule, the states of various nodes become statistically dependent, when they could otherwise be considered as independent. The fundamental mathematical tool for analysing networks with a congestion-counteracting packet admission rule are the results of queueing theory, in particular the product form representation theorem of the probabilities of the states of such networks. A review of the results of the theory of networks of queues which are used in this chapter is given in Appendix 7 and Appendix 8.

7.1 FUNDAMENTAL CONCEPTS

In this section we introduce the fundamental concepts related to congestion and we give a simple example illustrating the overloading of a single buffer. Then we give the classification of methods of counteracting congestion.

7.1.1 Behaviour of a system when its loading increases

We denote by $\lambda_0(m)$ the intensity of packets delivered by the mth source for transmission to the mth destination and by

$$\lambda = \sum_{m=1}^{M} \lambda_m \tag{7.1.1}$$

the total intensity of all external flows accessing the network. On the assumption that packets from all sources consist of the same average number $\bar{N}$ bits the intensities λ_m and λ are related by the formulae

$$X_m = \bar{N}\lambda_m \tag{7.1.2}$$

$$X = \bar{N}\lambda \tag{7.1.3}$$

to the intensities X_m, X of packet flow previously introduced.

As will be shown by a number of examples, the average delay τ' typically depends on λ as shown in Fig. 7.1. This shows that for small λ the growth of τ' is slow, but for large λ it becomes very rapid. One reason for this is that with large values of λ new mechanisms, such as packet circulation may appear, which are responsible for the rapid growth of τ'.

We have previously assumed that each packet entering the network is delivered to its destination. This would be so if the system were stable and the buffers in the network had infinite storage capacity. However real buffers can accommodate only a finite number of packets, if more packets arrive they are rejected. In a real network the average intensity λ^+ of the packets which go through the network

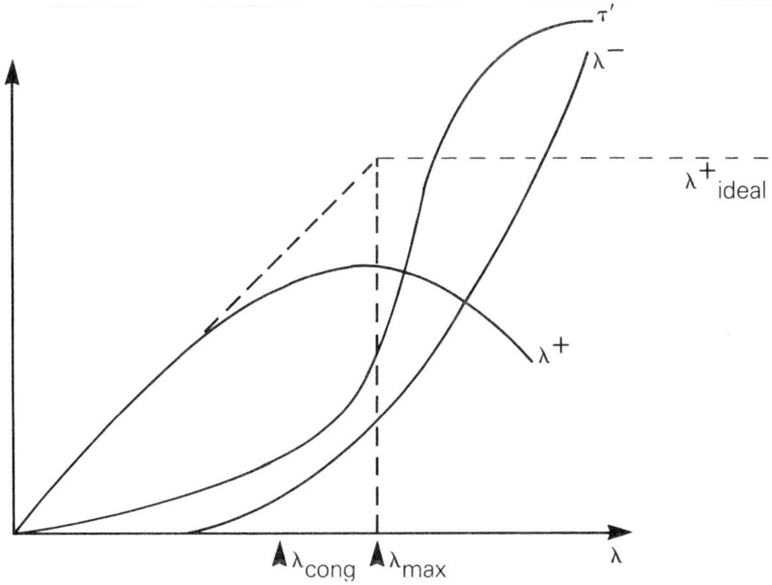

Fig. 7.1 – Typical dependence of average normalised delay τ, intensity λ^+ of packets going through the network, and intensity λ^- of lost packets on the total intensity λ of packets offered to the network by external sources λ_{id}, intensity of packets going through in an ideal system; λ_{max}, capacity bound for λ^+.

successfully is less than the average intensity λ of packets delivered to the network by external sources, even if the total intensity λ is smaller than

$$\lambda_{max} \equiv X_{max}/\bar{N} \tag{7.1.4}$$

where X_{max} is the maximum total intensity of flow which can be carried by the network. As we have shown in section 6.3 the latter is determined by the capacities of channels. The difference

$$\lambda^- = \lambda - \lambda^+ \tag{7.1.5}$$

is the average intensity of packets which are either not accepted by the network or which are lost during transit through the network. We may expect the dependence of the intensity λ^- on the total intensity λ to be shown in Fig. 7.1. For small λ the intensity λ^- is negligible. If, λ becomes too large, the intensity λ^- starts to grow very rapidly. A good example of systems performing in this way are multiaccess systems with feedback, analysed in Chapter 3. The curves shown in Figs. 3.11 and 3.12 are concrete examples of the illustration in Fig. 7.1.

The effect of the rapid reduction in the quality of packet transmission and the increase in intensity λ^- of lost packets with increasing λ we call **congestion.**

As the change in the growth rate of the quality and intensity of rejected packets and decrease of quality are usually continuous, the definition of the value of λ_{cong} when the network is be considered as congested is a matter of convention.

Each congestion control method causes in general an improvement of packet transmission quality e.g. decrease of the average delay, but an increase of intensity of lost packets. Different methods yield various values of quality improvement and loss increase, depending on the choice of parameters. Such pairs of values give us the operational characteristics of a given congestion control method.

To illustrate the effects of increasing load we take a very simple example, namely a single buffer–transmitter unit. The limitation of the access we obtain by assuming that the buffer capacity is limited.

Example 7.1.1

We consider the single buffer–transmitter unit (B–Tr) shown in Fig. 7.2. We assume that:

A1 The input is a Poisson exponential sequence; λ denotes the intensity of packet starting instants and T their average length.

A2 The capacity of the (B–Tr) unit is finite: at the most, L packets can reside in it. If a packet arrives when there are already L packets in the (B–Tr) unit the new packet is rejected.

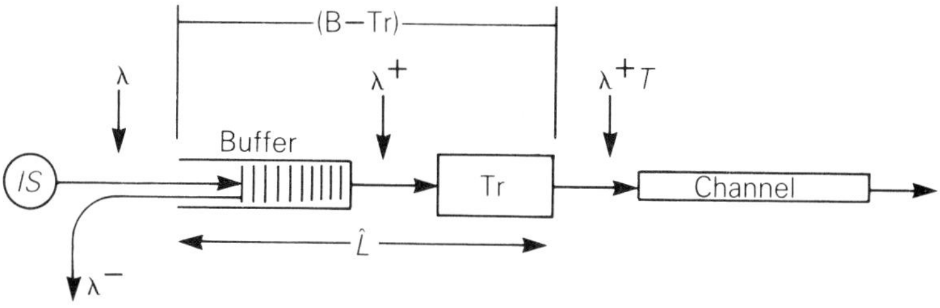

Fig. 7.2 – System considered in Example 7.1.1. Tr, transmitter, (B–Tr), Buffer–Transmitter unit.

Let $P(1)$ be the probability of finding 1 packet in the (B–Tr) unit. As shown in Appendix A2 (formula A.2.11)

$$P(1) = P(0)\nu^{l} \tag{7.1.6}$$

$l = 0, 1, \ldots, L$ where

$$\nu \equiv \lambda T \tag{7.1.7}$$

is the normalised intensity; it can be $\nu > 1$. Obviously

$$\nu = X/C \tag{7.1.8}$$

where X, the intensity of the flow of packets delivered by the source in bits/s, and C is channel capacity.

The coefficient $P(0)$ in (7.1.6) is determined from the normalisation constraint:

$$\sum_{l=0}^{\hat{L}} P(l) = 1 \; . \tag{7.1.9}$$

The average number of packets in the (B–Tr) is:

$$L = \sum_{l=1}^{\hat{L}} lP(1) = \frac{\nu - \nu^2 - (\hat{L}+1)\nu^{\hat{L}+1} + \nu^{\hat{L}+2}}{(1-\nu)^2\,(1-\nu^{\hat{L}+1})} \tag{7.1.10}$$

whereas the intensity of the rejected blocks

$$\lambda^- = \lambda P^- \tag{7.1.11}$$

where

$$P^- \equiv P(\hat{L}) \tag{7.1.12}$$

is the probability of non-acceptance of a new packet. The average intensity of packets ultimately accepted

$$\lambda^+ = \lambda(1-P^-) \tag{7.1.13}$$

The average waiting time of a block in the (B–Tr) unit is obtained from Little's formula:

$$\tau = \frac{\bar{L}}{\lambda^+} \tag{7.1.14}$$

The normalised routing time

$$\tau' = \tau/T \tag{7.1.15}$$

characterises the operation of the system, as do the dimensionless parameters

$$\nu^+ \equiv \lambda^+ T \tag{7.1.16}$$

$$\nu^- \equiv \lambda^- T \tag{7.1.17}$$

As the packet can only be fed into the channel after the transmission of the previous packet is completed, we have $\nu^+ \leqslant 1$.

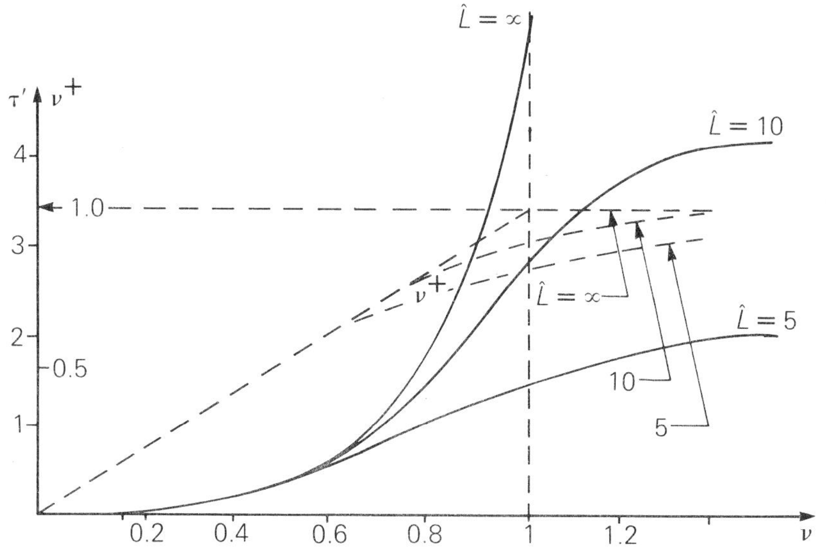

Fig. 7.3 – Dependence of the normalised intensity ν^+ of accepted packets (broken lines) and the normalised average waiting time τ' (continuous lines) on the normalised intensity ν of packets delivered by the source for the system shown in Fig. 7.2.

We can calculate the parameters ν^- and τ' using formulae (7.1.10) and (7.1.12) Fig. 7.3 shows graphs of the relationships between these parameters and ν. It may be seen from Fig. 7.3 that for a buffer of infinite capacity, we have $\nu^+ = \nu, \nu^- = 0$ for $\nu < 1$, and $\nu^+ = 1, \nu \equiv \nu - 1$ for $\nu > 1$. If $\hat{L}$ is finite, ν^+ rises for $\nu > 1$. For $\nu = 1$, we get from (7.1.3)

$$\nu^+ = \frac{\hat{L}}{\hat{L} + 1} \cdot \nu \ . \tag{7.1.18}$$

We see from Fig. 7.3 that for $\nu \to 1$, the waiting time grows infinitely if the capacity is unlimited. If the capacity is finite, the growth of τ' for ν around 1 is smooth. As is seen from Fig. 7.3 for the simple example considered the intensity λ^+ of packets going successfully through the system grows monotonically with the intensity λ of external packets put into the system. In more complex systems the dependence of the type shown in Fig. 7.1 may occur. Examples are multi-access systems with feedback considered in Chapter 3. In these systems with heavy loading the number of retransmissions grows rapidly and the multiple collisions cause the intensity of packets going successfully through to decrease with increasing load.

7.1.2 Classification of admission rules

The fundamental method of congestion control is not to allow a packet to enter an area of the network if storage or communication resources in this area are exhausted. In the extreme case, the area may cover the whole network. This is equivalent to adding to the the set of possible routing decisions an additional element: the decision that the packet must not enter the area, or in the extreme case, the network. We will call this the **non-admission decision**. The decision about how a packet arriving should be handled, either the route along which it should be sent or a rejection decision, we call the **handling decision.**

Like the routing decision discussed in Chapters 5 and 6, the handling decision is based on the information ξ_n about the state of the network and on the information ξ_p about the packet itself (contained usually in the organising part of the packet). The rule weighing the handling decision against the information (ξ_n, ξ_p) is called the **packet handling rule** and is denoted by $\mathbf{H}(\cdot)$. Thus $\mathbf{H}(\xi_p, \xi_n)$ can be either a path, the next node to which the packet should be fowarded, or the decision that the packet may not enter the area.

Let us introduce the auxiliary decisions:

α^+ a packet can be admitted into a given area to be routed according to a routing rule;

α^- it must not be admitted.

The binary decision, which can be either α^+ or α^-, is denoted by α, and called the **admission decision.** The rule which makes the admission decision on the basis of the information ξ_n, ξ_p is called the **admission rule** and is denoted by $A(\cdot)$.

We can consider the packet-handling decision as a two-stage decision rule. In the first stage we make the admission decision and if this is α^+, we then make a routing decision. Thus the packet-handling rule $\mathbf{H}(\cdot)$ can be considered to be a two-component rule consisting of the admission rule $A(\cdot)$ and the routing rule $R(\cdot)$, thus:

$$\mathbf{H}(\cdot) = \{A(\cdot), R(\cdot)\} \tag{7.1.19}$$

In general, the admission and routing rules should be considered jointly. This is because when making the admission decision, we have to take into account the path along which the packet could be forwarded, so that it is transmitted efficiently and does not disturb the transmission of other packets. The implementation of an admission rule taking into account the eventual subsequent routing is quite complicated, and in most networks we make admission decisions separately from the details of packet routing. Thus we consider the admission rule $A(\cdot)$ separately from the routing rule $R(\cdot)$. We will now take such an approach.

As in the case of routing rules, we can classify admission rules on the basis of the type of network identification information which is available. We will consider these types.

In section 6.1 we introduced the network state description corresponding to the most accurate individual packet model, which is based on division of the packets into I disjoint classes. Typical are divisions based on: (1) number of the source–destination pair, (2) history of the packet. Type 1 division we realise by dividing the set $\mathcal{M} = 1, 2, \ldots, M$ into I non-overlapping subsets $\mathcal{B}_i, i = 1,2,\ldots,I$, so that we have

$$\mathcal{M} = \bigcup_{i=1}^{I} \mathcal{B}_i \tag{7.1.20}$$

$$\mathcal{B}_i \cap \mathcal{B}_j = \phi \tag{7.1.21}$$

for $i \neq j$. We say that the packet belongs to ith class if the number of source–destination pairs for this packet belongs to $\mathcal{B}_i$. In the extreme case we take $I = M$ and $\mathcal{B}_m = m$, thus we say that the packet belongs to the mth class if the number of its source–destination is m.

Let $l_i(k)$ be the number of packets of ith class at the input of kth channel and let $l'_m(k)$ be the number of packets directed from mth source to mth destination (we also denote it by $l_{\mathrm{pq}}(k)$). It is

$$l_i(k) = \sum_{m \in \mathcal{B}_i} l'_m(k) \tag{7.1.22}$$

Typical type 2 division is the dichotomy into two classes

(1) external packets newly delivered by the local source;
(2) internal packets which were somehow processed, e.g. which passed through some channel.

The total number of packets of ith class in the whole network is

$$l_i = \sum_{k \in \mathcal{K}} l_i(k) \tag{7.1.23}$$

where K is the set of all nodes. The set

$$\mathbf{l} = \{\mathbf{l}_i,\ i = 1,2,\ldots,I\} \tag{7.1.24}$$

we call **global n.s.i.** In the extreme case, when we have only one class, i.e. $I = 1$ the number

$$l = \sum_{m=1}^{M} \sum_{k=1}^{K} l'_m(k) \tag{7.1.25}$$

is the total number of all packets in the network; we call it the **reduced global n.s.i.**

The global information is a synthetic characterisation of all nodes, hence we call it global. The admission decisions may also be based on more detailed but local n.s.i. Let us assume that the packet is actually at node w. We denote the upper neighbourhood of node w by $N_{out}(w)$, and the channels going out of node $u \in N_{out}(w)$ by $k_\mu(u)$, $\mu = 1, 2, \ldots, M_1$. The local information about the state of the network is the set:

$$\mathbf{l}_{loc}(w) = \{l_i[k_\mu(u)],\ i = 1, 2, \ldots, I,\ \mu = 1, 2, \ldots, M_1, u \in N_{out}(w)\} \quad (7.1.26)$$

i.e. the set of numbers of packets of various classes at the inputs of channels which can be reached by direct channels going out of node w.

Let us first take a system in which we have global information: $\mathbf{l} = \{l_1, \ldots, l_I\}$ about the total number of packets of a given class in the whole network. We choose a set of thresholds $\hat{L}_i$, $i = 1, 2, \ldots, I$, and admit a new packet only if the thresholds $\hat{L}_i$ are not exceeded; i.e. we apply the admission rule:

$$A_1(\mathbf{l}) = \alpha^+ \text{ if } l_i < \hat{L}_i \quad \text{for} \quad i = 1, 2, \ldots, I \quad (7.1.27)$$

Since the admission decision is binary we take decision α^- if we do not take α^+. Therefore describing $A(\cdot)$ we state only when α^+ is taken; we shall do similarly subsequently.

In the special case when $I = 1$, i.e. when we have only l, the total number of all packets in the network, we use the rule

$$A_2(l) = \alpha^+ \quad \text{if} \quad l < \hat{L} \quad (7.1.28)$$

where $\hat{L}$ is the threshold for the total number of packets knowing the number of packets l_i, $i = 1, 2, \ldots, I$, we can evaluate the total number of packets and apply the composite rule

$$A_3(\mathbf{l}) = \alpha^+ \quad \text{if} \quad l_i < L_i,\ i = 1, 2, \ldots, I \quad \text{and} \quad l < \hat{L} \quad (7.1.29)$$

The admission rule can be characterised by a set A^+ of sets $\mathbf{l}$ such that $\mathsf{A}(\mathbf{l}) = \alpha^+$ if and only if $\mathbf{l} \in \mathsf{A}^+$.

To illustrate the relationship between the above three rules, let us assume that $I = 2$. The sets A^+ in the $l_1 \times l_2$ plane corresponding to these rules are shown in Fig. 7.4. From these figures it is evident that the rule $A_3(l)$ is the most general one. Taking

$$\hat{L} = \sum_{i=1}^{I} \hat{L}_i \quad (7.1.30)$$

we obtain the rule $A_1(\cdot)$ as the special case, whereas taking

$$\hat{L} < \min\{\hat{L}_i,\ i = 1, 2, \ldots, I\} \quad (7.1.31)$$

we obtain the rule $A_2(\cdot)$.

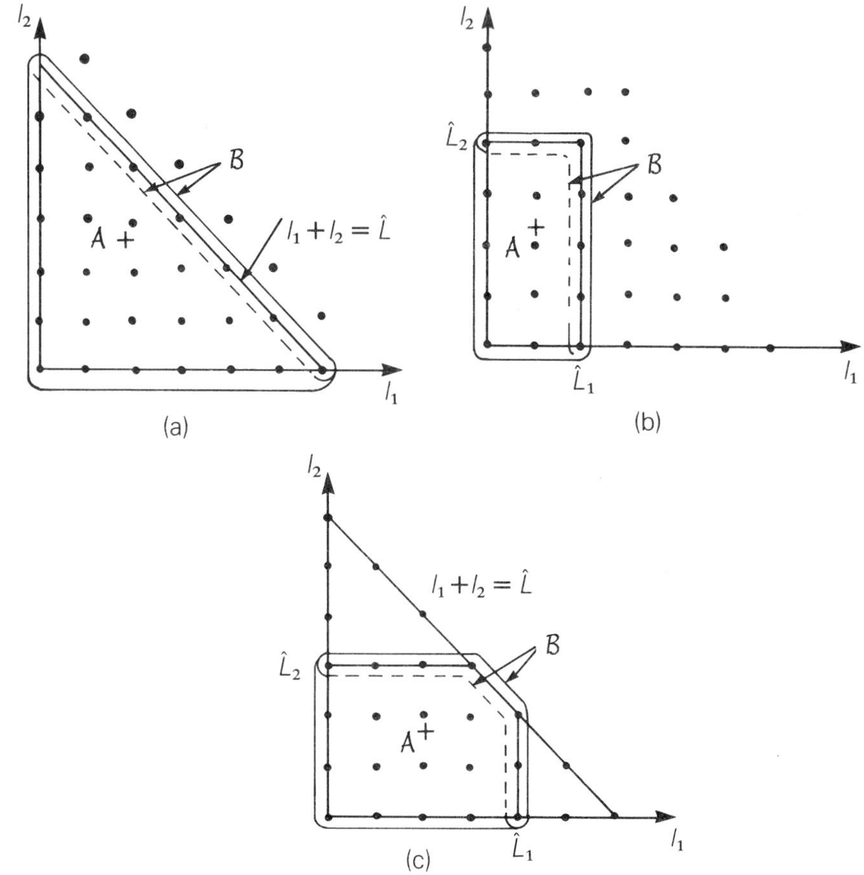

Fig. 7.4 – The sets A^+ in the $l_1 \times l_2$ space of admissible sets of packet numbers in the case of rule: (a) $A_1(\cdot)$, (b) $A_2(\cdot)$, (c) $A_3(\cdot)$, $\hat{L} < \max(\hat{L}_1, \hat{L}_2)$. B is the set of boundary points.

To make decisions according to rules $A_j(\cdot)$, $j = 1, 2, 3$, we must be able to check at the place where decisions are made if inequalities of type $l_i < \hat{L}_i$ are satisfied or not. This in turn requires a suitable n.s.i. subsystem delivering to the place where decision are made information about the numbers of packets $l_i(k)$ at all nodes k, so that we can evaluate l_i. There are a variety of possible n.s.i. subsystems described in section 1.3.2. We can expect that the implementation of such systems delivering n.s.i. without excessive delay would be costly.

We can, however, perform admission control similar to that previously considered by introducing entrance tickets of types corresponding to classes. A new packet is admitted to the network if an entrance ticket corresponding to the packet's class is available at the node adjacent to the information source which generated the packet. When the packet arrives at its destination it releases the ticket. The number of tickets of a given type is fixed. Obviously we can never have more packets of a given class than we have entrance tickets of the corresponding type in the network. Thus admission control based on entrance tickets is at least as restrictive as that based on the knowledge that the total number of packets of a given class does not surpass a threshold. However, it may be that a new packet cannot enter the network even if the threshold is not surpassed, merely because no ticket is available at the node adjacent to the packet's source.

To describe the system with entrance tickets we must specify the subsystem for distributing the released entrance tickets (abbreviation: e.t. subsystem). The principles of e.t. subsystem operation are similar to those of n.s.i. subsystem operation described in section 1.3.2. The simplest e.t. subsystem is the system with blind distribution, similar to purely random routing described in section 5.5. The difference is that the entrance ticket is not destined for a given node, but seized by the next new packet. The other e.t. subsystem is that with localised e.t. In this system the entrance ticket is bound to a given node and after its release it is returned to that particular node. A modification of this system is to attach the free entrance ticket to the first new packet directed from s to r and then to send from s to r $W-1$ packets without tickets. At the destination r the ticket is held until $W-1$ packets arrive, then the released ticket is sent back to the source s. The Wth new packet must wait at s until the localised entrance ticket returns. This procedure, called windowing, is equivalent to assembling the arriving packets into batches of size W, attaching one ticket in the front of the batch and returning it when the whole batch has arrived.

The e.t. subsystem can also be coupled with the working packet subsystem letting working packets carry piggyback the released entrance tickets.

Hitherto we have considered admission rules based on the global information. We now deal with rules based on local n.s.i., e.g. defined by (7.1.26). As a typical example of such a rule we take the rule based on the second type of division of packets into classes, namely the dichotomic division into external and internal packets described on pp. 348. Let us denote by

$l_1(v)$ the number of packets delivered by source at node v, not yet admitted to the node (we call them external packets);

$l_2(v)$ the number of packets being stored or transmitted by (at) node v (we call them internal packets).

The local admission rule is

$$D_4[l_1(\sigma), l_2(v)] = \alpha^+ \quad \text{if} \begin{cases} \text{the packet is an internal one and} \\ \qquad l_1(v) + l_2(v) \leqslant \hat{L} \\ \text{the packet is an external one and} \\ \qquad l_1(v) + l_2(v) \leqslant \hat{L} \\ \qquad l_1(v) \leqslant \hat{L}_1 \end{cases} \tag{7.1.32}$$

Usually we take $\hat{L}_1 < \hat{L}$, then the rule $D_4(\cdot)$ favours internal packets. We do so in order not to lose any processing work already done on internal packets. To make the admission rule precise we have to specify what we do with a non-admitted packet. To provide additional protection of internal packets, for such a packet at node w, we produce a copy and deliver to node w information about the admission decision $\alpha(v)$ taken at node v to which the packet from w was forwarded. If $\alpha(v) = \alpha^+$ we destroy the copy, if $\alpha(v) = \alpha^-$ then we proceed according to the rule for transmitting the copy as in systems with feedback, considered in Chapter 3.

This procedure applies local n.s.i. acquisition initiated by the user, based on feedback, considered in section 1.5.1. We can similarly apply user initiated n.s.i. acquisition based on requests for information signals or source initiated n.s.i. acquistion subsystems not transmitting the packet until the n.s.i. arrives. The admission rules described are heuristic. To choose them in an optimum way we have to introduce parameters characterising the rules. We must consider at least a parameter characterising the quality of packet transmission, usually the normalised delay and the probability of rejecting a packet. To define these parameters, we start with the corresponding parameters $\tau[\mathbf{H}(\cdot)]$ and $P^-[\mathbf{H}(\cdot)]$ characterising packet handling rules, the component of which constitutes the admission rule. We obtain the parameters characterising admission rules by removing the dependence on τ and P^- for the routing rule. The simplest approach is to choose a standard routing rule $\mathcal{R}_0(\cdot)$ and to take

$$\tau[A(\cdot)] = \tau[A(\cdot), \mathcal{R}_0(\cdot)] \quad (7.1.33a)$$

$$P^-[A(\cdot)] = P^-[A(\cdot), \mathcal{R}_0(\cdot)] \quad (7.1.33b)$$

as the parameters characterising the admission rule. Obviously, comparing two admission rules on the basis of these parameters may not be fair, because in general, the admission and routing rules should be matched. We can often analyse the effects of augmenting a given routing rule $\mathcal{R}(\cdot)$ by an admission rule. In such case, we characterise the admission rule by the increments

$$\Delta\tau[A(\cdot)] = \tau[R(\cdot)] - \tau[A(\cdot), R(\cdot)] \quad (7.1.34a)$$

$$\Delta P^-[A(\cdot)] = -\{P^-[R(\cdot)] - P^-[A(\cdot), R(\cdot)]\} \quad (7.1.34b)$$

where the first components on the right-hand side are the parameters characterising the system in which no admission decisions are made.

Most admission rules depend on some adjustable parameters. In the case of admission rules $A_j(\cdot)$, $j = 1, 2, 4$, these are the thresholds $\hat{L}_i$, $\hat{L}$. Changing the adjustable parameters we change both τ' and P^-. Thus each rule is characterised by the set of points with coordinates τ', P^- corresponding to various parameter settings. We call this set the **operational characteristic**.

7.2 PACKET ADMISSION RULES BASED ON GLOBAL INFORMATION

In this section we will analyse three types of admission rules using global state information. First a system with two packet classes, followed by one with several classes, and finally a system using entrance tickets.

7.2.1 Systems with admission based on the number of packets from one of two classes

Here we consider systems in which newly generated packets are admitted to the network providing the total number of packets generated by the same source and already in the network does not surpass a threshold. The simple model of such a system, as proposed by Pennotti and Schwartz [7.1] is shown in Fig. 7.5. The system is a chain of channels. At the head of the chain is the information source denoted by $IS_1(1)$ while the destination of the packets $ID_1(K)$ is at the end of the chain. We call packets forwarded from $IS_1(1)$ to $ID_1(K)$ **class 1 packets.** Besides class 1 packets, packets sent from other information sources to other destinations pass through each channel, termed **class 2 packets.**

The chain described can be as a model of a virtual channel determined by a routing rule from $IS_1(1)$ to $ID_1(K)$. We interpret class 1 packets as packets

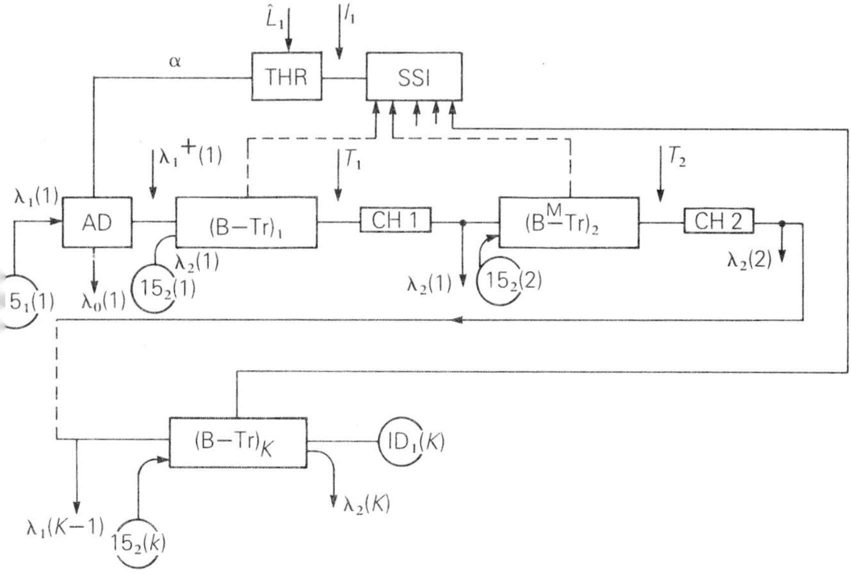

Fig. 7.5 – model of a system with admission rule based on the number of all class 1 packets in the system. AD, facility realising the admission rule: THR, threshold device; SSI, subsystem for system state information collecting; $IS(k)$, class i, $i = 1, 2$, packets information source at node k; $ID_1(K)$, class 1 information destination.

newly introduced to the network from the outside, while class 2 packets are interpreted as background packets previously admitted to the network. Packets of classes 1 and 2 are called **external** and **internal** packets respectively. We assume that only class 1 packets are subject to admission control.

The above general considerations lead to the assumptions:

A1 Admission control is performed only at the node at which the class 1 packet source is located. The admission rule is:

$$A(l_1) = \alpha^+ \quad \text{if} \quad l_1 \leqslant \hat{L}_1 \tag{7.2.1}$$

where l_1 is the total number of packets of class 1 in the network and $\hat{L}_1$ is the threshold.

A2 The capacity of all buffers is infinite; there are no admission restrictions for second-class packets.

Our aim is to derive the relationships between the average delays of class 1 and class 2 packets, the intensity of the flow of rejected class 1 packets and the threshold $\hat{L}_1$. Let:

$l_i(k)$ be the number of packets of class i, $i = 1, 2$, in the kth $(\text{B--Tr})_k$ unit, $k = 1, 2, \ldots, K$;
$\tau_i(k)$ be the average delay of class i packets caused by $(\text{B--Tr})_k$ unit;
$\lambda_i^+(k)$ be the average intensity of class i packets admitted to the $(\text{B--Tr})_k$ unit;
$\lambda_i^-(k)$ be the intensity of class i packets not admitted to the $(\text{B--Tr})_k$ unit;
$\lambda_i(k)$ be the intensity of class i packets delivered to the $(\text{B--Tr})_k$ unit.

From the definitions, it follows that

$$\lambda_i(k) = \lambda_i^+(k) + \lambda_i^-(k) \tag{7.2.2}$$

From Little's theorem we have:

$$\tau_i(k) = \frac{L_i(k)}{\lambda_i^+(k)} \tag{7.2.3}$$

where $L_i(k)$ is the average number of packets in the $(\text{B--Tr})_k$ unit. The total average delay of ith class packets is

$$\tau_i = \sum_{k=1}^{K} \tau_i(k) \tag{7.2.4}$$

From A1 and A2, it follows that

$$\lambda_1^+(k) = \lambda_1(k) \quad k = 2, 3, \ldots, K \tag{7.2.5a}$$

$$\lambda_2^+(k) = \lambda_2(k) \quad k = 1, 2, \ldots, K \tag{7.2.5b}$$

Now, let:

$$\mathbf{l}_i = \{l_i(k),\ k = 1, 2, \ldots, K\} \tag{7.2.6}$$

be the set of all numbers of class i packets;

$A^+[\hat{L}_1]$ be the set of all admissible sets $\{\mathbf{l}_1, \mathbf{l}_2\}$ such that:

$$l_i(k) \geqslant 0\ ,$$
$$l_1 < \hat{L}_1 \tag{7.2.7}$$

where

$$l_1 = \sum_{k=1}^{K} l_1(k) \tag{7.2.8}$$

$A^-(\hat{L}_1)$ be the set of all sets $\{\mathbf{l}_1, \mathbf{l}_2\}$ such that:

$$l_i(k) \geqslant 0\ ,$$
$$\sum_{k=1}^{K} l_1(k) = \hat{L}_1 \tag{7.2.9}$$

$A^+(1, \hat{L}_1)$ be the set of all sets $\mathbf{l}_1$ such that $l_1(k) \geqslant 0$ and (7.2.7) holds;
$A^-(1, \hat{L}_1)$ be the set of all sets $\mathbf{l}_1$ such that $l_1(k) \geqslant 0$ and (7.2.9) holds;
$A^+(2, \infty)$ be the set of all sets $\mathbf{l}_2$ such that $l_1(k) \geqslant 0$.

Examples of sets $A^+(1, \hat{L}_1)$ and $A^-(1, \hat{L}_1)$ for $K = 2$ are shown in Fig. 7.4. From the definitions it follows that:

$$A^+(\hat{L}_1) = A^+(1, \hat{L}_1) \times A^+(2, \infty) \tag{7.2.10}$$
$$A^-(\hat{L}_1) = A^-(1, \hat{L}_1) \times A^-(2, \infty) \tag{7.2.11}$$

where $\times$ denotes a Cartesian product, and

$$A^-(1, \hat{L}_1) = A^+(1, \hat{L}_1 + 1) - A^+(1, \hat{L}_1) \tag{7.2.12}$$

we have

$$\lambda_k^-(k) = P_i^-(k)\lambda_i(k) \tag{7.2.13}$$

where $P_{\mathrm{nad}}\, k^{(i)}$ is the probability that a newly arriving packet of class i will not be admitted to the input of kth channel. From the assumption A1 it follows immediately that, except for $k = 1, i = 1$, we have

$$P_i^-(k) = 0\ , \tag{7.2.14a}$$

while

$$P_i^-(1) = P[(\mathrm{L}_1, \mathrm{L}_2) \in A^-(\hat{L}_1)] = P[\mathrm{L}_1 \in A^-(1, \hat{L}_1)] \tag{7.2.15}$$

where $\mathrm{L}_1, \mathrm{L}_2$ are the random variables representing sets $\mathbf{l}_1$ and $\mathbf{l}_2$.

We will assume additionally that:

A3 The packets generated by each source form a Poisson-exponential sequence, the sequences generated by various sources being statistically independent.

If we consider our chain to be the model of a virtual channel, the assumption about the statistical independence of sequences then corresponds to the Kleinrock hypothesis.

Under assumptions A1–A3 we can use the formulae A.7.42 for joint equilibrium probabilities for the primary set $(\mathbf{l}_1, \mathbf{l}_2)$ derived in Appendix A1 which for the case considered take the form:

$$P(\mathbf{l}_1,\mathbf{l}_2) = C\prod_{k=1}^{K}[\nu_1(k)]^{l_1(k)}[\nu_2(k)]^{l_2(k)} \cdot \frac{[l_1(k)+l_2(k)]!}{[l_1(k)]!\,[l_2(k)]!} \tag{7.2.16}$$

where

$$\nu_i(k) = T_k\lambda_i(k) \tag{7.2.17}$$

is the normalised intensity of packets of class $i = 1, 2$ put into $(\mathrm{B{-}Tr})_k$ unit, and T_k is the average length of packets in the kth channel. Formula (7.2.16) holds for $(\mathbf{l}_1, \mathbf{l}_2) \in A^+(\hat{L}_1) \cup A^-(\hat{L}_1)$. Thus we obtain the constant C from the normalisation constraint

$$\sum_{(\mathbf{l}_1,\mathbf{l}_2)\in A^+(\hat{L}_1)\cup A^-(\hat{L}_1)} P(\mathbf{l}_1,\mathbf{l}_2) = 1 \tag{7.2.18}$$

As shown in Appendix A8, using (7.2.18) we can put (7.2.16) into the form

$$P(\mathbf{l}_1,\mathbf{l}_2) = \psi^{-1}(K,\hat{L}_1)\prod_{k=1}^{K}[\nu_1(k)]^{l_1(k)}[\nu_2(k)]^{l_2(k)} \cdot \frac{[l_1(k)+l_2(k)]!}{[l_1(k)]!\,[l_2(k)]!} \tag{7.2.19}$$

where the auxiliary function

$$\psi(K,L_1) \equiv \sum_{\mathbf{l}_1\in A^+(1,\hat{L}_1)\cup A^-(1,\hat{L}_1)} \prod_{k=1}^{K}\left[\frac{\nu_1(k)}{1-\nu_2(k)}\right]^{l_i(k)} \tag{7.2.20}$$

Having determined the joint probability $P(\mathbf{l}_1, \mathbf{l}_2)$, we can easily obtain the parameters we are interested in. For the average number of packets we obviously have:

$$\bar{L}_i(k) = \sum_{l=0}^{\infty} lP[\mathrm{L}_i(k) = l] \tag{7.2.21}$$

where $\mathrm{L}_i(k)$ is the random variable representing the number of class i packets in the kth channel. We obtain the probability occurring in (7.2.21) as the marginal probability:

$$P[\mathrm{L}_i(k) = l] = \sum_{(l_1,l_2) \in A^+(\hat{L}_1) \cap \{\mathbf{l}_1,\mathbf{l}_2;\, l_i(k) = l\}} P(\mathbf{l}_1,\mathbf{l}_2) \tag{7.2.22}$$

where we sum over all such admissible sets $(\mathbf{l}_1,\mathbf{l}_2)$ in which $l_i(k) = l$. As shown in Appendix A.8, the averages $\bar{L}_i(k)$ can be expressed by means of derivatives of the function $\psi[K, L]$ with respect to the auxiliary variable $z = \nu_1(k)[1-\nu_2(k)]^{-1}$.

Knowing $P(\mathbf{l}_1,\mathbf{l}_2)$, we can obtain the intensity $\lambda_1^-(1)$ of non-admitted packets from formulae (7.2.13), (7.2.14) and (7.2.19). As shown in Appendix A.8, the required probability $P_1^-(1)$ that the packet will not be admitted can again be expressed by means of the function $\psi(K,L)$. Total delay of class 1 packets is given by (7.2.4) and knowing $\lambda_1^-(1)$ we obtain $\tau_1(k)$ from (7.2.2) and (7.2.3).

We can express the parameters we are interested in by means of the auxiliary function $\psi(K,L)$. Regretably, this function can be evaluated only numerically. Therefore we will illustrate the relationship between the parameters characterising the system considered using a simple, concrete case, taking a chain consisting of two channels ($K = 2$), the average packet length $\bar{T}_k = T =$ const., and $\lambda_1(2) = \lambda_2(2)$. We will use the normalised intensities $\nu_1 = \nu_1(1)$, $\nu_2 = \nu_2(1) = \nu_2(2)$, $\nu_1^- = \lambda_1^-(1)$, and the normalised delay $\tau_i' = \tau_i/T$, $i = 1,2$.

Figure 7.6(a) shows the normalised delay τ_1' as a function of the normalised intensity ν_1 on the assumption that the class 2 packet normalised intensity is $\nu_2 = 0.3$. If there is no admission control ($\hat{L}_1 = \infty$) $\tau_1' \to \infty$ when $\nu_1 \to 0.7$, because then the normalised intensity of packets of both classes put into the channel $\nu_1 + \nu_2 \to 1$. Introduction of admission control sharply reduces ν_1. Figure 7.6(a) shows also how much we have to pay for it in terms of class 1 packet losses. Figure 7.6(b) shows the operational characteristic indicating the possibilities of exchanging a decrease of class1 packet delay for an increase in the intensity of non-admitted packets. Finally, Fig. 7.7 shows the dependence of class 2 packet normalised delay τ_2' on the normalised intensity ν_1 of class 1 packet input for $\nu_2 = 0.6$. Again, admission control gives a dramatic improvement. Similar relationships for $K = 3$ can be found in Penotti and Schwartz [7.1].

The model considered so far corresponds to a fixed deterministic routing rule in which packets of class 1 are always routed along the same path. The method described was generalised by Chatterjec *et al.* [7.2] for memoryless random routing causing flow branching.

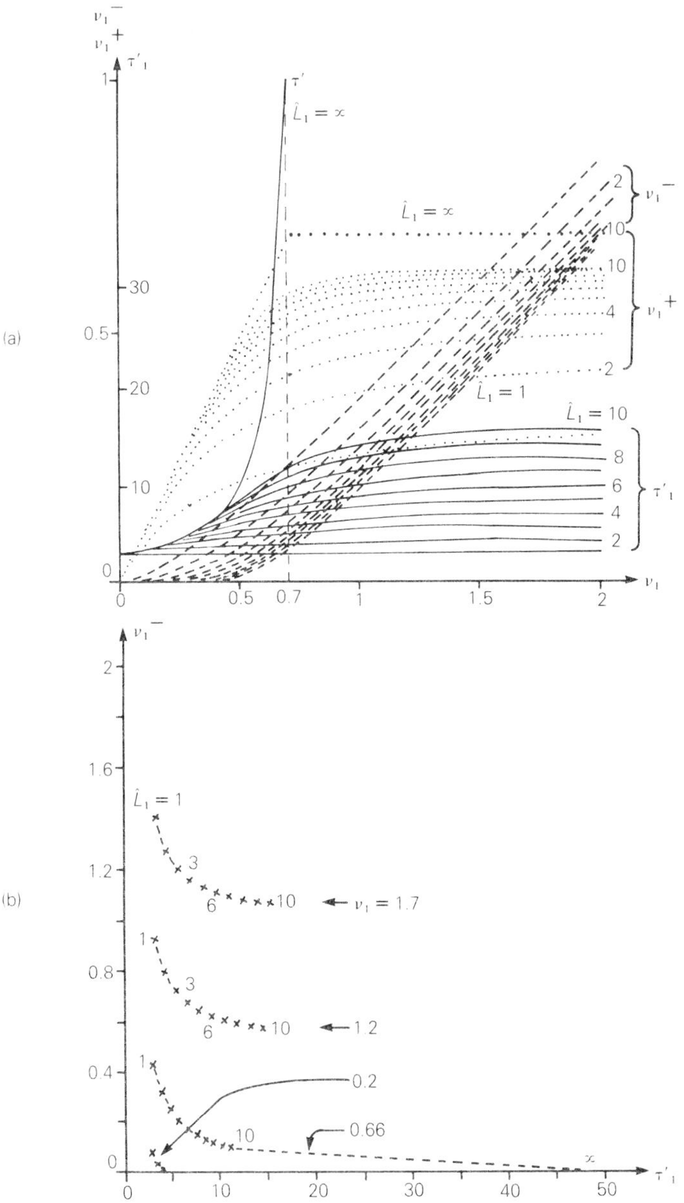

Fig. 7.6 – Dependence (a) of the average normalised class 1 packet delay τ_1' (continuous lines) and normalised intensity $\nu_1^- = \lambda_1^- T$ of non-admitted packets (broken lines) and ν_1^+ of admitted packets (dotted lines) on the normalised class 1 intensity $\nu_1 = \lambda_1(1)T$, (b) of the normalised intensity ν_1^- of non-admitted class 1 packets on the normalised class 1 packet delay τ_1' and on the maximum number L_1 of admissible class 1 packets; number of nodes $K = 2$, intensity of class 2 packets $\nu(2) = \lambda_2(k)T = 0.5$. Based on Papir [7.3].

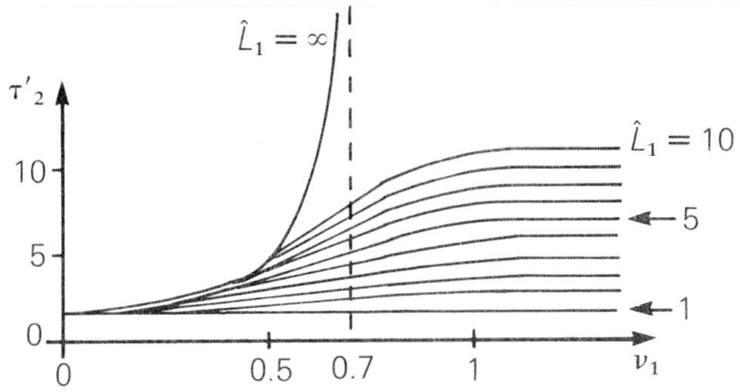

Fig. 7.7 – Dependence of the normalised class 2 packet delay τ_2' introduced by a single B–Tr unit on the normalised intensity ν_1 of class 1 packets and on the maximum number L_1 of admitted class 1 packets $\nu_2 = 0.5$. Based on Papir [7.3].

7.2.2 Systems based on information about numbers of packets from several classes

In the previous subsection we assumed that only packets of one class are subject to admission control, namely, packets directed from a given source to a destination. We now consider the general case when all source–destination pairs are divided into I classes and the admission rule (7.1.32) is applied. Thus a packet of class i is admitted only if

$$l_i < \hat{L}_i \tag{7.2.23}$$

and

$$l < \hat{L} \tag{7.2.24}$$

where l_i is the total number of packets from the ith class in the network given by (7.1.23) and

$$l = \sum_{i=1}^{I} l_i \tag{7.2.25}$$

is the total number of all packets in the network (see 7.1.25). We again make the assumption A3 that the sequences of packets delivered by information sources are Poisson-exponential sequences. We also assume that the buffer capacity is infinite; thus packet rejection only occurs as the result of the non-admission decision. Let

$l_i(k)$ be the number of packets of class i, $i = 1, 2, \ldots, I$ in the (B–Tr) unit in front of kth channel;

$\mathbf{l}_i$ $= \{l_i(k), k = 1, 2, \ldots, K\}$

$\mathbf{l}$ $= \{\mathbf{l}_i, i = 1, 2, \ldots, I\}$

$A^+(\hat{L}_1, \ldots, \hat{L}_I, \hat{L})$ be the set of sets l satisfying conditions (7.2.23) for i 1, 2, ..., I and condition (7.2.24);

$\lambda_i(k)$ be the intensity of class i packets delivered to the (B–Tr) unit in front c kth channel

$\bar{T}_i$ be the average length of packet of ith class

$$\nu_i(k) \equiv \lambda_i(k)\bar{T}_k \tag{7.2.26}$$

We have

$$\lambda_i(k) = \sum_{m \in M(i)} \lambda'_m(k) \tag{7.2.27}$$

where $\lambda'_m(k)$ is the intensity of packets directed from the mth source to the mt destination and passing through the kth channel.

Under the assumptions made before we can again use† the formula A.7.5 given in Appendix A.7 for the joint equilibrium probability $P(\mathbf{l})$

$$P(\mathbf{l}) = C \prod_{k=1}^{K} \left(\sum_{i=1}^{I} l_i(k) \right)! \prod_{i=1}^{I} \frac{1}{[l_i(k)]!} [\nu_i(k)]^{l_i(k)} \tag{7.2.28}$$

We again obtain the normalisation constant C from the normalisation equation Knowing the joint probability, we obtain the parameters characterising the system as in the previous subsection. As a generalisation of (7.2.21) we have the average value

$$\bar{L}_i(k) = \sum_{i=1}^{\hat{L}_i} l\mathbf{P}[\mathrm{L}_i(k) = l]$$

where

$$\mathbf{P}[L_i(k) = l] = \sum_{\mathbf{l} \in A^+ \cap \{\mathbf{l};\, l_i(k) = l\}} P(\mathbf{l}) \tag{7.2.29}$$

The intensity of packets belonging to the ith class which are admitted to the network is

$$\lambda_i^+ = \lambda_i[1 - P_i^-] \tag{7.2.30}$$

† According to the definition introduced here and in Appendix A.7 we have to take $\mathbf{l}$ and $l_i(k)$ for $\mathbf{l}'$ and $l'_i(k)$ entering in A.7.58.

here

$$\lambda_i = \sum_{m \in M(i)} \lambda_m(0) \tag{7.2.31}$$

the total intensity of packets delivered by sources belonging to the ith class, $_n(0)$ is the intensity of packets delivered by the source of mth node,

$$P_i^- = \sum_{\mathbf{l} \in A^+[L_1, L_2, \ldots, L_I, L]} P(\mathbf{l}) \tag{7.2.32}$$

the probability of not admitting a packet of the ith class to the network, and

$$A^-[\hat{L}_1, \hat{L}_2, \ldots, \hat{L}_I, \hat{L}]$$

the set of sets $\mathbf{l}$ for which equality for all i in (7.2.23) and (7.2.24) holds.

Knowing λ_i^+ and $\bar{L}_i$, we obtain the average passage time of an ith class packet

$$T_i = \frac{\bar{L}_i}{\lambda_i^+} . \tag{7.2.33}$$

his parameter and P_i^- given by (7.2.32) are the two fundamental parameters aracterising the admission rule considered. As in the previous subsection, we ust evaluate these parameters numerically, the main computational difficulty eing the evaluation of constant C from the normalisation constraint.

xample 7.2.1

o illustrate our considerations, we take an example from Wong and Unsoy [7.4]. he network is shown in Fig. 7.8. We use one-index numbering of nodes and vo-index numbering of channels. The source–destination intensities $\lambda_{sr}(0)$ (in e previous notation $\lambda_m(0)$) are given in Table 7.2.1.

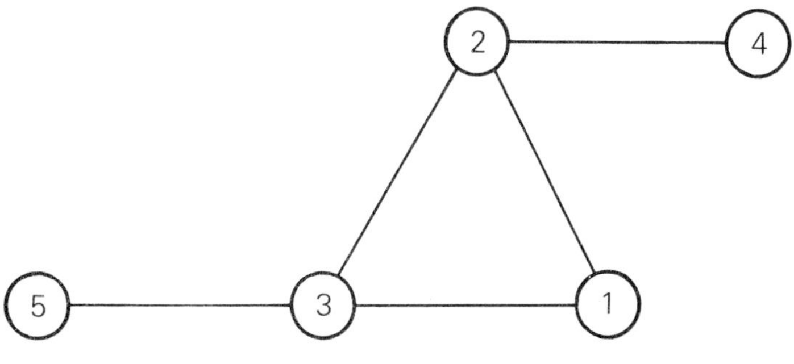

Fig. 7.8 – The network considered in Example 7.2.1.

Table 7.2.1

s \ r	1	2	3	4	5
1	0	$2a$	$2.5a$	$0.5b$	$0.5b$
2	$2a$	0	$2a$	$0.5b$	b
3	$2.5a$	$2a$	0	b	$0.5b$
4	$0.5b$	$0.5b$	b	0	b
5	$0.5b$	b	$0.5b$	b	0

As class 1 source–destination pairs, we take pairs of nodes 1, 2, 3, and as class 2 pairs 4, 5. The intensities of class 1 source–destination pairs are indicated by the thick-lined frame. The parameters a and b are proportionality parameters. By introducing them, we can analyse the behaviour of the network when all intensities in one class are changed simultaneously we assume $T_k = T =$ const. Figure 7.9(a) shows the dependence of normalised delay τ_i, on the normalised intensity ν obtained from formulae (7.2.35), (7.2.32) and (7.3.34) for various sets of thresholds $\hat{L}$, $\hat{L}_1$, $\hat{L}_2$. The dependence of the intensites $\nu_i^+ = \lambda_i^+ T$ on $\nu_2 = \lambda_2 T$ are shown in Fig. 7.9(b). We see that introducing admission control dramatically reduces the delays, at the cost of a tolerable increase in the intensity of non admitted packets.

7.2.3 Systems with entrance tickets

If we wish to implement the systems considered previously, we have to organise an auxiliary network for collecting and delivering information about the actual number of packets of a given class in the main network. The auxiliary information collection and delivery system can be either centralised or decentralised, but both types are quite costly. The system based on admission tickets is simple to implement. Each class of packets has a corresponding class of ticket. The total number of admission tickets of class i, $i = 1, 2, \ldots, I$, is constant and equal to the upper limit $\hat{L}_i$ of the number of packets belonging to class i admitted to the network. Tickets circulate in the network and may be either attached or free. A packet delivered by a source of the ith class may be put into the network if there is a free ticket of type i in the node adjacent to the information source. The free ticket is attached to the packet and becomes an attached ticket. It again becomes free when the working packet to which it was attached reaches its destination. There are two possible variants of such a delivery system for information about the total number of packets in the network:

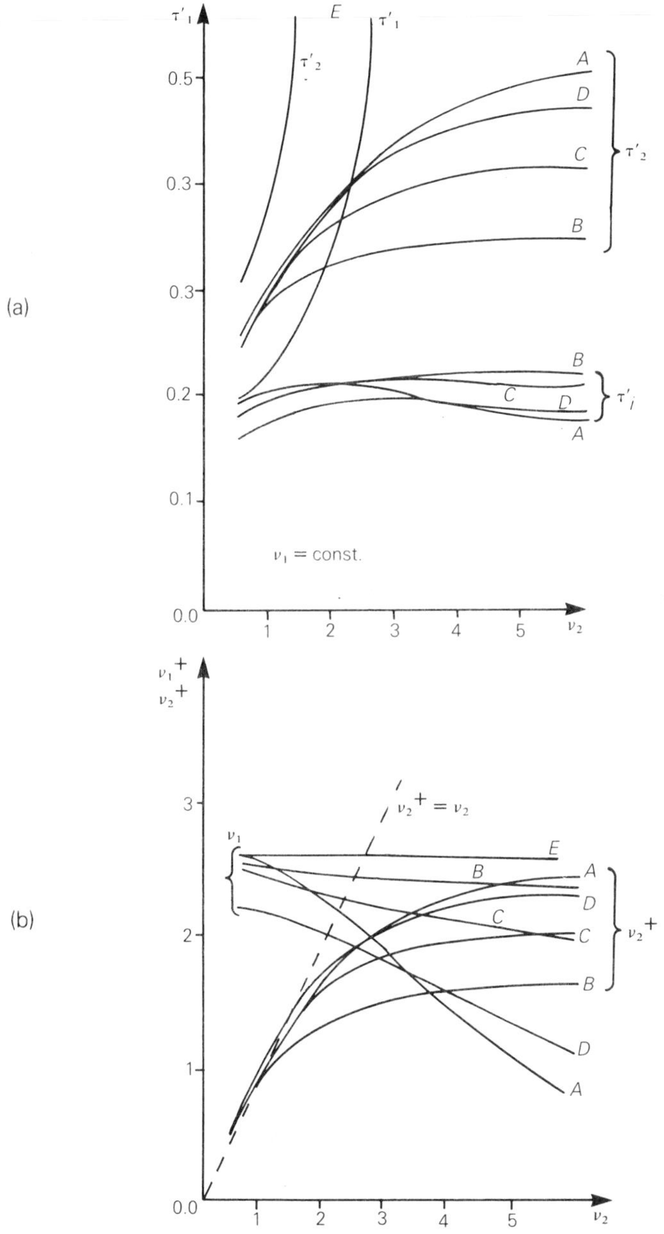

Fig. 7.9 – The dependence (a) of the normalised delay τ_i', $i = 1, 2$; (b) of the normalised intensities $\nu_i = \lambda_i^+ T$, $i = 1, 2$, of admitted class i packets on the normalised total intensity $\nu_2 = \lambda_2 T$ of class 2 packets, network shown in Fig.7.8. Normalised intensity of class 1 packets $\nu_1 = 2.6$, sets of thresholds $(\hat{L}, \hat{L}_1, \hat{L}_2)$: $A = (15, 15, 15)$, $B = (15, 12, 6)$, $C = (15, 9, 9)$, $D = (15, 6, 12)$, $E = (\infty, \infty, \infty)$.

A. separate packets are introduced for distributing free tickets about the network;
B. free tickets are attached to working packets; when the packet has reached the next node, free tickets can be stored at this node and then used by packets entering the network at this node, or they can be carried further by the same or another working packet.

System A is more flexible. In this system we can choose the routing rule for auxiliary packets carrying the tickets, their distribution can be made almost independent of the network load of working packets. We can expect the purely random routing rules described in section 6.2 to be especially favourable to the dissemination of free tickets.

The advantage of system B is its simplicity; it can be implemented without great changes in the uncontrolled primary system. We now consider such a system in more detail. We shall consider the simplest case where we have only one class and the admission of a packet is based only on the total number of packets of all types in the network. As all tickets are of the same type the basis for admitting an external packet is the presence in the node of at least one ticket. A packet which has got a ticket and has been introduced into the network is sent according to the established routing rule; there is no need to check if it has a ticket. We shall call such a packet an **internal** packet, or a class 2 packet. An **external** packet is a packet which has been put into a node of the network from an information source near that node, and which is directed another node in the network; we call it a class 1 packet. In each node there is a special buffer in which tickets are stored, the **ticket buffer**. The part of the node where tickets are taken from internal packets and attached to external packets is called the **ticket office**. We will assume here that:

A1 an internal packet carries at most a single ticket.

The rule 1 operating the ticket office consists out of subrules

(1.1) The external packet generated by the source is put into the entrance buffer; its capacity $\hat{L}_{b1}$.†

(1.2) If the internal packet carries a ticket and the ticket buffer is not full, the ticket is taken from the packet and put into the ticket buffer; its capacity is L_{b3}.‡ If the ticket buffer is full, the ticket continues travelling with the internal packet.

† We use subscript b to remind us that $\hat{L}_{b1}$ is the capacity of buffer but not a bound on the number of all packets in the network, which we denoted previously $\hat{L}_1$. The second subscript denotes the class of the packet (external).

‡ We consider tickets as class 3 packets. Hence the indexing of parameters related to entrance tickets.

(1.3) If at least one ticket is available in the ticket buffer and a working packet is waiting in the entrance buffer, the ticket is removed, the status of the packet is changed from external to internal, and the packet enters the unit implementing the routing rule.

(1.4) If the node is the destination node for an internal packet, a free ticket is generated and is put into the 'export' ticket buffer.

(1.5) After passing through the ticket office, the internal and external packets go to the unit implementing the routing rule.

(1.6) The free ticket is taken from the export ticket buffer and attached to a packet which has left the routing unit and which is capable of carrying a free ticket.

The model of a node operated by this rule is shown in Fig. 7.10.

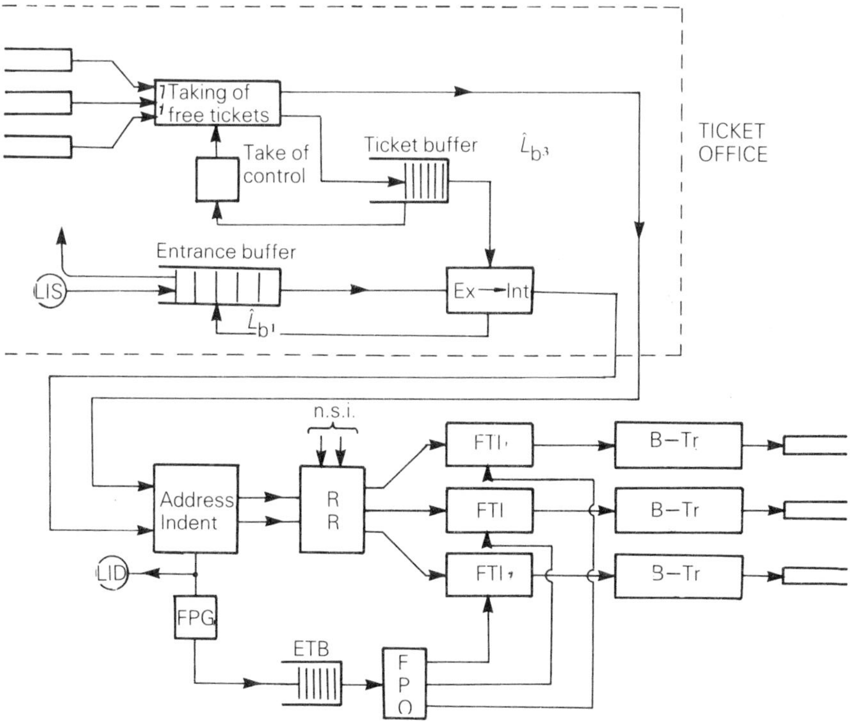

Fig. 7.10 – Model of a node in which admission is based on entrance tickets. LIS, local information source; LID, local information destination; RR, facility realising routing rule; FPG, free packet generator; FPD, facility for free packet distribution; FTI, facility for free ticket introduction into the packet; ETB, entrance ticket buffer.

The fundamental parameter characterising the operation of the ticket office is the average time the external packet must wait in the entrance buffer to obtain its ticket, i.e. to become an internal packet, denoted by τ_1 (we indicate parameters related to external packets by the index 1). The operation of the ticket office is also characterised by the average time τ_3 which the ticket spends in the ticket buffer (we indicate parameters related to tickets by the index 3). The time τ_3 is a measure of the tickets' mobility and we can expect that if it is large, the tickets may have a tendency to accumulate at some nodes while at others packets may have to wait a long time. To increase the packets' mobility we restrict the capacity of the ticket buffer. We will later derive the relationship between the average waiting time of packets and tickets, and the capacity of the ticket and entrance buffers.

We start with the simple case where a working packet can carry one free ticket and only one packet arrives at a given instant. Then we will consider the generalised case where a working packet can carry several free tickets, and packets arrive in batches. We assume that:

A2 The instants of arrival of external and internal packets are independent Poisson sequences with intensities λ_1 and λ_2 respectively (we use the index 2 for parameters of internal packets).

A3 The internal packet carries one ticket with a probability P_3; thus the probability that the internal packet is carrying no free ticket is $1-P_3$.

A4 The times to take a free ticket from an internal packet, and to attach a ticket to an external packet and forward it to the routing rule unit are negligibly small.

We say that the ticket office is in the state $\sigma(k,l)$ if we have k free tickets in the ticket buffer and l external packets in the entrance buffer waiting for an entrance ticket. From the ticket office operation rule and assumptions A2–A4, it follows that:

$$\text{The only possible states of the ticket office are the states } \sigma(k,0), k=0,1,2,\ldots,\hat{L}_{b3} \text{ and } \sigma(0,l), l=0,1,\ldots,\hat{L}_{b1} \tag{7.2.34}$$

L_{b3} and L_{b1} are here the capacities of the ticket and entrance buffers. In the course of arrivals of internal and external packets the state of the ticket office changes. Let $\sigma(t)$ be the state of the ticket office at instant t. We will now consider the transitions of the state of the ticket office in the time interval $\langle t, t+\Delta t\rangle$. We shall make Δt so small that in view of assumption A.3 and the properties of the Poisson sequences, we need only consider the situations when either no new packet or one new packet arrives.

We assume that at instant t we have $k \geqslant 0$ free tickets in the ticket buffer and no packet is in the entrance buffer, thus the ticket office is in the state $\sigma(k,0)$, $0 \leqslant k \leqslant L(0)-1$. At instant $t+\Delta t$ the ticket office will be in the state $s(k+1,0)$ if: (1) an internal packet arrives, (2) it is carrying a free ticket, and (3) no external packet arrives. Thus:

$$\begin{aligned} P[\Sigma(t+\Delta t) &= \sigma(k+1,0) \mid \Sigma(t) = \sigma(k,0)] \\ &= [\lambda_2 \Delta t] P_3 [1-\lambda_2 \Delta t] + 0(\Delta t) \\ &= P_3 \lambda_2 \Delta t + 0(\Delta t) \end{aligned} \tag{7.2.35}$$

The probability of a transition from the state $\sigma(k,0)$ to the state $\sigma(k+l, 0)$, $l \geqslant 1$ is of the order of magnitude $0(\Delta t)$. For $1 \leqslant k \leqslant L_{b3}$ the ticket office will be in state $\sigma(k-1,0)$ at instant $t + \Delta t$ if: (1) an internal packet carrying a free ticket arrives, (2) an external packet arrives. Thus for $1 \leqslant k \leqslant L$

$$\begin{aligned} P[\Sigma(t+\Delta t) &= \sigma(k-1,0) \mid \Sigma(t) = \sigma(k,0)] \\ &= [1-P_3 \lambda_2 \Delta t] \lambda_1 \Delta t + 0(\Delta t) \\ &= \lambda_1 \Delta t + 0(\Delta t) \end{aligned} \tag{7.2.36}$$

Let $\psi(k'' | k')$ be the transition intensity from state $\sigma(k',0)$ to the state $\sigma(k'',0)$, $k', k'' \geqslant 0$ defined as

$$\psi(k'' \mid k') = \lim_{\Delta t \to 0} \frac{P[\Sigma(t+\Delta t) = \sigma(k'',0) \mid \Sigma(t) = \sigma(k',0)]}{\Delta t} \tag{7.2.37}$$

From (7.2.35) and (7.2.36) it follows that:

$$\psi_0(k+m \mid k) = \begin{cases} 0 & \text{for } m > 1, \quad k = 0, 1, \ldots, \hat{L}_{b3} \\ P_1 \lambda_3 & \text{for } m = 1, \quad k = 0, 1, \ldots, \hat{L}_{b3} - 1 \\ \lambda_1 & \text{for } m = -1, \; k = 1, 2, \ldots, \hat{L}_{b3} \\ 0 & \text{for } m < -1, \; k = 1, 2, \ldots, \hat{L}_{b3} \; . \end{cases} \tag{7.2.38}$$

Next we assume that we have one packet in the entrance buffer and in view of conclusion (7.2.34), no tickets in the ticket buffer. Thus the ticket office is in the state $\sigma(0,l)$, $l = 0, 1, \ldots, L(1)$. As in (7.2.37), we define the transition intensity

$$\psi(l'' \mid l') = \lim_{\Delta t} \frac{P[\Sigma(t+\Delta t) = \sigma(0,l'') \mid \Sigma(t) = \sigma(0,l')]}{\Delta t} \tag{7.2.39}$$

During the time interval $\langle t, t+\Delta t \rangle$, the transition $\sigma(0,l) \to \sigma(0,l+1)$ occurs when a new external packet arrives but no new ticket, similarly $\sigma(0,l) \to \sigma(0,l-1)$ when a free ticket arrives but no external packet. It can be seen that as in (7.2.38) we have:

$$\psi_1(l+n \mid l) = \begin{cases} 0 & \text{for } n > 1, \quad l = 0, 1, \ldots, \hat{L}_{b1} - 1 \\ \lambda_1 & \text{for } n = 1, \quad l = 0, 1, \ldots, \hat{L}_{b1} - 1 \\ P_3 \lambda_2 & \text{for } n = -1, \; l = 1, 2, \ldots, \hat{L}_{b1} \\ 0 & \text{for } n < -1, \; l = 1, 2, \ldots, \hat{L}_{b1} \end{cases} \tag{7.2.40}$$

The states $\sigma(k,l)$ and the derived transition intensities are shown in Fig. 7.11. We observe that the transition diagram has the same topology and the same intensities as in the case of the buffer at which packets arrive with an intensity λ_1 and the intensity of completing the service is $P_3\lambda_2$. The interpretation of the

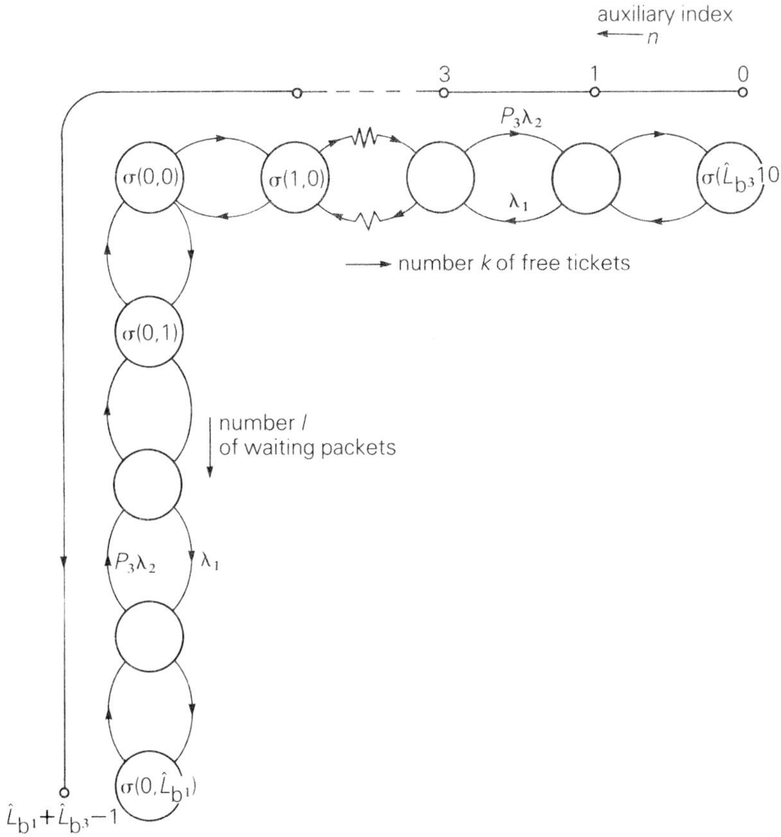

Fig. 7.11 – Transition intensities diagram of the states of the ticket office consisting of an entrance buffer and a ticket buffer; simple packet and ticket arrivals.

states of the ticket office and the single buffer are obviously different. However, if we number the states $\sigma(k,l)$ of the ticket office by a single index n as shown on Fig. 7.11, and denote the stationary probability of the state $\sigma(k,l)$ by P_n such that the pair (k,l) obtains the number n, we can directly use the formula which is valid for the single buffer. Thus:

$$P_n = \frac{\nu^n(1-\nu)}{1-\nu^{\hat{L}+1}} \qquad (7.2.41)$$

for $n = 0, 1, 2, \ldots, \hat{L}$ where

$$\hat{L} \equiv \hat{L}_{b1} + \hat{L}_{b3} - 1 \tag{7.2.42}$$

and

$$\nu \equiv \lambda_1 / P_3 \lambda_2 \tag{7.2.43}$$

Let us denote by $P(k,l)$ the equilibrium probability of the state $S(k,l)$. From Fig. 7.11 we see that

$$P(k,0) = P_{\hat{L}_{b3}-k} \quad k = 0, 1, \ldots, \hat{L}_{b3} \tag{7.2.44a}$$

and

$$P(0,l) = P_{\hat{L}_{b3}+l} \quad l = 0, 1, \ldots, \hat{L}_{b1} \tag{7.2.44b}$$

where P_n is given by (7.2.41).

We denote by $P_3(k)$ the probability that we have k tickets in the ticket buffer, and by $P_1(l)$ the probability that we have l external packet in the entrance buffer. We obtain these probabilities from $P(k,l)$ as marginal probabilities:

$$P_1(l) = \sum_{k=0}^{\hat{L}_{b1}} P(k,l) \tag{7.2.45a}$$

$$P_3(k) = \sum_{l=0}^{\hat{L}_{b3}} P(k,l) \tag{7.2.45b}$$

From Fig. 7.11 we see that for $k \neq 0, l \neq 0$ we have:

$$P_1(l) = P(0,l) \tag{7.2.46a}$$

$$P_3(k) = P(k,0) \tag{7.2.46b}$$

$$P_1(0) \equiv \sum_{k=0}^{\hat{L}_{b1}} P(k,0) \tag{7.2.47a}$$

$$P_3(0) \equiv \sum_{l=0}^{\hat{L}_{b3}} P(0,l) \tag{7.2.47b}$$

Knowing the probabilities $P_i(k)$, $i = 1, 3$, we obtain the average numbers of tickets (packets):

$$\bar{L}_i = \sum_{k=1}^{\hat{L}_{bi}} l P_i(l) \tag{7.2.48}$$

and the intensities of the accepted tickets (packets)

$$\lambda_i^+ = \lambda_i[1-P_i^-] \tag{7.2.49}$$

$i = 1, 3$, whereas the probabilities of not accepting a newly arriving tickets (packet)

$$P_i^- = P_i(\hat{L}_{bi}) \tag{7.2.50}$$

The average tickets (packets) waiting time is obtained from Little's theorem:

$$T_i^{(b)} = \frac{\bar{L}_i}{\lambda_i^+} . \tag{7.2.51}$$

It would be unfavourable to lose external packets because of limited entrance buffer capacity. We will therefore assume it is very large, taking:

$$\hat{L}_{b1} = \infty . \tag{7.2.52}$$

Assuming this, we see that the condition that the average packets waiting time is finite is that:

$$\nu < 1 \tag{7.2.53a}$$

thus

$$P_3\lambda_2 > \lambda_1 . \tag{7.2.53b}$$

Substituting (7.2.49) in (7.2.45a) and (7.2.50), we obtain

$$P_3^- = 1-\nu \tag{7.2.54}$$

This probability does not depend on the ticket buffer capacity, thus formula (7.2.54) holds even if we had no such buffer. In view of assumption (7.2.52) that the capacity of the entrance buffer is infinite, and (7.2.54), each packet eventually obtains its ticket; thus the intensity of absorbed free tickets is λ_1 and the intensity of tickets rejected by the ticket buffer and continuing to travel with the internal packet is

$$\lambda_3 - \lambda_2 = \lambda_3 \; 1 - \frac{\lambda_2}{\lambda_3} \tag{7.2.55}$$

This is equivalent to 7.2.54.

The external packet waiting time τ_1 depends on the parameter ν given by (7.2.43) characterising the intensity of free ticket delivery, and the ticket buffer capacity $\hat{L}_{b3}$. The dependence is obtained from (7.2.51) after using (7.2.48) and (7.2.49). Let us denote by

$$T_{ref} \equiv [P_3 \lambda_2]^{-1} \tag{7.2.56}$$

the average time between two consecutive arrivals of free tickets. This time is a suitable reference time for the average external packet queueing time τ_1. The diagram of $\tau_1' = \tau_1/T_{ref}$ as a function of the parameter ν given by (7.2.43) and the ticket buffer capacity $\hat{L}_{b3}$ are shown in Fig. 7.12, while Fig. 7.13 shows the dependence of the normalised time τ_3/T_{ref} which a free packet spreads in the packet buffer until it is needed by a packet.

Figures 7.12 and 7.13 confirm our expectation that increasing the ticket buffer capacity $\hat{L}_{b3}$ decreases the average external packet waiting time, but increases the average time spent by a ticket at a node.

We have only been considering a single isolated node, whereas we are interested not only in the external packets waiting time at a node w, which we now denote by $\tau_1(w)$, but also in a parameter characterising the waiting time at all nodes. We can define the latter as the weighted average

$$\bar{\tau} = \frac{1}{\bar{\lambda}_1} \sum \tau_1(w) \lambda_1(w) \tag{7.2.57}$$

where $\lambda_1(w)$ is the intensity of external packets generated at node w (previously denoted briefly by λ_1), and

$$\bar{\lambda}_1 = \sum_{w=1}^{W} \lambda_1(w) \tag{7.2.58}$$

is the total intensity of packets arriving at all nodes. The analytical evaluation of $\bar{\tau}$ is quite difficult because we have to take into account the fact that the intensity $\lambda_0(w)$ of free packets reaching node w depends on the external packet intensities put in at other nodes, and also in a complicated way on the routing and admission rules. Much work has been done in the UK (see [7.5] and [7.6]) to obtain this type of relationship by simulation. One of the important conclusions is that we have $\hat{L}_{b3}$ minimising τ'. This can be explained as follows: For a small ticket buffer capacity, increasing the capacity $\hat{L}_{b3}$ decreases $\bar{\tau}$, as in the previously considered simple model of the isolated node (see Fig. 7.12(b)). However, if the ticket buffer capacity grows more, the waiting time $\bar{\tau}$ starts to increase. This can be explained with the aid of Fig. 7.13(b). If $\hat{L}_{b3}$ is too large some nodes may become traps for free tickets, the distribution of tickets waiting at various nodes may become non-uniform and the advantages of having many free tickets waiting at some nodes does not compensate for the disadvantages of the excessively long time which external packets spend waiting for a ticket at other nodes.

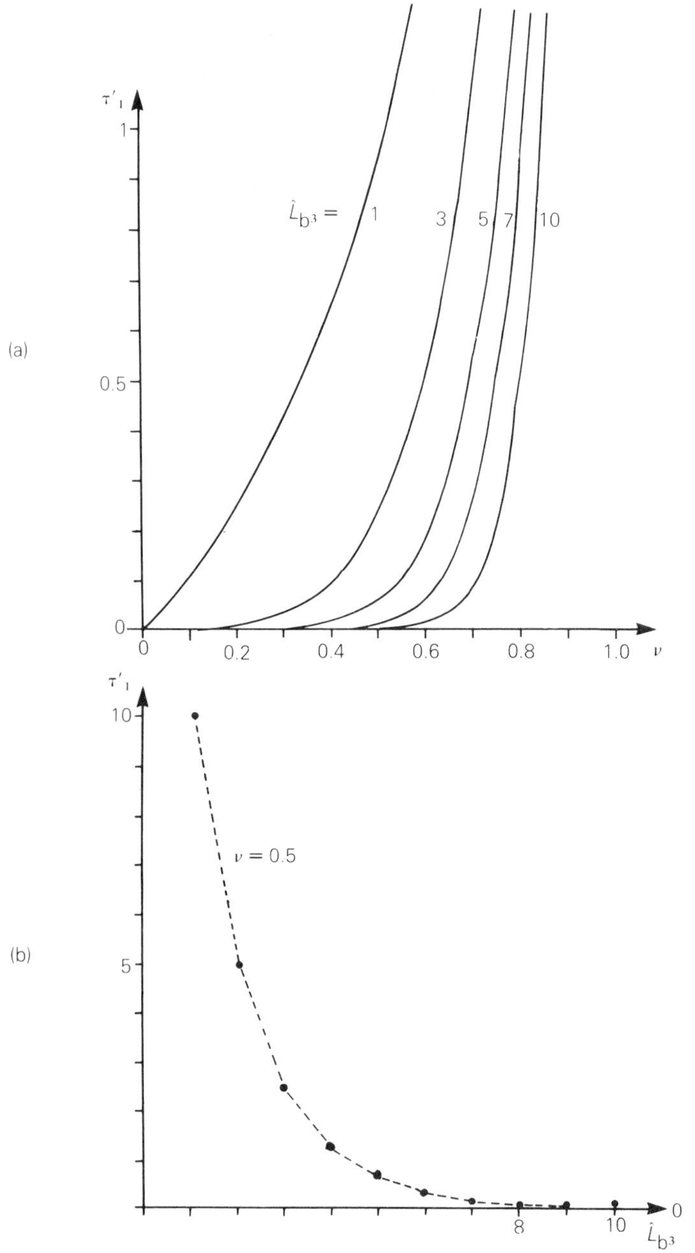

Fig. 7.12 – Dependence of the normalised average external packets waiting time τ_1/T_{ref} where T_{ref} is the average time between consecutive free ticket arrivals (a) on the normalised intensity $\nu = \lambda_1/P_3\lambda_2$ (see 7.4.43) and (b) on the ticket entrance buffer capacity $\hat{L}_{b3}$ for $\nu = 0.5$.

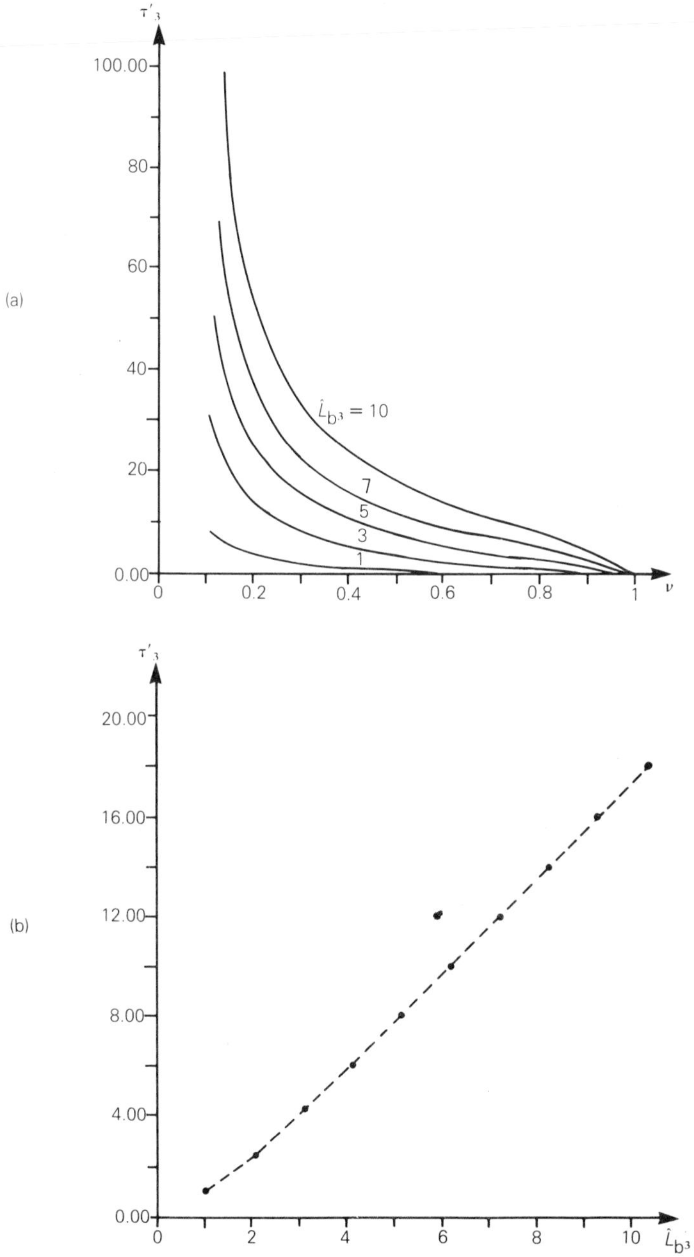

Fig. 7.13 – Dependence of the normalised average time $\tau_3' = \tau_3/T_{ref}$ which a free ticket spends in the buffer waiting for an external packet, (a) on the normalised intensity ν, (b) on the ticket buffer capacity $\hat{L}_{b3}$, $\nu = 0.5$ based on Papir [7.3].

7.3 A SYSTEM WITH ADMISSION CONTROL BASED ON LOCAL DATA

Here we consider systems in which admission control is based only on the state of local nodes. Packets arriving from another node connected by in-going channels which are rejected are not lost; auxiliary information that the packet must be retransmitted is sent through the feedback channel to the packet's source node. Exact analysis even of such simple systems is not possible. Therefore we will derive approximate relationships between the parameters characterising the system introducing several simplifying assumptions. We will first consider a simple chain of buffer transmitter units and then study a mesh network. To obtain at least some expressions in closed form, we assume that random routing is applied.

7.3.1 Admission rule based on local information in a chain of nodes

To illustrate the fundamental concepts and properties of systems with admission concepts based on local information about the state of nodes delivered by means of binary feedback signals we take a simple chain of nodes shown in Fig. 7.14. We assume that admission control is realised simply by limiting buffer capacity

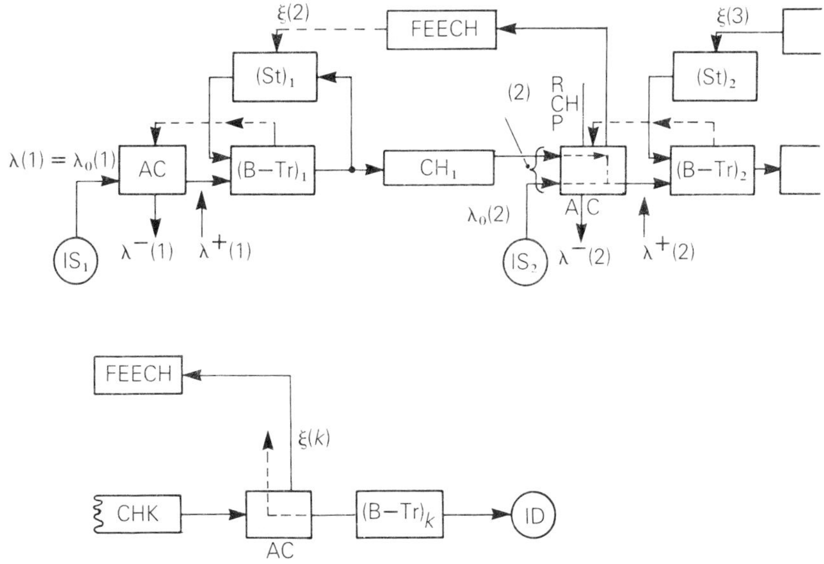

Fig. 7.14 – The chain of channels with feedback. $(\mathrm{IS})_k$, kth information source; $(\mathrm{B–Tr})_k$, kth buffer–transmitter unit for working packets; $(\mathrm{St})_k$, kth copy storage; CH, forward channel; FEECH, feedback channel; ACU, admission control unit; RCHP, rejected channel packet.

as we assumed in Example 7.1.1. The system operates according to the rule R1 which is the set of subrules:

(1.1) The buffer transmitter unit operates in the usual way on the FIFO principle.

(1.2) A copy of the packet being transmitted to the $(k + 1)$th node is put into the copy storage.

(1.3) Packets delivered by local sources and coming from an adjacent node are treated the same. Let us denote by $\hat{L}_b(k+1)$ the capacity of the $(B\text{–}Tr)_{k+1}$ unit, and by $l(k+1)$ the total number of packets in it. If $l(k+1) < \hat{L}_b(k+1)$ and a packet from kth node arrives the admission decision α^+ is taken and the packet is put in $(B\text{–}Tr)_{k+1}$. If $l(k+1) = \hat{L}_b(k+1)$ decision α^- is taken and the packet is destroyed.

(1.4) Packets from local sources are treated similarly, but in case of α^- decision the loss is unrecoverable.

(1.5) After a time T_r, counted from the instant of ending the transmission of the packet, the feedback channel delivers to node k the auxiliary information $\xi(k+1)$ about the admission decision taken at $(k+1)$th node.

(1.6) The auxiliary information $\xi(k+1)$ is binary and can take either of the forms: ξ^+ or ξ^-; ξ^+ means that the $(k + 1)$th node made α^+ decision (acceptance of the packet) while ξ^- means that the decision was α^- (non-acceptance decision).

(1.7) If ξ^+ is received, the copy of the packet is destroyed. If information ξ^- is received, the copy is transferred from the storage to the B–Tr unit.

Let us introduce the intensities:

$\lambda_0(k)$ – of packets delivered by the local source,
$\lambda(k)$ – of all packets put into kth B–Tr,
$\lambda^-(k)$ – of non-admitted packets,
$\lambda^+(k)$ – of admitted packets.

Obviously

$$\lambda(k) = \lambda^-(k) + \lambda^+(k) \tag{7.3.1}$$

From Fig. 7.14 we see that

$$\lambda(k) = \lambda_0(k) + \lambda^+(k-1) \tag{7.3.2}$$

Notice that the intensity of packets put into kth channel is $H(k)\lambda(k)$ where $H(k)$ is the average number of all transmisions including retransmissions (see (3.1.3) and (3.1.3), remembering that $\lambda(k)$ corresponds to $\lambda_m(0)$).

We assume

A1 The sequences of primary information delivered by the sources are Poisson-exponential independent sequences.

A2 The intensities $\lambda_0(k)$ of the packets delivered by local sources are chosen in such a way that the total intensity put into each node is the same, i.e.

$$\lambda(k) = \lambda_0(1) = \lambda = \text{const.} \tag{7.3.3}$$

The statistical properties of sequences of packets put into the system by the information sources and the rule of system operation unequivocally determine the statistical properties of the sequences of auxiliary information $\xi(k)$ and thus of retransmissions. However, we now make some heuristic simplifications. Let us denote by $\Xi(j, k+1)$ the binary random variable representing the jth, $j = 1, 2, \ldots,$ auxiliary information available at node k about the α decision taken at the $(k+1)$th node. We assume:

A3 For $j' \neq j$ and $k' \neq k$ the random variables $\Xi(j,k)$ are independent; the probability distribution of $\Xi(j,k)$ does not depend on j.

In view of this assumption we denote

$$P^+(k) = P[\Xi(j,k) = \xi^+] \tag{7.3.4a}$$

$$P^-(k) = P[\Xi(j,k) = \xi^-] = 1 - P^+(k) \tag{7.3.4b}$$

On the assumption that the feedback channel is ideal, the event $\xi(k) = \xi^-$ is equivalent to the event $\alpha(k) = \alpha^-$. In view of the subrules 1.3, 1.4 the latter takes place if the $(\text{B-Tr})_k$ unit is full. Thus

$$P^-(k) = P[\text{L}(k) = \hat{L}(k)] \tag{7.3.5}$$

where $\text{L}(k)$ is the random variable representing the total number of packets in $(\text{B–Tr})_k$, and $\hat{L}(k)$ is its capacity.

Let $\text{H}(k)$ be the random variable representing the number of retransmissions until the packet is ultimately accepted by the $(k + 1)$th node. From system operation rules and A2, A3 we have

$$P[\text{H}(k) = h] = [P^-(k+1)]^{h-1} P^+(k+1) \tag{7.3.6}$$

Thus the average number of transmissions

$$\bar{H}(k) = \frac{1}{P^+(k+1)} = \frac{1}{1 - P^-(k+1)} \tag{7.3.7}$$

and the average total duration of all transmissions of the same packet is:

$$\bar{T}'(k) = \bar{T}(k) H(k) = \frac{\bar{T}(k)}{1 - P^-(k+1)} \tag{7.3.8}$$

We assume next that the propagation time in the forward and feedback channels is much smaller than the duration of the signals. This justifies the simplifying assumption:

A4 The transmission of packets by means of retransmissions is equivalent to the single transmission of an equivalent packet whose length has an exponential distribution with the average $T'(k)$.

Assuming this we can replace the chain with feedback links by the open chain shown in Fig. 7.15.

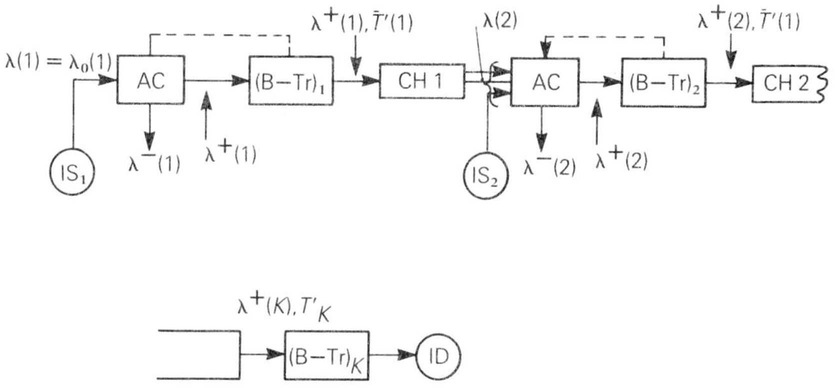

Fig. 7.15 – The open chain of channels which on assumption A4 is equivalent to the chain with feedback shown in Fig. 7.14.

For the open system we have

$$P^{-}(k) = P[\mathrm{L}(k) = \hat{L}(k)] \tag{7.3.9}$$

$$\lambda^{+}(k) = \lambda(k)[1 - P^{-}(k)] \tag{7.3.10}$$

The delay

$$\tau(k) = \frac{\bar{L}(k)}{\lambda^{+}(k)} \tag{7.3.11}$$

Where average number of packets in $(\mathrm{B{-}Tr})_k$

$$\bar{L}(k) = \sum_{l=1}^{\hat{L}(k)} l P[\mathrm{L}(k) = l] \tag{7.3.12}$$

$L(k)$ is the random variable representing the number of packets at $(B\text{–}Tr)_k$ unit. From these formulae it is evident that to obtain the parameters we are interested in we have to obtain the probabilities $\mathbf{P}[L(k) = l]$. Exact evaluation in closed form of these probabilities, even for the simple chain shown in Fig. 7.14 is not possible. The reason for the difficulties is the constraint that the B–Tr unit capacity is finite. Even for two nodes in tandem the exact solution given by Konheim and Reiser [7.7] is very complicated. However, for the system analysed with additional input at each intermediate node it can be expected that the input at each node can be considered approximately as a Poisson-exponential sequence. Then for each node we can use the results of Example 7.1.1, in particular the formula (A.2.11). Obviously this is only a tentative hypothesis; its justification in more detail is discussed in Pennotti and Schwartz [7.1] and Rudin [7.8]. In particular simulation experiments have shown that the results obtained using the probability distribution given by A.2.11 are reasonably accurate.

Hitherto we have considered the parameters characterising the single node. From (7.3.8) we see that $\bar{T}_k'$ depends on the probability $P^-(k+1)$ and this probability depends on the normalised intensity of the sequence of packets put into this buffer, which depends in turn on T_{k+1}'. Starting with the last node we can successively evaluate T_k' and $P^-(k+1)$.

Let us denote by $\tau_{k,K}$ the delay introduced on the path from the kth node to the destination node K. It is

$$\tau_{k,K} = \sum_{\mu=1}^{K} \tau(\mu) \tag{7.3.13}$$

According to the definition $\nu^+(k)$ characterises an individual node. The segment of chain starting with kth node is characterised by the intensity $\lambda_{k,K}^+$ of packets which, put into the kth node, reach the end of the chain. We have:

$$\lambda_{k,K}^+ = \lambda_{k-1} \prod_{\mu=k}^{K} [1 - P^-(\mu)] \tag{7.3.14a}$$

Figure 7.16 shows the dependence of the normalised delay $\tau_{k,K}' \equiv \tau_{k,K}/\bar{T}$, the dependence of the normalised intensity of packets going through

$$\nu_{k,K}^+ = T\lambda_{k,K}^+ \tag{7.3.14b}$$

and the dependence of the normalised intensity $\nu_{k,K}^- = \nu - \nu_{k,K}^+$ of lost packets on the normalised intensity $\nu = \lambda(1)\bar{T}$, for a chain consisting of $K = 3$ nodes, on the assumption that $\bar{T}_k = \bar{T} = \text{const.}$

These dependences are typical of the congestion phenomena described at the introduction to this chapter (see Fig. 7.1).

(a)

(b)

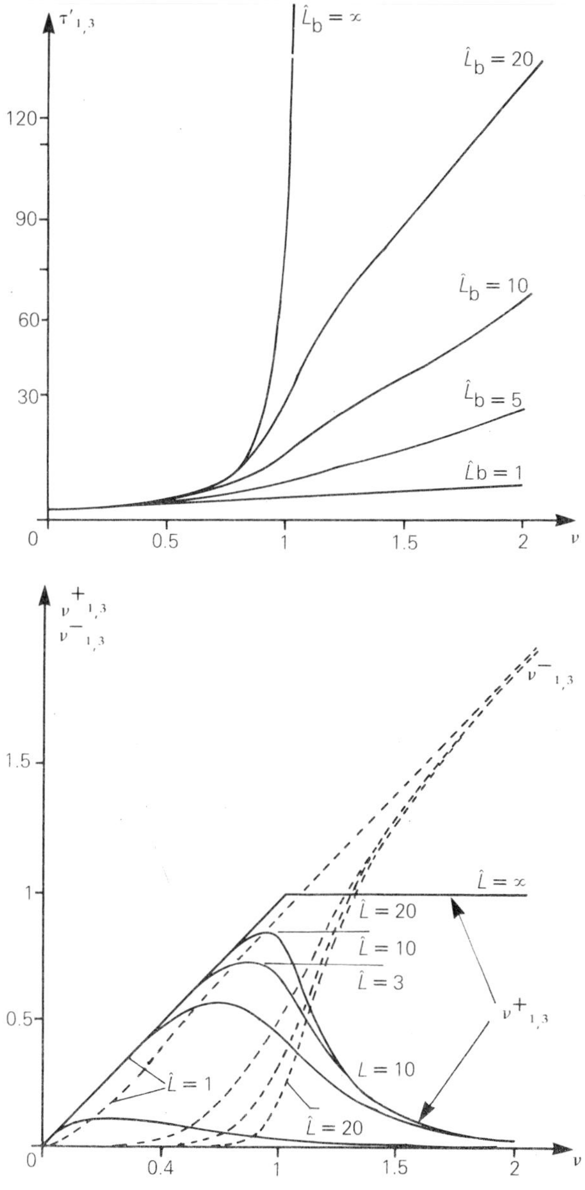

Fig. 7.16 – Dependence (a) of normalised delay $\tau'_{1,3}$ and (b) of the normalised intensity $\nu^{+}_{1,3}$ (continuous lines) of packets going through the chain shown in Fig. 7.14 consisting of $K = 3$ nodes and of the normalised intensity $\nu^{-}_{1,3}$ (broken lines) of lost packets on the normalised intensity $\nu = \lambda(1)\bar{T}$, $\bar{T}_k = \bar{T} =$ const. of packets delivered by the source; $\hat{L}_b(k) = \hat{L}_b =$ const. is the capacity of each buffer–transmitter unit. Based on Papir [7.3].

7.3.2 Admission rule based on local information in a mesh network

In the system considered previously there was only one path from the source to the destination. In this subsection we will consider a meshed network in which several paths from source to destination are possible. To get at least some results in closed form which would give us insight into the properties of system with access control based on local data obtained by means of a feedback channel, we shall assume that a random routing rule is applied. We will first describe the system. We assume that the rule for handling the packets and copies are similar to those in the case of the chain of nodes considered previously. One of the differences is that we now introduce two classes of packets: (1) external packets (class 1 packets) generated by the source at the node we are considering; (2) internal packets (class 2 packets) arriving from other nodes.

A block diagram of the node is given in Fig. 7.17. Both internal and external packets arrive at the node. Let us begin by considering internal packets. They are first fed into the unit implementing the internal packet admission rule (abbreviation: InAD). Any non-admitted packet is rejected. An admitted packet is directed to the entrance buffer, where initial processing of the packet takes place. At the output of the entrance buffer is the unit implementing the routing

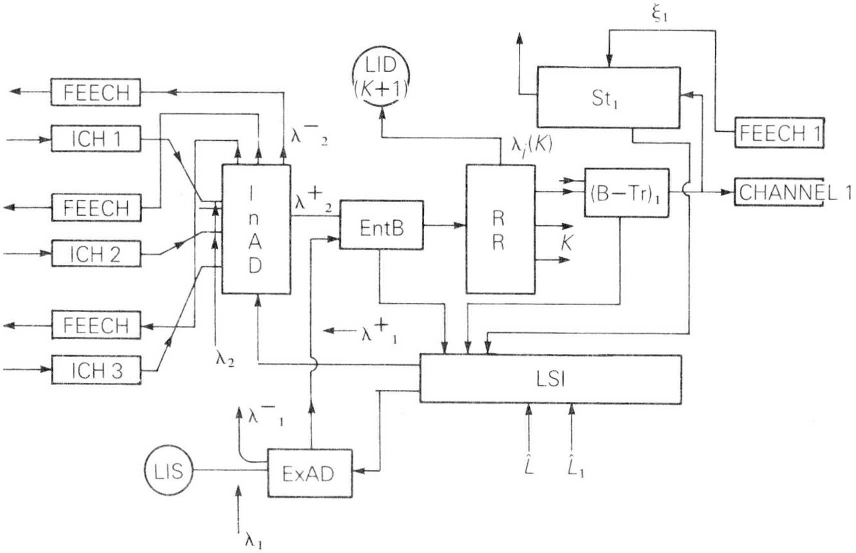

Fig. 7.17 – Model of the node in the network with admission control based on local information. InAD, facility realising the internal packet admission rule; ExAD, facility realising the external packet admision rule, LSI, facility for local state information collecting and preprocessing; FEECH, feedback channels; EntB, entrance buffer; RR, facility realising the routing rule; CHR, facility realising the copy handling rule; St, copy storage.

rule. The channels leaving the node are given numbers $k = 1, 2, \ldots, K$. At the input to each channel there is a line buffer $k = 1, 2, \ldots, K$, which is followed by a transmitter. We call this set the $(\text{B--Tr})_k$ unit. The entrance buffer has the number $k = 0$, the local destination buffer the number $k = K+1$. We also have the copy storage. The line buffer, transmitter and the copy storage operate as in the simple chain considered previously. Thus, at the same time as a packet is put into the channel a copy is placed in the copy storage. The subrules 1.3, 1.4 of the rule R1 of section 7.3.1 are then applied.

We call external packets class 1 packets, and internal ones class 2 packets; we indicate the parameters characterising these packets by the appropriate index. Let:†

$l_i(k)$ be the number of packets of ith, $i = 1, 2$ class in the $(\text{B--Tr})_k$ unit, $k = 0, 1, \ldots, K+1$;

$l_i = \sum_{k=0}^{K} l_i(k)$ be the total number of packets of class i at all $(\text{B--Tr})_k$ units;

$l_i^{(c)}$ be the total number of copies of packets of class i in all copy stores $k = 1, \ldots, K$;

$$l_i' = l_i + l_i^{(c)} \tag{7.3.15}$$

be the total number of packets of class i and their copies in the node;

$\hat{L}$ be the maximum admissible number of all packets and copies in the node;

$\hat{L}_1$ be the maximum admissible number of class 1 packets in the node.

Channels are numbered $k = 1, 2, \ldots, K$. The packet admittance rule to the entrance buffer is:

R1 An external packet is admitted if

$$l_1' \leqslant \hat{L}_1 \tag{7.3.16}$$

and

$$l_1' + l_2' < \hat{L} \tag{7.3.17}$$

An internal packet is admitted if

$$l_1' + l_2' < \hat{L} \,. \tag{7.3.18}$$

The admission rule is obviously more restrictive for external packets than for internal ones. Notice that non-admission of an external packet causes its loss,

† Since we consider a fixed node we do not indicate that the parameters depend on its number.

whereas the non-admission of an internal packet only necessitates its retransmission. Let us denote by:

λ_i – the intensity of packets delivered to the node;
λ_i^+ – the intensity of packets accepted by the node;
P_i^- – the probability of non-acceptance of a packet directed to the node considered;
τ_i – the average waiting time of packets;
L_i – the average number of packets in the node,

where $i = 1, 2$ is the packet's class. The intensity of non-admitted packets is

$$\lambda_i^+ = \lambda_i - \lambda_i^- \tag{7.3.19}$$

and

$$\lambda_i^- = \lambda_i P_i^- \, . \tag{7.3.20}$$

From Little's theorem

$$\tau_i = \frac{\bar{L}_i}{\lambda_i^+} \, . \tag{7.3.21}$$

So far we have been concerned with a fixed node and have not indicated the dependence of the parameters introduced at that node. We now proceed as in section 1.5.1 and, on the basis of parameters characterising the single node, define parameters characterising the whole network. Deriving the fundamental properties of the system considered, we assume that the sequences of packets delivered by sources are independent, Poisson-exponential sequences. We denote by λ_1 the intensity of packets delivered by the source at the node considered. Even under this assumption and as for the simple chain previously considered, the exact analysis of this system is excessively complicated. One reason is that although the starting instants of the internal packets passing through a channel are independent at first, they become statistically dependent as a result of feedback. Another reason is that the sequences of internal and external packets are interrelated in a complicated way through the routing rule. One way of taking these dependences into account would be simulation. The other possibility, which we shall follow here, is to introduce a series of simplifying assumptions which permit us to decompose the problem of analysing the whole network into a set of problems analysing single nodes and buffers. The first simplifying assumption which we will now introduce is:

A1 The routing rule is a memoryless random routing rule described by the probability $P_i(k)$, $k = 1, 2, \ldots, K+1$ of putting a packet of class i into the kth buffer.

Remember that in the node considered we give the number $K + 1$ to the local destination. Thus $P_i(K+1)$ is the probability that an i-class packet ends its journey through the network at the node considered.

Let us denote by

$\lambda_i(k)$ – intensity of packets of ith class put into the $(B\text{–}Tr)_k$ unit.

We have

$$\lambda_i(k) = P_i(k)\lambda_i^+ \tag{7.3.22}$$

where λ_i^+ is given by (7.3.19), (7.3.20).

Let us consider the lengths of packets put into the outgoing channels. Since the process of transmission of both the internal and external packets admitted into the node is the same, calculating the length of the packet we omit the class number i. Retransmissions may cause a packet to be transmitted more than once. We will allow for this by introducing assumption A4 from the previous subsection. The equivalent packet duration in the open outgoing link k, $k = 1, 2, \ldots, K$ is

$$\bar{T}'(k) = \bar{H}(k)\bar{T}(k) \tag{7.3.23}$$

Let us denote by $P^-(k)$ the probability that a packet put into the kth channel will not be accepted at the channels output. It is

$$\bar{H}(k) = \frac{1}{1-P^-(k)} \quad . \tag{7.3.24}$$

We characterise the packets put into outgoing channels by the normalised intensity

$$\nu_i(k) = \lambda_i(k)\bar{T}_i'(k) \tag{7.3.25}$$

From (7.3.22)–(7.3.24) we obtain $\nu_i(k)$ for $k = 1, 2, \ldots, K$. Because there are no retransmissions for the entrance buffer, we define

$$\nu_i(0) = \lambda_i\bar{T}_i(0) \tag{7.3.26}$$

and similarly for the local destination

$$\nu_i(K+1) = \lambda_i P_i(K+1)\bar{T}_i(K+1) \tag{7.3.27}$$

where $T_i(0)$ and $T_i(K+1)$ are the corresponding packet lengths. We next consider the flows of copies from the copy store. Two events are possible: (A) as a result of the packet being rejected by the next node either the auxiliary information ξ^- arrives or the time-out period for acknowledgement elapses, and the copy is transferred to the transmitter buffer; (B) as the result of accepting the packet, the auxiliary information ξ^+ arrives and the copy is destroyed.

Let us consider event A. The total intensity of this event is $\bar{H}(k)-1$ times larger than the intensity of input packet intensity, where $\bar{H}(k)$ is the average number of packet retransmissions which can be obtained from (7.3.7). Thus the intensity of event A

$$\lambda_i^{(A)}(k) = \lambda_i(k)[\bar{H}(k)-1] \qquad (7.3.28)$$

Next we look at event B. On the assumption that:

A2 the average numbers of packets in the network buffers are finite, and
A3 that the capacities of the buffers are infinite,

each internal packet (class 1) forwarded to the next node will ultimately, possibly after a number of retransmissions, be accepted by it. Thus the intensity of event B is the same as the intensity of working packets. Thus the intensity of event B is:

$$\lambda_i^{(B)}(k) = \lambda_i(k) \qquad (7.3.29)$$

Let $T_i^{(A)}$ and $T_i^{(B)}$ denote the average times the copy is kept in store until either event A or B occurs. Appendix A.1 explains that the operation of the copy store is characterised by the dimensionless parameter as in the operation of the buffer:

$$\nu_i^{(c)}(k) = \lambda_i^{(A)}(k)T_i^{(A)} + \lambda_i^{(B)}(k)T_i^{(B)} \quad . \qquad (7.3.30)$$

If we know the primary input intensities $\lambda_i, i=1,2$, and the probabilities of non-acceptance $P^-(k)$, formulae (7.3.13)–(7.3.18) enable us to evaluate the dimensionless parameters $\nu_i(k)$ characterising the operation of the (B–Tr)$_k$ unit and the parameters $\nu_i^{(c)}(k)$ characterising the copy store. So far we have considered the primary intensities λ_1 and λ_2 as independent. This is a valid assumption as long as we are considering an isolated node. However, if we consider the whole network we have to take into account the fact that the external intensities determine the internal packet intensities by means of the routing and admission rules. We now show that it is possible to derive a simple relationship between λ_1 and λ_2 by making two simplifying assumptions. The first is:

A4 that the network is homogeneous in the sense that the values of parameters characterising nodes are the same for all nodes.

The second is an assumption about the equilibrium of packets' absorption and delivery by each node. Let λ_{abs} be the intensity of absorption by the local destination. We have:

$$\lambda_{abs} = \lambda_1(1-P_1^-)P_1(K+1) + \lambda_2(1-P_2^-)P_2(K+1) \qquad (7.3.31)$$

where on the basis of A4 we denote P_i^- as the probability of not admitting a packet of class i, $i=1,2$, into the node considered. We assume that:

A5 the network is in equilibrium in the sense that the intensity of external packets introduced at each node is equal to the intensity of packets absorbed by the destination at that node.

This assumption can be stated as the condition

$$\lambda_{abs} = \lambda_1^+ \ . \qquad (7.3.32)$$

After substituting (7.3.31), (7.3.19) and (7.3.20) in condition (7.3.32) we obtain

$$\lambda_2 = H''\lambda_1 \qquad (7.3.33)$$

where

$$H'' = \frac{(1-P_1^-)[1-P_1(K+1)]}{(1-P_2^-)P_2(K+1)} \ . \qquad (7.3.34)$$

Formula (7.3.33) gives the relationship between the intensities of the internal and external packets. We now show that the parameter H'' has a simple interpretation. We assume that the network is homogeneous in the sense of A4. Consider a packet delivered by an external source to a node. It will be admitted to the network with a probability $1 - P_1^-$ and it will not be absorbed by the local destination with a probability $1 - P_1(K+1)$. Thus it will start a journey through the network with a probability $P_{st} \equiv (1 - P_1^-)(1 - P_1(K + 1))$. The packet is accepted by the next node and completes its journey with a probability $\Pi \equiv (1 - P_2^-)P_2(K + 1)$, or continues its journey with a probability $1 - \Pi$. If the successive steps of the packet are independent, we see that the probability that the packet completes its journey after exactly k hops is $P_{st}(1 - \Pi)^{k-1}\Pi$.

Thus we have the same situation as when deriving the average number of retransmissions, i.e. as in (7.3.11) we have the average number of hops $\bar{H}'' = P_{st}/\Pi$.

Comparing this formua with (7.3.34), we see that auxiliary parameter H'' can be interpreted as the average number of packet hops, including retransmissions.

Under the simplifying assumptions we can apply formula A.7.58 given in Appendix A.7. Notice that because at each copy store each copy is served individually, we can consider all copy stores as one store. Thus in the node being considered, we have $K + 1$ buffers and one infinite server in which packets of one of the two classes (internal, external) may be waiting. Thus the systems state description is given by the set

$$\mathbf{l} = (\mathbf{l}_1, l_1^c, \mathbf{l}_2, l_2^c) \qquad (7.3.35)$$

where

$$\mathbf{l}_i \equiv \{l_i(k), k = 0, 1, \ldots, K+1\} \qquad (7.3.36)$$

Let us denote by $A^{+}(\hat{L},\hat{L}_1)$ the set of sets L satisfying conditions (7.3.16)–(7.3.18). The probability $P(\mathbf{l})$ of state $\mathbf{l} \in A[\hat{L},\hat{L}_1]$ occurring is given by the formula (see A.7.58).

$$P(\mathbf{l}) = C \prod_{k=0}^{K+1} \frac{[l_1(k)+l_2(k)]!}{[l_1(k)]!\,[l_2(k)]!} [\nu_1(k)]^{l_1(k)} [\nu_2(k)]^{l_2(k)}$$

$$\frac{1}{(l_1^{(c)})!\,(l_2^{(c)})!} [\nu_1^{(c)}]^{l_1^{(c)}} [\nu_2^{(c)}]^{l_2^{(c)}} \tag{7.3.37}$$

where $\nu_i(k)$ are given by (7.3.25) and

$$\nu_i^{(c)} = \sum_{k=1}^{K} \nu_i^{(c)}(k) \tag{7.3.38}$$

where $\nu_i^{(c)}(k)$ is given by (7.3.30).

The normalisation constraint is determined by the condition

$$\sum_{\mathbf{l} \in A^{+}[\hat{L},\hat{L}_1]} P(\mathbf{l}) = 1 \ . \tag{7.3.39}$$

The average number of packets L_i in the node, and the probability of not accepting a packet P_i^-, can be expressed by means of the probabilities $P(\mathbf{l})$, as in the previous section. For numerical purposes it is, however, convenient to introduce the aggregated state description and its probability distribution.

Let the aggregated state description be the set

$$\mathbf{l}' = (l_1', l_2') \tag{7.3.40}$$

where

$$l_i' = \sum_{k=0}^{K+1} l_i(k) + l_i^{(c)} \tag{7.3.41}$$

is the total number of packets and copies of the ith class, and let $P'(\mathbf{l})$ be the probability of the pair (l_1', l_2')

We have

$$P'(l') = \sum_{l \in L(l')} P(l) \tag{7.3.42}$$

where $L(l')$ is a subset of $A^+(\hat{L},\hat{L}_1)$ such that

$$\sum_{k=0}^{K+1} l_i(k) + l_i^{(c)} = l_i, \; L = 1,2$$

Reiser and Kobayqshi [A.4] gave an effective method for evaluating the sum occurring in (7.3.42).

For the probability of external packet non-acceptance we have

$$P_1^- = \sum_{l_1=0}^{\hat{L}_1} P'(l_1, \hat{L}_1 - l_1) + + \sum_{l_2=0}^{\hat{L}-\hat{L}_1} P[\hat{L}_1, l_2] \tag{7.3.43}$$

The first sum corresponds to the event that the external packet is not accepted because $l_1 + l_2 = \hat{L}$, while the second sum corresponds to the event that $l_1 = \hat{L}_1$. Similarly,

$$P_2^- = \sum_{l_1=0}^{\hat{L}_1} P'(l_1, \hat{L} - l_i) \tag{7.3.44}$$

because an internal packet is not accepted only if the total number of packets has reached L. Finally the average number of packets in the node

$$\bar{L}_i = \sum_{l_1, l_2} l_i \cdot P(l_1, l_2) \tag{7.3.45}$$

Having evaluated P_i^- and L_i we obtain the intensity λ_i^+ and delay τ_i from (7.3.19)–(7.3.21). As an example of application of the formulae derived, we consider a chain of 2 channels and buffers similar to that shown in Fig. 7.14. We assume that we have no entrance buffer, ($T_i(0) = 0$, $T_i(K + 1) = T$), $T^{(A)} = T^{(B)} = T_i$, $\lambda(1)$ is variable.

Figure 7.18 shows the dependence of the normalised delay and the normalised intensity of non-accepted packets $\nu_1^- = T\lambda_1^-$ on the normalised intensity of external packets $\nu_1 = \lambda(1)T$ and on $\hat{L}_1$.

As may be expected, the growth of ν_1 causes the growth of T and ν_1^-. Figure 7.19 shows the operational characteristics, i.e. the dependence of the normalised intensity ν_1^- on the normalised delay τ_1'; both these are changed by altering the threshold $\hat{L}_1$ while $\hat{L}$ is kept fixed.

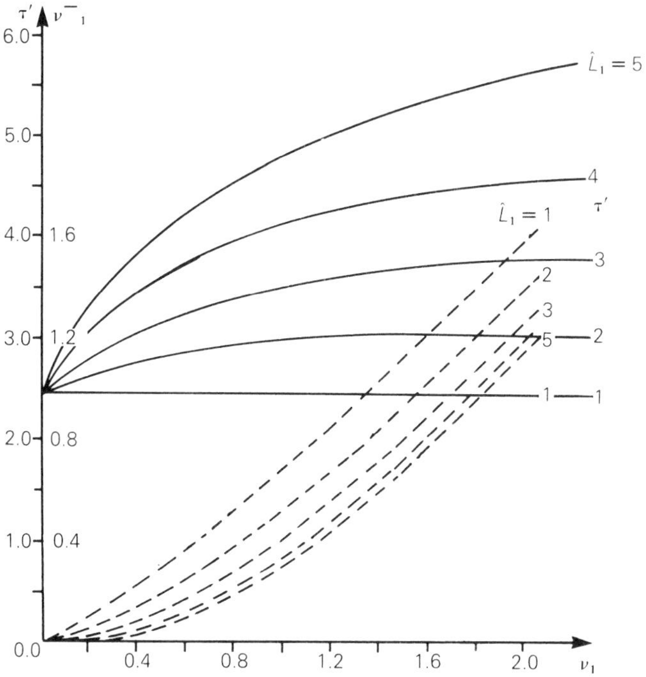

Fig. 7.18 – Dependence of the normalised delay τ_1' (continuous lines) and the normalised intensity ν_1^- of non-accepted external packets (broken lines) of on the intensity of external packets put into a chain, threshold $\hat{L}_1$ variable; rule R1 based on local information. $K = 2$; $\lambda(1)$ = variable; $\lambda(2) = 1$ = const.; routing probabilities: $P_1(1) = P_2(1) = 0.5$; $P_1(2) = 1 - P_2(2) = 0.2$; $P_k^- = 0.2, k = 1, 2$; normalised intensities $\nu_0(1) = 0.1\lambda(1)$; $\nu_0(2) = 0.1$; $\nu_1(1) = 1.25\lambda(1)$, $\nu_1(2) = 0.5$; $\nu_2(1) = 0.625\lambda(1)$; $\nu_2(2) = 1$; $\nu_1^c(1) = 0.0625\lambda(1)$; $\nu_1(2) = 0.025$; $\nu_2^c(1) = 0.125\lambda(1)$; $\nu^2(2) = 0.125$; maximum number of all packets $\hat{L} = 10$; maximum number of class 1 packets $\hat{L}_1 \leqslant 10$ variable.

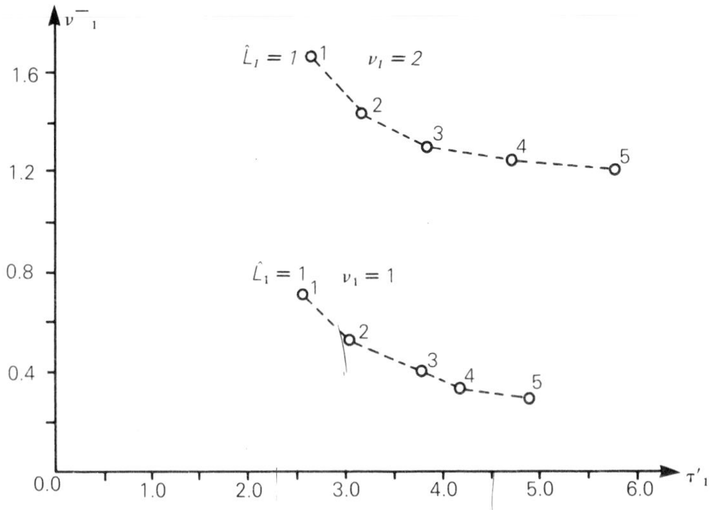

Fig. 7.19 – Operational characteristic of a system with access rule based on local information; ν_1^-, normalised intensity of external (class 1) rejected packet; τ_1', their normalised delay. Threshold $\hat{L} = 5$ = const.; other data as for Fig. 7.18.

REFERENCES

[7.1] Pennotti, M., and Schwartz, M., (1975), Congestion control in store and forward tandem links, *IEEE Trans. on Comm.*, **COM-23**, No. 12, 1434–1443.

[7.2] Chatterjee, A., Georgans, P., and Vermas, P., (1976), Analysis of a packet switched network with end-to-end congestion control and random routing, *International Conference on Computer Communications 1976, Toronto*, 488–494.

[7.3] Papir, Z., (1979), Congestion and methods of counteracting it, Doctoral dissertation, AGH, Kraków, in Polish.

[7.4] Wong, J. W., and Unsoy, M. S., (1977), Analysis of flow control in switched data network, *IFIP Congress Proceedings 1977*, 315–320.

[7.5] Okada, H., *et al.*, (1976), Analysis of isorhythmic flow control method in packet switching computer networks, *Electronics and Comm. in Japan*, **59-A**, No. 3, 22–30.

[7.6] Lam, S. S., and Reiser, M., (1977), Congestion control of store-and-forward networks by input buffer limits, *Proc. Com. Conference, Los Angeles, 1977*, 813–817.

[7.7] Konheim, A. G., and Reiser, M., (1974), A queueing model with finite waiting room and blocking, *IBM res. Rep. RC 5066.*

[7.8] Rudin, H., (1976), An introduction to flow control, *Proc. of International Conference of Computer Communications 1976, Toronto*.

8

Optimisation of channel capacities and network topologies

In the previous three chapters we have assumed that the capacities and layout of channels in the network are fixed. We attempted to optimise use of the channels by adjusting the routing rules to the properties of the information sources and to the existing channels connecting the nodes. However, we can often change the properties of channels. By increasing channel capacity, we can improve the quality of packet transmission, but in doing so, we increase the cost of the channels. When choosing channel capacities we must take at least two parameters into account: the cost of increasing the channel capacities, and the gain resulting from any increase in the quality of transmission. In the first three sections of this chapter, we consider the optimisation of the set of capacities of a network with a given topology, taking both these effects into consideration. We start with a discussion of parameters characterising the set of channel capacities, we will formulate the channel capacities optimisation problem and illustrate it by two simple examples. As explained in Chapter 1, we must in general use the results of routing rule optimisation considered previously, because, in order to compare fairly two sets of channel capacities, we must assume that for each set we apply the optimal routing rule for that set. This difficulty does not arise in the inflow or outflow tree network because we have no routing problem: there is only a single path from the source node to the central node or from the central node to the destination node. This is why we shall be paying a good deal of attention to tree networks when trying to explain the fundamental properties of channel capacity optimisation.

We secondly consider the problem of finding the set of channel capacities in a mesh network while minimising their cost, assuming that the cost of each channel is non-linearly dependent on the channel capacity. However, instead of the constraint imposed on the quality of packet transmission, we introduce only the capacity constraint.

In the third subsection, we will deal with the complementary problem of finding the set of channel capacities maximising the quality of packet transmission on the assumption that the total cost of all channels is fixed. In general, the solution of such optimisation problems is very complicated. We will restrict ourselves to the special case when the cost of a channel is a linear function of its capacity. It is then possible to use the results of the subchannel capacity optimisation obtained in section 3.2 and reduce the problem of the optimisation of the set of channel capacities to one of flow pattern optimisation. This latter problem can be solved using the methods described in Chapter 6.

Topology optimisation is the most general problem, and its systematic solution is quite complicated because, as we explained in Chapter 1, to optimise the network's topology, we must use all the conclusions about optimum routing and optimum choice of channel capacities. Only heuristic methods exist to find 'good' topologies of general mesh-type networks. We will concentrate here on the simplest type of tree network topology optimisation. For this type of network, important from the practical point of view, there exist algorithms which, although heuristic, in most cases yield topologies which can be expected to be close to the optimum. In order to find good tree network topologies, we will describe the algorithms in greater detail, to show by the example of these particular networks the fundamental problems arising when searching for 'good' topologies in the general case of a mesh network.

8.1 CHANNEL CAPACITY OPTIMISATION – FUNDAMENTAL CONCEPTS, SIMPLE EXAMPLES

In this section we introduce the parameters characterising the quality of a set of channel capacities and formulate their optimisation. We will illustrate the general concepts by two examples. One will be the optimisation of channel capacities in a tree network, the other in a mesh network, albeit for the special case when we do not take quality of packet transmission into account, and when the cost function is linear. The general case when the cost function is non-linear will be the subject of the next section.

8.1.1 Parameters characterising channel capacities

In this and the next two sections we assume that the topology of the network is fixed, but that we can choose the channel capacities. With this possibility, we can change the topology to some extent, because by giving zero capacity to a channel, we effectively delete it.

The general methodology of formulating the channel capacity optimisation problem was given in section 1.5. As we explained there, the set of channel capacities is characterised by two sets of parameters: (a) the cost of obtaining the desired channel capacities; (b) the quality of packet transmission. We now consider these parameters in more detail.

We usually define the parameter characterising the cost of the network on the basis of parameters characterising the costs of constructing the individual channels and nodes. The cost of constructing a single channel depends both on its geometrical shape, especially its length, and on its capacity. Since the latter relationship is fundamental, we shall denote the cost of constructing a channel (w, v) of capacity C by $\kappa[(w, v), C]$; in situations where no confusion can arise we will write briefly $\kappa(C)$. The function $\kappa(C)$ is usually a function of increasing capacity, so

$$\phi(C) > 0 \tag{8.1.1}$$

where

$$\phi(C) \equiv \frac{d\kappa}{dC} \tag{8.1.2}$$

is the rate at which the construction cost of the channel increases with its capacity. Figure 8.1(a) shows a typical graph of the dependence of $\kappa(C)$ on

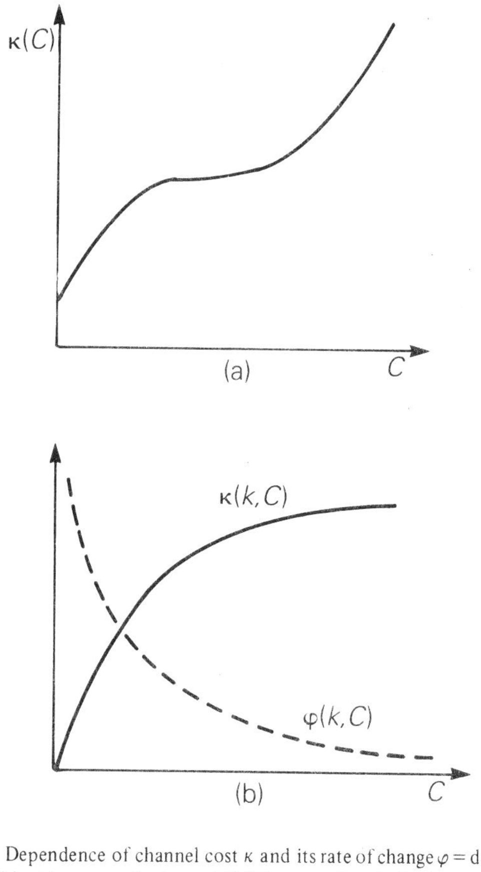

Fig. 8.1 – Dependence of channel cost κ and its rate of change $\varphi = d\kappa/dC$ channel capacity: (a) wide range of values of C, (b) range of typical values of C.

capacity C. When $C \to 0$ the function $\kappa(C)$ does not approach zero as a consequence of the fact that certain permanent costs are generally involved in the construction of the channel and are independent of its capacity. As the capacity increases from small values, the rate of growth of the channel cost usually decreases at first, i.e. within a range of C we have

$$\frac{d\phi}{dC} < 0 \tag{8.1.3a}$$

or, which is equivalent,

$$\frac{d^2\kappa}{dC^2} < 0 \ . \tag{8.1.3b}$$

A typical graph of the functions $\kappa(C)$ and $\phi(C)$ in this range is given in Fig. 8.1(b). An example of a cost function of this type is the empirically obtained function of the cost of constructing a wide class of channels:

$$\kappa(C) = A + BC^{\alpha} \tag{8.1.4}$$

where $0 < \alpha \leqslant 1$, and the constants A and B depend on the shape of the channel, chiefly its length. The function A is a component corresponding to the permanent cost of channel construction, independent of its capacity. In some discussions, the function

$$\kappa(C) = \phi C \tag{8.1.5}$$

is taken to be an approximation of the cost of channel construction, where ϕ is a constant coefficient. Such a function is called the **linear function** of the cost of channel construction.

As we explained• previously when we use a channel, we usually divide it into subchannels of smaller capacity. When the channel capacity becomes very large, and hence also the number of subchannels, the costs of organising subchannel operation begin to rise rapidly. The rate of increase of cost increases with capacity, and the derivative $d\phi/dC$ becomes positive. The capacity ranges for which an increase in channel construction cost is less or greater than linear (derivative $d\phi/dC$ is negative or positive) depends on the type of channel; this is illustrated by Fig. 8.2.

The construction cost of a node depends both on the functions realised by that node, and on the capacity of the node C', defined as the greatest flow intensity of signals that can be correctly processed by the node. In general, the construction cost of a node $\kappa(C')$ processes properties similar to those in (8.1.1) and (8.1.3) of the channel construction cost. If we include the construction of a node in the costs of constructing the channels using that node, the new channel construction cost will have properties similar to the original cost of constructing

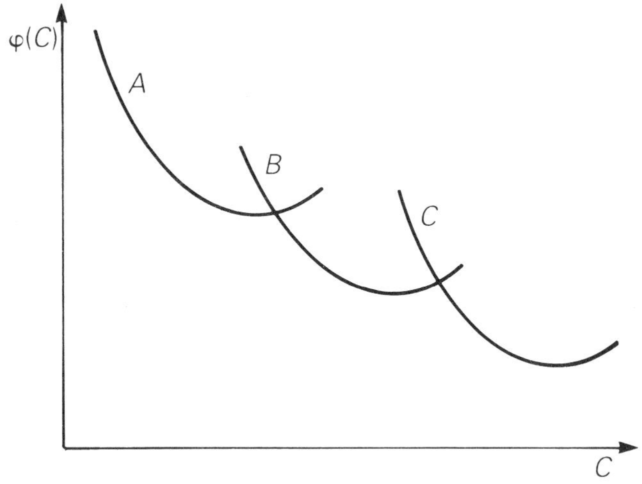

Fig. 8.2 – Dependence of rate of change of cost on channel capacity for various types of channel: A, microwave links; B, coaxial cables; C, waveguides.

the channel alone. For this reason, we shall subsequently assume that the cost of constructing a node is included in the cost of constructing the channels going out from that node.

The cost of network construction depends on the cost of constructing the channels. To a good approximation, we can assume the cost of channel construction

$$\kappa(\mathbf{C}) = \sum_{(w,v)\in K} \kappa\,[(w,v), C(w,v)] \tag{8.1.6}$$

where

$$\mathbf{C} \equiv \{C(w,v); (w,v) \in K\} \tag{8.1.7}$$

is the set of capacities and K is the set of all channels forming the network. We take the parameter $\kappa(\mathbf{C})$ to be the basic parameter characterising the set of channel capacities from the point of view of the costs of obtaining channels of such capacities, which we call the **capacity set cost.**

Notice that the network construction cost includes not only the cost of constructing channels for transmitting working information, but also that of constructing a subsystem for the collection and transmission of n.s.i. This latter cost depends on the channel capacities in quite a complex manner, because as the capacity and the number of channels increase the cost of the subsystem for n.s.i. collection and transmission rises non-linearly. However, this cost is usually small in comparison with the cost of constructing working channels, so we shall only deal with the capacity set cost $\kappa(C)$. Apart from the cost of constructing the set of capacities this set is also characterised by parameters related to the quality of packet transmission, in particular, the packet transit time. We define the latter parameters on the basis of the parameters characterising the routing rule or the flow pattern from the point of view of packet transmission quality (for a detailed discussion of these parameters, see sections 5.2 and 6.1), using the general methods described in section 1.4. We shall illustrate the methodology in defining a parameter characterising the set of capacities from the point of view of packet transmission quality, assuming that it is based on a parameter characterising the flow pattern quality.

Notice that the parameter $Q(\mathbf{F})$ characterising the quality of the total flow pattern $\mathbf{F}$ between all the source–destination pairs considered in section 6.1, depends in general on the set of channel capacities $\mathbf{C}$ and the flow pattern $\mathbf{F}$. We indicate this by writing $Q(\mathbf{F},\mathbf{C})$ instead of $Q(\mathbf{F})$ which we used in Chapter 6.

As a typical example of such a parameter, consider the packets passage time through the network given by the formula:

$$\tau(\mathbf{F},\mathbf{C}) = A_1 \sum_{(w,v)\in K} \frac{F(w,v)}{C(w,v)-F(w,v)} + A(w,v)\,F(w,v) \tag{8.1.8}$$

where $F(w,v)$ is the flow intensity through channel (w,v), and A_1 is a normalising coefficient.

If, on the basis of parameters characterising the flow pattern quality, we wish to define the parameter $Q(\mathbf{C})$ characterising the set of capacities, we must apply a suitable operation on $Q(\mathbf{F},\mathbf{C})$ to remove the dependence on the flow pattern $\mathbf{F}$. The most consistent approach would be to take the best flow pattern from the point of view of packets transmission quality. Assuming we want to minimise parameter ϵ, for example if ϵ is packet transit time, we would define:

$$Q_1(\mathbf{C}) \equiv \min_{\mathbf{F}} Q(\mathbf{F},\mathbf{C}) \tag{8.1.9}$$

Although consistent, the application of this definition would be difficult, because to use it we must solve the flow optimisation problem OP$Q\mathbf{F}\,|\,\mathbf{C},\mathcal{C}$ where $\mathcal{C}$ is the set of constraints imposed on the flows in the network considered, a rather difficult task. Therefore we frequently remove the dependence of $Q(\mathbf{F},\mathbf{C})$ on $\mathbf{F}$ by assuming that the flow is predetermined; thus we define

$$Q_2(C) \equiv Q(\hat{\mathbf{F}},\mathbf{C}) \tag{8.1.10}$$

where $\hat{\mathbf{F}}$ is the predetermined flow. This definition is justifed where the statistical properties of information sources are fixed and we apply a standardised routing rule. The flow pattern is then also fixed and we take it to be $\mathbf{F}$. We should remember that in general definition (8.1.10) is not completely consistent. To compare the quality of two capacity sets is possible in principle on the basis of a comparison of the quality of packet transmission, calculated under the assumption that we use the best possible routing rule for the given set of capacities.

So far, we have assumed our definition of the set of capacities **C** is based on the parameter $Q(\mathbf{F},\mathbf{C})$ characterising the total flow pattern. We often start with the parameter $Q_{sr}(\mathbf{F}_{sr},\mathbf{C})$ characterising the flow pattern from source s to destination r, define the parameter $Q_{sr}(\mathbf{C})$ characterising the set **C**, and finally remove the dependence on s,r, for example, by taking weighted averaging.

We now consider the special case of tree networks. To simplify the terminology we assume that the tree network is an inflow network (see section 1.1) in which packets from terminals are delivered to central node. This is not a restrictive assumption, because the outflow network which has to deliver packets from a central node to many destination nodes can be treated in a similar way. The tree structure we will study is shown in Fig. 8.3. In such a network, no routing problem arises because there is only one path from the source pole to the central node determined by the topology of the tree. As a result, the operation to remove the dependence of the parameter characterising the quality of information transmission on the routing rule or flow pattern is no longer necessary.

We start our discussion of parameters characterising a tree network by describing such a network. We take the central node of such a network to have the number $w = 0$, and the remaining nodes to be numbered by the indices $w = 1,2,\ldots,M$. We will call them terminal nodes.

A1 An information source is located at each node.

In accordance with the previously introduced notation,

$$N = M+1 \; . \tag{8.1.11}$$

As in previous chapters, the parameter M indicates the number of information sources. Of course, assumption A1 does not diminish the generality of the discussion, because assuming the intensity of information to be zero, we can, with the aid of our model, describe networks in which, apart from the sources, we also have nodes at which there is no information source.

A node in a tree network with no incoming channel and connected only with a local information source is called a **hanging node**. We call a node at which channels arrive an **intermediate node**. A set consisting of an intermediate node and hanging nodes joined by direct channels or chains of channels is called a set of hanging nodes joined to node w, and we denote it by $H(w)$. Obviously, $H(0)$ includes all nodes in the network. The channels and nodes belonging to $H(w)$ form a sub-tree based on w. Let:

$$X_w \equiv X_{w0} \tag{8.1.12}$$

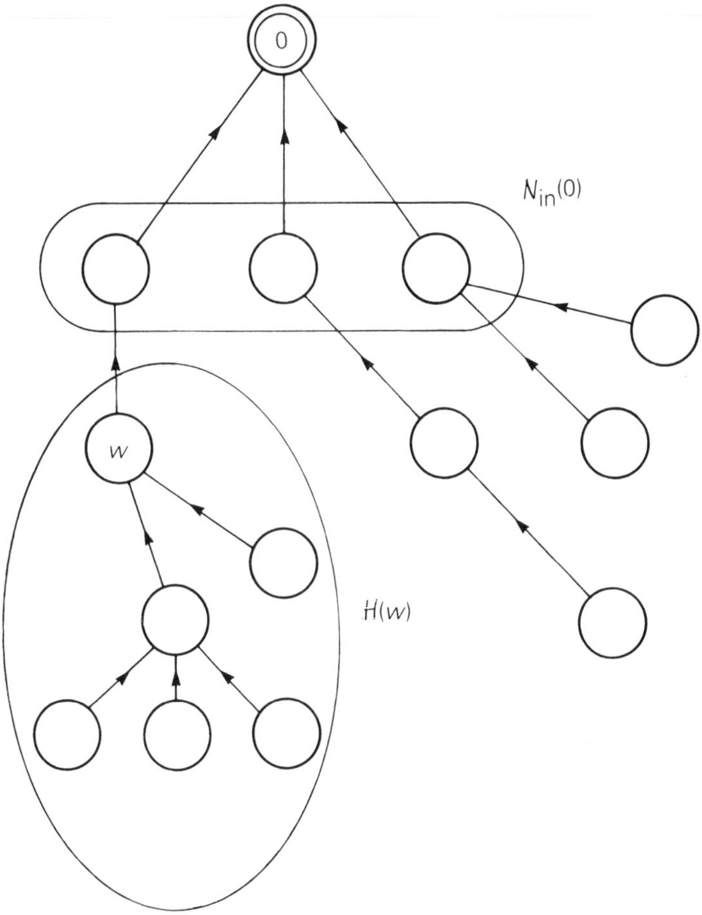

Fig. 8.3 – Tree network and concepts related to it: $N_{in}(0)$, set of channels connected directly to the central node; $H(w)$, set of nodes hanging on node w, full circles, hanging nodes; set of channels cut by a wavy line, a bunch of channels.

be the flow intensity of information delivered by the source at node w directed to the central node, and let

$$F_w \equiv F_{w0} \tag{8.1.13}$$

be the total intensity of the flow directed from node w to the central node.

We assume here that:

A2 No information flow is lost in the network.

Under such an assumption, the continuity constraints (constraints 6.2.11) take the form

$$F_w = \sum_{v \in H(w)} F_v \qquad (8.1.14)$$

We denote the set of these constraints for $w = 1, 2, \ldots, M$ by $A(\mathbf{X})$, as in Chapter 6, where

$$\mathbf{X} \equiv \{X_1, X_2, \ldots, X_M\} \qquad (8.1.15)$$

In a tree network only one channel leaves each node, so the capacity constraints take the form

$$F_w \leqslant C(w, v) \qquad (8.1.16)$$

where (w, v) is the only channel leaving node w. The set of constraints (8.1.13) for $w = 1, 2, \ldots, L$ will be denoted by $B(\mathbf{C})$.

As we showed in section 5.2, the quality of transmission through a single channel depends only on the intensity of the total flow passing through that channel. By indicating that this quality depends also on the capacity of the channels of the tree network, we can put the parameter characterising the set of channel capacities $\mathbf{C}$, from the point of view of the quality of transmission of packets delivered from the terminal node w to the central node 0 in the form:

$$Q_{w0}(C) = \sum_{(u,v) \in P_{w0}} Q_1[(u, v), C(u, v), F(u, v)] \qquad (8.1.17)$$

In this formula, P_{w0} is the unique path going from node w to the central node, and $Q[(u, v), C(u, v), F(u, v)]$ is the quality of transmission through the single channel (u, v) which has capacity $C(w, v)$ when a flow of intensity $F(w, v)$ is passing through it.

To obtain the parameter $Q(\mathbf{C})$ characterising the set of channel capacities $\mathbf{C}$ from the standpoint of the quality of tranmission of packets from all sources, we introduce the operation removing the dependence of $Q_{w0}(\mathbf{C})$ on w mentioned on page 395. Taking the weighted summation, we get

$$Q(\mathbf{C}) = \frac{1}{X} \left\{ \sum_{w=1}^{M} X_w [Q_w(C)]^{\alpha} \right\}^{\alpha} \qquad (8.1.18)$$

where

$$X \equiv \sum_{w=1}^{M} X_w$$

is the total intensity of all flows put into the network, and α is a parameter. For $\alpha \to \infty$, we obtain the quality index

$$Q(\mathbf{C}) = \max_{w} \sum_{(u,v) \in P_{w0}} Q_1[(u,v), C(u,v), F(u,v)] \tag{8.1.19}$$

8.1.2 Formulation of the optimisation problem

To formulate the optimisation of the set of channel capacities we usually have to introduce some constraints. An example of such a constraint is:

> the capacity of the channel $C(w, v)$ can take only one value out of the set $\mathcal{C}_{\text{ad}} = (C_1, \ldots, C_L)$ of admissible values. (8.1.20)

The capacities satisfying such a constraint will be called **standardised.**

A typical optimisation problem is:

> We have to find a set $\mathbf{C}_0$ of channel capacities minimising the total cost $\kappa(\mathbf{C})$ under the constraint that for given statistical properties S_{IS} of the information source, the parameter characterising set $\mathbf{C}$ from the point of view of quality transmission has a given value $\hat{Q}$ and the set of additional constraints $\mathcal{C}$ is satisfied. (8.1.21)

This optimisation problem can be denoted breifly by OP $\mathbf{C}\kappa \mid \mathcal{C}_Q, \mathcal{C}, S_{\text{IS}}$, where $\mathcal{C}_Q$ denotes the constraint $Q(\mathbf{C}) = \hat{Q}$ where $\hat{Q}$ is given. Because we often assume that the primary information sources deliver a Poisson-exponential sequence, the set of statistical properties is completely determined by the set $\mathbf{X}$ of intensities of flows put into the network. We can then write the optimisation problem as OP $\mathbf{C}\kappa \mid \mathcal{C}_Q, \mathcal{C}, \mathbf{X}$.

As explained in section 8.1.1 we define the parameter $Q(\mathbf{C})$ on the basis of the primary parameter $Q[\mathbf{R}(\cdot), \mathbf{C}]$ characterising the set $\mathbf{R}(\cdot)$ of routing rules, or the parameter $Q(\mathbf{F}, \mathbf{C})$ characterising the flow pattern. To simplify the terminology we assume that the definition of $Q(\mathbf{C})$ is based on $Q(\mathbf{F}, \mathbf{C})$. Assuming, for example, that when defining $Q(\mathbf{C})$ we use definition (8.1.10), we can put (8.1.21), in the equivalent form:

> We have to find a set $\mathbf{C}_0$ of channel capacities such that under the constraint $Q(\hat{\mathbf{F}}, \mathbf{C}) = \hat{Q}$ where $\hat{\mathbf{F}}$ is a fixed flow pattern and additional constraints $\mathcal{C}$, the cost of channel capacities is minimal. (8.1.22a)

We denote this problem as OP $\mathbf{C}\kappa \mid \mathcal{C}_Q, \mathcal{C}, \hat{\mathbf{F}}, \mathbf{X}$ where $\mathcal{C}_Q$ denotes the constraint $Q(\hat{\mathbf{F}}, \mathbf{C}) = \hat{Q}$.

Using (8.1.9) for defining $Q(\mathbf{C})$, we formulate the problem:

We have to find the set $\mathbf{C}_0$ of channel capacities and the corresponding flow $\mathbf{F}_0$ such that under the constraint $Q(\mathbf{F},\mathbf{C}) = \hat{Q}$ and constraints $\mathcal{C}$ the cost of channel capacities is minimal. (8.1.22b)

This problem can be briefly written as OP $\mathbf{C},\mathbf{F}\kappa \mid \mathcal{C}_{\hat{Q}}', \mathcal{C}, \mathbf{X}$ where $\mathcal{C}_{\hat{Q}}'$ is the constraint $Q(\mathbf{F},\mathbf{C}) = \hat{Q}$.

Taking into account the constraints $\mathcal{C}_Q$ or $\mathcal{C}_{Q'}$ is usually difficult. Therefore instead we often use a secondary constraint which requires that the channel capacity constraints

$$F(w,v) \leqslant C(w,v) \tag{8.1.23}$$

$(w,v) \in \mathcal{K}$ are met, where $F(w,v)$ is the total flow intensity satisfying the continuity constraints $\mathcal{A}(\mathbf{X})$, and $\mathbf{X}$ is the set of given external flow intensities. We denote the set of constraints (8.1.23) by $\mathcal{B}$. The optimisation problem under constraints (8.1.23) can be formulated as OP $\mathbf{C}\kappa \mid \mathcal{A}(\mathbf{X}), \mathcal{B}$.

Taking into account only the capacity constraint, we can assume that all channels are saturated, i.e. for all channels

$$F(w,v) = C(w,v) \tag{8.1.24}$$

Were this not so, we could have at least one channel w',v' for which $F(w',v') < C(w',v')$. Without violating the constraints $\mathcal{A}(\mathbf{X})$, $\mathcal{B}$, we could then decrease the capacity $C(w',v')$ by $C(w',v') - F(w',v')$. In view of property (8.1.2) of the cost function, such a decrease of channel capacity would decrease the cost of the network.

When (8.1.24) holds, we can consider $\kappa[(w,v), F(w,v)]$ as a parameter characterising the flow intensity $F(w,v)$, and $\mathcal{C}$ as the constraints imposed on the flow pattern. Thus the OP $\mathbf{C}\kappa \mid \mathcal{A}(\mathbf{X}), \mathcal{B}, \mathcal{C}$ becomes equivalent to the flow pattern OP $\mathbf{F}\kappa \mid \mathcal{A}(\mathbf{X}), \mathcal{C}$ where we take

$$\kappa(\mathbf{F}) \equiv \sum_{(w,v)\in\mathcal{K}} \kappa[(w,v), F(w,v)] \tag{8.1.25}$$

Notice that in the latter problem we do not take into account the capacity constraints $\mathcal{B}$ because as a result of (8.1.24) they are satisfied automatically.

Now consider the relationship between OP $\mathbf{C}\kappa \mid \mathcal{A}(\mathbf{X}), \mathcal{B}, \mathcal{C}$ and OP $\mathbf{C},\mathbf{F},\kappa \mid \mathcal{C}_Q, \mathcal{C}, \mathbf{X}$. We assume that the parameter $Q(\mathbf{F},\mathbf{C})$ is such that if at least one channel is saturated, i.e. if for some (w',v'), we have $C(w',v') = F(w',v')$, then $Q(\mathbf{F},\mathbf{C}) = \infty$. On this assumption, if $\hat{Q} < +\infty$, and we can satisfy the constraint $Q(\mathbf{F},\mathbf{C}) = \hat{Q}$, we shall automatically satisfy the capacity constraints $\mathcal{B}$. The converse does not hold. Thus the solution of OP $\mathbf{C}\kappa \mid \mathcal{A}(\mathbf{X}), \mathcal{B}, \mathcal{C}$ is not usually a solution of OP $\mathbf{C},\mathbf{F}\kappa \mid \mathcal{C}_Q, \mathcal{C}$. The more so because, as we explained previously, the channel cost is an increasing function of channel capacity, so we must expect the solution of OP $\mathbf{F},\kappa \mid \mathcal{A}(\mathbf{X})$ to be such that all channels are saturated, and thus $Q(\mathbf{F},\mathbf{C}_0) = \infty$. However, the solution $\mathbf{C}_0$ of OP $\mathbf{C},\kappa \mid \mathcal{A}(\mathbf{X}), \mathcal{B}, \mathcal{C}$ can be used to create the set $\mathbf{C}_0 + \mathbf{\Delta C}$ of capacities $\mathbf{C}_0(w,v) + \Delta C$, where the increment ΔC is chosen so that the constraint $\mathcal{C}_\epsilon$ is satisfied. Obviously the set $\mathbf{C}_0 + \mathbf{\Delta C}$ is in general not the solution of OP $\mathbf{C},\mathbf{F}\kappa \mid \mathcal{C}_Q, \mathcal{C}, \mathbf{X}$, but we can expect that the set $\mathbf{C}_0 + \mathbf{\Delta C}$ will be close to the solution.

The roles of κ and Q can be interchanged. We then get the problem OP $\mathbf{C},Q \mid \mathcal{C}_\kappa, \mathcal{C}, \mathbf{X}$ where $\mathcal{C}_\kappa$ is the constraint $\kappa(\mathbf{C}) = \hat{\kappa}$, where $\hat{\kappa}$ is the total permitted cost of the set of channel capacities. Almost all our considerations about OP $\mathbf{C}\kappa \mid \mathcal{C}_Q, \mathcal{C}, \mathbf{X}$ have their exact counterpart in OP $\mathbf{C},Q \mid \mathcal{C}_\kappa, \mathcal{C}, \mathbf{X}$.

We now illustrate our general considerations about the channel capacity optimisation by two simple examples.

8.1.3 Optimisation of channel capacities in tree networks

We shall consider here a tree network. We assume that: A(1) the topology of the network if fixed, A(2) the set $\mathbf{X}$ of flow intensities put into the network is fixed, A(3) the channel capacity $C(w,v)$ can take only one value out of the finite set $\mathcal{C}_{ad}(w,v)$, A(4) the parameter characterising the quality of transmission through the channel (w,v) depends only on the capacity $C(w,v)$ and total flow $F(w,v)$; denoted by: $Q[(w,v),C(w,v),F(w,v)]$.

Because the topology and the intensities of input flows are given, we can find the total intensities of flow in each channel. So, in view of assumption A3, the quality of the transmission through a channel (w,v) depends only upon its capacity. Also, the cost depends only on the capacity, which we indicate by writing $\kappa[(w,v),C(w,v)]$. Assuming that both Q_1 and κ are increasing functions of the channel capacity, we can conclude that each of the numbers

$$Q[(w,v),C(w,v),F(w,v)],\ \kappa[(w,v),C(w,v)],\ C(w,v) \tag{8.1.26}$$

determines the other two.

According to assumption A3, the channel capacity can take only predetermined values. Because both κ and ϵ are functions of the capacity these parameters also take predetermined values. Thus we can completely characterise the channel using the pairs $Q[(w,v),C(w,v),F(w,v)]$, $\kappa[(w,v),C(w,v)]$. We shall henceforth write

$$\kappa(w,v) \equiv \kappa[(w,v),C(w,v)], \tag{8.1.27}$$

$$Q(w,v) \equiv Q[(w,v),C(w,v),F(w,v)], \tag{8.1.28}$$

whereby the pair of numbers $\kappa(w, v)$, $Q(w, v)$ always indicate a pair corresponding to the same capacity. The result of conclusion (8.1.26) is that $\kappa(w, v)$ determines $\epsilon(w, v)$ and vice versa. A typical sequence of pairs is:

$\kappa(w, v)$	1	2	3	5	10
$Q(w, v)$	10	8	6	4	1
$C(w, v)$ bit/s	100	200	300	500	1000

We assume here that both κ and Q are dimensionless and normalised with respect to some reference values, and we use typical values of C.

We next assume that the cost characterising the set $\mathbf{C}$ is

$$\kappa(\mathbf{C}) = \sum_{(w, v) \in K} \kappa[(w, v), C(w, v)] \tag{8.1.29}$$

and that the parameter characterising the quality

$$Q(\mathbf{C}) = \max_{w} \sum_{(u, v) \in P_{wo}} Q[(u, v), C(u, v), F(u, v)] \tag{8.1.30}$$

We consider here OP $\mathbf{C}\kappa \mid C_Q, C_{\text{ad}}, \mathbf{X}$, where C_Q denotes the constraint

$$Q(\mathbf{C}) = \hat{Q} \tag{8.1.31}$$

and C_{ad} is the set of sets $C_{\text{ad}}(w, v)$ of admissible channel capacities.

Before describing the method for solving the optimisation problem, we introduce a number of concepts. A **hanging node** is one which is joined to the network by one channel only. A **bunch** of channels is a set of channels joining all the hanging nodes with a common node from which, besides the channels to the hanging nodes, only one channel goes out joining it with the rest of the network (see Fig. 8.3). A chain of channels is a sequence of channels connected in series, without branchings at intermediate nodes. The essence of the method to be described is that we replace the initial tree network with an ever-simpler network, applying the following operations:

(a) substitution of a bunch of channels by one equivalent channel,
(b) substitution of a chain of channels by one equivalent channel.

By 'equivalent' we mean a channel which has the same parameters κ and Q as the optimised primary bunch or chain, which is the solution of OP $\mathbf{C}\kappa \mid C_Q, C_{\text{ad}}, \mathbf{X}$.

By applying both substitutions a sufficiently large number of times, we reduce the original network to a single equivalent channel in which a cost is minimised. The operation of substitution of a bunch or chain is such that knowing the parameters of the equivalent channel we can identify the original channels which give us these values. Thus reversing the procedure which resulted in a single channel replacing the network, we can find the optimum set of capacities of the channels in the original network. Let us first examine the substitution of a bunch by one channel. Let $v_1, v_2, \ldots, v_I$ be the hanging nodes joined by direct channels to node w (see Fig. 8.4), and let $\mathbf{C}$ be the set of capacities of these

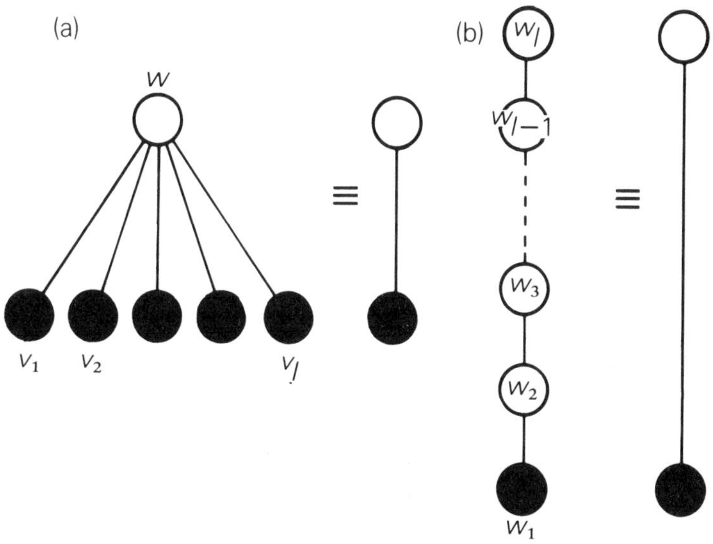

Fig. 8.4 – Illustration to the replacement of (a) a bunch of channels, and (b) a chain of channels by a single equivalent channel.

channels. The maximum value of $Q(\mathbf{C})$ does not alter if we reject from this bunch all channels except (v_{i^*}, w) which introduces the greatest distortion of all the channels making up the bunch, i.e. a distortion such that

$$Q(v_{i^*}, w) = \max_{v_i} Q(v_i, w) \tag{8.1.32}$$

Let:

$$Q'_b(C) \equiv Q(v_{i^*}, w) \tag{8.1.33}$$

be the parameter characterising the bunch considered from the point of view of transmission quality. By writing $Q'_b(\mathbf{C})$ we emphasise that the maximum value given by (8.1.32) depends on the set of capacities **C**. As the parameter characterising the cost of the bunch we take the cost of the channels making up the bunch:

$$\kappa'_b(\mathbf{C}) = \sum_{i=1}^{I} \kappa(v_i, w) \tag{8.1.34}$$

Similarly as in definition (8.1.33) we introduce the prime, because, as will be seen, the parameters Q'_b and κ'_b are only auxiliary parameters. If we take various sets **C**, we get various pairs $Q'_b(\mathbf{C})$, $\kappa'_b(\mathbf{C})$. It may happen that for various sets **C** we obtain the same value of Q'. Let Q_b be one of the values which $Q'_b(\mathbf{C})$ can take, and let $\mathcal{C}(Q_b)$ be a set of capacity sets of bunches of channels such that if $\mathbf{C} \in \mathcal{C}(Q_b)$, then:

$$Q'_b(\mathbf{C}) = Q_b\ . \tag{8.1.35}$$

Since we have taken the cost of the channels as our criterion, we are interested in the set of capacities $\mathbf{C}^*_{Q_b} \in \mathcal{C}(Q_b)$ for which

$$\kappa(C^*_{Q_b}) = \min_{\mathbf{C} \in \mathcal{C}_{Q_b}} \kappa(\mathbf{C}) \tag{8.1.36}$$

Let

$$\kappa_b \equiv \kappa(\mathbf{C}^*_{\epsilon_b}) \tag{8.1.37}$$

The pair κ_b and ϵ_b can be treated as the cost and quality of an equivalent channel whose cost is equal to that of the cheapest bunch of channels and which has the same quality as that bunch. If we take a diminishing sequence of successive admissible values of ϵ_b, we may get a non-diminishing sequence of numbers κ_b, that is, we find two successive values $Q_b^{(1)} < Q_b^{(2)}$ such that $\kappa_b^{(1)} < \kappa_b^{(2)}$. In such a case, we shall not take the pair $\kappa_b^{(2)}$, $\epsilon_b^{(2)}$ into consideration because it does not pay to have a channel in which increased cost does not achieve increased quality. Finally, the sequence of pairs κ_b, Q_b which we have obtained will be treated as a characteristic of the channel equivalent to the solution of the optimisation problem OP $C\kappa \mid C_\epsilon, C_{ad}, \mathbf{X}$ for the bunch of channels we have been examining.

Since we have a finite number of pairs κ, ϵ for each channel, finding the pairs κ_b and ϵ_b reduces to checking a finite number of combinations. Operation (8.1.36) can be made easier to carry out if we introduce auxiliary tables. In the columns of these tables we write the pairs κ, Q which correspond to the different channels; we start with the greatest possible values of Q corresponding to the worst quality. Then, having found a pair κ_b, Q_b, we exchange the pair κ, Q for the next pair with a lower value of Q. The following example will illustrate this.

Example 8.1.1

Consider the bunch of 3 channels described by the tables given below:

(a) (8.1.38a)

κ	1	2	3	5	10
Q	10	8	6	4	1

(b) (8.1.38b)

κ	1	2	3	5	10
Q	8	4	4	1	5

(c) (8.1.38c)

κ	1	2	3	5	10
Q	20	10	8	6	4

We denote the channels in the same way as the tables, i.e. with bold letters **a**, **b**, **c**.

In order to find the sequence of pairs κ_b, Q_b characterising the equivalent channel, arranged in order of decreasing Q_b, we make a table whose three rows correspond respectively to the pairs κ, Q and the number ψ, which we define as the number of changes in a given column arising from this procedure. According to this, $\psi = 1$ indicates the cost of the channel assumed at the start, $\psi = 2$ means that the second highest cost has been taken etc.

In the first stage, we write in each column the values from the first column from the tables for the channels forming the bunch, corresponding to the highest values of Q, and we put ones in the last row.

	a	b	c
κ	1	1	1
Q	10	8	20
ψ	1	1	1

(8.1.39a)

As we are seeking a sequence of pairs κ_b, Q_b arranged in order of decreasing Q_b, we look for the column with the greatest ϵ; this is column **c**. If we choose for channel **c** the value $Q_b = 20$, the parameter Q for the other channels will be smaller than Q_b even for the smallest values of κ. Therefore for $Q_b = 20$ the minimum total cost for the bunch under consideration is 3, i.e. we get $Q_b = 20$, $\kappa_b = 3$.

We change column **c**, inserting the second column from the table (8.1.38c) which corresponds to the second-largest value of Q, for channel **c** and we take $\psi = 2$:

	a	b	c
κ	1	1	2
Q	10	8	10
ψ	1	1	2

(8.1.39b)

We now look again for the column with the highest Q; this can be either column **a** or column **c** since $Q = 10$ for both of them. Let us take column **c**. Because the value $Q = 10$ has appeared for the first time, and we can only increase κ in later steps, we take $Q_b = 10$, $\kappa_b = 4$. We again change column **c**, putting in the third column from the table and take $\psi = 3$.

	a	b	c
κ	1	1	3
Q	10	8	8
ψ	1	1	3

(8.1.39c)

Again we take $Q = 10$ as the maximum value, the minimum cost being $\kappa_b = 5$. As this cost is greater than in the previous step we take no account of the pair $Q_b = 10$, $\kappa_b = 5$. Now we change column **a**, entering 4 in it from the second column of the table (8.1.38a). We obtain the table:

	a	b	c
κ	2	1	3
Q	8	8	8
ψ	2	1	3

(8.1.39d)

From this table it follows that $Q_b = 80$, $\kappa_b = 6$. Continuing as before, we finally obtain a table characterising the equivalent channel of the bunch we have been discussing:

κ_b	3	4	6	11	18
Q_b	20	10	8	6	4

(8.1.40)

Apart from deriving the above table, it is necessary to record intermediate tables. The last lines of these tables enables us to determine the optimum parameters of primary channels **a**, **b**, **c**, corresponding to the equivalent channel.

Consider, for example, OP $C\kappa \mid Q = 8$, C_{ad}. From the table (8.1.40) we can read off $Q_b = 8$, $\kappa_b = 6$. This pair was obtained from the table (8.1.39d). The last line of this table gives us the following information about the pair κ_b, Q_b: (1) channel **a** corresponding to the ψ = 2nd pair of values of κ, Q from the table (8.1.38a), i.e. the pair $\kappa = 2$, $Q = 8$; (2) channel **b** corresponding to the ψ = 1st pair from the table (8.1.38b), i.e. $\kappa = 1$, $Q = 8$; (3) channel **c** corresponding to the ψ = 3rd pair from the table (8.1.38c), i.e. $\kappa = 3, Q = 8$.

We now discuss the operation of replacing a chain of channels (w_1, w_2), (w_2, w_3), ..., (w_{J-1}, w_J), see Fig. 8.4(b), by a single channel which is equivalent from the optimisation point of view. We again assume that the set of values the channel capacity can take is fixed, and thus also the set of values the cost of these channels can take. The cost

$$\kappa'_{ch}(\mathbf{C}) = \sum_{j=1}^{J-1} \kappa(w_{m-1}, w_m) \tag{8.1.41}$$

and the parameter

$$Q'_{ch}(\mathbf{C}) = \sum_{j=1}^{J-1} Q(w_{m-1}, w_m) \tag{8.1.42}$$

characterise the chain. As with the bunch of channels we indicate in this notation that both parameters depend on the set of capacities of channels forming the chain. Let Q_{ch} indicate the value which $Q'_{ch}(\mathbf{C})$ can take, and let $\mathcal{C}(Q_{ch})$ be a set of capacity sets $\mathbf{C}$ such that

$$Q'_{ch}(\mathbf{C}) = Q_{ch} \tag{8.1.43}$$

for each $\mathbf{C} \in \mathcal{C}(Q_{ch})$.

When solving the OP $C\kappa \mid \mathcal{C}_Q\ \mathcal{C}_{ad}$ it is essential to have such a set of channel capacities taken from the set $\mathbf{C}(Q_{ch})$ for which the cost of the chain, given by (8.1.42), is minimal. Let:

$$\kappa_{ch} = \min_{\mathbf{C} \in \mathcal{C}(Q_{ch})} \kappa'_{ch}(\mathbf{C}) \tag{8.1.44}$$

As in the case of the single channel equivalent to a bunch of channels, if we take successive increasing values of Q_{ch}, we may get a non-increasing sequence of costs κ_{ch}. In this case we reject pairs (κ_{ch}, Q_{ch}) which correspond to non-increasing κ_{ch}. We finally get a sequence of pairs (κ_{ch}, Q_{ch}) characterising a channel equivalent to the chain from the standpoint of the OP $C\kappa \mid C_Q, C_{ad}$. The construction of an equivalent channel and the sequence of pairs (κ_{ch}, Q_{ch}) corresponding to it can be reduced to the search for a channel equivalent to two series-connected channels, replacing the first two channels by one equivalent channel, then substituting the pair made up of this equivalent channel and the next channel etc. Therefore we limit ourselves to a description of the method for finding a channel equivalent to a pair of neighbouring channels. This method is illustrated in the following example.

Example 8.1.2

Consider channels **a**,**b** characterised by (8.1.38a,b); note that we assume they are connected in series. We construct a table K_1 in which the columns are the sum of the first column from (8.1.38b) and the successive columns from (8.1.38b) and the successive columns from (8.1.38a). Thus $\kappa'_{ch}(n) = \kappa_a(n) + \kappa_b(1)$, $n = 1, 2, \ldots$ and the sequence corresponding to it $Q'_{ch}(n) = Q_a(n) + Q_b(1)$. We get:

κ'_{ch}	2	3	4	6	11
Q'_{ch}	18	16	14	12	9

(8.1.45a)

As the first pair we take $\epsilon_{ch} = 180$, $\kappa_{ch} = 2$, because the value $\epsilon = 180$ cannot be obtained with any combination of costs of channels **a** and **b** cheaper than 2. In the second step we insert into the column containing the selected pair, i.e. the first column, the sum of the second column of (8.1.38d) and the first column of (8.1.38a); we assign a value of 2 to the count of the number of changes of values in the column. We thus obtain the table:

κ'_{ch}	3	3	4	6	11
Q'_{ch}	14	16	14	12	9
ψ	2	1	1	1	1

(8.1.45b)

Again we choose a column with the smallest κ'_{ch}, e.g. column 1. In this way we get the pair $\kappa_{ch} = 3$, $Q_{ch} = 140$. In the third step we write in column 1 the sum of the third column from (8.1.38a) and the first column from (8.1.38b), and we take the index $\psi = 3$. We get:

κ'_{ch}	4	4	4	6	11
Q'_{ch}	14	12	14	12	9
ψ	3	2	1	1	1

(8.1.45c)

From this table we get the next pair $\kappa_{ch} = 4$, $Q_{ch} = 120$. In general, we write the sum of the appropriate column from (8.1.38b) and the next column from (8.1.38a) in the column where in the given step we have found the maximum value of Q_{ch} after the one which was added previously. This procedure leads to a sequence of pairs arranged in order of decreasing Q_{ch}. Any pairs with non-decreasing Q_{ch} are removed in the same way as when finding the sequence for the channel equivalent to a bunch of channels. Thus we obtain from (8.1.45c) the final table.

κ_{ch}	2	3	4	5	7	8	10	15	20
Q_{ch}	18	14	12	10	8	7	5	2	1.5

(8.1.46)

Notice that in this procedure, the recording of values of κ_a and κ_b corresponding to the chosen pair Q_{ch} and κ_{ch} is made easier by the relationship between κ_a and the number of the column containing the corresponding κ_{ch}, Q_{ch} pair.

The procedure described for finding the pairs κ, Q characterising channels equivalent to a bunch or chain which is a solution of the auxiliary function OP $C\kappa \,|\, C_Q, C_{ad}$ for a bunch or chain, can be iterated in order to find the sequence of pairs κ, Q for a channel which is equivalent to a given tree network. Going backwards from the single equivalent channel. We get the final solution to the optimisation problem for the primary tree network.

8.1.4 Optimisation of channel capacities when the cost function is linear

The optimisation of the channel capacities for the tree network considered previously is untypical in the sense that the routing rule for such a network is predetermined. As explained in section 8.1.2, when more than one path exists between the source and the destination, we have to solve the routing rule optimisation problem as an auxiliary subproblem while solving the channel capacity optimisation problem. As in introduction to the subproblems of channel capacity optimisation requiring the solution of an auxiliary routing optimisation problem, we consider here the optimisation of channel capacities in a general mesh network, but with the following simplifying assumptions:

(1) the cost function for the channel is a linear function i.e.

$$\kappa(k, C) = C\phi(k) \tag{8.1.47}$$

(2) instead of the constraint $Q(C) \leqslant \hat{Q}$ we take the capacity constraint $\mathcal{B}$, and the continuity constraint $\mathcal{A}(\mathbf{X})$, where $\mathbf{X}$ is the set of external flow intensities put into the network.

In formula (8.1.47) and henceforth we use the one-index numbering of channels, corresponding to the mapping $(w, v) \Rightarrow k$.

As we explained in the previous section, if we introduce constraint $\mathcal{B}$, the channel capacity optimisation problem becomes equivalent to the flow optimisation problem OP $\mathbf{F}\kappa \,|\, \mathcal{A}(\mathbf{X})$ in which we do not take into account the capacity constraints. To obtain the capacities which are the solution to the primary OP $\mathbf{C}\kappa \,|\, \mathcal{A}(\mathbf{X}), \mathcal{B}$ we take

$$\mathbf{C}(k) = F(k) \tag{8.1.48}$$

We will show that for a linear cost function, finding the solution to OP $\mathbf{F}\kappa \,|\, \mathcal{A}(\mathbf{X})$ is a straightforward task. We apply here the path-orientated flow description (see section 6.3.2). We number the source–destination pairs p, q by the single index m, $m = 1, 2, \ldots, M$, and denote by $P_m(j)$, $j = 1, 2, \ldots, J(m)$ all paths going from the mth source to the mth destination node, and by $G_m(j)$ the intensity flowing along this path. We have (see (6.1.25)):

$$\sum_{j=1}^{J(m)} G_m(j) = X_m \tag{8.1.49}$$

where X_m is the external flow intensity. We further introduce the coincidence coefficients $a_m(j,k)$ of the path $\mathcal{P}_m(j)$ and the kth channel which appear in (6.1.27). For the total intensity of flow $F(k)$ in the kth channel, we have:

$$F(k) = \sum_{m=1}^{M} \sum_{j=1}^{J(m)} a_m(j,k)\, G_m(j) \tag{8.1.50}$$

Taking $C(k) = F(k)$, and substituting (8.1.47) and (8.1.50) in (8.1.6), we obtain the parameter characterising the cost of flow:

$$\kappa(G) = \sum_{k=1}^{K} \sum_{m=1}^{M} \sum_{j=1}^{J(m)} \phi(k) a_m(j,k)\, G_m(j) \tag{8.1.51}$$

where **G** is the total path flow pattern (see section 6.1.2). Let P be a path and G the flow intensity along it. We define:

$$\phi(P,G) \equiv G \sum_{k \in P} \phi(k) \tag{8.1.52}$$

Taking (8.1.47) into account, we see that $\phi(P,G)$ can be interpreted either as the cost of building a path P capable of carrying a flow of intensity G, or the cost of building a chain P of channels each with a capacity G. We will call $\phi(P,Q)$ the **path cost**. We now interpret the coefficient $\phi(k)$ appearing in (8.1.47) as the length of the channel. The path cost can then be interpreted as the path length. Thus we can write:

$$d(k) = \phi(k) \tag{8.1.53}$$

$$d(P) = \phi(P) \tag{8.1.54}$$

Using (8.1.52) and (8.1.54), we can put (8.1.51) in the form:

$$\kappa(\mathbf{G}) = \sum_{m=1}^{M} \sum_{j=1}^{J(m)} G_m(j) d[P_m(j)] \tag{8.1.55}$$

Consider two paths $P_m(i)$ and $P_m(j)$ such that $G_m(j) > 0$, and

$$d[P_m(i)] < d[P_m(j)] \tag{8.1.56}$$

We make changes in the flows along these paths so that the flows after alteration become

$$G'_m(i) = G_m(i) + G_m(j) \tag{8.1.57}$$

$$G'_m(j) = 0 \tag{8.1.58}$$

where the prime indicates the changed intensities. Obviously, the new path flow pattern $\mathbf{G}'$ fulfills the constraint $A(\mathbf{R})$. At the same time bearing in mind (8.1.57) we have:

$$\kappa(\mathbf{G}') < \kappa(\mathbf{G}) \tag{8.1.59}$$

We can keep reducing the cost $\kappa(\mathbf{G}')$ as long as we have non-zero flows of the mth component in the paths, whose length is greater than the minimum length

$$d_{\min}(m) \equiv \min d[P_m(j)] \tag{8.1.60}$$

This leads to the following conclusion:

> The optimum flow pattern $\mathbf{G}_0$ which is the solution of the optimisation problem OP $\mathbf{G}\kappa \,|\, A(\mathbf{X})$ is the flow such that each

component flows only along the path which is shortest as regards the length defined by (8.1.52) and (8.1.53). (8.1.61)

If there are several paths of the same length, shorter than the length of the other paths, the optimum flow may be any combination of superimposed flows along the shortest paths. If we are considering only the criterion of cost, sending flows along a number of paths is unnecessary and we should choose only one of them.

Conclusion (8.1.61) immediately gives us the following procedure for solving the optimisation problem OP $\mathbf{C}\kappa \mid A(\mathbf{X}), B$.

(1) We treat the coefficient $\phi(k)$ as the channel length.
(2) We find the path $P_m^{(0)}$ which is shortest as regards this length.
(3) We direct flows of the mth component along the path $P_m^{(0)}$.
(4) We apply procedures (1)–(3) to all components.
(5) We calculate the capacity of the kth channel from the equation

$$C_0(k) = \sum_{m=1}^{M} a_m^{(0)}(k) X_m \tag{8.1.62}$$

where $a_m^{(0)}(k)$ is the coincidence coefficient of the path $P_m^{(0)}$ and the kth path.

Example 8.1.3

Consider the network in Fig. 8.5. For convenience, we indicate a channel not by the number k but by the pair of nodes (w,v) at the input and output; similarly, we denote a component by the pair of poles (p,q) and not by the number m. We assume that:

(1) the channels are symmetrical, i.e.

$$C(w,v) = C(v,w)$$

(2) the cost corresponding to unit capacity is symmetrical: $\phi(w,v) = \phi(v,w)$; values of this cost are given as numbers next to the appropriate channels in Fig. 8.5.

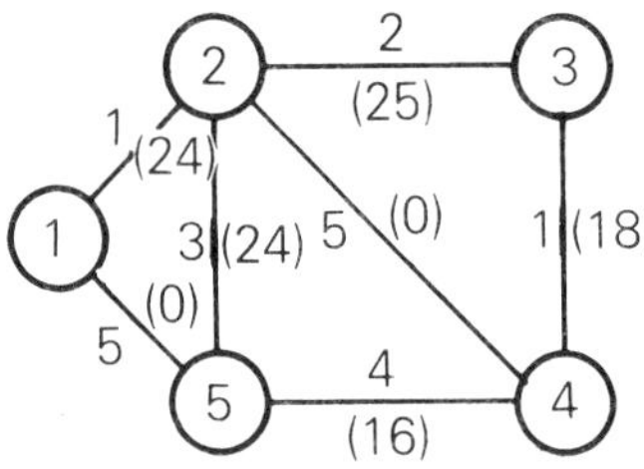

Fig. 8.5 – Network assumed in Example 8.1.3. Symmetrical channels; the number next to the channel gives the value of $\phi(w,v)$, the number in brackets gives the optimum capacity.

(3) the external flow intensities X_{sr} are given by the table

$$\mathbf{X} = \begin{bmatrix} - & 4 & 6 & 5 & 9 \\ 4 & - & 7 & 7 & 8 \\ 6 & 7 & - & 6 & 7 \\ 5 & 7 & 6 & - & 16 \\ 9 & 8 & 7 & 16 & - \end{bmatrix}$$

The set of paths joining each pair of poles is characterised as follows: for a given pair (s,r) we give the number of the penultimate node $u(s,r)$ on the path P_{sr}. Instead of channel length, we take the numbers $\phi(w, v)$ given on Fig. 8.5, and we apply Algorithm 5.1.2, to obtain the set of shortest paths, which is described using a table giving the numbers $u(p,q)$ of the penultimate node on the path P_{sr}.

r \ s	1	2	3	4	5
1	–	1	2	3	2
2	1	–	2	3	2
3	2	2	–	3	2
4	3	3	3	–	4
5	2	2	2	4	–

Let us take, for instance, $w = 1$, $v = 4$. From the table we read off that the penultimate node on the shortest path $P_{14}^{(0)}$ is node $u_1 = 3$. Then in a similar way, we deduce from the table that the penultimate node on the path $P_{13}^{(0)}$ is node $u_2 = 2$, and that on the path $P_{12}^{(0)}$ it is node 1. Therefore $P_{14}^{(0)} = (1, 2, 3, 4)$. From Fig. 8.5 we can read off the matrix $A^{(0)}$ made up of coincidence coefficients $a^{(0)}(w, v;pq)$

w, v \ s, r	1,2	1,3	1,4	1,5	2,3	2,4	2,5	3,4	3,5	4,5
1,2	1	1	1	1	0	0	0	0	0	0
2,3	0	1	1	0	1	1	0	0	0	0
2,5	0	0	0	1	0	0	1	0	1	0
3,4	0	0	1	0	0	1	0	1	0	0
4,5	0	0	0	0	0	0	0	0	0	1

Using equation (8.1.62) we get:

$$
\begin{aligned}
C(1,2) &= X_{12} + X_{13} + X_{14} + X_{15} = 4 + 6 + 5 + 9 = 24 \\
C(2,3) &= X_{13} + X_{14} + X_{23} + X_{24} = 6 + 5 + 2 + 2 = 25 \\
C(2,5) &= X_{15} + X_{25} + X_{35} = 9 + 8 + 7 = 24 \\
C(3,4) &= X_{14} + X_{24} + X_{34} = 5 + 7 + 6 = 18 \\
C(4,5) &= X_{15} = 16
\end{aligned}
$$

The remaining $C(1,5) = C(2,4) = 0$.

These capacities are given in brackets next to the lines in Fig. 8.5; obviously, channels with zero capacity can be removed from the network. Equation (8.1.29) gives us the cost $\kappa(\mathbf{C}_0)$ of the network with optimum capacities through which one can send a set of flows of intensity $\mathbf{X}$.

8.2 OPTIMISATION OF CHANNEL CAPACITIES WITH NON-LINEAR COST FUNCTION

In this section we consider the problem of optimising the set of capacities of channels forming a mesh network in the general case when the cost of constructing a channel is a non-linear, convex, increasing function of the channel capacity. We deal here with the problem of minimising the total cost under the capacity contraint, i.e. with the same optimisation problem as in section 8.1.4. The method which we will describe is essentially a generalisation of the method explained in that section. As in the case of the linear cost function, the solution of the capacity optimisation problem can be reduced to the problem of finding paths shortest in the sense of a suitably defined channel length. However, difficulties arise, because in the case of the non-linear cost function, the channel lengths are not consistent but depend on the flow pattern. This makes it impossible to find a closed solution and forces us to apply iterative procedures.

8.2.1 Properties of the optimum flow

As in section 8.1.4, except in examples, we will number the channels by a single index $k = 1, 2, \ldots, K$, and similarly number the source–destination pairs by the single index $m = 1, 2, \ldots, M$. We deal here with the problem of minimising the total cost $\kappa(\mathbf{C})$ given by (8.1.29) under the continuity constraints $\mathcal{A}(\mathbf{X})$ and the capacity constraints $\mathcal{B}$ which guarantee that the set of external flows with given intensities $\mathbf{X} \equiv \{X_m, m = 1, 2, \ldots, M\}$ will go through the network. Thus we are dealing with OP $\mathbf{C}\kappa \,|\, \mathcal{A}(\mathbf{X})\, \mathcal{B}$. As explained in section 8.1.1 and illustrated in section 8.1.4, this problem is equivalent to the flow pattern optimisation problem OP $\mathbf{F}\kappa \,|\, \mathcal{A}(\mathbf{X})$ in which we do not take the capacity constraints into consideration because we assume that the capacity of the kth channel:

$$C(k) = F(k) \tag{8.2.1}$$

where $F(k)$ is the intensity of total flow in the kth channel.

We considered flow pattern optimisation problems in section 6.2, where we derived the fundamental property (6.2.1) of the optimum flow pattern, stating that it is the superposition of flows along paths shortest in the sense of the channel length, defined as derivatives of the criterial function. We now give a somewhat different justification of the basic conclusion, but using assumption (8.1.11) about the convexity of the function $\kappa(k,C)$, and the path-orientated flow description. Let us denote:

$$\phi(P,\mathbf{G}) \equiv \sum_{k\in P} \left(\frac{\partial\kappa(k,C)}{\partial C}\right)_{C=F} \tag{8.2.2}$$

where $\mathbf{G}$ is the path flow pattern corresponding to the channel flow pattern $\mathbf{F}$. This function is the generalisation of the function defined by (8.1.55) for the linear cost function, the main difference being that $\phi(P,\mathbf{G})$ depends now on the whole set of path flow intensities $\mathbf{G}$, and not only on the intensity G of flow along the path P as it did in the case of the linear cost function. Next we denote:

$$d(k) \equiv \left(\frac{\partial\kappa(k,C)}{\partial C}\right)_{C=F(k)} \tag{8.2.3}$$

and

$$d(P) \equiv \sum_{k\in P} d(k) = \phi(P,\mathbf{G}) \tag{8.2.4}$$

Obviously,

$$d(k) = \phi[k,F(k)] \tag{8.2.5}$$

where $\phi(k,F)$ is the rate of change of cost. We will call $d(k)$ the **channel length** and dP the **path length.** Taking (8.2.2) into account, we can interpret $\phi(P,G)$, and thus dP, as the rate of change of the total cost of the network if we introduce an infinitesimal increase in the capacities of channels forming the path P. Let:

$P_m(j)$, $j=1,2,\ldots,J$ be the path from pole p_m to q_m;
$G_m(j)$ be the flow intensity of the mth component along the path $P_m(j)$.

Consider two paths $P_m(i)$ and $P_m(j)$ with flows of intensities $R_m(i)>0$ and $R_m(j)>0$, and assume that

$$d[P_m(i)] < d[P_m(j)] \tag{8.2.6}$$

Let us change the intensities, taking $R'_m(i) = R_m(i) + \delta R$, $R'_m(j) = R_m(j) - \delta R$, where δR is an infinitesimally small change of intensity of flow along both paths considered; the intensities along other paths remaining unchanged. When choosing the new intensities, we are satisfying the continuity constraint,

$$\sum_{j=1}^{J(m)} G_m(j) = X_m \;. \tag{8.2.7}$$

The flow intensity change causes a change in the costs of network construction:

$$\delta\kappa = \delta G \; d[P_m(j)] - d[P_m(i)] \tag{8.2.8}$$

Taking into account assumption (8.2.5) we get:

$$\delta\kappa < 0 \; . \tag{8.2.9}$$

Thus the change introduced reduces the cost of the network. From the convexity assumption we get:

$$\phi[P_m(j), G_m(j) + \delta G] < \phi[P_m(j), G_m(j)] \tag{8.2.10a}$$

and

$$\phi[P_m(i), G_m(i) + \delta G] > \phi[P_m(i), G_m(i)] \tag{8.2.10b}$$

So after making the change of flow intensities considered above, constraint (8.2.5) is still satisfied. We can therefore further reduce the cost by transferring the flow from path $P_m(j)$ to path $P_m(i)$. From this we can draw the following conclusion:

> The optimum flow pattern can be represented as the superposition of the component flows along the path shortest in the sense of definition (8.2.4). (8.2.11)

As we have seen in section 6.3.1, the fundamental difficulty in the application of this conclusion when looking for the optimum flow pattern, and therefore according to (8.2.1) the optimum channel capacities, is related to the fact that the partial derivatives appearing in the definition of channel lengths (8.2.3) depend on the flow intensities. Those, in turn, when directed on to the shortest paths, depend on the channel lengths.

8.2.2 Properties of flows along shortest paths

Before moving to an interative method of determining the flow pattern having the property (8.2.11), we consider the properties of flows along shortest paths in the situation where channel lengths are treated as variable. We assume that:

(1) the flow from the mth source to the destination takes place along the shortest path;
(2) the intensities X_m of the flows delivered by the sources are given; in view of assumption (1), this is the intensity of a flow along the shortest path;
(3) the channels are saturated, i.e. (8.2.1) holds.

Let $\mathbf{d} = \{d_1, d_2, \ldots, d_K\}$ be a set of non-negative numbers which we interpret as the channel lengths. Under assumptions (1)–(3), the numbers d determine the set of channel capacities $\mathbf{C} = (C(1), \ldots, C(K))$. This depedence can be presented in the form:

$$\mathbf{C} = \mathbf{\Gamma}\,\mathbf{d} \tag{8.2.12}$$

where $\mathbf{\Gamma}$ can be interpreted as an operator transforming set $\mathbf{d}$ into set $\mathbf{C}$. To illustrate this dependence, we give an example (Example 8.2.1). Consider the network shown in Fig. 8.6(a). Note that we now use two-index numbering of channels and source–destination pairs. We assume that the intensities of external flows are identical and unitary.

$$R_{sr} = 1 \tag{8.2.13}$$

$s = 1, 2, \ldots, N, r = 1, 2, \ldots, N$, where N is the number of information sources. To illustrate the dependence (8.2.12), the length of the channel (2,6) will be treated as a variable, d. The lengths of the other channels will be treated as fixed; they are given in Fig. 8.6(a). First take $d = 1$. As we showed in section 5.1, the set of optimum paths going out from a given node to others forms a tree; these paths are shown in Fig. 8.6(b). To indicate where channel (2,6) belongs, it is convenient to introduce the channel-path incidence coefficients:

$$a_{s,r}^{(0)}(2,6) = \begin{cases} 1, \text{ if channel } (2,6) \text{ belongs to the shortest path } P_{s,r}^{(0)} \\ 0, \text{ if the channel does not belong to this path.} \end{cases} \tag{8.2.14}$$

The tables of these coefficients are shown in Fig. 8.6(c). For the value $d = 2, 6$, only the table formed by the coefficients $a_{s,r}^{(0)}(2,6)$ has been given. The optimum paths for $d = 4$ and 5 are the same as for $d = 3$ and for $d \geqslant 7$; channel (2,6) is not part of any of the optimum paths. Knowing the incidence coefficients for channel (2,6) – optimum path, we find the capacity $C^{(0)}(2,6)$ from equation (8.2.1) which in the notation used here takes the form

$$C^{(0)}(2,6) = \sum_{s=1}^{W} \sum_{r=1}^{W} R_{sr} a_{s,r}^{(0)}(2,6) \tag{8.2.15}$$

The dependence of $C^{(0)}(2,6)$ on $d(2,6)$ obtained in this way is shown in Fig. 8.6(d).

Let us return to general considerations and to the single-index notation of channels and source–destination pairs. From the example, we see that for each channel, e.g. $k = 1$, the dependence of channel capacity $C^{(0)}(1)$, ensuring flow along the shortest path, on the length of that channel $d(1)$ will, in general, have the character of a staircase function falling to zero. This is because for small $d(1)$, we usually choose the path so that channel $k = 1$ is part of them. Thus $C^{(0)}$ will be large. If $d(1)$ is slightly increased, optimum paths do not generally change,

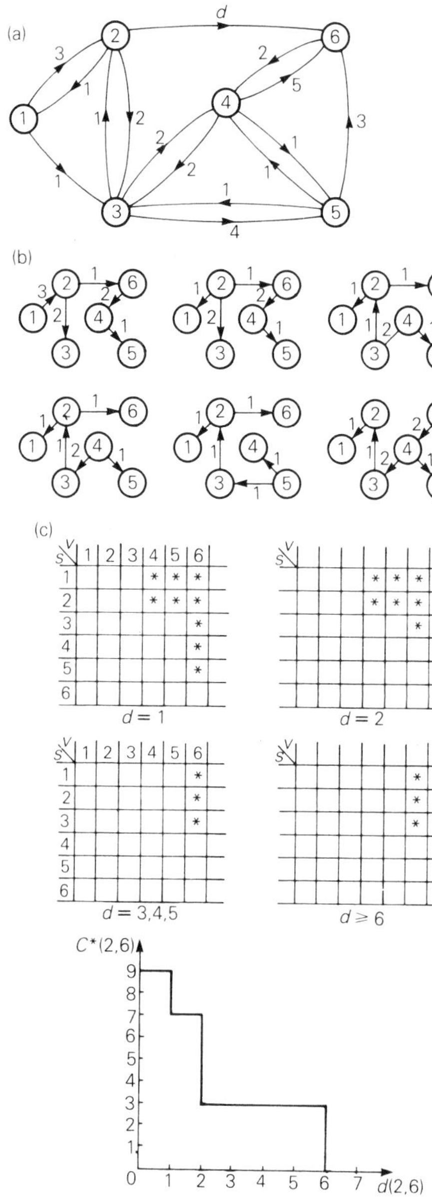

Fig. 8.6 – Network assumed in Example 8.2.1 and sets of optimum paths for various lengths of channel (2,6). (a) Network, number next to the arrow indicates channel length; (b) the thick circle $d = 1$ gives the set of optimum paths leaving node w, (c) incidence coefficients $a^*_{2,6;s,r}$ of the channel (2,6) and the paths P^*_{rs} are given by values of $a^*_{s,r}(2,6) = 1$ indicated by an asterisk; values of $a^*_{sr}(2,6) = 0$ are not marked; (d) dependence of $C^*(2,6)$ on length $d(2,6)$.

so $C^{(0)}(1)$ will be constant. If, however, $d(1)$ becomes large, the shortest paths may be those which do not include channel 1 for one or several pole node pairs. The required capacity is then reduced dramatically. As $d(1)$ continues to increase the optimum paths will at first be the same, but if $d(1)$ is large enough, the optimum paths again change. Channel $k = 1$ ceases to belong to several such paths. Finally, when $d(1)$ becomes so large that there exists a path shorter than $d(1)$ joining the beginning and end of channel $k = 1$, we no longer use this channel and $C^{(0)}(1) = 0$.

Let us denote:

$$\phi \equiv \{\phi[k,c(k)]; k = 1,2,\ldots,K\} \tag{8.2.16}$$

where $\phi(k,C)$ is the rate of change of the channel's cost. Because the cost function $\kappa(k,C)$ is given, the value of $\phi[k,C(k)]$ is determined by the channel capacity C, and so the set ϕ is determined by the set of channel capacities $\mathbf{C}$. We can write this relationship in the form

$$\phi = \mathbf{BC} \tag{8.2.17}$$

where $\mathbf{B}$ is the operation defined in (8.1.1). Using (8.2.12), we have:

$$\phi = \mathbf{B\Gamma d} \ . \tag{8.2.18}$$

It follows from conclusion (8.2.11) that for an optimum set of paths we must have

$$\phi = \mathbf{d} \tag{8.2.19}$$

Thus the set of path lengths d_0 corresponding to the optimum set of paths is the solution of the equation

$$\mathbf{d} = \mathbf{B\Gamma d} \tag{8.2.20}$$

In other words, the optimum lengths are a fixed point of the operator $\mathbf{B}$.

Knowing the set of optimum lengths d_0, we get from (8.2.19) the corresponding optimum values $\phi_0[k,C(k)]$. Knowing these values, we can find the final optimum capacities we are looking for. For this reason we continue to deal with the solution of equation (8.2.20).

8.2.3 An iterative algorithm for finding optimum 'lengths'.

Let us introduce the operator $\mathbf{A} \equiv \mathbf{B\Gamma}$. Equation (8.2.20) can be written thus:

$$(\mathbf{A} - \mathbf{I})\mathbf{d} = \mathbf{0} \tag{8.2.21}$$

where $\mathbf{I}$ is an identity operator.

The general iterative method for finding the zero point of the equation

$$\mathbf{Fd} = \mathbf{0} \tag{8.2.22}$$

where **F** is a certain operator, is known: we choose a certain $\mathbf{d}_1$, and then we calculate the series for $n = 2, 3, \ldots$

$$\mathbf{d}_n = \mathbf{d}_{n-1} + \lambda_n \mathbf{F} \mathbf{d}_{n-1} \tag{8.2.23}$$

where λ_n is a certain fixed numerical series. It can be shown that with very general assumptions about operator **F**, one can find a series λ_n such that the series (8.2.23) converges to the solution of equation (8.2.22). In particular, under quite general assumptions about the operator **F**, we can take $\lambda_n = 1$. After substituting $\mathbf{F} = \mathbf{A} - \mathbf{I}$, the series (8.2.23) becomes

$$\mathbf{d}_n = \mathbf{A}\mathbf{d}_{n-1} \ . \tag{8.2.24}$$

The difficulty in using theorems about the convergence of the series (8.2.23) to the solution of (8.2.21) is the fact that the operator **B** is in general non-continuous and non-linear, and does not satisfy the assumptions usually made about the operator **A** in classical convergence theorems. In order to get an insight into the properties of operator **B**, we investigate the simple case where the parameters of all channels, with the exception of one, e.g. channel $k = 1$, are treated as fixed. As in Example 8.2.1, the dependence of the optimum capacity $C^{(0)}[1, d(1)]$ on $d(1)$ has the character of a staircase function falling to zero, as shown in Fig. 8.7. The thick line on this graph shows the dependence of the rate of change of channel cost increase $\phi[1, C(1)]$ on the capacity C(1). It is obvious that the solutions of equation (8.2.20) correspond to the points where the smooth curve intersects the staircase line. In this example we have two such

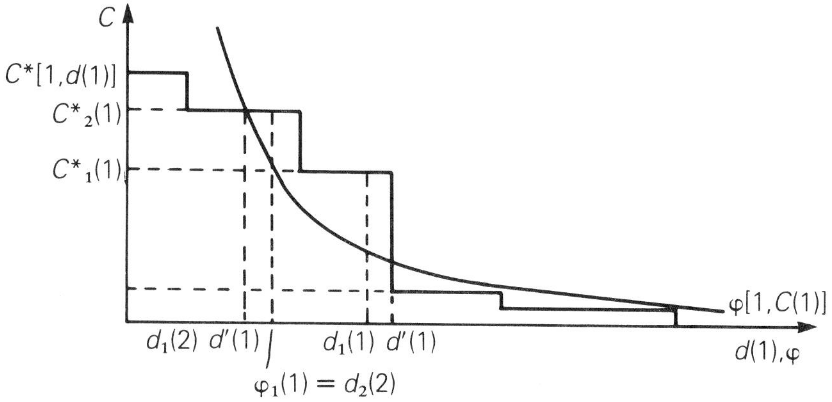

Fig. 8.7 – Illustration to the iterative algorithm (8.2.24) for finding the solution of equation (8.2.20). Staircase line, dependence of the capacity $C[1, d(1)]$ of channel 1 with optimum control of flow capacity on the 'assumed' length $d(1)$ of that channel; thick line, dependence of the rate of cost increase $\phi[1, C(1)]$ on the capacity $C(1)$.

points, corresponding to the values $d'(1), d''(1)$. If we assume that $\phi[1,C(1)] \to \infty$ for $C(1) \to 0$, we get a third intersection point $d'''(1) = \infty$.

Let us look at the operation of the algorithm (8.2.16) on the example shown in Fig. 8.7. We start with the value $d_1(1)$. For this value, a capacity of $C_1^{(0)}(1) = C[1,d_1(1)]$ is required. The value $\phi_1(1) = \phi[1,C_1^{(0)}(1)]$ corresponds to this capacity.

According to algorithm (8.2.24) we take

$$d_2(1) = \phi_1(1) \tag{8.2.25}$$

As in the first step we find $C_2^{(0)}(1) = C[1,d_2(1)]$ and then $\phi_2(1) = \phi[1,C_2^{(0)}(1)]$. As can be seen from the figure, $\phi_2(1) = d'(1)$, where $d'(1)$ is the solution of equation (8.2.20) we are looking for. As we mentioned, apart from $d'(1)$ we have two other solutions, namely, $d''(1)$ and $d'''(1) = \infty$, which of these three solutions is the correct one? Applying the algorithm we find that the intersection points of the graphs $d'(1)$ and $d'''(1) = \infty$ correspond to stable solutions, whereas $d''(1)$ corresponds to an unstable solution. If we make a small shift in the position of the intersection point, and the series still converges to that shifted point, we have a stable solution. Since solution $d'''(1) = \infty$ is obviously not favourable, $d''(1)$ remains as the correct solution. This is precisely the solution which the algorithm brought us to after only two steps.

In general, when we use algorithm (8.2.24) to find the set d corresponding to the optimum total flow pattern, there is the problem of choosing the starting set of lengths d_1. This problem has been studied by Yaged [8.2]. He proposes that in the solutions of concrete problems we should take

$$d_1(k) = A\,l_k \tag{8.2.26}$$

where l_k is the physical length of the channel, and A is a constant. The concrete applications of algorithm (8.2.23) shows that it converges relatively slowly. We can accelerate the convergence by using a modification of the form:

$$d_n = A[\mu d_{n-1} + (1-\mu)d_{n-2}] \tag{8.2.27}$$

where $0 \leqslant \mu \leqslant 1$ is an auxiliary parameter.

Notice finally, that the assumption that the channel cost is a convex function is essential in the applications of this algorithm. Let us take, for example, a non-convex function which corresponds to function $\phi(1,C)$ shown in Fig. 8.8. It can easily be verified graphically, that for such a function for some values of $d_1(1)$, the series (8.2.23) is not convergent, but becomes a periodic oscillating series.

The property (8.2.11), which is the basis for our deliberations, is a necessary condition for the occurrence of a local minimum. Frequently, the function $\kappa(C)$ can have many local minima and the algorithms discussed here lead to one of these minima but not to a global minimum. In order to illustrate this, we take

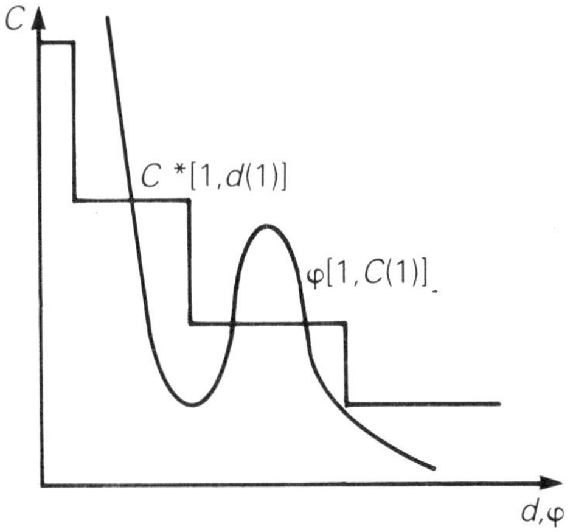

Fig. 8.8 – The situation when algorithm (8.2.24) leads to a divergent series. Notation as for Fig. 8.7.

two channel cost functions, one with small constant coefficients $A(k)$, the other with large values of $A(k)$; the channel lengths defined by (8.2.3) are the same. It is obvious that the positions of the optima can be different in both cases. Especially, if the constant cost component $A(k)$ is large, while the intensity of the flow through the channel is small, it pays not to use this channel at all, but to transfer the whole flow to other channels. We might expect, that if we take d corresponding to the situation where there is a certain flow through k', the algorithm, depending only on the derivatives $\mathrm{d}\kappa/\mathrm{d}C(k)$, thus depending on the values of the function $B(k)$ occurring in (8.1.17), does not lead to the channel k' being removed from the network. We shall now briefly describe the method of counteracting these effects as proposed by Yaged [8.2]. It can be expected that the effects of not considering the constant cost component $A(k)$ mentioned earlier can be overcome by introducing the following definition of channel length

$$d'(k) \equiv \frac{\kappa(k,C)}{C} \tag{8.2.28}$$

and thus taking the cost per unit capacity as the channel length. Let $\mathbf{B}'$ be the operator associating the length set with the set of capabilities $\mathbf{C}$ according to equation (8.2.28). Using the arguments which led us to equation (8.2.20), the problem of changing the flow pattern in such a way as to direct the flow along paths of minimum length according to definition (8.2.28) can be reduced to the solution of the equation

$$\mathbf{d}' = \mathbf{B}'\mathbf{\Gamma}\mathbf{d} \ . \tag{8.2.29}$$

The process of finding the optimum flow pattern, and therefore the optimum channel capacities, can be broken down into two parts. In the first, we find the flow pattern minimising the path length according to definition (8.2.28). This flow pattern and the lengths corresponding to it are taken as the starting length for algorithm (8.2.24). This algorithm leads us to the minimisation of path lengths according to definition (8.2.3). The fact that we began the procedure with the flow minimising path lengths according to definition (8.2.28) allows us to expect that the solution obtained using algorithm (8.2.24) is the global minimum. Numerous examples of the application of this procedure, described by Yaged [8.2] confirms this supposition.

8.3 OPTIMISATION OF THE SET OF CAPACITIES FROM THE POINT OF VIEW OF PACKET TRANSMISSION QUALITY

We now deal with the optimisation problem OP $\mathbf{C}\,Q\,|\,C_\kappa,\mathbf{R}$, where C_κ is the constraint $\kappa(C) = \hat{\kappa}$, and $\hat{\kappa}$ is a predetermined limit on total cost. We assume that the parameter $Q(\mathbf{C})$ characterising the set of capacities from the point of view of transmission quality is obtained from the primary parameter $Q(\mathbf{F},\mathbf{C})$, characterising the quality of the flow pattern **F**, by removing the dependence on **F** using the operation given by (8.1.9). As we explained in section 8.1.1, OP $\mathbf{C},\epsilon\,|\,C_\kappa,\mathbf{X}$ is then equivalent to the joint optimisation of the flow pattern and the set of capacities, which can be written as OP $\mathbf{F},\mathbf{C},Q\,|\,C_\kappa,\mathcal{A}(\mathbf{X}),\mathcal{B},\mathcal{D}$, where $\mathcal{D}$ are the non-negativity constraints. We will now deal with this latter problem.

8.3.1 Formulation and general method of solving the optimisation problem

We assume here that the cost of constructing the channels $\kappa(\mathbf{C})$ is a linear function:

$$\kappa(\mathbf{C}) = \sum_{k=1}^{K} \phi(k)C(k) \tag{8.3.1}$$

where $\phi(k) > 0$ is the cost of obtaining unit capacity in the kth channel.

Under general assumptions about the criterial function and constraints, OP $\mathbf{F},\mathbf{C},Q\,|\,C_\kappa,\mathcal{A}(\mathbf{X}),\mathcal{B},\mathcal{D}$, can be solved as follows: we fix one of the sets of variables, e.g. **F**, and look for a second set $\mathbf{C}_0(\mathbf{F})$ for which the function $Q(\mathbf{F},\mathbf{C})$ takes its extreme value. Then we look for a set $\mathbf{F}_0$ for which the function $Q[\mathbf{F},\mathbf{C}_0(\mathbf{F})]$ takes its extreme value; the pair F_0 and $\mathbf{C}_0(\mathbf{F}_0)$ constitute the solution to the optimisation problem. We now give an example of the application of this general method. We assume that:

(1) As criterial function we choose the average packet delay τ through the network; since we will be considering a multicomponent flow pattern, instead of X_m we take

$$X = \sum_{m=1}^{M} X_m \,.$$

(2) Kleinrock's hypothesis is valid for flow patterns in the network, so the average delay contributed by the channel is given by (8.1.8).

Under such assumptions, the criterial function takes the form:

$$Q(\mathbf{F},\mathbf{C}) = A_1 \sum_{k=1}^{K} \frac{F(k)}{C(k)-F(k)} + A(k)F(k) \tag{8.3.2}$$

where A_1 is a normalisation constant.

Notice, that if we treat the flow pattern $\mathbf{F}$ as fixed, the problem of minimising the function $Q(\mathbf{F},\mathbf{C})$ with respect to the capacity $\mathbf{C}$ with $\kappa(\mathbf{C}) = \kappa_u$ is formally equivalent to the problem of optimising subchannel capacities (see section 3.2), whereby we take $\alpha = 1$ and $C(k) = \lambda_k N_k$. We can use the optimum solution in which the notation used here becomes:

$$C_0(k) = F(k) + \frac{\Delta\kappa}{\phi(k)} \frac{\sqrt{\phi(k)F(k)}}{\sum_{k=1}^{K}\sqrt{\phi(k)F(k)}} \tag{8.3.3}$$

where

$$\Delta\kappa \equiv \kappa_u - \sum_{k=1}^{K} \phi(k)F(k) \tag{8.3.4}$$

and the condition for a maximum is

$$\Delta\kappa > 0 \ . \tag{8.3.5}$$

We shall be referring to this condition as constraint E. As explained in section 3.2, constraint E is equivalent to the constraint that the fixed cost κ_u per channel is greater than the cost which would be required for the realisation of a channel capacity $C(k) = F(k)$.

After substituting (8.3.5) in (8.3.4) we get:

$$Q[\mathbf{F},\mathbf{C}_0(\mathbf{F})] = \frac{A_1}{\kappa\pi} \left[\sum_{k=1}^{K} \sqrt{(k)F(k)}\right]^2 + A_1 \sum_{k=1}^{K} A(k)F(k) \tag{8.3.6}$$

Thus we reduce OP$\mathbf{F},\mathbf{C}Q \mid C_\kappa, A(\mathbf{X}), B, F^+, E$ to the auxiliary optimisation problem:

Find the flow pattern $\mathbf{F}$ minimising the function

$$Q_1(\mathbf{F}) \equiv Q[\mathbf{F},\mathbf{C}_0(\mathbf{F})]$$

for a fixed set $\mathbf{X}$ of external flow intensities and total cost κ_u, whereby the flow pattern $\mathbf{F}$ satisfies the constraints $A(\mathbf{X})$, B, F^+ and E. (8.3.7)

8.3.2 An iterative method for solving the auxiliary optimisation problem

The auxiliary problem (8.3.7) to which we reduced our original problem (8.3.2) is similar to the problem of optimising the flow pattern, which we discussed in Chapter 6. The differences between them are that (a) constraint $\mathcal{E}$ now appears, and (b) the capacities occurring in the set of constraints $\mathcal{B}$ are dependent on the flow pattern (see (8.3.5)). The latter constraint is not essential because, as can be seen from equation (8.3.5), constraint $\mathcal{E}$ ensures the fulfilment of the set of constraints $\mathcal{D}$. It is thus sufficient to take constraints $\mathcal{A}$, $\mathcal{B}$ and $\mathcal{E}$ into consideration.

Notice that reasoning as in section 6.1.4, we can prove that for a set $\mathcal{F}_{ABE}$ of vectors satisfying constraints $\mathcal{A}$, $\mathcal{B}$, $\mathcal{E}$, conclusion 6.2.3 holds, and therefore the set $\mathcal{F}_{ABE}$ is a convex polyhedron. Further, we can apply the method of flow deviation, described in section 6.3, for if the flow pattern $\mathbf{F} \in \mathcal{F}_{ABE}$, then the flow pattern $\psi\mathbf{F} \in \mathcal{F}_{ABE}$ where ψ is an operation described by (6.4.1). So, in order to solve the optimisation problem (8.3.9), we can use:

Algorithm 8.3.1

Step 1

We find the flow pattern $\mathbf{F}_1 \in \mathcal{F}_{ABE}$.

Step n

$n1$ We take:

$$\mathbf{F}_{n+1} = \Psi_n \mathbf{F}_n \tag{8.3.8}$$

where Ψ_n is an operator defined by (6.4.1), and consider shortest length paths

$$d(k) \equiv \left(\frac{\partial Q_1}{\partial F(k)}\right)_{F_n} \tag{8.3.9}$$

$n2$ If $Q_1(\mathbf{F}_{n+1}) > Q_1(F_n)$, we end the procedure and take F_n as the solution. Otherwise we go on to step $n+1$.

After substituting (8.3.6) in (8.3.9), we obtain:

$$d(k) = A_1\left[\frac{\sum_{k=1}^{K} \phi(k)F(k)}{\Delta\kappa}\sqrt{\frac{\phi(k)}{F(k)}} + \frac{\sum_{k=1}^{K} \phi(k) + F(k)}{\Delta\kappa}\phi(k) + B(k)\right] \tag{8.3.10}$$

From this we see that: (1) $d(k) > 0$, therefore no loops occur on the shortest paths, (2) if $F(k) \to 0$, $d(k) \to \infty$, thus if the flow intensity in a channel falls to zero, that channel will not be used in later steps. This property indicates that we should select the initial flow pattern $\mathbf{F}_1$ with non-zero intensities in the largest possible number of channels. In later steps, the non-essential channels will quickly be eliminated. As we have already emphasised, algorithms of this type lead to a local minimum, so Algorithm 8.3.1 should be executed with various initial flow patterns. One of the methods proposed by Fratta [6.8] is based on a random selection of channels, after which $\mathbf{F}_1$ is taken to be the flow pattern along the shortest length paths satisfying constraints $\mathcal{A}, \mathcal{B}, \mathcal{D}$. As channel capacities are standardised, the cost function $\kappa(C)$ is a staircase function. In such a situation, Algorithm 8.3.1 needs modifying. Fratta [6.8] suggests using an approximation of the primary staircase function $\kappa[C(k)]$ by means of the auxiliary continuous function $\kappa_1[C(k)]$. Having arrived at the solution, we increase all the capacities to the nearest admissible values, and then apply the algorithm again using those capacities. Fratta [6.8] quotes results from the application of the procedure to the ARPA network shown in Fig. 6.14. He assumes that the flow intensity between the poles for each pair of poles is identical: we denote this by R. Fig. 8.9 shows the dependence of the average transit time $\bar{\tau}[\mathbf{F}_0, \mathbf{C}_0(\mathbf{F}_0)]$, using the optimum capacities $\mathbf{C}_0(\mathbf{F}_0)$ and the optimum flow pattern $\mathbf{F}_0$, on the assumed κ_u and intensity $\mathbf{X}$. This figure confirms the intuitive supposition that with external flow patterns of fixed intensity R, the quality of the optimum flow pattern using optimum capacities is greater, the larger the admissible cost κ_u of constructing the network.

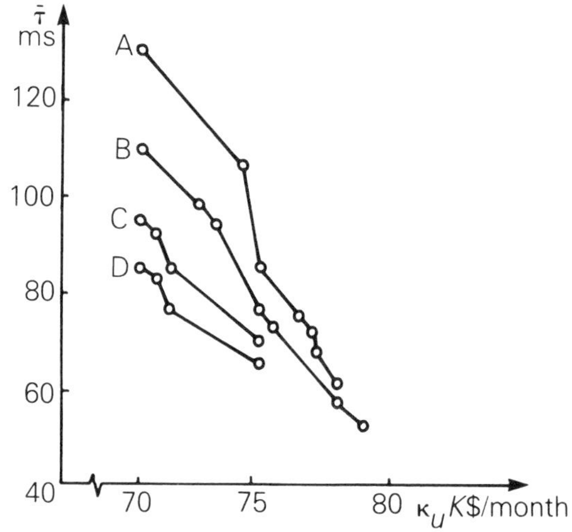

Fig. 8.9 — The dependence of the average weighted packet transit time $\bar{\tau}$ on the total cost κ obtained using Algorithm 8.3.1. External flow intensity $X_{sr} = X =$ const. Curve A, $X = 1005$ Mbit/s, B, $X = 925$ Mbit/s, C, $X = 848$ Mbit/s.

8.4 TOPOLOGICAL OPTIMISATION OF TREE NETWORKS

In this section we examine the problem of optimising the topology of a tree network. We assume that the position of the nodes (terminal nodes, concentrators) is fixed and that we know the cost of building channels connecting given pairs of nodes. Our aim is to find a set of channels such that they form a tree establishing one path from each terminal node to the central node. Such a tree is called a spanning tree. The problem is similar to that of finding optimum channel capacities. Our 'variable' is the set K of channels forming the tree. We assume that the parameter characterising the cost of the set of channels K is as in (8.1.6):

$$\kappa(k) = \sum_{(w,v)\in K} \kappa[(w,v), C(w,v)]$$

where $\kappa(K)$ is the cost of building the network consisting of the set K of channels and $\kappa[(w,v),C(w,v)]$ is, as before, the cost of building a channel (w,v) with capacity $C(w,v)$.

The other parameter characterising the set of channels K is that describing the quality of packet transmission when packets are delivered with intensities X_{w0}, $w = 1,2,\ldots,N$, from the terminal nodes to the central node. As in the case of channel capacities optimisation, we introduce the quality parameter $Q(K)$ defined in the same way as the parameter $Q(\mathbf{C})$. To define such a parameter, we start with the parameter $Q(\mathbf{C})$ and then remove its dependence on $\mathbf{C}$, but leaving the dependence on K. Owing to difficulties in carrying out such a procedure, we introduce the capacity constraint instead of taking into account the quality of packet transmission. As explained in section 8.1.3, the capacity constraint takes the form of constraints (8.1.16) in the case of tree networks.

Let β_l, $l = 1,2,\ldots,L$ be the elements of the lower neighbourhood $N_{\text{in}}(0)$ of the central node, i.e. nodes connected directly to the central node. We can often assume:

A1 The capacity $C(\beta_l, 0)$ of the direct channel linking node β_l with the central node 0 is greater than or equal to the capacity of any channel linking nodes hanging on node β_l.

This assumption is usually justified because at node β_l we have a concentrator which can operate with a high capacity channel going to the central node, while terminal nodes are connected with β_l by low capacity local channels. If we make assumption A1, the capacity constraints B will be satisfied if for all β_l, $l = 1,2,\ldots,L$ we have

$$F(\beta_l,0) \leqslant C(\beta_l,0) \tag{8.4.1}$$

where

$$F(\beta_l,0) = \sum_{v\in H(\beta_l)} X_{v0} \tag{8.4.2}$$

and $H(\beta_l)$ is the set of terminal nodes hanging on node β_l.

Channel capacities will be standardised, i.e. the capacity of each channel can take values from the same set $\mathcal{C}_{ad}$ of admissible channel capacity values. If $\mathcal{C}$ is the largest admissible value, the capacity constraints take the form:

$$F(\beta_l, 0) \leqslant C \tag{8.4.3}$$

for each $\beta_l \in \mathcal{N}_{in}(0)$.

In this section we review the methods of solving the OP $\mathcal{K}\kappa | \mathcal{B}, \mathbf{X}$. The common idea behind these methods is that we compile the set of channels $\mathcal{K}$ considered earlier by adding one channel after another as an approximation of the optimum set $\mathcal{K}_0$, which is the solution of OP $\mathcal{K}\kappa | \mathcal{B}, \mathbf{X}$. To introduce some order into the descriptions of the methods, we divide them into node- and channel-orientated methods, depending on whether, in choosing a new channel, emphasis is put on the new node joined to the set of nodes connected by the channels chosen in earlier steps, or on the new channel itself. We start with the simplest node-orientated procedure in which no constraints are introduced. Then we show how this procedure can be modified to take into account the capacity constraint, and to overcome, at least to some extent, the drawback of the primary procedure, namely that this procedure makes irreversible decisions about the choice of the channels. In the last subsection we consider channel-orientation procedures. We again start with a simple procedure, not taking any constraints into account, and then build a generalised but efficient procedure. We end with a comparison of all the procedures discussed.

8.4.1 Node-orientated algorithms

In this section we describe three node-orientated algorithms for finding minimum spanning trees. We start with a description of a simplified version of the algorithms not taking into account the quality or capacity constraints, and then indicate how the algorithms can be modified to satisfy such constraints.

The basic idea behind the first algorithm is to divide the set of all nodes into two auxiliary subsets: set $\mathcal{A}$ consisting of nodes already connected by the channels belonging to set $\mathcal{K}^*$ of channels previously chosen, and set $\mathcal{B}$, made up of the remaining isolated nodes. In each step a new channel is chosen, and as a result elements of set $\mathcal{B}$ are successively transferred to set $\mathcal{A}$. The choice is based on the cost of connecting an element $b \in B$ to the set $\mathcal{A}$. This cost, the counterpart of the distance element-set used in pattern recognition theory, is defined by

$$\kappa(b, \mathcal{A}) \equiv \min_{a \in \mathcal{A}} \{\kappa(b, a)\} \tag{8.4.4}$$

The element of the set $\mathcal{A}$ for which this cost is achieved is denoted by $a^*(b)$. We thus have

$$\kappa[b, a^*(b)] = \kappa(b, \mathcal{A}) \tag{8.4.5}$$

In each step we transfer element b from set $\mathcal{B}$ to set $\mathcal{A}$ whose cost of connection to set $\mathcal{A}$ is minimal, i.e. such that

$$\kappa(b^*, A) = \min_{b \in B} \{\kappa(b, A)\} \tag{8.4.6}$$

and we add channel $(b^*, a^*(b^*))$ to the set K^* of chosen channels. We find node b^* by forming table **T**, which contains in each column: an element $b \in B$, the cost $\kappa(b, A)$ of connecting this element and the element $a^*(b) \in A$, for which this cost has been achieved. This algorithm, which we call the **algorithm for adding a node of least connection** cost, can be formulated as follows:

Algorithm 8.4.1

Step 1

The central node $w = 0$ is included in set $A(1)$, all terminal nodes are included in set $B(1)$; set $K^*(1)$ is empty.

Step n

We compose Table $\mathbf{T}(n)$ for sets $A(n-1)$ and $B(n-1)$. From this table we choose the node $b^*(n)$, to which the minimum cost $\kappa(b^*(n), A(n-1))$ corresponds. We transfer node $b^*(n)$ from set $B(n-1)$ to $A(n-1)$ that is, we create the sets:

$$A(n) = A(n-1) \quad \{b^*(n)\} \tag{8.4.7a}$$

$$B(n) = B(n-1) - \{b^*(n)\} \tag{8.4.7b}$$

$$K^*(n) = K^*(n-1) \quad \{a^*[b^*(n)], b^*(n)\} \tag{8.4.7c}$$

We stop the procedure when set B becomes empty. This requirement is equivalent to the requirement that the set K^* of channels chosen contains K^* channels.

The following example illustrates this algorithm.

Example 8.4.1

We take a network with $N = 5$ nodes. The channel costs $\kappa(w, v)$ are defined for all pairs w, v and are given by the following table:

$\mathbf{K} =$ (8.4.8)

v \ w	0	1	2	3	4
0	0	11	6	30	16
1	11	0	15	17	13
2	6	15	0	21	7
3	30	17	21	0	15
4	16	13	7	15	0

We assume that the central node is node $w = 0$.

Step 1

$$A(1) = \{0\}$$
$$B(1) = \{1,2,3,4\}$$
$$K^*(1) = \emptyset$$

where $\emptyset$ is the empty set.

Step 2

We now form table $\mathbf{T}(2)$ on the basis of the table 8.4.8:

b	1	2	3	4
$\kappa[b, A(1)]$	11	6	30	16
$a^*(b)$	0	0	0	0

From this table we find $b^*(2) = 2, a^*[b^*(2)] = 0$. We have

$$A(2) = \{0,2\}$$
$$B(2) = \{1,3,4\}$$
$$K^*(2) = \{(0,2)\}$$

Step 3

Table $\mathbf{T}(3)$ is of the following form:

b	1	3	4
$\kappa[b, A(2)]$	11	21	7
$a^*(b)$	0	2	2

From this table we find $b^*(3) = 4$, $a^*[b(3)] = 2$, and we choose channel $(2,4)$. We take:

$$A(3) = \{0,2,4\}$$
$$B(3) = \{1,3\}$$
$$K^*(3) = \{(0,2),(2,4)\}$$

Step 4

We now find table **T**(4)

b	1	3
$\kappa[b, A(3)]$	11	15
$a^*(b)$	0	4

From this table we find $b^*(4) = 1, a^*[b^*(4)] = 0$. We have:

$$A(4) = \{0,2,4,1\}$$
$$B(4) = \{3\}$$
$$K^*(4) = \{(0,2),(2,4),(0,1)\}$$

Step 5

Table **T**(5) has the following form:

b	3
$\kappa[b, A(4)]$	15
$a^*(b)$	4

Channel (3,4) is included in the set of channels chosen. As all the nodes are now connected directly or indirectly to the central node, the procedure stops. The ultimate network obtained is shown in Fig. 8.10.

The algorithm just described does not take into account either quality or capacity constraints. We can account for these constraints by considering, instead of set B of isolated nodes, only a subset of nodes which, when joined to the set A of nodes chosen, does not violate the constraints. We illustrate this idea

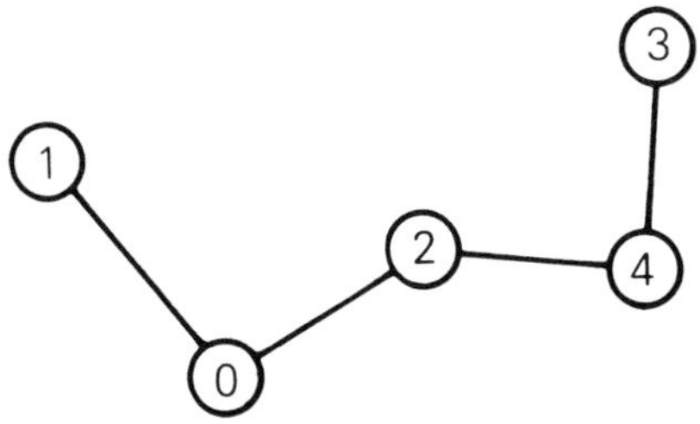

Fig. 8.10 – The optimum network obtained in Examples 8.4.1 and 8.4.3.

making the assumption (8.4.2) and thus taking into account consideration the capacity constraint (8.4.3). Let:

$N_{in}(0)$ be the lower neighbourhood of the central node, i.e. the set of nodes connected by channels with the central node: let β_l, $l = 1, 2, \ldots, L$ be the elements of this set, i.e.

$$\{\beta_l; l = 1, 2, \ldots, L\} = N_{in}(0) \tag{8.4.9}$$

$a^*(b)$ be a node belonging to the set A of nodes chosen in earlier steps of the algorithm so that the cost of joining the node $b \notin A$ to node $a^*(b)$ is as small as possible;

$\beta(b)$ be a node belonging to the set $N_{in}(0)$ such that $a^*(b) \in H[\beta(b)]$;

B' be a subset of set B of nodes not yet joined by channels so that for each $b \in B'$ the capacity constraint (8.4.8) for node $\beta(b)$ is not yet violated.

This notation is illustrated in Fig. 8.11.

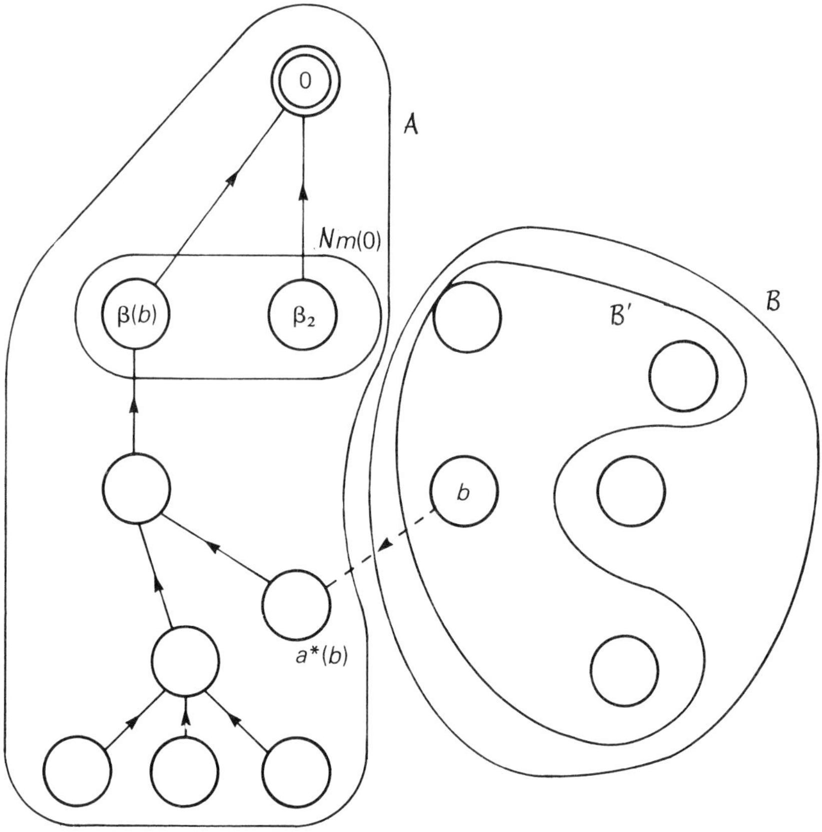

Fig. 8.11 – Illustration to the definition of set B'.

The idea behind the modified Algorithm 8.4.1 taking into account constraints (8.4.8) is that instead of the set of nodes not yet joined, we consider only set $\mathcal{B}'$. The algorithm is:

Algortihm 8.4.2

Step 1

We take

$$\mathcal{A}(1) = \{0\}$$
$$\mathcal{B}(1) = \mathcal{N}'$$

where $\mathcal{N}'$ is the set of all terminal nodes.

Step n

Let $b^*(n)$ be a node such that

$$\kappa[b^*(n), \mathcal{A}(n-1)] = \min_{b \in \mathcal{B}'(n)} \kappa[b, A(n-1)] \quad (8.4.10)$$

where $\mathcal{B}(n) \subset \mathcal{B}(n-1)$ is a set of nodes such that

$$R_{bo} + \sum_{v \in \mathcal{H}[\beta(b)]} R_{vo} \leqslant C[\beta(b), 0] \quad (8.4.11)$$

where $\mathcal{H}[\beta(b)]$ is the set of nodes hanging on a node $\beta(b)$ such that $a^*(b) \in \mathcal{H}[\beta(b)]$. We take:

$$\mathcal{A}^*(n) = \mathcal{A}^*(n-1) \cup b^*(n) \quad (8.4.12a)$$
$$\mathcal{B}(n) = \mathcal{B}(n-1) - b^*(n) \quad (8.4.12b)$$
$$\mathcal{K}^*(n) = \mathcal{K}^*(n-1) \cup (b^*(n), a^*[b^*(n)]) \quad (8.4.12c)$$

The procedure stops when set $\mathcal{B}(n)$ is empty.

It is obvious from the consideration in section 6.1 that for given sets $\mathcal{C}_{ad}$ of values which the channel capacity can take, and for a given set $\mathbf{R}$ of external flow intensities, the solution of OP $\mathcal{K}\kappa | \mathcal{A}(\mathbf{R}), \mathcal{B}, \mathcal{C}_{ad}$ may not exist, simply because we do not have enough channel capacity at out disposal. However, even if the solution of OP $\mathcal{K}\kappa | \mathcal{A}(\mathbf{R}), \mathcal{B}, \mathcal{C}_{ad}$ does exist, the set $\mathcal{B}'$ may become empty, even though the set of isolated nodes is not empty, and Algorithm 8.4.2 does not yield a network connecting all terminal nodes to the central node. This is possible only when an element of the set $C_{ad}(\beta', 0)$ of possible channel capacities contains a large value and the algorithm puts terminal nodes delivering small external flow intensities into the set of nodes hanging on node β', while in set $\mathcal{B}$ there remains a node delivering an external flow of such a large intensity that only channel

$(\beta',0)$ can handle it. This situation cannot arise when each channel $(w,0)$ can have a capacity not smaller than the external flow intensity R_{w0}. This will be assumed in the following example.

Example 8.4.2

We assume that we have $N = 5$ channels and that the external flow intensities R_{w0}, $w = 1, 2, \ldots,$ are:

w	1	2	3	4
X_{w0}	6	2	5	4

We also assume that the capacity of each channel can be only $C = 6$. To find node $b^*(n)$ we compose a table as in Example 8.4.1, except that we add a fourth row in which we place

$$X_b \equiv X_{b0} + \sum_{v \in H[\beta(b)]} X_{v0} \tag{8.4.13}$$

where $H[\beta(b)]$ is the set of nodes hanging from a node $\beta(b)$ such that the node $a^*(b)$ minimising the cost of joining belongs to $H[\beta(b)]$. The parameter X_b is the criterion used for including node b into set B'.

Step 1

$$A(1) = \{0\}$$
$$B(1) = \{1, 2, 3, 4\}$$
$$K^*(1) = \emptyset$$

Step 2

We compile table $\mathbf{T}(2)$:

b	1	2	3	4
$a^*(b)$	0	0	0	0
$\kappa[b, a^*(b)]$	11	6	30	16
X_b	6	2	5	4

Because for all b we have $R_{b\Sigma} \leqslant 6$, the set $B^*(2) = \{1, 2, 3, 4\}$. From the table we read off $b^* = 2$, $a^*(2) = 0$. Thus we have:

$$A(2) = \{0,2\}$$
$$B(2) = \{1,3,4\}$$
$$K^*(2) = \{(0,2)\}$$

Step 3

Table **T**(3) takes the form:

b	1	3	4
$a^*(b)$	0	2	2
$\kappa[b,a^*(b)]$	11	21	7
X_b	6	7	6

Now for $b = 3$ the constraint $X_b \leqslant 6$ is violated, thus $B^*(3) = \{1,4\}$. From this table we have: $b^*(3) = 4, a^*[b^*(3)] = 2$. So we get:

$$A(3) = \{0,2,4\}$$
$$B(3) = \{1,3\}$$
$$K^*(3) = \{(0,2),(2,4)\}$$

Step 4

Table **T**(4) is written down:

b	1	3
$a^*(b)$	0	0
$\kappa[b,a^*(b)]$	11	30
X_b	6	5

The capacity constraint is again satisfied for all b.

From this table we obtain: $b^*(4) = 1, a^*[b^*(4)] = 0$. We increase the network by adding channel $(1,0)$ and assume:

$$A(4) = \{0,1,2,4\}$$
$$B(4) = \{3\}$$
$$K^*(4) = \{(0,2),(2,4),(0,1)\}$$

The final table $\mathbf{T}(5)$ take the form:

b	3
$a^*(b)$	0
$\kappa[b,a^*(b)]$	30
X_b	5

From table $\mathbf{T}(5)$ we have $b^*(5) = 3$, $a^*[b^*(5)] = 0$. We thus include $(0,3)$ in $K^*(5)$. We take $K^*(5)$ as the network we are looking for – it is shown in Fig. 8.12. For this network $\kappa[K^*(5)] = 54$ and the constraint $\Sigma X_{\beta 0} \leqslant 6$ is satisfied.

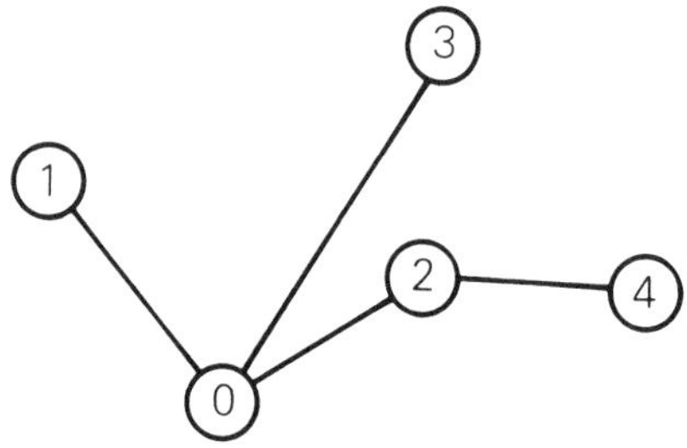

Fig. 8.12 – The optimum network obtained in Example 8.4.2.

An obvious disadvantage of Algorithms 8.4.1 and 8.4.2 is that the decisions about including channels in the set of channels just given are irreversible. The result of this is that the algorithm may choose an expensive direct channel for a connection, because other connections along channels selected earlier do not satisfy the constraints imposed, e.g. of type (8.4.2). We can attempt to prevent the occurrence of such situations by choosing a node v_1, to which one can get only along the most expensive channels. To such a node we then add terminal nodes, which can be joined to node v_1, by channels which are as cheap as possible. If we get so many of these terminal nodes that increasing their number would lead to the sum of the flow intensities coming from them exceeding the capacity C of each of the channels, we stop the procedure. Let A_1 denote a set obtained in this way. We do not consider this set to be the ultimate one, but we apply Algorithm 8.4.1 to set A_1 and find a channel joining one of the nodes from set A_1 to the central node. Here we can use Algorithm 8.4.1 rather than 8.4.2, because while constructing set A_1, we ensured the fulfilment of the constraint (8.4.2). If set A_1 does not include all the nodes, then starting from a node not belonging to set A_1 which can be reached from other nodes not belonging to set

A_1 only along the most expensive channels, we construct set A_2 etc. in like manner, until all the nodes are used up (see Fig. 8.13). The search for nodes to be included into a given set A_k can be simplified if we consider only nodes satisfying the condition that:

The cost of connection to the central node is greater than the cost of connection to previously selected nodes belonging to set A_k. (8.4.14)

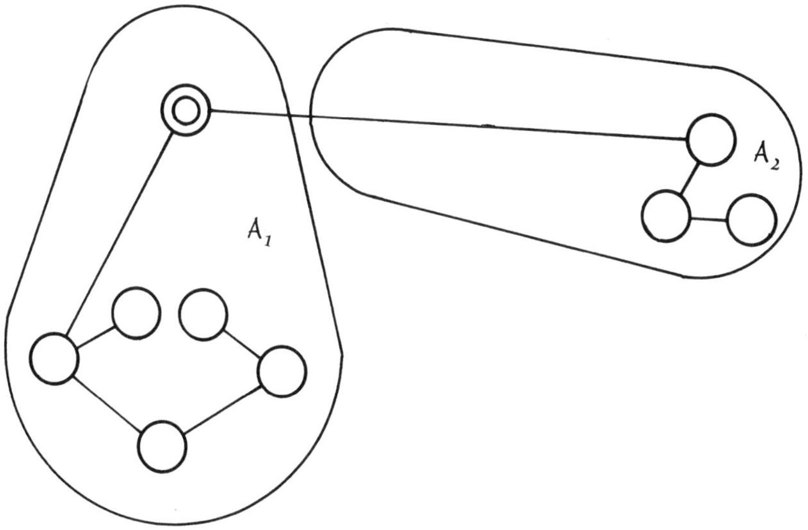

Fig. 8.13 – Illustration to the definition of sets A_k in the inverted tree algorithm. Thin lines, original channels.

It is obvious the nodes not satisfying this condition will in further steps belong to the set A_{k_1}, $k_1 \neq k$. We also need not consider nodes for which the following condition is satisfied:

the cost of connecting node $a^*(b)$ with set A_k, for which the minimum cost of connecting node b lying outside set A_k to set A_k has been attained, is greater than the cost of connecting $a^*(b)$ directly to the central node. (8.4.15)

Rejection of nodes satisfying this condition is justified by the fact that after applying Algorithm 8.4.2 to the set A_k, the node $a^*(b)$ may be connected to the central node by node b, which is of course disadvantageous. From these remarks it appears that the node, for which the cost of connection with a previously chosen set of nodes is lowest, should be looked for in set $\mathcal{B}$ which is formed by rejecting from the set $\mathcal{N}' - \mathcal{A}$, where $\mathcal{N}'$ is a set of all terminal nodes u, such that

after the connection of node u to set $\mathcal{A}$, the total flow intensity does not satisfy condition (8.4.2), and thus exceeds the channel capacity C. (8.4.16)

or

$$\kappa(u, \mathcal{A}_k) > \kappa(u, 0) \tag{8.4.17}$$

or

$$\kappa[u, a^*(u)] > \kappa[a^*(u), 0] \tag{8.4.18}$$

In the above inequalities $a^*(u)$ is the node belonging to set $\mathcal{A}$ for which the cost of connection to node u is the lowest.

The inequality (8:4.17) is equivalent to the condition (8.4.14), and the inequality (8.4.18) to the condition (8.4.16). Our considerations suggest the following algorithm consisting of two parts:

Algorithm 8.4.3 (part I)

FIRST ITERATION

Step 1

We find a terminal node $v_{1,1}$ such that:

$$\kappa(v_{1,1}, 0) \geqslant \kappa(w, 0) \tag{8.4.19}$$

for all terminal nodes. In other words, $v_{1,1}$ is the node whose cost of direct connection to the central node is greatest. We take:

$$\mathcal{A}_1(1) = \{v_{1,1}\} \tag{8.4.20a}$$

$$\mathcal{B}_1(1) = \mathcal{N}' - \{v_{1,1}\} \tag{8.4.20b}$$

Step n

Taking set $\mathcal{A}_1(n-1)$ in place of set $\mathcal{A}$, we create set $\mathcal{B}$ in accordance with the principles previously laid down (8.4.16)–(8.4.18). This set is denoted by $\mathcal{B}_1(n-1)$. We find node $v_{1,n} \in \mathcal{B}_1(n-1)$ such that the cost of adding this node to set $\mathcal{A}_1(n-1)$ is minimal:

$$\kappa[v_{1,n} \mathcal{A}_1(n-1)] \leqslant \kappa[v, \mathcal{A}_1(n-1)] \tag{8.4.21}$$

for all $v \in \mathcal{B}_1(n-1)$. We take:

$$\mathcal{A}_1(n) = \mathcal{A}_1(n-1) \cup \{v_{1,n}\} \tag{8.4.22}$$

We finish the iteration in step N_1, when the set $B_1(N_1)$ becomes empty. If the set $N' - A_1(N_1)$ is not empty, we begin a second iteration ($k = 2$). Otherwise we go straight on to part II of the algorithm.

kTH ITERATION

We proceed as in iteration 1, taking the set

$$N'_k = N' - \bigcup_{j=1}^{k=1} A_j(N_j) \qquad (8.4.23)$$

instead of set N'. We end part I of the algorithm after the Ith iteration, after which the set $N'(I+1)$ becomes empty.

Algorithm 8.4.3 (part II)

We apply Algorithm 8.4.2 to each of the sets $A'_j(N) = A_j(N_j) \cup \{0\}, j = 1, 2, \ldots, I$. Just as in the case of the algorithms previously discussed, in order to find the node with minimal cost of connection to set A, it is convenient to use a table similar to that introduced in Example 8.4.1. Initially we place in this table columns corresponding to all the nodes from the set $N' - A$. Then, taking constraints (8.4.14) and (8.4.15) into account, we cross out the columns corresponding to nodes not satisfying these constraints. Finally, there remain nodes from set B. This is illustrated in the following example.

Example 8.4.3

We take the assumptions made in Example 8.4.1. According to Algorithm 8.4.3 we get:

PART I, ITERATION 1

Step 1

Find node $v_{1,1} \in N'$ such that

$$\kappa(v_{1,1}, 0) \geqslant \kappa(w, 0) \quad \text{for} \quad w \in N' .$$

For our assumptions we have

$$v_{1,1} = 3$$

Therefore

$$A_1(1) = \{3\}$$
$$B_1(1) = \{1, 2, 4\}$$

Step 2

According to rules (8.4.14)–(8.4.16) we find the set $B_1(2) = \{4\}$ and we find $v_{1,2} = 4$; thus $A_1(2) = \{3,4\}$. Since the sets B and $B_1(2)$ are empty sets, and

$$N'(2) = N' - A_1(2) = \{1,2\}$$

is not empty, we pass on to Iteration 2.

PART I, ITERATION 2

Consider set $N_2'(2)$.

Step 1

Since $\kappa(1,0) > \kappa(2,0)$ we take $v_{2,1} = 1$. We have

$$N_2(1) = \{1\}$$
$$B_2(1) = \{2\}$$

Step 2

Since set $B_2(2)$ is empty, and

$$N'(3) = N' - A_1(2) - A_2(1) = \{2\}$$

is not an empty set, we move on to Iteration 3.

PART I, ITERATION 3

Step 1

Consider set $N_3' = \{2\}$. We get $v_{3,1} = 2$ and $N_3(1) = \{2\}$.

Step 2

Since the sets $B_3(1)$, and $N'(1) = N' - A_1(2) - A_2(1) - A_3(1)$.

PART II

As a result of applying Part II of the algorithm, we find:

(1) channels (0,4), (4,3) for set $A_1(2)$
(2) channel (0,1) for set $A_2(1)$
(3) channel (0,2) for set $A_3(1)$.

The network obtained, having a total cost of 48, is shown in Fig. 8.14.

8.4.2 Channel-orientated algorithms

The algorithms described in the previous subsection are based on rules of choosing suitable nodes and determining channels interconnecting them. In this subsection we deal with algorithms in which channels are of primary interest. However, as we explained earlier the difference between node- and channel-orientated

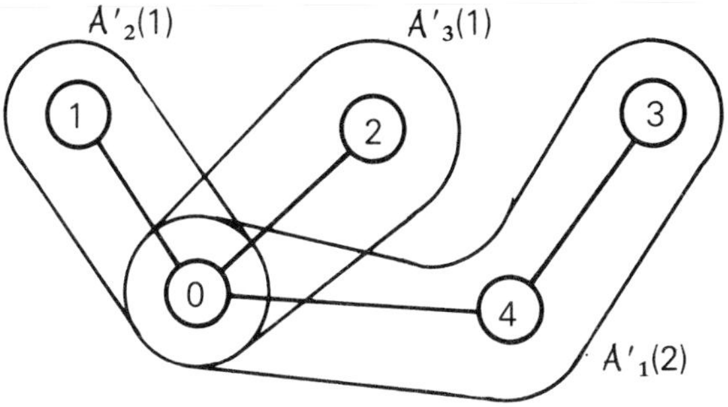

Fig. 8.14 – Network obtained after using Algorithm 8.4.3 in Example 8.4.3; $A'_j(N_j)$, auxiliary sets used in Part II.

algorithms is rather superficial because in both types of algorithm we choose both nodes and channel.

The basic idea behind the algorithm to be described is that we start with the cheapest channel, and connect to the network increasingly expensive channels, so long as they do not make loops with the channels already selected. For this reason it is called the **algorithm for connecting the cheapest channel.** Since we are only dealing with channels and not nodes here, we use one-index notation of channels, numbering them $k = 1, 2, \ldots, K$. The cost of constructing a channel, according to the above principles, will be denoted by $\kappa(k, C)$. However, as we are not considering the capacity constraints we shall not show the dependence of cost on the capacity, and shall use $\kappa(k)$ as the channel construction cost.

Let us arrange the channels in order of increasing cost such that:

$$\kappa(k_1) \leqslant \kappa(k_2) \leqslant \ldots \leqslant \kappa(k_K) \qquad (8.4.24)$$

Let:

$K^*(n)$	be the set of channels after n steps;
$F(n)$	be the event when, after adding channel k_n to the set $K^*(n-1)$, no loop is closed;
$M = N-1$	be the number of terminal nodes;
N	be the number of terminal nodes plus the central node;
K	be the number of channels
K	be the total number of channels.

The algorithm is of the following form.

Algorithm 8.4.4

Step 1

As the set $K^*(1)$ let us take the single element set

$$K^*(1) = \{k_1\} \qquad (8.4.25a)$$

Step 2

$$K^*(2) = K^*(1) \cup \{k_2\} \tag{8.4.25b}$$

Step n

We take:

$$K^*(n) = \begin{cases} K^*(n-1) \cup \{k_n\} & \text{if } F(n) \text{ occurs} \\ K^*(n-1) & \text{if } F(n) \text{ does not occur} \end{cases} \tag{8.4.26}$$

If $F(n)$ does not occur, i.e. if channel k_n closes a loop with previously chosen channels, we take no account of channel k_n in further steps. We complete the procedure when M channels are in the set $K^*(n)$. This is an obvious condition, because the algorithm is so constructed that it leads to the formation of a tree, and this tree has as many channels as there are terminal nodes. A basic difficulty in the implementation of Algorithm 8.4.4 is in checking to see whether the event $F(n)$ does occur, i.e. whether the channel added does not close a loop. We now describe a method of overcoming this difficulty. Let us introduce the matrix

$$\mathbf{A} \equiv \begin{bmatrix} a(0,1)\, a(0,1) \ldots\ldots a\,(0,M) \\ a(1,0)\, a(1,1) \ldots\ldots a\,(1,M) \\ \ldots\ldots\ldots\ldots\ldots\ldots\ldots\ldots \\ a(M,0)\, a(M,1) \;\ldots\; a(M',M) \end{bmatrix} \tag{8.4.27}$$

where for $v \neq w$,

$$a(w,v) \equiv \begin{cases} 1, & \text{if channel } (w,v) \text{ exists} \\ 0, & \text{if channel } (w,v) \text{ does not exist} \end{cases} \tag{8.4.28}$$

whereas

$$a(w,w) \equiv 1 \;.$$

Let us define a rule of multiplying zero–one matrices, defining as a product $\mathbf{B} = \mathbf{A}_1 * \mathbf{A}_2$ of the matrices $\mathbf{A}_1$ and $\mathbf{A}_2$ of $a^{(1)}(w,v)$, $a^{(2)}(w,v)$ the elements of matrix $\mathbf{B}$ are defined in the following way:

$$b(m,n) \equiv \begin{cases} 1, & \text{if } \alpha(m,n) \geqslant 1 \\ 0, & \text{if } \alpha(m,n) = 0 \end{cases} \tag{8.4.29}$$

where

$$\alpha(m,n) \equiv \sum_{w=0}^{M} a^{(1)}(m,w)\, a^{(2)}(n,w) \tag{8.4.30}$$

The condition $\alpha(m,n) \geqslant 1$ is equivalent to the condition that there is at least one product $a^{(1)}(m,w)$, $a^{(2)}(m,w)$ differing from zero. Taking into account the network to which matrix **A** defined by formula (8.2.28) corresponds, consider the matrix:

$$\mathbf{A}^{(2)} \equiv \mathbf{A} * \mathbf{A} \tag{8.4.31}$$

Suppose there is a channel joining nodes w and v, since $a(w,v) = 1, a_{vw}a_{wv} = 1$. According to (8.4.29),

$$a^{(2)}(w,v) = 1 \ . \tag{8.4.32a}$$

Let us now assume that channels (w,u) and (u,v) exist, but that channel (w,v) does not exist. We have $a(w,u)\,a(u,v) = 1$, therefore

$$a^{(2)}(w,v) = 1 \ . \tag{8.4.32b}$$

Thus we conclude that the matrix $\mathbf{A}^{(2)}$ contains ones for those nodes which are either directly connected, or which can be connected by a route passing through one node. It is easy to see that if we have to pass through two or more intermediate nodes in order to get from one given node to another, the corresponding element of the matrix $\mathbf{A}^{(2)}$ is equal to zero. If we introduce the nth power of the matrix **A**, defined by the recurring formula:

$$\mathbf{A}^{(n)} \equiv \mathbf{A}^{(n-1)} \cdot \mathbf{A} \tag{8.4.33}$$

it is easily seen that for elements of this matrix $a^{(n)}(w,v) = 1$ when there exists a route made up of not more than $(n+1)$ nodes (including terminal nodes) joining the wth node with the vth one. Because the set $K^*(n)$, defined by formula (8.4.26), and occurring in the description of Algorithm 8.4.4, consists of isolated nodes or trees, we can immediately check to see if event $F(n)$ arises or not, by calculating the appropriate power of the matrix **A**.

The following example will illustrate the algorithm for connecting the cheapest channel. The occurrence of event $F(n)$ will be checked using the matrix **A**.

Example 8.4.4

We assume that the costs $\kappa(w,v)$ are those given by the table (8.4.7). We put the channel costs in order of magnitude according to the formula (8.4.2):

$$k_1 = (0,2),\ k_2 = (2,4),\ k_3 = (0,1),\ k_4 = (1,4),\ k_5 = (3,4),$$
$$k_6 = (1,2),\ k_7 = (0,4),\ k_8 = (1,3),\ k_9 = (2,3),\ k_{10} = (0,3).$$

We now apply Algorithm 8.4.4.

Step 1

$$K^*(1) = \{(0,2)\}$$

Step 2

$$K^*(2) = \{(0,2),(2,4)\}$$

Step 3

We check to see if event $F(3)$ takes place. In order to do this, we allocate the second power to the corresponding network formed from the set of channels $K^*(2)$:

$$\mathbf{A} = \begin{bmatrix} 1 & 0 & 1 & 0 & 0 \\ 0 & 1 & 0 & 0 & 0 \\ 1 & 0 & 1 & 0 & 1 \\ 0 & 0 & 0 & 1 & 0 \\ 0 & 0 & 1 & 0 & 1 \end{bmatrix}$$

After multiplying out according to (8.4.30) we get:

$$\mathbf{A}^{(2)} = \begin{bmatrix} 1 & 0 & 1 & 0 & 1 \\ 0 & 1 & 0 & 0 & 0 \\ 1 & 0 & 1 & 0 & 1 \\ 0 & 0 & 0 & 1 & 0 \\ 1 & 0 & 1 & 0 & 1 \end{bmatrix}$$

From this matrix we get $a(0,1) = 0$. Therefore event $F(3)$ does occur and we thus take

$$K^*(3) = \{(0,2),(2,4),(0,1)\}$$

Step 4

To check whether the event $F(4)$ takes place, we allot the third power to the following matrix $\mathbf{A}$, corresponding to the network formed by the set of channels $K^*(3)$:

$$\mathbf{A} = \begin{bmatrix} 1 & 1 & 1 & 0 & 0 \\ 1 & 1 & 0 & 0 & 0 \\ 0 & 1 & 1 & 0 & 1 \\ 0 & 0 & 0 & 1 & 0 \\ 0 & 0 & 1 & 0 & 1 \end{bmatrix}$$

After having calculated the third power of this matrix according to the multiplication rule (8.4.31), we get:

$$\mathbf{A}^{(3)} = \begin{bmatrix} 1 & 1 & 1 & 0 & 1 \\ 1 & 1 & 1 & 0 & 1 \\ 1 & 1 & 1 & 0 & 1 \\ 0 & 0 & 0 & 1 & 0 \\ 1 & 1 & 1 & 0 & 1 \end{bmatrix}$$

This matrix indicates that $a(1,0) = 1$. Thus event $F(4)$ does not occur, channel $k_4 = (1,4)$ is not taken into consideration, so

$$K^*(4) = K^*(3) = \{(0,2),(2,4),(0,1)\}$$

Step 5

As in the previous steps, we check to see whether : (5) occurs. Thus

$$K^*(5) = \{(0,2),(2,4),(0,1),(3,4)\}$$

In set $K^*(5)$ we have $N' = 4$ channels, thus the procedure stops.

The network obtained is illustrated in Fig. 8.10. As we could expect this is the same network as obtained in Example 8.4.1.

The iterative procedures which apply the principle of steepest descent are both universal and effective. The procedures based on the gradient are their best known representatives. Here we shall examine more closely an algorithm of this type, called the Essau–Williams algorithm. In its simplest form, this algorithm can be used for finding networks close to the solution of OP $K\kappa$, but with a slight modification can also be used to obtain networks close to the solution of OP $K\kappa \,|\, A(\mathbf{R}), B$.

Consider a set of channels K connecting terminal nodes with the central node. Let:

- β_l — be a node belonging to $N_{\text{in}}(0)$ i.e. connected by a direct channel to the central node $w = 0$;
- $K(\beta_l)$ — be a set of channels connecting to node β_l nodes from the set $H(\beta_l)$ of nodes hanging from node β_l;
- $K_{\beta_l,\,u,v}$ — be the set of channels arising from the removal of the direct channel $(\beta_l, 0)$ from set K of the channels previously chosen and the addition of channel (u,v) connecting a node $u \in H(\beta_l)$ to the node $v \in H(\beta_l)$ but being one of input channels from K (this definition is illustrated in Fig. 8.15);

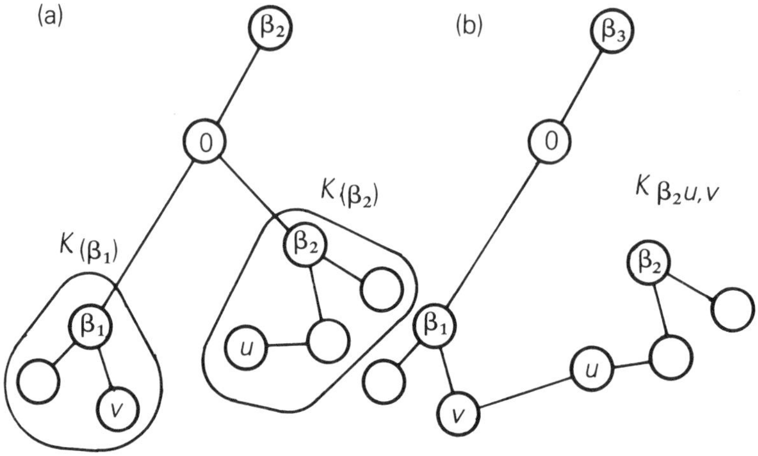

Fig. 8.15 – Illustration to the definition of the network $K_{\beta_l,u,v}$; (a) initial network K; (b) network $K_{\beta_2,u,v}$.

$\kappa(K_{\beta_l,u,v})$ be the cost of formation of the set of channels

$K_{\beta_l,u,v}$

$$\delta\kappa(\beta_l, u, v) \equiv \kappa(K_{\beta_l,u,v}) - \kappa(K) \tag{8.4.34}$$

where $\kappa(K)$ is the cost of the primary set of channels K

$$\delta\kappa(\beta_l) \equiv \min_{u \in H(\beta_l),\, v \notin H(\beta_l)} \delta\kappa(\beta_l, u, v) \tag{8.4.35}$$

$$\Delta \equiv \min_{\beta_l} \delta\kappa(\beta_l) \tag{8.4.36}$$

The parameter $\delta\kappa(\beta_l)$ may be interpreted as the greatest cost saving which can be obtained by replacing the central channel $(\beta_l, 0)$ by a channel connecting one of the nodes belonging to the set of nodes hanging from node β_l to any other node in the network. The idea underlying the algorithm we are going to describe is that starting with an initial set of channels $K^*(1)$ chosen in a heuristic way, we improve it by replacing the central channel $(\beta^*, 0)$, where β^* is the channel for which the maximum saving $\Delta\kappa(\beta_l)$ is obtained, by the channel $(u(\beta^*), v(\beta^*))$, where $u(\beta^*) \in H(\beta^*), v(\beta^*) \notin H(\beta^*)$ are a pair of nodes, for which the minimum value $\delta\kappa(\beta^*)$, defined by (8.4.35), is achieved.

When we take into account capacity constraint B which requires that the intensity of the total flow through the channel does not exceed a fixed capacity, this procedure can be modified by searching for the maximum values occurring in definitions (8.4.34)–(8.4.35) only among nodes satisfying the constraints laid on them. An algorithm modified in this way has the following form:

Algorithm 8.4.5

Step 1

We take $K^*(1)$ to be a set of channels forming a star network with $w = 0$ as centre.

Step n

For set $K^*(n-1)$ we find a set of nodes for which the minimum defined by (8.4.35) and (8.4.36) is obtained, whereby we search for this minimum among the sets satisfying the imposed constraints. To find this minimum, we can make use of tables, as in Example 8.4.1. We stop the procedure when $\Delta\kappa \geqslant 0$.

The following example illustrates the application of this algorithm.

Example 8.4.5

We take the costs $\kappa(w, 0)$ of forming the channels from the table (8.4.8).

Step 1

As $K^*(1)$ we take the star network shown in Fig. 8.16(a); its cost is 63.

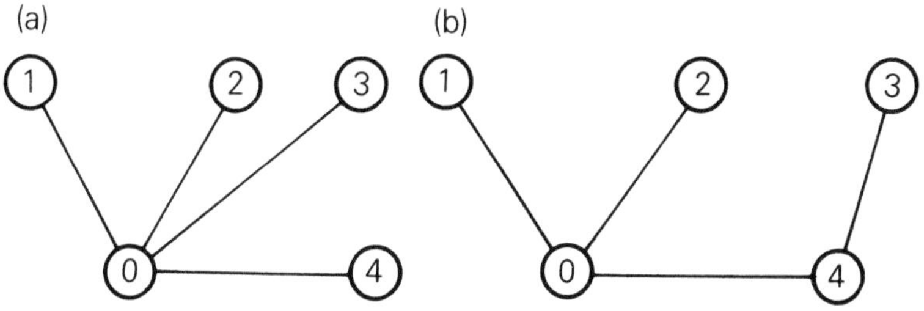

Fig. 8.16(a) Initial network, (b) final network obtained after using Algorithm 8.4.5 in Example 8.4.5.

Step 2

Construct the following tables:

For channel (0, 1)

pair (u, v)	(1,2)	(1,3)	(1,4)
$\kappa(K^*(1), u, v)$	8	7	6
$\delta\kappa(1, u, v)$	4	6	2

For channel (0, 2)

pair (u, v)	(2,1)	(2,3)	(2,4)
$\kappa(K^*(2), u, v)$	8	7	6
$\delta\kappa(2, u, v)$	9	15	1

For channel (0, 3)

pair (u, v)	(3, 1)	(3, 2)	(3,4)
$\kappa(K^*(3), u, v)$	11	7	9
$\delta\kappa(3, u, v)$	−13	−9	−15

For channel (0, 4)

pair (u, v)	(4,1)	(4, 2)	(4, 3)
$\kappa(K^*(4), u, v)$	10	6	9
$\delta\kappa(4, u, v)$	−3	−9	−1

From these tables we get:

$$\begin{aligned}\delta\kappa(1) &= 2\\ \delta\kappa(2) &= 1\\ \delta\kappa(3) &= -15\\ \delta\kappa(4) &= -9\end{aligned}$$

Therefore $\Delta = -15$, where this value is attained for node $\beta_2^* = 3$ and also channel $(u(\beta_2^*), v(\beta_2^*)) = (3, 4)$. The network $K^*(2)$ obtained in step 2 thus has the form shown in Fig. 8.16(b).

Step 3

Having constructed tables similar to those in step 2, we find that $\Delta > 0$. The algorithm is therefore complete, thus the network $K^*(2)$ obtained in step 2 is the final network.

Returing to general considerations, we can now show that the concepts underlying both channel-orientated algorithms examined suggest a universal algorithm. Special cases of this algorithm are not only the channel-orientated algorithms mentioned but also the first two node-orientated algorithms discussed in the previous subsection.

We introduce:

(1) an auxiliary set of non-overlapping sets of nodes covering the set of all nodes in the auxiliary sets; the auxiliary set to which the node w belongs is denoted by $\mathcal{D}(w)$;

(2) the function of the node, which we call the weight of the node and denote it by $\alpha(w)$; it may be changed after adding a new channel to the set K^* of channels chosen in the previous steps;

(3) the function of the channel, on the basis of which we choose the next channel; we call this the criterial function and denote it by $\gamma(w, v)$. It is defined by the formula:

$$\gamma(w, v) \equiv \kappa(w, v) - \alpha(w) \tag{8.4.37}$$

The algorithm for chooosing the channels forming the network which we expect to be close to the solution of the OP $K\kappa \mid C$, where C is a set of constraints, is determined by the way we define the auxilary sets, the auxiliary function $\alpha_1(w)$ used in step 1, and the rule of changing it. The algorithm is as follows.

Algorithm 8.5.6

Step 1

We take:

$$\mathcal{D}_1(w) = \{w\}, \; w = 0, 1, \ldots, M$$

$$\gamma(w, v) = \begin{cases} \kappa(w, v) - \alpha_1(w) & \text{if } (w, v) \notin V_c \\ \infty & \text{if } (w, v) \in V_c \end{cases}$$

where by V_c we denote the set of pairs of nodes such that linking them by a channel violates the constraints; in particular, $(w, v) \in V_c$ if no channel (w, v) exists. We find such a pair of nodes $w^*(1), v^*(1)$ for which the auxiliary function $\gamma(w, v)$ takes the minimum value, i.e.

$$\gamma[w^*(1), v^*(1)] = \min_{(w, v) \notin V_c} \gamma(w, v) \tag{8.4.38}$$

We take

$$K^*(1) = \{w^*(1), v^*(1)\} \; . \tag{8.4.39}$$

and we define

$$\mathcal{D}_2(w) = \{w\} \quad \text{if} \quad w \neq w^*(1), v^*(1)$$

$$\mathcal{D}_2[w^*(1)] = \mathcal{D}_2[v^*(1)] = \{w^*(1), v^*(1)\} \tag{8.4.40}$$

Step n

$n1$ Take $\mathcal{D}_n(w)$ as defined in step $n-1$.

$n2$ Using $\alpha_{n-1}(w)$ and the rule of changing α, evaluate $\alpha_n(w)$.

$n3$ Find $w^*(n), v^*(n)$, minimising $\gamma_n(w,v) = \kappa(w,v) - \alpha_n(w)$, i.e. such that

$$\gamma_n[w^*(n), v^*(n)] = \min_{\substack{w,v \\ \mathcal{D}_n(w) \neq \mathcal{D}_n(v)}} \gamma_n(w,v) \tag{8.4.41}$$

$n4$ If $\gamma_n[w^*(n), v^*(n)] = \infty$, stop the procedure.
If $\gamma_n[w^*(n), v^*(n)] < +\infty$, proceed as follows:

$n5$ If $[w^*(n), v^*(n)] \notin \mathcal{V}_{c_{n-1}}$, take:

$$K^*(n) = K^*(n-1) \cup [w^*(n), v^*(n)] \tag{8.4.42}$$

$$\mathcal{D}_{n+1}[w^*(n)] = \mathcal{D}_{n+1}[v^*(n)] = \mathcal{D}_n[w^*(n)] \cup \mathcal{D}_n[v^*(n)] \,,$$

leaving the remaining $\mathcal{D}$s unchanged.

$\mathcal{V}_{c_{n-1}}$ denotes the set of pairs (w, v) violating the constraints determined in step $n-1$.

$n6$ Define new constraints C_n following on from the primary constraints, and the structure of sets $\mathcal{D}$. Go on to step $n+1$.

$n7$ If $[w^*(n), v^*(n)] \in \mathcal{V}_{c_{n-1}}$, take $\gamma_n[w^*(n), v^*(n)] = \infty$, leave the remaining functions unchanged and return to $n3$.

Let us illustrate the algorithms with a few examples. To simplify them, we will not take the constraints into account.

Example 8.4.6

We take:

$$\alpha_1(0) = 0, \; \alpha_1(w) = -\infty, \; w = 1, 2, \ldots, M \,.$$

The rule of changing the weight $\alpha(w)$ is: after choosing the channel (w^*, v^*) for all $m > n$ at step n, we take $\alpha_m(v^*) = 0$. According to (8.4.37), in step $n = 1$ we have $\gamma_1(w, 0) = \kappa(w, 0)$, while for $v \neq 0$ we have $\gamma_1(w, v) = \infty$. Thus the channel $[w^*(1), v^*(1)]$ is the cheapest channel going from the terminal node to the central node. In step $n = 2$, we have:

$$\mathcal{D}_2(w) = w \,, \; w = 1, 2, \ldots, M, \; w \neq w^*(1) \,,$$

$$\mathcal{D}_2[w^*(1)] = \mathcal{D}_2(0) = \{w^*(1) \cup 0\},$$

and

$$\gamma(w, 0) = \kappa(w, 0), \; w = 1, 2, \ldots, M, w \neq w^*(1)$$

$$\gamma_2[w, w^*(1)] = \kappa[w, w^*(1)] \,,$$

$$\gamma(w, v) = \infty, \; v = 1, 2, \ldots, M, \; v \neq w^*(1) \,.$$

Thus the node $w^*(2)$ is a node such that connecting it to either the central node or the node $w^*(1)$ is cheapest. It is evident that in general for all n, under the assumptions made in this example, Algorithm 8.4.6 becomes an algorithm for adding the node of least connection cost, it becomes Algorithm 8.4.1.

Example 8.4.7

We take:

$$\alpha_n(w) = 0, \ n = 1, 2, \ldots, \ w = 0, 1, \ldots, M.$$

Thus we do not change the weight and for all n we have

$$\gamma_n(w, v) = \kappa(w, v) \ .$$

In step $n = 1$, we choose the channel $[w^*(1), v^*(1)]$ which has the lowest cost. In step 2, we have:

$$\mathcal{D}_2(w) = \{w\}, \ w \neq w^*(1), w \neq v^*(1),$$

$$\mathcal{D}_2[w^*(1)] = \mathcal{D}_2[v^*(1)] = \{w^*(1), v^*(1)\} \ .$$

Because $\gamma_2(w, v) = \kappa(w, v)$, in step $n = 2$ we choose the second cheapest channel $[w^*(2), v^*(2)]$. It is again evident that in step n we choose the cheapest of the as yet unselected channels, if adding this channel to the set K^* of channels chosen previously does not cause a loop to be formed. If it does, we go on to the next cheapest channel. Thus it is evident under the assumptions made in this example that Algorithm 8.4.6 becomes Algorithm 8.4.4.

Example 8.4.8

We take:

$$\alpha_1(w) = \kappa(0, w), \ w = 1, 2, \ldots, M.$$

The rule of changing the weight is that after introducing the channel $[w^*(n), v^*(n)]$ at step n, we take

$$\alpha_{n+1}(v) = \alpha_n(v) \quad \text{for all } v \in \mathcal{D}_n[v^*(n)] \ .$$

In step $n = 1$ we have

$$\gamma_1(w, v) = \kappa(w, v) - \kappa(w, 0) \quad \text{for } w, v \neq 0 \ .$$

Let:

$$\gamma_1'(v) = -\max_{w \neq 0} [\kappa(w, 0) - \kappa(w, v)] = \min \kappa(w, v) - \kappa(w, 0)$$

This parameter can be interpreted as the maximum decrease of channel cost if we take a channel (w, v) instead of the direct channel $\kappa(w, 0)$. According to Algorithm 8.4.6, we look for the node $v^*(1)$ for which this decrease is the greatest. In other words, in step $n = 1$ we find a node $w^*(1)$ such that the gain from replacing the direct channel $[w^*(1),(0)]$ by the paths $w^*(1), v^*(1), 0$ is the greatest. In step $n = 2$, we have $\alpha_2(w) = \kappa(w, v)$ for $w \neq w^*(1)$ and $\alpha_2[w^*(1)] = \alpha_2[v^*(1)]$. Thus we look again for a channel $[w^*(2), v^*(2)]$ such that replacing the direct channel $[w^*(2), 0]$ by a path $[w^*(2), v^*(2), 0]$, $v^*(2) \neq w^*(1)$ or the path $[w^*(2), w^*(1), v^*(1), 0]$ gives the greatest possible gain. It is thus evident that under the assumption made in this example, Algorithm 8.4.6 becomes Algorithm 8.4.5.

From the examples above we see that Algorithm 8.4.6 can be considered as a generalisation of Algorithms 8.4.1, 8.4.4, and 8.4.5. If we take into account the constraints, we can also consider Algorithm 8.4.2 as a special case of Algorithm 8.4.6. There are, however, several other possible special forms of Algorithm 8.4.6. For example, let us consider the cost $\kappa[w, \mathcal{D}(w)]$ where $\mathcal{D}(w) = N - \mathcal{D}(w)$ and $\mathcal{D}(w)$ is the auxiliary set to which node w belongs. Let $\alpha'(w)$ be the minimum value of $\kappa[w, \mathcal{D}(w)]$ and $\alpha''(w)$ the next lowest value. If we define

$$\alpha(w) = \alpha''(w) - \alpha'(w)$$

and change it by taking $\alpha_{n+1}(w) = \alpha_n(w)$, and if channel w was chosen in step n (as in Example 8.4.8), we get the algorithm called Vogel's Approximation Method.

REFERENCES

[8.1] Frank, H., Frisch, I. T., Van Slyke, R., and Chou, W. S., (1971), Optimal design of centralized computer networks, *Networks*, **1**, 43–47.

[8.2] Yaged, B., (1971), Minimum cost routing for static network models, *Networks*, **1**, 139–172.

[8.3] Prim, R. C., (1957), Shortest connection networks and some generalizations, *BSTJ*, **36**, 1389–1401.

[8.4] Sharma, R. L., and El-Bardai, M. T., (1970), Suboptimal communications networks sysnthesis, *Proc. of the IEEE International Conference of Communications 1970*, 19.11–19.16.

[8.5] Esau, L. R., and Williams, K. C., (1966), On teleprocessing system design. A method for approximating the optimal network, *IBM System Journal*, **5**, 142–147.

[8.6] Doll, D. R., (1971), Topology and transmission rate considerations in the design of centralized computer communication network, *IEEE Trans. on Comm.*, **CT-9**, 339–344.

[8.7] Whitney, V. K. M., (1972), Comparison of network topology optimization algorithms, *Proc. of the First International Conference on Computer Communication, New York, 1972*, 332–337.

[8.8] Kerschenbaum, A., and Chou, W., (1974), A unified algorithm for designing multidrop teleprocessing networks, *IEEE Trans. on Comm.*, **COM-22**, 1762–1771.

Appendices

APPENDIX A.1 – ANALYSIS OF A PERIODICALLY EMPTIED BUFFER

The primary purpose of this appendix is to derive the formulae for the average time a packet spends on a periodically emptied buffer which is used in several sections of the book where we consider systems operating synchronously.

The second aim is to introduce the method of obtaining the generating function of the probability distribution of the states of a system described by recursive equations. An extension of this method is used in Appendix A.4 to obtain formulae for the waiting time of packets in a multiaccess system with access *en route*.

We start the description of the buffer emptied periodically by assuming that:

A1 The packets can be taken out of the buffer only at the buffer content checking instants:

$$t_j \equiv jT_1 \tag{A.1.1}$$

where $j = 1, 2, \ldots$ and T_1 is the checking period; K packets can be taken out simultaneously.

A2 The removal is instantaneous.

A3 The duration T_1 of the packet is equal to the duration of the slot.

Let:

$l(t)$ be the number of packets in the buffer at instant $t \neq t_j$;

$l(t_j) \equiv \lim\limits_{t \to t_j - 0} l(t)$ be the number in the buffer at an instant just prior to the jth checking instant.

The operation of the buffer for $j = 2, 3, \ldots$ is described by the formula:

$$l(t_j) = \begin{cases} l_1(t_j) & \text{if } l_1(t_j) \leqslant \hat{L} \\ \hat{L} & \text{if } l_1(t_j) > L \end{cases} \tag{A.1.2}$$

where $\hat{L}$ is the buffer capacity,

$$l_1(t_j) = [l(t_{j-1}) - K]^+ + \Lambda_j \tag{A.1.3}$$

and

$$u^+ = \begin{cases} u & \text{if} \quad u \geqslant 0 \\ 0 & \text{if} \quad u < 0 \end{cases} \tag{A.1.4}$$

$[l(t_{j-1}) - K]^+$ on the right-hand side of (A.1.3) is the number of packets in the buffer just after the checking instant t_{j-1} while Λ_j is the number of packets which arrive during the time interval $\langle t_{j-1}, t_j \rangle$. Formula (A.1.2) states that the number of packets in the buffer cannot exceed $\hat{L}$. For a buffer of infinite capacity, i.e. for $\hat{L} = \infty$, we have simply:

$$l(t_j) = [l(t_{j-1}) - K]^+ + \Lambda_j \ . \tag{A.1.5}$$

Next we perform the statistical analysis of the buffer. We assume here that:

A4 The model of the starting instants of the packets delivered to the buffer is a stochastic random process with stationary independent increments.

Let:

Λ_j be the random variable representing the number of packets arriving during the time interval $\langle t_{j-1}, t_j \rangle$. We assume

A5 the random variables Λ_j, Λ_i for $i \neq j$ are independent variables with the same probability distribution.

Therefore we denote briefly:

$$P_1(l) = P(\Lambda_j = l) \tag{A.1.6}$$

We next define the buffer state. We say that it is in state l if l packets are in the buffer. Let us denote by $\mathrm{L}(t)$ the random variable representing buffer state at instant t. From the assumption that the random variables Λ_j representing the numbers of packets arriving during various periods $\langle t_{j-1}, t_j \rangle$ $j = 1, 2, \ldots$ are statistically independent, it follows that the sequence of $\mathrm{L}(t_j)$ $j = 1, 2, \ldots,$ is a Markovian sequence. The statistical properties of such a sequence are determined by the probability distribution in the first checking instant and the state transition probabilities. We now show that the latter can be easily determined.

We call the event where $L(t_{j-1}) = l$ on the condition that $L(t_j) = k$ an $l \rightarrow k$ transition.

Let us first consider the case when at most one packet can be taken out, i.e. we take $K = 1$ in (A.1.3). We assume that $l \geqslant 1$. Then at the checking instant t_{j-1} one packet is taken out. If during the interval $\langle t_{j-1}, t_j \rangle$ m packets are delivered to the buffer by the source, just before the checking instant t_j we will have $l-1+m$

packets. Thus for $k \geqslant l-1$ the transition $l \to k$ is eqivalent to the event $\Lambda_j = k-l+1$. Let us denote the transition probability by

$$P(k\,|\,l,t_j) = P[L(t_j) = k\,|\,L(t_{j-1}) = 1] \tag{A.1.7}$$

From our considerations, it follows that for $k \geqslant 1, l \geqslant k$. We have:

$$P(k|l,t_j) = P_\Lambda(\Lambda_j = k-l+1)$$

Similarly, we find transition probabilities for all possible pairs k, l. It is helpful to represent the buffer operation by means of a state transition graph. An example

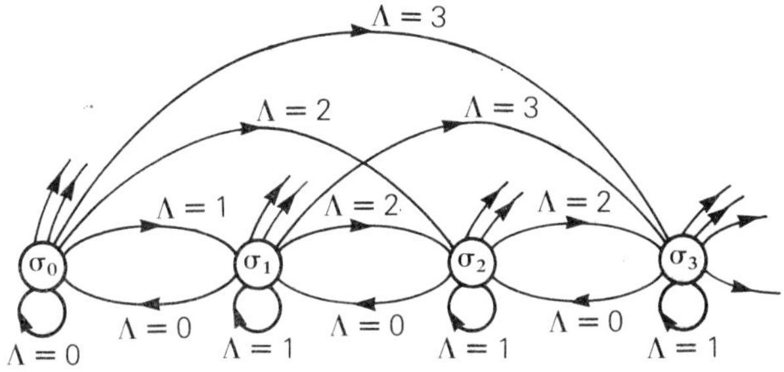

Fig. A.1 – Graph representing transition probabilities for the states of the buffer described by (A.1.2), $\hat{L} = \infty, K = 1$, Λ, number of packets delivered by the source.

of such a graph for $\hat{L} = \infty$ is shown in Fig. A.1. Knowing the transition probabilities, we can determine the unconditional state probabilites:

$$P_j(k) = P[L(t_j) = k] \tag{A.1.8}$$

from the Chapman–Kolmogorov equations:

$$\begin{aligned}
P_j(0) &= P_{j-1}(1)P_\Lambda(0) + P_{j-1}(0)P_\Lambda(1) && \vdots \\
P_j(1) &= P_{j-1}(2)P_\Lambda(0) + P_{j-1}(1)P_\Lambda(1) + P_{j-1}(0)P_\Lambda(1) && \vdots\; z \\
P_j(2) &= P_{j-1}(3)P_\Lambda(0) + P_{j-1}(2)P_\Lambda(1) + P_{j-1}(1)P_\Lambda(2) + P_{j-1}(0)P_\Lambda(2) && \vdots\; z^2 \\
P_j(3) &= P_{j-1}(4)P_\Lambda(0) + P_{j-1}(3)P_\Lambda(1) + P_{j-1}(2)P_\Lambda(2) + P_{j-1}(1)P_\Lambda(3) + && \vdots \\
&\quad + P_{j-1}(0)P_\Lambda(3) && \vdots\; z^3
\end{aligned} \tag{A.1.9}$$

We now give a method for solving this set of equations using the z-transformation or, in probability theory terminology, the generating function method. Let:

$$\varphi_\Lambda(z) \equiv \sum_{k=0}^{\infty} P_\Lambda(k) z^k \tag{A.1.10}$$

$$\varphi_j(z) \equiv \sum_{n=0}^{\infty} P_j(n) z^n \tag{A.1.11}$$

be the generating fucntions of the probability distributions $P_\Lambda(k)$ and $P_j(n)$. By multiplying the equations from the set (A.1.9) by the appropriate powers of the variable z indicated on the left-hand side of the set, grouping the expressions in the way shown and by adding both sides we get:

$$z\phi_j(z) = \phi_\Lambda(z)[\phi_{j-1}(z) - (1-z)P_{j-1}(0)] \tag{A.1.12}$$

From (A.1.11), it is evident that

$$P_{j-1}(0) = \phi_{j-1}(0) \tag{A.1.13}$$

Finally:

$$\phi_j(z) = \phi_\Lambda(z)\frac{\phi_{j-1}(z) - (1-z)\phi_{j-1}(0)}{z} \tag{A.1.14}$$

Let:

$$\Phi(w,z) = \sum_{j=0}^{\infty} \phi_j(z)w^j \tag{A.1.15}$$

be the double w, z transformation of the set of numbers $P_j(n)$, whereby

$$\phi_0(z) \equiv \sum_{n=0}^{\infty} P_0(n)z^n \tag{A.1.16}$$

where $P_0(k) = P[\mathrm{L}(t_0) = k]$, $k = 0, 1, 2, \ldots$ is the probability distribution of the initial state of the buffer. In particular, if we assume that the buffer is initially empty, we have:

$$P_0(0) = 1, P_0(k) = 0 \quad k \geqslant 1 \tag{A.1.17}$$

Multiplying (A.1.14) by w^j and summing for j, $1 \leqslant j \leqslant +\infty$, we get:

$$\Phi(w,z) = \frac{z\phi_0(z) - w(1-z)\phi_\Lambda(z)\Phi(w,0)}{z - w\phi_\Lambda(z)} \tag{A.1.18}$$

The difficulty in obtaining the double transformation $\Phi(w,z)$ from this formula lies in the fact that the boundary value $\Phi(w,0)$, also unknown, appears on the right-hand side. However, we can determine this value from the condition that the function $\Phi(w,z)$ over the area $|z| < 1$, $|w| < 1$ is an analytical function. Let $\alpha(w)$ be the root of the equation

$$z - w\phi_\Lambda(z) = 0 \ . \tag{A.1.19}$$

It is not difficult to show that in the circle $|z| < 1$ this is the only root, therefore:

$$\alpha(w)\phi_0[\alpha(w)] - w[1-\alpha(w)]\phi_\Lambda[\alpha(w)]\Phi(w,0) = 0$$

We finally get:

$$\Phi(w,z) = \frac{z\phi_0(z) - w(1-z)[1-\alpha(w)]^{-1}\phi_\Lambda(z)\phi_0[\alpha(w)]}{z - w\phi_\Lambda(z)} \tag{A.1.20}$$

Knowing $\Phi(w,z)$ we can obtain by means of the inverse transformation the marginal probabilities $P_j(k)$ which are the solution of the fundamental set of equations (A.1.9). As is well known, under quite general assumptions, there exists a limit

$$P(k) = \lim_{j\to\infty} P_j(k) \tag{A.1.21}$$

not depending on the *a priori* probabilities $P[\mathrm{L}(t_0) = k]$. We call the probabilities $P(k)$ the stationary probabilities and it is in these that we are most interested. Let $\phi_\infty(z)$ be the generating function of the stationary probabilities $P(k)$. Using Tauber's theorem, we can find $\phi_\infty(z)$ knowing $\Phi(w,z)$, namely:

$$\phi_\infty(z) = \lim_{w\to 1} (1-w)\Phi(w,z) \tag{A.1.22}$$

Applying l'Hospital's rule to equation (A.1.20), we obtain:

$$\phi_\infty(z) = (1-E\Lambda)\frac{(z-1)\phi_\Lambda(z)}{z-\phi_\Lambda(z)} \tag{A.1.23}$$

where by Λ we denote a random variable representing the number of packets arriving during the time interval between consecutive checking instants. We denoted it earlier by Λ_j, but since according to the stationarity assumption A4, it does not depend on j, we omit the index. We now illustrate the method of finding $\Phi(w,z)$ and $\phi_\infty(z)$.

Example A.1.1

Let us assume that: (1) the starting instants of the packets delivered to the buffer form a Poisson sequence of intensity λ, (2) $P_0(0) = 1$, $P_0(k) = 0$ for $k \geqslant 1$.

Under assumption (1) we have:

$$P_\Lambda(l) = \frac{(\lambda T_1)l}{l!} \exp(-\lambda T_1) \tag{A.1.24}$$

and

$$\phi_\Lambda(z) = \exp[\lambda T_1(z-1)] \tag{A.1.25}$$

Under assumption (2) we have:

$$\phi_0(z) = 1 \tag{A.1.26}$$

The solution of equation (A.1.9) is

$$\alpha(w) = \frac{1}{\lambda T_1} \sum_{k=1}^{\infty} \frac{k^{k-1}}{k!} (\lambda T_1 w \exp[-\lambda T_1])^k \tag{A.1.27}$$

for

$$|\lambda T_1 w \exp[-\lambda T_1]| < 1$$

From (A.1.18) we have:

$$\Phi(w,z) = \frac{z - \dfrac{w(1-z)\exp[\lambda T_1(z-1)]}{1 - \dfrac{1}{\lambda} \displaystyle\sum_{k=1}^{\infty} \frac{k^{k-1}}{k!} (\lambda T_1 w \exp[-\lambda T_1])^k}}{z - w\exp[\lambda T_1(z-1)]} \tag{A.1.28}$$

and

$$\phi_\infty(z) = (1-\lambda T_1)\frac{(z-1)\exp[\lambda T_1(z-1)]}{z - \exp[\lambda T_1(z-1)]} \tag{A.1.29}$$

Let L_∞ be the random variable representing the number of packets in the buffer at instant $t_j - 0$ for $j \to \infty$. The average value in the stationary state

$$E L_\infty = \sum_{l=1}^{\infty} l P_\infty(l) \tag{A.1.30}$$

As is known,

$$E L_\infty = \left(\frac{d\phi_\infty(z)}{dz}\right)_{z=1} \tag{A.1.31}$$

From (A.1.29) we ultimately obtain

$$E L_\infty = \frac{\text{var}(\Lambda)}{2(1 - E\Lambda)} + \frac{1}{2} E\Lambda \tag{A.1.32}$$

Notice that although we assumed that the process representing the starting instants of the packets is stationary, as the result of introducing periodic buffer content checking, and the possible removal of a packet, we ensure that the process $L(t)$ representing the number of packets in the buffer is no longer stationary even for $t \to \infty$. The diagram of the average $E L(t)$ for large t is shown in Fig. A.2. The increase in the average $L(t)$ during the interval between two consecutive chacking instants is equal to the average number $E\Lambda$ of packets delivered during that interval by the packet source. The average $E L_\infty$ evaluated previously is the average number of packets just before the checking instant. Let

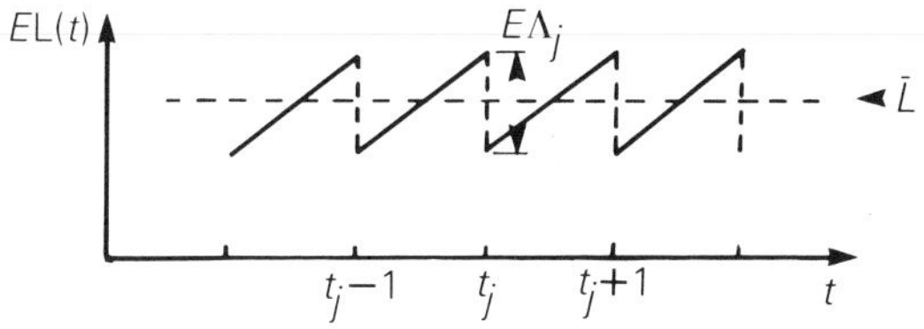

Fig. A.2 – Average number of packets in a buffer emptied rhythmically.

$\bar{L}$ be the time average of the average $\bar{L}(t)$, and thus the double average of the random process $L(t)$. From Fig. A.2 we see that

$$\bar{L} = EL_{\infty} - 1/2E\Lambda \tag{A.1.33}$$

Thus from (A.1.32),

$$\bar{L} = \frac{\text{var}(\Lambda)}{2(1-E\Lambda)} \tag{A.1.34}$$

For the assumptions made in Example A.1.1, we have $\text{var}(\Lambda) = \lambda T_1$, $E\Lambda = \lambda T_1$, and thus

$$\bar{L} = \frac{\lambda T_1}{2(1-\lambda T_1)} \tag{A.1.35}$$

From Little's theorem, the average time spent by the packet in the buffer queueing time is:

$$\bar{T}_{qu} = \frac{\bar{L}}{\lambda} = T_1 \frac{1}{2(1-\lambda T_1)} \tag{A.1.36}$$

Notice that if $\lambda T_1 \to 0$ then $T_{qu} \to T_1/2$. It must be so, since the packet must wait until the slot arrives, and this is on average $T_1/2$.

Hitherto we have been considering the case when at most one packet can be taken out of a checking instant. The method can be generalised for the general case when $K > 1$ packets can be taken out.

Attention has to be drawn to the basic limitation of the method, which is that we can express the double transformation in a closed form only because the sums cover an infinite number of components, i.e. because we assumed that the buffer capacity is infinite.

APPENDIX A.2 – ANALYSIS OF A CONTINUOUSLY EMPTIED BUFFER

The main purpose of this appendix is to derive the formula for the average time spent by a packet in a continuously emptied buffer. The final result is used in several places in the book.

The second aim of this appendix (which determines its structure) is to give an introduction to the method by which the probabilities of the states of systems described by recurrent equations can be analysed. This method is based on the concept of intensities of introduction and removal of packets from the system, and on the probability equilibrium conditions. It is important that it can be generalised to permit the analysis of networks of interconnected buffers. Such an analysis, which is essential for studying congestion phenomena in mesh networks, will be given in Appendix A.6. We consider here systems consisting of a single buffer and a single transmitter, called a buffer–transmitter unit (B–Tr unit). We assume here that:

A1 Packet input to and removal from the buffer is instantaneous.

A2 The packet waiting in the buffer is taken immediately if the transmission of the previous packet is completed; if a packet arrives in the buffer when no other packet is being transmitted, the transmission of the newly arriving packet starts immediately.

A3 There can be at most $\hat{L}$ packets in the B–Tr facilty.

We assume for the packet arrival instants and durations of transmission that:

A4 The model of packet starting instants is a Poisson process of intensity μ.

Parameter μ occurring in A4 we call intensity of completing the transmission. It can be easily seen that A4 is equivalent to

A4′ The random variable T representing the duration of the packet has an exponential distribution with average

$$\bar{T}_k = 1/\mu \tag{A.2.1}$$

Let l be the number of packets in the B–Tr facility†. We identify the state of the B–Tr facility by the number of packets in it. Hence we shall now refer to l as the state of the B–Tr facility. Because of assumption A3, the only admissible states are those from the set $L = \{0, 1, \ldots, \hat{L}\}$, which we call the set of admissible states for the B–Tr facility.

Let $\mathrm{L}(t)$; $t \in \langle 0, +\infty\rangle$, be a process representing the state of the B–Tr facility in time. Under the above assumptions, the $\mathrm{L}(t)$ process is a stationary

† Notice that now we consider the total number of packets in the buffer and eventually the one just being transmitted, while in A.1 we considered only packets in the buffer.

Markovian process defined by the set of states L. If the L(t) process has such properties, the following limits exist:

$$P(1) \equiv \lim_{t\to+\infty} P[\mathrm{L}(t)=1] \qquad l = 0,1,\ldots,L \tag{A.2.2}$$

We call these the **stationary** set of probabilities.

Consider the state of the B–Tr facility at instant $t+\Delta t$, where $\Delta t \to 0$. The first column of Table A.2.1 gives the states from which the B–Tr facility can reach state L after a time Δt, the second column gives the events causing transitions, the third gives the probabilities of transition. The symbol $0(\Delta t)$ indicates values approaching zero more quickly than Δt. The probability of reaching state l from states other than those given in the table is of the order $0(\Delta t)$.

Table A.2.1

$L(t)$	Event causing the transition	Probability of passage into state l at instant $t+\Delta t$
l	no new packet arrives nor is the transmission of a packet being transmitted completed	$1-(\lambda+\mu)\Delta t + 0(\Delta t)$
$l-1$ $l \geqslant 1$	a new packet arrives	$\lambda\Delta t + 0(\Delta t)$
$l+1$	the transmission of a packet being transmitted is completed	$\mu\Delta t + 0(\Delta t)$

The probability that at instant $t+\Delta t$ the B–Tr faciltiy is in state l can be written in the form:

$$\begin{aligned} P[-\mathrm{L}(t+\Delta t)=l] &= P[\mathrm{L}(t+\Delta t)=l\,|\,\mathrm{L}(t)=l]\,P[\mathrm{L}(t)=l]+\\ &+P[-\mathrm{L}(t+\Delta t)=L\,|\,\mathrm{L}(t)=l-1]\,P[\mathrm{L}(t)=l-1]+\\ &+P[-\mathrm{L}(t+\Delta t)=l\,|\,\mathrm{L}(t)=l+1]\,P[\mathrm{L}(t)=l+1] \end{aligned} \tag{A.2.3}$$

After substituting the probabilities from Table A.2.1 in equation (A.2.3), and after some simple manipulation with $\Delta t \to 0$, we obtain the differential equation:

$$\begin{aligned} \mathrm{d}/\mathrm{d}t\,P[\mathrm{L}(t)=l] &= -(\lambda+\mu)P[\mathrm{L}(t)=l]+\lambda P[\mathrm{L}(t)=l-1]+\\ &+\mu P[\mathrm{L}(t)=l+1] \end{aligned} \tag{A.2.4}$$

which is a particular form of the equation known in the literature as Kolmogorov's differential equation, see Parzen [A.1]. Assuming that the limits (A.2.2) exist, the differential equation (A.2.4) with $t \to +\infty$ becomes an algebraic equation of the form:

$$0 = -(\lambda + \mu)P(l) + \lambda P(l-1) + \mu P(l+1) \qquad \text{(A.2.5)}$$

whereby $l = 1, 2, \ldots, \hat{L} - 1$.

Analogously, we find that for $l = 0$, we get the equation:

$$0 = -\lambda P(0) + \mu P(1) \qquad \text{(A.2.6)}$$

since $P(L = 1) = 0$, as the B–Tr facility does not attain state −1. For $L = \hat{L}$, we obtain the equation:

$$0 = -\mu P(\hat{L}) + \lambda P(\hat{L} - 1) \qquad \text{(A.2.7)}$$

We can write equations (A.2.5)–(A.2.7) in the form:

$$\mu P(1) = \lambda P(0)$$

$$\lambda P(l-1) + \mu P(l+1) = (\lambda + \mu)P(l), \; l = 1, 2, \ldots, \hat{L} - 1 \qquad \text{(A.2.8)}$$

$$\lambda P(\hat{L} - 1) = \mu P(\hat{L})$$

We consider $P(0)$ as a parameter. Then from the first equation we obtain $P(1)$. Substituting it we obtain $P(2)$ from the second and so on. Finally we obtain $P(0)$ from the normalisation constraint.

Notice that the left-hand side of each equation in the set (A.2.8) can be interpreted as the intensity of respective entry into the state $l = 0, 1, \ldots, \hat{L}$, whereas the right-hand side indicates the intensity of leaving that state. In consequence, we can write each of the equations in the set (A.2.8) as the condition:

$$\text{(intensity of entering state } l\text{)} = \text{(intensity of leaving state } l\text{)} \qquad \text{(A.2.9)}$$
$$l = 0, 1, \ldots, \hat{L}$$

Condition (A.2.19) is called the **equilibrium equation of state** l. The individual equations in the set (A.2.8) can be interpreted graphically in the form of a graph of the change of states shown in Fig. A.3.

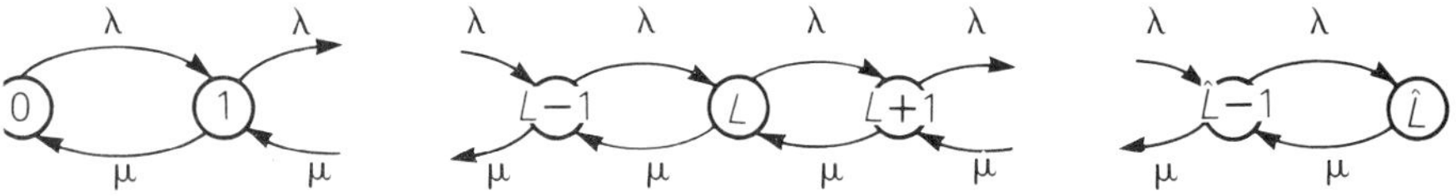

Fig. A.3 – Graph representing intensities of state transitions in a buffer emptied continuously.

Let us denote:

$$\nu \equiv \lambda/\mu \tag{A.2.10}$$

the solution of the set (A.2.8) takes the form

$$P(l) = P(0)\nu^l, \; l = 1, 2, \ldots, \hat{L} \; . \tag{A.2.11}$$

Obviously the following condition must be satisfied:

$$\sum_{l=0}^{\hat{L}} P(l) = 1 \; . \tag{A.2.12}$$

From (A.2.11), (A.2.12) we obtain:

$$P(0) = \begin{cases} \dfrac{1-\nu}{1-\nu^{\hat{L}+1}} & \text{if } \nu \neq 1 \\[2ex] \dfrac{1}{\hat{L}+1} & \text{if } \nu = 1 \end{cases} \tag{A.2.13}$$

Equations (A.2.10) and (A.2.12) give us the desired stationary probability distribution of states of the B–Tr facility. In particular, if $\hat{L} \to +\infty$, we must have $\nu < 1$ if the distribution is to be stationary. This is because, if this condition is not fulfilled, the sum on the left-hand side of equation (A.2.12) becomes a divergent series.

Knowing the probabilities of states we immediately obtain the average number of packets in the B–Tr unit:

$$\bar{L} = \sum_{l=1}^{\hat{L}} lP(\mathrm{L}\equiv l) = \frac{\nu - \nu^2 - (\hat{L}+1)\nu^{\hat{L}+1} + \nu^{\hat{L}+2}}{(1-\nu)^2(1-\nu^{\hat{L}+1})} \; . \tag{A.2.14}$$

A packet delivered by the source can enter the buffer only if it is not full, i.e. if $L < L$. Thus the intensity of packets entering the B–Tr unit is:

$$\lambda^+ = \lambda[1 - P(\mathrm{L}\equiv\hat{L})] = \lambda\left[\frac{1-\nu^{\hat{L}}}{1-\nu^{\hat{L}+1}}\right] \tag{A.2.15}$$

From Little's theorem, the average time the packet admitted to the buffer spends in the B–Tr unit is

$$\bar{T}_{\mathrm{btr}} = \frac{\bar{L}}{\lambda^+} \; . \tag{A.2.16}$$

For the buffer of infinite capacity $\hat{L} = \infty$ we have $\lambda^+ = \lambda$ and from (A.2.14), (A.2.16) it follows

$$\bar{T}_{btr} = \frac{1}{\lambda}\frac{\nu}{1-\nu} = \bar{T}\frac{1}{1-\nu} \tag{A.2.17}$$

Let us assume that the packet consists on average on $\bar{N}_p$ bits and channel capacity is C bit/sec. Than the rate of transmission is

$$\bar{T}_{btr} = \frac{\bar{N}_p}{C-\lambda\bar{N}_p} \tag{A.2.18}$$

and $\bar{T} = \bar{N}_p/C$. Formula (A.2.17) takes the form

$$\bar{T}_{btr} = \frac{\bar{N}_p}{C-\lambda\bar{N}_p} \tag{A.2.19}$$

The average time spent in the buffer (queueing time)

$$\bar{T}_{qu} = \bar{T}_{btr} - \bar{T} = \bar{T}\frac{\nu}{1-\nu} \tag{A.2.20}$$

If the probability distribution of packet duration is not geometric the methods of Markov processes can not be directly applied. However, on assumption A2 the average queueing delay is given by the Pollaczek formula

$$\bar{T}_{qu} = \bar{T}\frac{\nu}{2(1-\nu)}\left[1+\frac{\mathrm{var}(\mathrm{T})}{\bar{T}^2}\right] \tag{A.2.21}$$

For packets of constant duration var $(T) = 0$ and we have

$$T_{qu} = T\frac{\nu}{2(1-\nu)} \tag{A.2.22}$$

APPENDIX A.3 – THE OPTIMISATION OF CHANNEL CAPACITIES IN A SYSTEM WITH INDIVIDUAL BUFFERS AND FIXED SUBCHANNEL ASSIGNMENT

The problem of optimising the assignment of subchannel capacities leads us to find the capacities $C_{m0}(\alpha)$ minimising the function

$$\bar{\tau}_\beta(C_1, \ldots, C_M) = \left[\sum_{m=1}^{M} \frac{F_m}{(C_m - G_m)^\beta}\right]^{1/\beta} \tag{A.3.1}$$

under the condition that

$$\kappa(C_1, \ldots, C_M) = \sum_{m=1}^{M} \phi_m C_m = \text{const.} \tag{A.3.2}$$

whereby $\beta > 0, \phi_m > 0$ and

$$F_m \equiv \frac{\lambda_m \bar{N}_{pm}^\beta}{\sum_{m=1}^{M} \lambda_m} \tag{A.3.3}$$

and

$$G_m \equiv \lambda_m \bar{N}_{pm} \quad . \tag{A.3.4}$$

The minimal subchannel capacities are a solution of the equations

$$\frac{\partial}{\partial C_m} (\bar{\tau}_\beta + A\kappa) = 0 \tag{A.3.5}$$

$m = 1, 2, \ldots, M$ and equation (A.3.2); A is a Lagrange multiplier. After substituting (A.3.1) and (A.3.2), the mth equation (A.3.5) becomes:

$$\frac{1}{\beta} (\bar{\tau}_\beta)^{1/\beta - 1} \cdot \frac{-F_m \beta}{(C_m - G_m)^{\beta - 1}} + A\phi_m = 0 \tag{A.3.6}$$

From this equation, we obtain:

$$C_{m0}(\beta) = G_+ \left(\frac{\beta F_m}{\phi_m A'}\right)^{1/\beta + 1} \quad . \tag{A.3.7}$$

The constant

$$A' \equiv \frac{\beta^2 A}{\bar{\tau}_\beta (1 - \beta)} \tag{A.3.8}$$

appearing here is derived from condition (A.3.2). After substituting (A.3.7) in (A.3.2) we get

$$\sum_{m=1}^{M} \phi_m G_m + \frac{1}{(A')^{1/\beta+1}} \sum_{m=1}^{M} \frac{(\beta F_m)^{1/\beta+1}}{\phi_m^{\beta/\beta+1}} = \kappa \tag{A.3.9}$$

Notice that the minimum capacity for sending packets of length N_{pm} at an intensity of λ_m is $\lambda_m N_{pm}$, hence it is equal to G_m according to (A.3.4). However, with such a capacity, the waiting time in the buffers would be infinitely great. The cost of channels having such a capacity would amount to:

$$\kappa^* \equiv \sum_{m=1}^{M} \phi_m G_m \tag{A.3.10}$$

It is apparent from (A.3.9) that if there is to be a solution to this problem, we must have:

$$\kappa > \kappa^* \ . \tag{A.3.11}$$

If this inequality is satisfied, then from (A.3.9) we get

$$A' = \left(\frac{\psi}{\Delta\kappa}\right)^{\beta+1} \tag{A.3.12}$$

where

$$\psi \triangleq \sum_{m=1}^{M} \frac{(\beta F_m)^{1/\beta+1}}{\phi_m^{1/\beta+1}} \tag{A.3.13}$$

$$\Delta\kappa \equiv \kappa - \kappa^* \tag{A.3.14}$$

After substituting (A.3.12) in (A.3.7) we finally get:

$$C_m^*(\beta) = G_m + \Delta\kappa \frac{\left(\dfrac{\beta F_m}{\phi_m}\right)^{1/\beta+1}}{\displaystyle\sum_{m=1}^{M} \frac{(\beta F_m)^{1/\beta+1}}{\phi_m^{1/\beta+1}}} \tag{A.3.15}$$

APPENDIX A.4 – DERIVATION OF AVERAGE SOURCE – TRANSMITTER PASSAGE TIME IN POLLING SYSTEMS

We introduce here the assumptions formulated in section 4.1. We start with derivation of the generating function† for a variable T_{cy} representing the systems cycle. Let:

$T_{ml}(j)$ be the duration of the lth packet in the mth buffer in the jth cycle; note that the packets are numbered starting from the end of the operation of the mth node in the $(j-1)$th cycle;

$T_{cy}(j)$ be the duration of the jth system cycle;

$\Lambda_m(j)$ be the total number of packets delivered by the source during the cycle $\langle \vartheta_m(j-1), \vartheta_m(j) \rangle$.

$\mathrm{T}_{ml}, \mathrm{T}_{cy}, \Lambda_m$ are the corresponding random variables. Since we are assuming that the system is stationary, their properties do not depend on j.

Since we apply rule R4.1 we have:

$$\mathrm{T}_{cy} \equiv \sum_{m=1}^{M} \mathrm{T}_m^* + \mathrm{T}_{pol} \tag{A.4.1}$$

where

$$\mathrm{T}_m^* \equiv \sum_{l=1}^{\mathrm{L}_{xm}} \mathrm{T}_{ml} \tag{A.4.2}$$

We first derive the generating function of Λ_m. From the definition of Λ_m it follows that it is the number of Poissonian events occurring in an interval of random duration T_{cy}. Let $p_{cy}(T)$ be the probability density of T_{cy}. We have:

$$P(\Lambda_m = l) = \int_0^{\infty} \frac{\exp(-\lambda_1 T)(\lambda_1 T)^l}{l!} P_{cy}(T) \mathrm{d}T \, . \tag{A.4.3}$$

The generating function of L_{xm}, which we denote by $\varphi_{xm}(z)$ is:

$$\varphi_m(z) = \mathrm{E}\, z^{j\Lambda m} = \sum_{L=0}^{\infty} z^{jl} P(\Lambda_m = l) \tag{A.4.4}$$

Substituting (A.4.3), and rearranging, we obtain:

$$\varphi_m(z) = \varphi_{cy}(\lambda_1 - \lambda_1 z) \tag{A.4.5}$$

† We call the Laplace transform of the probability density of a random variable taking only non-negative values the generating function of that variable.

where

$$\varphi_{\mathrm{cy}}(z) = \mathrm{E}\exp(j\mathrm{T}_{\mathrm{cy}}) = \int_0^\infty \exp(jzT)p_{\mathrm{cy}}(T)\mathrm{d}T \tag{A.4.6}$$

is the generating function of $\mathrm{T_{cy}}$, which we will evaluate. The generating function for $\mathrm{T}_m^{(\Sigma)}$ defined by (A.4.2) is:

$$\varphi_m^*(z) = \underset{\mathrm{T}_{m,l,\Lambda m}}{\mathrm{E}} z^{\mathrm{T}_m^*} = \underset{\Lambda_m}{\mathrm{E}} \underset{\mathrm{T}_{ml}|\Lambda_m}{\mathrm{E}} z^{j\sum_{m=1}^{\Lambda m} T_{ml}}$$

$$= \underset{\Lambda_m}{\mathrm{E}} [\varphi(z)]^{j\Lambda_m} = \varphi_m[\varphi_1(z)] \tag{A.4.7}$$

where $\varphi_1(z)$ is the generating function of T_{ml} which depends neither on m nor on l. Using (A.4.5), (A.4.7) we get:

$$\varphi_{\mathrm{cy}}(z) = z^{M\,T_{\mathrm{pol}}}\{\varphi_{\mathrm{cy}}[\lambda_1 - \lambda_1\varphi_1(z)]\}^M \tag{A.4.8}$$

Note that using the well-known formula

$$\mathrm{E\,T_{cy}} = \left(\frac{\mathrm{d}\varphi_{\mathrm{cy}}(z)}{\mathrm{d}z}\right)_{z=0}$$

equation (A.4.8) yields (4.1.19).

Let us denote:

ϑ' – the instant of arrival of the packet considered;

$T_{\mathrm{w}} = \vartheta_m(j+1) - \vartheta$ – the time the packet must wait until its node is permitted to transmit;

T_{qu} – the time the packet spends in the buffer from the instant the node obtained the permission to transmit to the instant the packet is put into transmitter;

$T_{\mathrm{s\text{-}t}}$ – the time taken to transfer the packet from the source to the transmitter;

Λ' – the number of packets delivered by the source during the interval $\langle \vartheta_m(j), \vartheta' \rangle$.

The notation is illustrated in Fig. A.4(a).

Obviously:

$$\mathrm{T_{qu}} = \sum_{l=1}^{\Lambda'} \mathrm{T}_{ml} \tag{A.4.9}$$

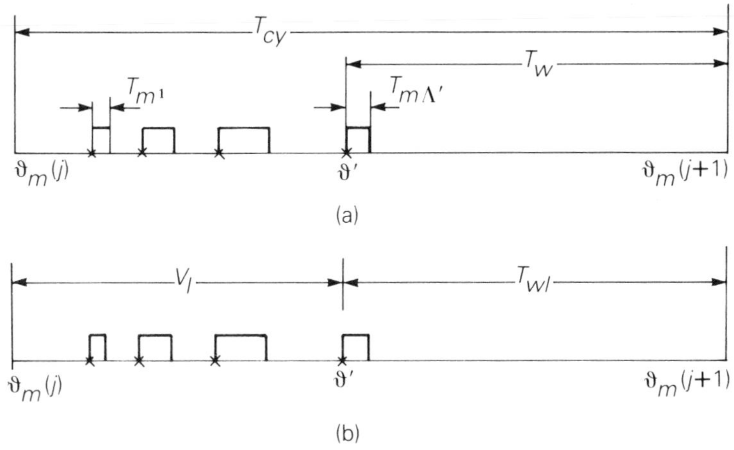

Fig. A.4 – Illustration of the notation used in Appendix A.4.

where T_{ml} is the duration of the lth packet which arrived in the interval $\langle\vartheta_m(j), \vartheta')$, starting to count l just after $\vartheta_m(j)$, and

$$T_{s\text{-}t} = T_w + T_{qu} \quad . \tag{A.4.10}$$

We denote

$p_w(l,\tau)\,d\tau$ – joint probability of the events $L' = l, \tau \leqslant T_w \leqslant \tau + d\tau$;
$p_{qu}(u|l)$ – probability density of T_{qu} given by (A.4.9) with $\Lambda' = l$;
$p_{s\text{-}t}(\vartheta)$ – probability density of $T_{s\text{-}t}$.

From (A.4.10) it follows that

$$p_{s\text{-}t}(\vartheta) = \int_0^\infty \sum_{k=0}^{\infty} p_{qu}(\vartheta - \tau)\, p_w(l,\tau)\,d\tau \tag{A.4.11}$$

Let: V_l be the random variable representing the length of such an interval that inside it arrived l packets and the $l+1-st$ is at the right-hand end of the interval, T_{wl} the random variable representing T_w on condition $\Lambda' = l$, and $p_l(v)$ and $p_{wl}(\tau)$ be the corresponding p.d.s (see Fig. A.4(b)). It is

$$T_{wl} = T_{cy} - V_l \tag{A.4.12}$$

$$p_l(v) = \begin{cases} \dfrac{(\lambda v)^l}{l!} \exp(-\lambda v) & \text{if } v \geqslant 0 \\ 0 & \text{if } v < 0 \end{cases} \tag{A.4.13}$$

$$p_{wl}(\tau) = \int_0^{\infty} p_l(\vartheta - \tau) p_{cy}(\vartheta) d\vartheta \ . \tag{A.4.14}$$

From Fig. A.4(b) we see that the event $\Lambda' = l, \tau \leqslant T_w \leqslant \tau + d\tau$ is equivalent to the event $\tau \leqslant T_{cy} - V_l < \tau + d\tau$ on the condition $T_{wl} \geqslant 0$. Thus

$$p(l,\tau) = p'_{wl}(\tau) \tag{A.4.15}$$

where $p'_{wl}(\tau)$ is the probability density of T_{wl} on the condition $T_{wl} \geqslant 0$; this condition must be satisfied on view of the definition of ϑ' which precedes $\vartheta_m(j+1)$. It is

$$p'_{wl}(\tau) = \begin{cases} A p_{wl}(\tau) & \text{if } \tau \geqslant 0 \\ 0 & \text{if } \tau < 0 \end{cases} \tag{A.4.16}$$

where A is a normalised constant. It can be easily checked that $A = \lambda^{-1} \bar{T}_{cy}$ where $\bar{T}_{cy} = \mathrm{E}\, T_{cy}$. From (A.4.15), (A.4.16), (A.4.14) we obtain

$$p_w(l,\tau) = \bar{T}_{cy}^{-1} \int_{\tau}^{\infty} \frac{[\lambda(\vartheta - \tau)]^l}{l!} \exp[-\lambda(\vartheta - \tau)] p_{cy}(\vartheta) d\vartheta \tag{A.4.17}$$

Substituting this in (A.4.11), performing the Laplace transform, taking into account that the Laplace transform of $P_{qu}(w|l)$ is $[p_1(z)]^l$ after some algebra we obtain:

$$\varphi_{s\text{-}t}(z) = \frac{\varphi_{cy}[\lambda - \lambda\varphi_1(z)] - \varphi_{cy}(z)}{\bar{T}_{cy}[z - \lambda + \lambda\varphi_1(z)]} \tag{A.4.18}$$

The average $\bar{T}_{s\text{-}t}$ we were looking for is obtained by differentiation

$$\bar{T}_{s\text{-}t} = \left. \frac{d\varphi_{s\text{-}t}(z)}{dz} \right|_{z=0} \tag{A.4.19}$$

The ultimate result can be found substituting (4.2.18); it is given by formula (4.1.15).

APPENDIX A.5 – ANALYSIS OF FLEXIBLE ACCESS *EN ROUTE*

As explained in section 4.3.3, the essential problem of the analysis of parameters characterising the rule of flexible access *en route* is to find the stationary joint probability distribution of the two-dimensional random process

$$\mathbf{L}_m[t_m(j)] \equiv \left(\sum_{n=1}^{m-1} \mathrm{L}_n[t_n(j)], \mathrm{L}_m[t_m(j)] \right) \tag{A.5.1}$$

where $\mathrm{L}_n[t_n(j)]$ satisfies the set of recursive equations (4.3.23) and (4.3.24). Our aim is to determine the mean value of $\bar{L}_m[t_m(j)]$. To solve the problem we apply the method described in Appendix A.1. As will be seen, although much more complicated, the steps of the solution are the exact counterparts of the steps of the solution of the simple problem of single buffer analysis carried out in Appendix A.1. We first find the generating function of the two-dimensional stationary probability distribution of component variables, next the generating function of the marginal distribution, and finally the mean value. Let us denote the following generating functions by:

$$\varphi_j(z_1 z_2) \equiv \sum_{k=0}^{\infty} \sum_{l=0}^{\infty} P\left[\sum_{n=1}^{m-1} \mathrm{L}_n(t_j) = k_1 \mathrm{L}_m(t_j) - l \;\; z_1^k z_2^l \right] \tag{A.5.2}$$

$$\varphi(z_1 z_2) \equiv \lim_{j \to \infty} \varphi j(z_1 z_2) \tag{A.5.3}$$

$$\varphi_{\Lambda m}(z) \equiv \sum_{k=0}^{\infty} P[\Lambda_m^{(1)}(j) = k] z^k \tag{A.5.4}$$

where we write briefly $\mathrm{L}_n(t_j)$ in place of $\mathrm{L}_n[t_n(j)]$. In view of assumptions A1 and A2 from section 4.3 (processes representing the numbers of packets delivered by the sources are independent), the two-dimensional chain determined by equations (4.3.23) and (4.3.24) is a first-order Markovian process. The transition probabilities for this process are:

$$P[L_m(t_j) = (l_1, l_2) \,|\, L_m(t_{j-1}) = (k_1, k_2)] =$$

$$= P\left[\sum_{n=1}^{m-1} \Lambda_n^{(1)}(j) = l_1 - (k_1 - 1)^+ \right] P\{\Lambda_n^{(1)}(j) = l_2 - [k_2 - (1 - k_1)^+]^+\} \tag{A.5.5}$$

Let us introduce the following definitions:

$$P_j(l_1, l_2) \equiv P[\mathrm{L}_m(t_j) = (l_1, l_2)] \tag{A.5.6a}$$

$$P_1(k) \equiv P\left[\sum_{n=1}^{m-1} \Delta_n^{(1)}(j) = k\right] \tag{A.5.6b}$$

$$P_2(k) \equiv P[\Delta_n^{(1)}(j) = k] \tag{A.5.6c}$$

We multiply both sides of equation (A.5.5) by $P_{j-1}(k_1, k_2) z_1 z_2$ and sum over k_1, k_2, $0 \leqslant k_1 < +\infty$, $0 \leqslant k_2 < +\infty$. First we transform the left-hand side of the equation:

$$\sum_{l_1} \sum_{l_2} \sum_{k_1} \sum_{k_2} P[\mathrm{L}_m(t_j) = (l_1, l_2), \mathrm{L}_m(t_{j-1}) = (k_1, k_2)]\, z_1^{l_1} z_2^{l_2} =$$

$$= \sum_{l_1} \sum_{l_2} P_j(l_1, l_2) z_1^{l_1} z_2^{l_2} = \varphi_j(z_1 z_2) \tag{A.5.7}$$

where $\varphi_j(z_1, z_2)$ is the generating function for the variable $\mathrm{L}(t_j)$. Now we transform the right-hand side of the equation (A.5.7):

$$\sum_{l_1} \sum_{l_2} \sum_{k_1} \sum_{k_2} P_1[l_1 - (k_1 - 1)^+]\, P_2\{l_2 - [k_2 - (1 - l_1)^+]^+\} P_{j-1}(k_1, k_2) z_1^{l_1} z_2^{l_2} =$$

$$\begin{aligned}
= \sum_{l_1} \sum_{l_2} \{ & P_1(l_1) p_2(l_2) P_{j-1}(0,0) + p_1(l_1) p_2(l_2) P_{j-1}(0,1) + \\
& + p_1(l_1) p_2(l_2 - 1) P_{j-1}(0,2) + \ldots + \\
& + p_1(l_1) p_2(l_2) P_{j-1}(1,0) + p_1(l_1) p_2(l_2 - 1) P_{j-1}(1,1) + \\
& + p_1(l_1) p_2(l_2 - 2) P_{j-1}(1,2) + \ldots + \\
& + p_1(l_1 - 1) p_2(l_2) P_{j-1}(2,0) + p_1(l_1 - 1) p_2(l_2 - 1) P_{j-1}(2,1) + \\
& + p_1(l_1 - 1) p_2(l_2 - 2) P_{j-1}(2,2) + \ldots + \\
& + p_1(l_1 - 2) p_2(l_2) P_{j-1}(3,0) + p_1(l_1 - 2) p_2(l_2 - 1) P_{j-1}(3,1) + \\
& + p_1(l_1 - 2) p_2(l_2 - 2) P_{j-1}(3,2) + \ldots + \} \cdot z_1^{l_1} z_2^{l_2} =
\end{aligned}$$

$$\begin{aligned}
= \sum_{l_1} p_1(l_1) z_1^{l_1} \sum_{l_2} p_2(l_2) z_2^{l_2} \{ & P_{j-1}(0,0) + P_{j-1}(0,1) + P_{j-1}(0,2) z_2 + \\
& + P_{j-1}(0,3) z_2^2 + \ldots + \\
& + P_{j-1}(1,0) + P_{j-1}(1,1) z_2 + P_{j-1}(1,2) z_2^2 + \\
& + P_{j-1}(1,3) z_2^3 + \ldots + \\
& + P_{j-1}(2,0) z_1 + P_{j-1}(2,1) z_1 z_2 + P_{j-1}(2,2) z_1 z_2^2 + \\
& + P_{j-1}(2,3) z_1 z_2^3 + \ldots + \\
& + P_{j-1}(3,0) z_1^2 + P_{j-1}(3,1) z_1^2 z_2 + P_{j-1}(3,2) z_1^2 z_2^2 + \\
& + P_{j-1}(3,3) z_1^2 z_2^3 + \ldots + \} =
\end{aligned}$$

$$= \prod_{n=1}^{m-1} \varphi_{\Lambda n}(z_1)\varphi_{\Lambda m}(z_2)\left\{P_{j-1}(0,0) + \sum_{l=1}^{\infty} P_{j-1}(0,l)z_2^{l-1} + \sum_{k=1}^{\infty} P_{j-1}(k,0)z_1^{k-1} + \right.$$

$$\left. + \sum_{k=1}^{\infty}\sum_{l=1}^{\infty} P_{j-1}(k,l)z_1^{k-1}z_2^{l}\right\} = (z_1z_2)^{-1}\prod_{n=1}^{m-1}\varphi_{\Lambda a}(z_1)\varphi_{\Lambda m}(z_2)\left\{z_1z_2P_{j-1}(0,0) + \right.$$

$$+ z_1\sum_{l=0}^{\infty} P_{j-1}(0,l)z_2^{l} - z_1P_{j-1}(0,0) + z_2\sum_{k=0}^{\infty} P_{j-1}(k,0)z_1^{k} - z_2P_{j-1}(0,0) +$$

$$+ z_2\sum_{k=0}^{\infty}\sum_{l=0}^{\infty} P_{j-1}(k,l)z_1^{k}z_2^{l} - z_2\sum_{k=0}^{\infty} P_{j-1}(k,0)z_1^{k} - z_2\sum_{l=0}^{\infty} P_{j-1}(0,l)z_2^{l} +$$

$$\left. + z_2P_{j-1}(0,0)\right\} =$$

$$= (z_1)^{-1}\prod_{n=1}^{m-1}\varphi_{\Lambda n}(z_1)\varphi_{\Lambda m}(z_2)\left\{P_{j-1}(z_1,z_2) + z_1\left(1-\frac{1}{z_2}\right)P_{j-1}(0,0) + \right.$$

$$\left. + \sum_{l=0}^{\infty}(z_1z_2^{l-1} - z_2^{l})P_{j-1}(0,l)\right\} \qquad (A.5.8)$$

From the final forms of the transformations (A.5.7) and (A.5.8) we get:

$$\frac{z_1\varphi_j(z_1,z_2)}{\prod_{n=1}^{m-1}\varphi_{\Lambda n}(z_1)\varphi_{\Lambda m}(z_2)} = \varphi_{j-1}(z_1,z_2) + z_1\left(1-\frac{1}{z_2}\right)P\left[\sum_{k=0}^{m} \mathbf{L}(t_k(j)) = 0\right] +$$

$$+ \sum_{l=0}^{\infty}(z_1z_2^{l-1} - z_2^{l})P_{j-1}(0,l) \qquad (A.5.9)$$

In order to calculate the generating function of the two-dimensional random variable $\mathbf{L}(t_j)$, $j = 0, 1, 2, \ldots$, in the state of statistical equilibrium, we introduce a function forming the sequence of functions $\{\varphi_j(z_1,z_2),\ j = 0, 1, 2, \ldots\}$

$$\Phi(z_1,z_2,v) \equiv \sum_{j=0}^{\infty}\varphi_j(z_1,z_2)v^j \ . \qquad (A.5.10)$$

Multiplying both sides of (A.5.9) by v^j and summing over j, $1 \leqslant j < +\infty$, we obtain

$$\Phi(z_1,z_2,v) =$$

$$= \frac{z_1\varphi_0(z_1,z_2) + v\prod_{n=1}^{m-1}\varphi_{\Lambda n}(z_1)\varphi_{\Lambda m}(z_2)\left[\frac{z_1}{z_2}(z_2-1)A_0(v)+\left(\frac{z_1}{z_2}-1\right)B_0(z_2,v)\right]}{z_1 - v\prod_{n=1}^{m-1}\varphi_{\Lambda n}(z_1)\varphi_{\Lambda m}(z_2)} \tag{A.5.11}$$

where

$$A_0(v) \equiv \sum_{j=0}^{\infty} P\left[\sum_{n=1}^{m} L(t_n(j)) = 0\right] v^j \tag{A.5.12}$$

$$B_0(z_2,v) \equiv \sum_{j=0}^{\infty}\sum_{k=0}^{\infty} P_j(0,l)z_2^l v^j \ . \tag{A.5.13}$$

We define the function $A_0(v)$ on the basis of the generating function of the random variable

$$\sum_{n=1}^{m} L_n\,(t_n(j))$$

i.e. of the number of packets in the virtual buffer into which we put packets from all nodes downstream from node m. Notice that from the formula

$$\sum_{n=1}^{m} \mathrm{L}_n(t_n(j)) = \left[\sum_{n=1}^{m} \mathrm{L}_n(t_n(j-1)) - 1\right]^+ + \sum_{n=1}^{m} \Lambda_n^{(1)}(j) \tag{A.5.14}$$

or from the comparison of (A.5.14) with (A.1.5) for $M = 1$ it follows that the function $A_0(v)$ corresponds to the function $\Phi(v,0)$ from equation (A.1.18). Therefore:

$$A_0(v) = \frac{\varphi_0[\alpha_m(v)]}{1-\alpha_m(v)} \tag{A.5.15}$$

where

$$\varphi_0(z) \equiv \sum_{l=0}^{\infty} P\sum_{n=1}^{m}\ [\mathrm{L}_m(t_n(0)) = l]\,z^l$$

is distribution of the sums of gueue lengths at instants $t = t_n(0) - 0$, whereas $\alpha_m(v)$ is the root of the equation

$$z - v\prod_{n=1}^{m}\varphi_{\Lambda n}(z) = 0 \ . \tag{A.5.16}$$

in the domain $|z|<1$, $|v|<1$.

The function $B_0(z_2, v)$ we determine from the condition that the function $\Phi(z_1, z_2, v)$ is an analytical function in the circle $|z_1| < 1$, for $0 \leqslant z_2 < 1, 0 \leqslant v < 1$. Since the denominator of this function has a single zero $z_1 = \alpha_{m-1}[v\varphi_{\Lambda m}(z)]$ the function $B_0(z_2, v)$ can be found from the equation

$$\varphi_{m-1}(a)\varphi_0[\alpha_{m-1}(a)z_2] + a\prod_{n=1}^{m-1}\varphi_{\Lambda n}[\alpha_{m-1}(a)]$$

$$\left[\frac{\alpha_{m-1}(a)}{z_2}(z_2 - 1)A_0(v) + \left(\frac{\alpha_{m-1}(a)}{z_2} - 1\right)B_0(z, v)\right] = 0 \qquad \text{(A.5.17)}$$

where $a = v\varphi_{\Lambda m}(z_2)$. We obtain:

$$B_0(v, z_2) = \frac{1}{z_2 - \alpha_{m-1}[v\varphi_{\Lambda m}(z_2)]}\Big\{\varphi_0\{\alpha_{m-1}[v\varphi_{\Lambda m}(z_2)]z_2\} +$$

$$+ (z_2 - 1)A_0(v)\alpha_{m-1}[v\varphi_{\Lambda m}(z_2)]\Big\} \qquad \text{(A.5.18)}$$

where the function $A_0(v)$ is given by equation (A.5.15), and function $\alpha_{m-1}(\cdot)$ is the solution of equation (A.5.16).

From equations (A.5.11), (A.5.15) and (A.5.17) we ultimately get the function $\Phi(z_1, z_2, v)$, which is the generating function of the sequence $\{\varphi_j(z_1, z_2)\}$, $j = 0, 1, 2, \ldots$. The limit of this sequence, i.e. the generating function for the random variable $L(t_j)$ in the stationary state can be calculated from Tauber's theorem:

$$\varphi(z_1, z_2) = \lim_{v \to 1-0} (1 - v)\Phi(z_1, z_2, v) \qquad \text{(A.5.19)}$$

Applying de l'Hospital's rule in the numerator of the function $(1 - v)D(z_1, z_2, v)$, we get:

$$\varphi(z_1, z_2) = \frac{1}{\frac{d}{dv}[\alpha_m(1)]} \; \frac{(z_2 - 1)\prod_{n=1}^{m-1}\varphi_{\Lambda n}(z_1)\varphi_{\Lambda m}(z_2)}{z_1 - \prod_{n=1}^{m-1}\varphi_{\Lambda n}(z_1)\varphi_{\Lambda m}(z_2)} \cdot$$

$$\cdot \frac{z_1 - \alpha_{m-1}[\varphi_{\Lambda m}(z_2)]}{z_2 - \alpha_{m-1}[\varphi_{\Lambda m}(z_2)]} \qquad \text{(A.5.20)}$$

We obtain $d/dv[\alpha_m(1)]$ by differentiating both sides of equation (A.5.16) taking $z = \alpha_m(v)$. Ultimately we have:

$$\varphi(z_1, z_2) = \left[1 - \sum_{n=1}^{m} \mathrm{E}\,\Lambda_m^{(1)}(j)\right] \frac{(z_1 - 1)\prod_{n=1}^{m-1} \varphi_{\Lambda n}(z_1)\varphi_{\Lambda m}(z_2)}{z_1 - \prod_{n=1}^{m-1} \varphi_{\Lambda n}(z_1)\varphi_{\Lambda m}(z_1)}$$

$$\frac{z_1 - \alpha_{m-1}[\varphi_{\Lambda m}(z_2)]}{z_2 - \alpha_{m-1}[\varphi_{\Lambda m}(z_2)]} \tag{A.5.21}$$

The sought-after generating function of the number of packets in the buffer of the mth node is the marginal distribution $\varphi_{\infty,m}(z)$ of the variable $\mathrm{L}_m(t_j)$. This is given by the formula:

$$\varphi_{\infty,m}(z) = \lim_{z_1 \to 1} \varphi(z_1, z) \tag{A.5.22}$$

Finally

$$\varphi_{\infty,m}(z) = \left[1 - \sum_{n=1}^{m-1} \mathrm{E}\,\Lambda_n^{(1)}(j)\right] \frac{(z-1)\varphi_{\Lambda m}(z)}{z - \varphi_m(z)} \; \frac{1 - \alpha[\varphi_{\Lambda m}(z)]}{z - \alpha[\varphi_{\Lambda m}(z)]} \tag{A.5.23}$$

where $\alpha_{m-1}(v)$ is the solution of equation (A.5.16). Hence the mean value we are looking for is

$$\mathrm{E}\,\mathrm{L} = \lim_{j \to \infty} \mathrm{E}\,L_m(t_j) = \varphi_{\infty,m}(0) \tag{A.5.24}$$

APPENDIX A.6 – ITERATIVE METHODS FOR FINDING THE EXTREME WITHIN INCIDENTAL LINEAR CONSTRAINTS

Consider the function $f(\mathbf{x})$ of a vector $\mathbf{x}$:

$$\mathbf{x} = \begin{pmatrix} x(1) \\ x(2) \\ \vdots \\ x(K) \end{pmatrix} \tag{A.6.1}$$

We shall describe the iterative or projection gradient method for solving the following minimising problem (see Rosen [A.2]).

Find the vector $\mathbf{x}_0$ minimising the function $Q(\mathbf{x})$.
We search for the minimum within the following linearly independent constraints:

$$\sum_{n=1}^{K} b_{jk}\, x(k) = b_j \tag{A.6.2}$$

$j = 1, 2, \ldots, J, J < K$ and

$$x_k \geqslant 0 \tag{A.6.3}$$

where b_{jk}, b_j, $j = 1, 2, \ldots, J$, $k = 1, 2, \ldots, K$, are given coefficients. As is known, if we ignore the incidental constraints (A.6.2), (A.6.3), we could, under fairly general assumptions, find the vector $\mathbf{x}_0$ minimising $f(x)$ as the boundary of the sequence x_n defined by the recurrent relationship

$$\mathbf{x}_{n+1} = \mathbf{x}_n - (\Delta\mathbf{x})_n \tag{A.6.4}$$

where

$$(\Delta\mathbf{x})_n = \alpha_n[\text{grad } Q(\mathbf{x})]_{x_n} \tag{A.6.5}$$

and α_n is a suitably chosen numerical sequence; we often have $\alpha_n = \alpha = \text{const.}$ Initially we shall look for the minimum assuming only the linear restrictions (A.6.2) and ignoring restrictions (A.6.3). Our intention is to construct a sequence defined by a recurrent relationship similar to (A.6.4). Let us suppose we have found vector $\mathbf{x}_1$ which fulfils constraints (A.6.2). If vector $\mathbf{x}(2)$ in the form

$$\mathbf{x}_2 = \mathbf{x}_1 - (\Delta\mathbf{x}) \tag{A.6.6}$$

where $\Delta\mathbf{x} \equiv [\Delta x(1), \Delta x(2), \ldots, \Delta x(K)]$ is also to fulfil constraint (A.6.2), we must have:

$$\sum_{k=1}^{K} b_{jk}\,\Delta x(k) = 0 \tag{A.6.7}$$

for $j = 1, 2, \ldots, J$.

Let $\mathcal{B}_j$ be the linear subspace of an N-dimensional Euclidean space. This subspace is defined by the constraints:

$$\sum_{k=1}^{K} b_{jk}\, x(k) = 0 \tag{A.6.8}$$

$j = 1, 2, \ldots, J$. The constraints (A.6.8) can be written in the form:

$$\Delta \mathbf{x} \in \mathcal{B}_j \tag{A.6.9}$$

If $\mathbf{x}_1$ fulfils constraints (A.6.2) (notice that these constraints have different right-hand sides from constraints (A.6.7)), the vector $\alpha(\text{grad}\, f)_{\mathbf{x}_1}$ does not usually fulfil constraints (A.6.7). Let Π_1 be the projection matrix of vector $\mathbf{y}$ on to the subspace $\mathcal{B}_1$ such that the length of the vector $(\mathbf{y} - \Pi_1 \mathbf{y})$ is minimal. We can show (e.g. Rosen [A.2]), that these constraints are fulfilled by the matrix

$$\Pi_1 = \mathbf{I} - \mathbf{B}_1^t (\mathbf{B}_1 \mathbf{B}_1^t)^{-1} \mathbf{B}_1 \tag{A.6.10}$$

where

$$\mathbf{B}_1 = \begin{pmatrix} b_{11} & b_{12} & \ldots & b_{1K} \\ b_{21} & b_{22} & \ldots & b_{2K} \\ \vdots & & & \\ b_{J1} & b_{M2} & \ldots & b_{JK} \end{pmatrix} \tag{A.6.11}$$

This reasoning leads to the modification in the calculation of the second approximation on the basis of equations (A.6.4), (A.6.5), which is the relationship

$$\mathbf{x}_2 = \mathbf{x}_1 - \alpha_1 \Pi_1 [\text{grad}\, Q]_{\mathbf{x}_1} \;. \tag{A.6.12}$$

So far, we have not taken the non-negativity constraints into consideration. We now show that they can be fulfilled by choosing a suitable coefficient A_i and introducing certain additional modifications into the projection matrix.

In geometrical terms, the non-negativity constraints mean we must find the solution in that part of the linear subspace $\mathcal{B}_1$ delimited by the planes $\mathcal{Q}_k$, $k = 1, \ldots, K$ and defined by the equation

$$x(k) = 0 \;. \tag{A.6.13}$$

We now introduce the unit vector $\mathbf{U}_k$ directed along the $x(k)$ axis i.e. a vector with a 1 in the kth position and 0 in the other positions. Notice that the scalar product of the vectors $\mathbf{a}$ and $\mathbf{b}$ can be written thus:

$$(\mathbf{a}, \mathbf{b}) = \mathbf{a}^t \mathbf{b} \tag{A.6.14}$$

in which the expression on the right-hand side is treated as the matrix product of the column matrices. Equation (A.6.13) defining Q_k can be written in the form:

$$\mathbf{U}_k^t \mathbf{x} = 0 . \tag{A.6.15}$$

We now define α_1 so that the vector $\mathbf{x}_2$ given by (A.6.12) fulfils constraints (A.6.5), and also that there is a minimal difference between it and the vector $\mathbf{x}^*$ minimising the function $Q(\mathbf{x})$. We treat $\mathbf{x}$ as a variable. The family of vectors

$$\mathbf{x}_\alpha = \mathbf{x}(1) - \alpha \Pi(\operatorname{grad} Q)_{\mathbf{x}_1} \tag{A.6.16}$$

can be interpreted as a straight line; let it be L_1. Furthermore, let $\mathbf{C}_k$ be the point at which the straight line L_1 cuts the plane Q_k, and let $\alpha(k)$ be the value of the parameter α corresponding to that point. Using equation (A.6.15), we can find this value from:

$$\mathbf{U}_k^t \mathbf{x}_1 - \alpha \mathbf{U}_k^t \mathbf{h}_1 = 0 \tag{A.6.17}$$

where

$$\mathbf{h}_1 \equiv \Pi(\operatorname{grad} Q)_{\mathbf{x}_1} . \tag{A.6.18}$$

Therefore:

$$\alpha(k) = \frac{\mathbf{U}_k^t \mathbf{x}_1}{\mathbf{U}_k^t \mathbf{h}_1} \tag{A.6.19}$$

Let α^* be the smallest of the non-negative $\alpha(k)$/s:

$$\alpha^* = \min_k \{\alpha(h); \alpha(k) > 0\} \tag{A.6.20}$$

and let k^* be the number of the component for which this minimum is reached. We thus have:

$$\alpha^* = \kappa(k^*) \tag{A.6.21}$$

If we take the values

$$0 \leqslant \alpha \leqslant \alpha^* \tag{A.6.22}$$

the non-negativity constraint for the components of vector $\mathbf{x}(2)$ will always be fulfilled. There remains the problem of selecting the best value of α within the range defined by (A.6.22). Let $L(\alpha^*)$ be a section of the straight line L_1 given by constraint (A.6.21). There are two possibilities: (a) as α increases, the function $Q(x)$ decreases along the section $L(\alpha^*)$, (b) a minimum is reached at a certain internal point. This minimum is not usually the one we are looking for, but the minimum under the additional constraint that we take into account only vectors lying on the straight line L_1. Situation (a) is characterised by the fact that the projection of the gradient calculated at the point C_{k^*}, where L_1 cuts the plane $\mathcal{Q}_{k^*}$, has the same sign as the gradient calculated at the initial point $\mathbf{x}_1$. This constraint can be written in the form:

$$[\Pi(\operatorname{grad} Q)_{\mathbf{x}_1}, \Pi(\operatorname{grad} Q)_{\mathbf{C}_{k^*}}] \geqslant 0 \ . \tag{A.6.23}$$

When calculating the scalar product of the vector projection $(\operatorname{grad} Q)_{\mathbf{c}_{k^*}}$ on to the subspace B_1 and the vector lying in this subarea, we can omit the projection operation. Thus we have:

$$[\Pi(\operatorname{grad} Q)_{\mathbf{x}_1}, \Pi(\operatorname{grad} Q)_{\mathbf{c}_{k^*}}] = [\Pi(\operatorname{grad} Q)_{\mathbf{x}_1}, (\operatorname{grad} Q)_{\mathbf{c}_{k^*}}] \tag{A.6.24}$$

Hence, we can write the inequality (A.6.23) in the form:

$$[\Pi(\operatorname{grad} Q)_{\mathbf{x}_1}]^t \cdot (\operatorname{grad} Q)_{\mathbf{c}_{k^*}} \geqslant 0 \ . \tag{A.6.25}$$

If situation (b) occurs, in which having searched along the section $L_1(\alpha^*)$ we find a minimum, we get an inverse inequality:

$$[\Pi(\operatorname{grad} Q)_{\mathbf{x}_1}]^t \cdot (\operatorname{grad} Q)_{\mathbf{c}_{k^*}} < 0 \ . \tag{A.6.26}$$

In situation (a) (fulfilment of the inequality (A.6.25)), it seems reasonable to move as far as possible along the section $L(\alpha^*)$, that is, as far as the plane $\mathcal{Q}_{k^*}$; this corresponds to the following coefficient apearing in the second iteration of (A.6.12):

$$\alpha_1 = \alpha(k^*) \tag{A.6.27}$$

In situation (b) (fulfilment of the inequality (A.6.25)), the obvious thing to do is to select α in such a way that it is located as near to the minimum as possible. To simplify the determination of theis value, we assume that the scalar product of the vector $\Pi(\operatorname{grad} Q)_{\mathbf{x}_1}$ and the vector chosen from the section $L(\alpha^*)$ varies linearly with A. This gives us the value where

$$\alpha_1 = \gamma\alpha(k^*)$$

where

$$\gamma \equiv \frac{\|\Pi(\operatorname{grad} Q)_{\mathbf{x}_1}\|^2}{\|\Pi(\operatorname{grad} Q)_{\mathbf{x}_1}\|^2 + [\Pi(\operatorname{grad} Q)_{\mathbf{x}_1}]^t(\operatorname{grad} Q)_{\mathbf{c}_{k^*}}} \tag{A.6.28}$$

If situation (a) occurs, we reach plane $\mathcal{Q}_{k^*}$. In order to remain on this plane, the constraint that $\mathbf{x}_3 \in \mathcal{Q}_{k^*}$ must be added to the constraints (A.6.3), i.e. the constraints that the next approximation $\mathbf{x}_3 \in B$. In other words, in each successive step we must add to constraints (A.6.3) the constraint that:

$$\mathbf{x}_{k^*} = 0 \tag{A.6.29}$$

after which we appropriately modify the matrix Π_1.

It can be seen that the transition from $\mathbf{x}_1$ to $\mathbf{x}_2$ shown here is of a general nature. The principle of calculating the sequence $\mathbf{x}_n$, which is to be an approximate solution of the optimisation problem being considered here, can be formulated as follows:

$$\mathbf{x}_{n+1} = \mathbf{x}_n - \alpha_n \Pi_n (\text{grad}\, Q)_{\mathbf{x}_n} \tag{A.6.30}$$

whereby the projection matrix Π_n corresponds to constraints (A.6.3) and possible constaints of type (A.6.29). In order to calculate the coefficient α_n, we first work out the coefficients

$$\alpha_n(k) = \frac{\mathbf{U}_k^t \mathbf{x}_n}{\mathbf{U}_k^t \Pi_n (\text{grad}\, Q)_{\mathbf{x}_n}} \tag{A.6.31}$$

$j = 1, 2, \ldots, J_n$. The we find the smallest† parameter α_n^* the coordinate k_n^* corresponding to it, and the vector $\mathbf{C}_{k_n^*}$ corresponding to the point at which the straight line is cut, defined in the same way as the point where L_n cuts the plane $\mathcal{Q}_{k_n^*}$.

If

$$\Pi_n (\text{grad}\, Q)^t_{\mathbf{x}_n} (\text{grad}\, Q)_{\mathbf{c}_{k_n^*}} \geqslant 0 \ . \tag{A.6.32}$$

we take

$$\alpha_n = \alpha_{k_n^*} \ . \tag{A.6.33}$$

In the opposite case, we take

$$\alpha_n = \gamma_n \alpha_{k_n^*} \tag{A.6.34}$$

where

$$\gamma_n = \frac{\|\Pi_n (\text{grad}\, Q)_{\mathbf{x}_n}\|^2}{\|\Pi_n (\text{grad}\, Q)_{\mathbf{x}_n}\|^2 + \Pi_n (\text{grad}\, Q)^t_{\mathbf{x}_n} (\text{grad}\, Q)_{\mathbf{c}_{k_n^*}}} \tag{A.6.35}$$

We add the constraint $x_{k_n^*} = 0$ to the earlier set of constraints and get the matrix Π_{n+1}. If the successive correction $\alpha_{n+1} \Pi_{n+1} (\text{grad}\, Q)_{\mathbf{x}_{n+1}}$ has all its components equal to zero, we end the procedure and take $\mathbf{x}^* = \mathbf{x}_{n+1}$.

† In the previous description of this procedure, we used the abbreviated notation α^*, k^* in step 2; obviously these values depend on the number of the step, which we shall now indicate.

APPENDIX A.7 – ANALYSIS OF NETWORKS OF BUFFERS AND STORAGE UNITS

In this appendix we derive formulae which are used in Chapter 7 on congestion. Although much more complicated, the analysis is a fairly exact counterpart of the analysis of the single buffer–transmitter unit presented in Appendix A.2, and it is based on the concept of equilibrium equations. To explain the idea of extending the analysis of the single buffer–transmitter unit to the general mesh network of buffer–transmitter and storage units we start in A.7.1 with the analysis if a chain of buffer–transmitter units. Next in A.7.2 we introduce the fundamental concepts needed for the analysis of meshed networks, in A.7.3 we derive the equilibrium equations, and subsequently in A.7.4 obtain the probability distribution of the detailed network states. Using the distribution, we ultimately derive in A.7.5 the probability distribution of locally aggregated states the numbers of packets at network nodes on which the congestion analysis presented in Chapter 7 is based.

The material presented in this appendix is a comprehensive summary of the results of the recently developed theory of networks of queues. The fundamental paper in this field is the paper by Baskett *et al.* [A.3]. An extension of the reults of that paper is given by the paper by Reiser and Kobayashi [A.4]. It also contains an extensive bibliography on the subject.

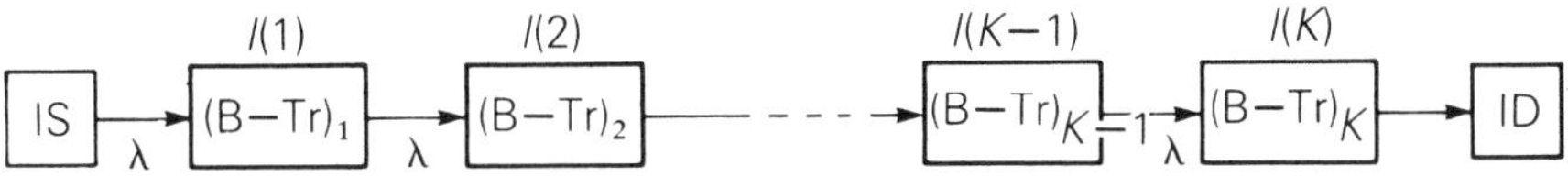

Fig. A.5 – The block diagram of a chain of buffer–transmitter units.

A.7.1 Analysis of a chain of buffer–transmitter units

Consider the chain of B–Tr units illustrated by Fig. A.5; we term it a B–Tr chain. We assume that the sequence of packets delivered by the source satisfies the assumptions A1, A2, and:

A5 The random variables T_k representing the packet duration in various channels are statistically independent.

In place of A3 we assume:

A3′ The buffer of each $(B\text{–}Tr)_k$ unit, $k = 1, \ldots, K$ has an infinite capacity.

The set $\mathbf{l} \equiv [l(1) \ldots, l(K)]$ will be called the B–Tr chain state, $l(k)$ will be the state of a single $(B\text{–}Tr)_k$ unit. Admissible states of the B–Tr chain are states from set L which is the K-fold cartesian product of the set of integers $\{0, 1, \ldots\}$. We shall call set L the set of admissible B–Tr chain states.

Let $\mathbf{L}(t)$, $t \in \langle 0, +\infty)$ be the process representing the state of the B–Tr chain in time. Under the above assumptions, the process $L(t)$ is a stationary Markovian process. We further assume that there exists limits

$$P(l) = \lim_{t \to +\infty} P[\mathbf{L}(t) = \mathbf{l}], \mathbf{l} \in L. \tag{A.7.1}$$

The probabilities $P(l)$ are called the stationary probabilities of the B–Tr chain states. When determining these probabilities, we proceed as in the case of the stationary probabilities of states for the single B–Tr unit considered in Appendix A2. Let $\mathbf{s}_k$ be a sequence of K elements, of which all but the kth are equal to zero, the kth being equal to one, i.e.

$$\mathbf{s}_k \equiv (0, 0, \ldots, \underset{k}{1}, 0, \ldots, 0) \tag{A.7.2}$$

By $\mathbf{l} \pm \mathbf{s}_k$ we mean the sequence which in all positions except the kth has the same elements as $\mathbf{l}$, while the kth position we have $[l(k) \pm 1]^+$ where $u^+ = u$ if $u \geqslant 0$ and $u^+ = 0$ if $u < 0$.

Consider a state $\mathbf{l} \in L$. In the second column of Table A.7.1 are given the states at instant t from which the chain caused by the events E_m listed in the

Table A.7.1

m	$\mathbf{L}(t)$	Event E_m causing the transition	Probability of passage into the state $\mathbf{l}$ at the instant $t + \Delta t$
1	$\mathbf{l}$	A new packet does not arrive, nor is the transmission of a packet being transmitted completed	$1 - [\lambda + \sum_{k=1}^{K} \epsilon[l(k)]\mu(k)]\Delta t + o(\Delta t)$
2	$\mathbf{l} - \mathbf{s}(1)$	A new packet is put into the first B–Tr unit	$\lambda \Delta t + o(\Delta t)$
3	$\mathbf{l} + \mathbf{s}(k-1) - \mathbf{s}(k)$ $2 \leqslant k \leqslant K$	The transfer of a packet from $(k-1)$st to kth B–Tr is completed	$\epsilon[l(k-1)]\mu(k-1)\Delta t + o(\Delta t)$
4	$\mathbf{l} + \mathbf{s}(K)$	The packet leaves the chain	$\epsilon[l(K)]\mu(K)\Delta t + o(\Delta t)$

second column may go to state **l** after time Δt. The last column gives the corresponding probabilities of transition. The probability of reaching state **l** from states other than those listed in Table A.7.1 is of the order of $O(\Delta t)$.

The function $\epsilon(l)$ appearing in the last column of Table A.7.1 is defined for integers

$$\epsilon(l) \equiv \begin{cases} 0 & \text{if} \quad l = 0 \\ 1 & \text{if} \quad l = 1, 2, \ldots \end{cases} \tag{A.7.3}$$

We introduce this function, since if there is no packet at a B–Tr unit, we must not take into account the probability of the events that the transmission of a packet is completed. From Table A.7.1 and from the formula for marginal probabilities, it follows that:

$$\begin{aligned} P[\mathbf{L}(t+\Delta t) = \mathbf{l}] &= P[\mathbf{L}(t+\Delta t) = \mathbf{l} \mid \mathbf{L}(t) = \mathbf{l}]\, P[\mathbf{L}(t) = \mathbf{l}] + \\ &+ P[\mathbf{L}(t+\Delta t) = \mathbf{l} \mid \mathbf{L}(t) = \mathbf{l} - \mathbf{s}_1]\, P[\mathbf{L}(t) = \mathbf{l} - \mathbf{s}_1] + \\ &+ \sum_{k=2}^{K} P[\mathbf{L}(t+\Delta t) = \mathbf{l} \mid \mathbf{L}(t) = \mathbf{l} + \mathbf{s}_{k-1} - \mathbf{s}_k]\, P[\mathbf{L}(t) = \mathbf{l} + \mathbf{s}_{k-1} - \mathbf{s}_k] + \\ &+ P[\mathbf{L}(t+\Delta t) = \mathbf{l} \mid \mathbf{L}(t) = \mathbf{l} + \mathbf{s}_K]\, P[\mathbf{L}(t) = \mathbf{l} + \mathbf{s}_K] + o(\Delta t) \end{aligned} \tag{A.7.4}$$

After substituting the probabilities given in Table A.7.1 and after checking the limit

$$\lim_{\Delta t \to 0} \frac{P[\mathbf{L}(t+\Delta t) = \mathbf{l}] - P[\mathbf{L}(t) = \mathbf{l}]}{\Delta t} = \frac{\mathrm{d}}{\mathrm{d}t} P[\mathbf{L}(t) = \mathbf{L}] \tag{A.7.5}$$

we obtain the differential equation

$$\begin{aligned} \frac{\mathrm{d}}{\mathrm{d}t} P[\mathbf{L}(t) = \mathbf{l}] &= -\left[\lambda + \sum_{k=1}^{K} \epsilon[(l(k)]\mu(k)\right] P[\mathbf{L}(t) = \mathbf{l}] \\ &\lambda P[\mathbf{L}(t) = \mathbf{l} - \mathrm{s}(1)] + \sum_{k=2}^{K} \epsilon[l(k-1)]\mu(k-1) \\ &P[\mathbf{L}(t) = \mathbf{l} + \mathrm{s}(k-1) - \mathrm{s}(k)] + \epsilon[l(K)]\mu(K) P[\mathbf{L}(t) = \mathbf{l} + \mathrm{s}(K)] \end{aligned} \tag{A.7.6}$$

which corresponds to equation (A.2.4) for a single B–Tr unit. For stationary probabilities

$$\frac{\mathrm{d}}{\mathrm{d}t} P[\mathbf{L}(t) = \mathbf{l}] = 0 \ . \tag{A.7.7}$$

Assuming that the limits given by (A.7.5) exist, the differential equation (A.7.6) reduces for $t \to \infty$ to the algebraic equation:

$$\lambda P[\mathbf{l}-\mathrm{s}(1)] + \sum_{k=2}^{K} \epsilon[l(k-1)]\mu(k-1)P[\mathbf{l}+s(k-1)-\mathrm{s}(k)] +$$

$$+ \epsilon[l(k)]\mu_K P[\mathbf{l}+\mathrm{s}(K)] = [\lambda + \sum_{k=1}^{K} \epsilon[l(k)]\mu(k)]P(\mathbf{l}) \quad \text{(A.7.8)}$$

This equation can again be interpreted as the condition:

$$\text{(intensity of entering state } \mathbf{l}) = \text{(intensity of leaving state } \mathbf{l}) \quad \text{(A.7.9)}$$

For this reason, equation (A.7.8) is called the **equation of global equilibrium for state l**. Notice that the global equilibrium equation (A.7.8) is satisfied if the following set of equations is also satisfied:

$$\lambda P(\mathbf{l}-\mathrm{s}_1) = \epsilon[l(1)]\mu(1)P(\mathbf{l}) \quad \text{(A.7.10a)}$$

$$\epsilon[l(k)]\mu(k-1)P[\mathbf{l}+\mathrm{s}(k-1)-\mathrm{s}(k)] = \epsilon[l(k)]\mu(k)P(\mathbf{l}) \quad \text{(A.7.10b)}$$

$$k = 2, \ldots, K$$

$$\lambda P(K) = \epsilon[l(k)]P\mu(K)P[\mathbf{l}+\mathrm{s}(K)] \quad \text{(A.7.10c)}$$

Consider a single B–Tr unit. The intensity of packets entering it is λ, while the intensity with which the packets leave it is $\mu(k)$. Therefore equations (A.7.10a), (A.7.10b) can be interpreted as the following conditions:

$$\begin{pmatrix}\text{the intensity of entering state } \mathbf{l} \text{ due to the arrival} \\ \text{of a packet at the } (\text{B–Tr})_k \text{ unit}\end{pmatrix} = \quad \text{(A.7.11a)}$$

$$= \begin{pmatrix}\text{the intensity of leaving state } \mathbf{l} \text{ due to the departure} \\ \text{of a packet from the } (\text{B–Tr})_k \text{ unit}\end{pmatrix} \quad \text{(A.7.11b)}$$

$$k = 1, \ldots, K$$

Equations (A.7.11) are called the **local equilibrium equations** since they are associated with single B–Tr units. Any solution of the local equilibrium equations will satisfy the global equilibrium equations; in general the converse does not always hold. Therefore, if we find a probability distribution satisfying the local equilibrium equations, the global equilbrium equation will also be satisfied. For this reason, the set of local equilibrium equations is helpful in determining the stationary probability distribution. Let:

$$\nu(k) \equiv \frac{\lambda}{\mu(k)} \qquad k = 1, \ldots, K \, . \quad \text{(A.7.12)}$$

As can be checked by substitution, the solution of the set of local equilibrium equations (A.7.10), and thus of the global equilbrium equation (A.7.8) is:

$$P(\mathbf{l}) = C\prod_{k=1}^{K} \nu(k)^{l(k)} \tag{A.7.13}$$

where C is a constant determined from the condition that

$$\sum_{l_1=0}^{+\infty} \dots \sum_{l_K=0}^{+\infty} P(\mathbf{l}) = 1 \ .$$

This condition can be written in the form

$$C\prod_{k=1}^{K} \sum_{L(k)=0}^{+\infty} \nu(k)^{l(k)} = 1 \tag{A.7.14}$$

For $\nu_k < 1$:

$$\sum_{l(k)=0}^{+\infty} \nu_k^{l(k)} = \frac{1}{1-\nu_k(k)}$$

Thus if $\nu(k) < 1$ for $k = 1, \dots, K$, there exists a stationary distribution defined by formula (A.7.9) in which

$$C = \prod_{k=1}^{K} [1-\nu(k)] \tag{A.7.15}$$

Notice that the probability $P(L)$ can be presented in the form:

$$P(\mathbf{l}) = \prod_{k=1}^{K} P_k[l(k)]$$

where

$$P_k[l(k)] \equiv [1-\nu(k)]\,[\nu(k)]^{l(k)} l(k) = 0, 1, \dots \tag{A.7.16}$$

defines the form of the stationary probability distribution of states for a single $(\text{B--Tr})_k$ unit, (formulas (A.2.11), (A.2.13) with $L = \infty$). Thus we formally calculate the probability of the state of a B–Tr chain as if we were calculating the probability of the state of a set of independent units such that the probability of the state of each of them is defined by equation (A.7.16). Notice that this is a consequence of our calculations and not a simplifying assumption.

A.7.2 Analysis of a mesh network – fundamental concepts

We shall now consider the mesh network. We assume that at the nodes we have either B–Tr units or storage units (S-units). By the latter we mean a storage device in which a packet is put in and is taken out after a time depending only on the packet considered and not on other packets. In queue theory terminology, the S-unit is called an infinite server, since it can be interpreted as an infinite set of servers to one of which the incoming packet is directed immediately after its arrival. We assume that the buffer capacity is infinite (A3′) and that the transfer times are negligible (A1) from Appendix A.1. We shall assume that the node is either a B–Tr unit or an S-unit. If at a physical node we have both these units, we split that node into nodes which are either single B–Tr units or single S-units.

We further assume that there is a source which generates packets which are to be put into the network at each node. We call a newly generated packet an external packet; a packet which has been put into the network and continues its journey through it is called an internal packet. We make the additional assumption that each packet can belong to one of I classes. We will number the classes by the index i. A packet can change its class during its journey through the network.

We also assume that:

A4 The model of the starting instants of external packets of class i generated by the source at the kth node is a Poisson process of intensity $\lambda_i^{(0)}(k)$; the superscript (0) denotes 'external packet'.

A5′ The Poisson processes for various values of k and i are independent.

In general, we call the time to transmit the packet or to keep it in the storage unit the packet processing time. We shall assume that:

A3″ The packet processing time is represented by an independent random variable with an exponential distribution, the same for all classes of packets at a given node.

We call the rule controlling routing of the packet and changing its class the packet handling rule. We assume that:

A7 The packet handling rule is a purely randomised memoryless rule.

Assumption A7 can also be formulated by saying that if a packet is of class i and it is at the kth node, then the probability that in the next step its class will be i' and that it will be directed to node k' does not depend on the packet's previous history. The memoryless randomised packet handling rule is completely described by the conditional probability $P_{i'|i}(k'|k)$ of transferring a packet from node k to node k' and of changing its class from i to i'.

When describing the network, it is convenient to treat the process of putting new packets into the network in the same way as the process of circulating packets inside the network. We do this by defining a virtual supersource which generates packets of class 0 with an intensity of

$$\lambda(0) \equiv \sum_i \sum_k \lambda_i^{(0)}(k) \tag{A.7.17}$$

The packet delivered by the supersource is put into the packet distribution unit which in a random way assigns a class $i, i = 1, 2, \ldots, I$ to the external packet and directs it to a node as shown in Fig. A.7. We give the index 0 to the supersource and consider packets generated by that source as '0' class packets. We denote by $P_{i|0}(k|0)$ the probability that an 0-class packet from t the supersource is assigned to class i and is put into the kth node. This system with the superstore and packet distribution unit is obviously equivalent to the system considered previously if we take:

$$P_{i|0}(k|0) = \frac{\lambda_i^{(0)}(k)}{\lambda(0)} \quad . \tag{A.7.18}$$

Similarly, we can describe the process of removing the packets from the network by introducing a supersink which we consider to be the $(K + 1)$st node, assigning the packets leaving to class $I + 1$, and indicating by $P_{I+1|i}(K + 1|k)$ the probability that a packet of class i at node k will leave the network in the next step. We call the supersource and the supersink virtual nodes, the others, physical nodes. Since a packet can change its class, be forwarded to another physical node, or leave the network, we have:

$$\sum_{k'=1}^{K+1} \sum_{i'=1}^{I+1} P_{i'|i}(k'|k) = 1 \tag{A.7.19}$$

for $k = 1, 2, \ldots, K$, $i = 1, 2, \ldots, I$.

Having defined the probabilities $P_{i|i'}(k|k')$, we introduce the description of the network by means of state transition graphs. We say that a packet is in state $s_k(i)$ if it is a class i packet located at node k. We denote the set of all possible states by:

$$\Pi \equiv \{\pi_i(k); (i, k) \in (I \times K)\} \tag{A.7.20}$$

where $(I \times K)$ is the set of all pairs (i, k), $i = 1, 2, \ldots, I$, $k = 1, 2, \ldots, K$.

Let us denote by $\lambda_i(k)$ the intensity of entering the state $\pi_i(k)$, i.e. the intensity of all packets of class i put into node k. The flow conservation constraints are:

$$\lambda_i(k) = \lambda(0) \cdot P_{i|0}(k|0) + \sum_{i'=1}^{I} \sum_{k'=1}^{K} \lambda_{i'}(k') P_{i|i'}(k|k') \tag{A.7.21}$$

for every $k = 1, 2, \ldots, K, i = 1, 2, \ldots, I$. If we introduce the normalised intensity

$$\lambda'_i(k) \equiv \frac{\lambda_i(k)}{\lambda(0)} \tag{A.7.22}$$

we can write (A.7.20) in the form:

$$\lambda_{i'}(k) = P_{i|0}(k|0) + \sum_{i'=1}^{I} \sum_{k'=1}^{K} \lambda'_{i'}(k')P_{i|i'}(k|k') \tag{A.7.23}$$

In general, packets of some classes may not be able to reach some nodes. The pair (i,k), where k is the class of a packet which can reach node i, is called a feasible pair, and the corresponding state $\pi_i(k)$ a feasible pair. We denote the set of feasible pairs by $(I \times K)$ and the set of feasible states by Π, i.e.:

$$\Pi \equiv \{\pi_i(k); (i,k) \in (I \times K)\} \tag{A.7.24}$$

Next, we interpret the states of packets as nodes of a graph which we will call the **packet state graph**; we denote it by G_p. To distinguish the node in the packet state graph from nodes in the primary network, we call the latter physical nodes. If $P_{i'|i}(k'|k) \neq 0$, we introduce an arc going from the state node $\pi_i(k)$ to state node $\pi_{i'}(k')$ and we interpret $P_{i|i'}(k'|k)$ as its weight.

Notice that the packet state graph introduced here is not a counterpart of the state transition graph which we used in the previous subsection. We will introduce the generalisation of this in the next subsection.

Hitherto we have considered the packet state graph G_p with nodes corresponding to the packet states $\pi_i(k)$, $(i,k) \in (I \times K)$. If we add to the graph the states $\pi_0(0)$, $\pi_{I+1}(K+1)$ corresponding to the supersource and the supersink, we call the graph the extended graph and denote it by G'_p. An example of a packet state graph and of an extended packet state graph is shown in Fig. A.6.

In general, the extended packet state graph G'_p can be decomposed into a set of disjointed subgraphs G'_{pj}, $j = 1, \ldots, J$, such that for $j \neq j'$, the two state nodes $\pi_i(k) \in G_j$ and $\pi_{i,}(k') \in G'_{pj}$ are not connected by an arc. Further it is not possible to decompose subgraphs G'_{pj} into smaller subgraphs having such a property. If $J = 1$, i.e. if the decomposition of G'_p is not possible, we say that the state transition graph G'_p is not decomposable.

Let us consider again the subgraph G_{pj}. We say that this subgraph is open for ith class packets if an external packet of this class can achieve a state which is represented by the node of subgraph G'_{pj}. Obviously this is the case if a node k exists such that $P_{i|0}(k|0) > 0$ and $s_i(k) \in G_{pj}$. If the opposite is true we say that the subgraph G_{pj} is closed for packets of the ith class. If a subgraph is open for packets of all classes we say that the graph is open, if it is closed for packets of all classes we say it is closed. In general a subgraph can be open for packets of

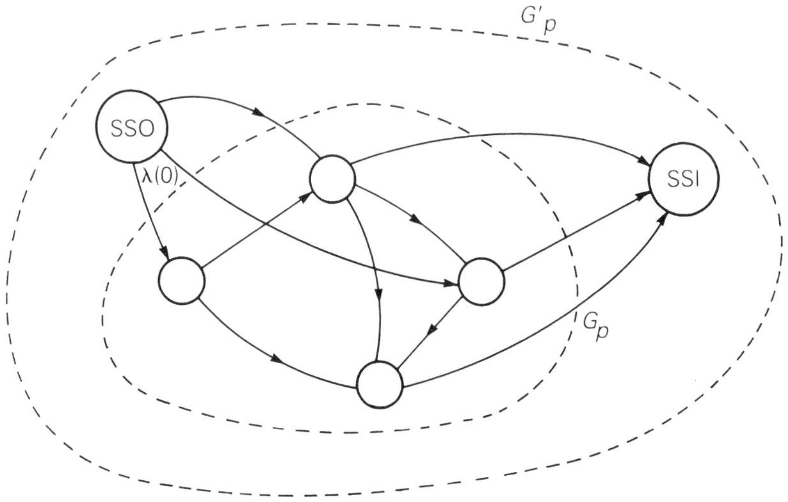

Fig. A.6 – Illustration of the definitions of supersink and supersource; G_p, primary graph, G_p', extended graph.

some classes and closed for packets of other classes; such a subgraph is called a mixed subgraph.

In order to illustrate the concepts just introduced, we shall take the following example:

Example A.7.1

Consider the network shown in Fig. A.7. It is a chain of B–Tr units. Packets generated by the source $IS_1(1)$ are called class 1 packets, while those generated by sources $IS_2(k)$, $k = 1, 2, \ldots, K$ are class 2 packets. The intensities of the packets generated are denoted by $\lambda_1^{(0)}(1)$ and $\lambda_2^{(0)}(k)$, $k = 1, 2, \ldots, K$. The supersource has the intensity

$$\lambda(0) = \lambda_1^{(0)}(1) + \sum_{k=1}^{K} \lambda_2^{(0)}(k)$$

We obtain the proababilities $P_{i|0}(k|0)$ from (A.7.18). We assume that the packets do not change their class, i.e. that

$$P_{i'|i}(k'|k) = 0$$

for $i \neq i'$. From Fig. A.7 it follows that

$$P_{1|1}(k'|k) = \begin{cases} 1 & \text{if} \quad k' = k+1 \\ 0 & \text{if} \quad k' \neq k+1 \end{cases}$$

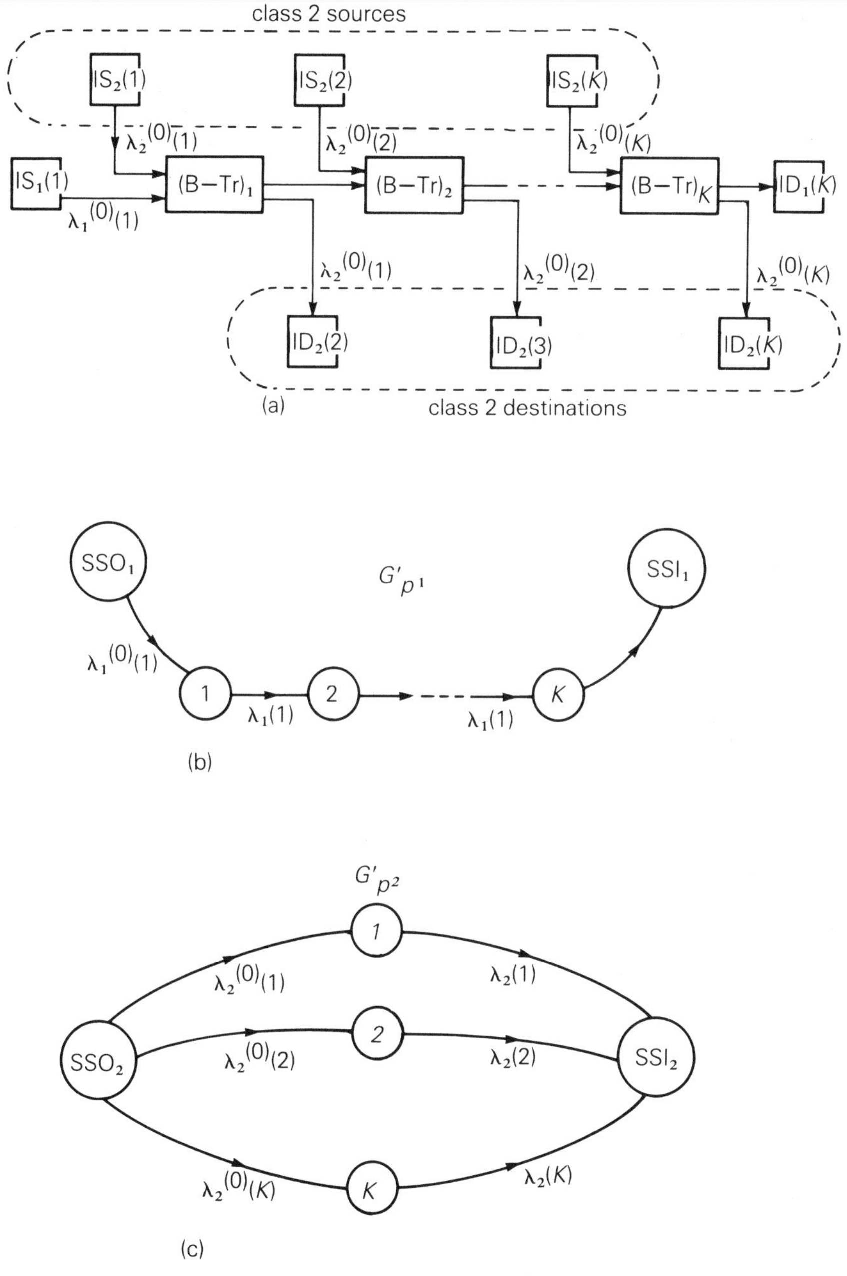

Fig. A.7 — A chain of B–Tr units with flows of 2 classes: end to end flow (class 1)

and $P_{2|2}(k'|k) = 0$ for $k, k' = 1, \ldots, K$ since class 2 packets pass only a single B–Tr unit and then leave the chain.

Next we consider the packet state graph. Since class 2 packets do not change their class, the graph consists of two disjointed graphs G'_{p1} and G'_{p2} which are shown in Fig. A.7(b) and (c) this figure we see that the intensities of entering the states are as given in Table A.7.2.:

Table A.7.2

State $\pi_i(k)$	Intensity $\lambda_i(k)$
$\pi_1(1)$	$\lambda_1^{(0)}(1)$
$\pi_1(k),\ k = 2, \ldots, K$	$\lambda_1(k-1) = \lambda_1(k)$
$\pi_2(k),\ k = 1, 2, \ldots, K$	$\lambda_2^{(0)}(k)$

From Table A.7.2, it follows immediately that $\lambda_1(k) = \lambda_1^{(0)}(1) = \text{const.}$ Hence $\lambda'(1) = 1$ and $\lambda'_2(k) = P_{2|0}(k|0)$.

A.7.3 Equilibrium equations for detailed network states

We now derive the fundamental equilibrium equations relating the stationary probabilities and packet intensities. These equations can be considered to be the generalisations of the equilibrium equations which we derived previously for a single buffer–transmitter unit (A.2) and the chain of buffers (A.6.1). Although much more complicated, the method for deriving the equilibrium equations for the general case is an extension of the method for deriving the above-mentioned special cases of equilibrium equations. It is based on the concept of the states of the nodes and of the network, which we will now introduce. Notice that in the previous subsection we considered the states of a packet. Let:

$l_i(k)$ be the number of ith class packets at the kth node;

$l(k) = \sum_{k=1}^{K} l_i(k)$ be the number of all packets at the kth node;

$i(k,j),\ j = 1, 2, \ldots, l_k$ be the class of the jth packet at the kth B–Tr unit, ordered according to their arrival instants.

$$\mathrm{l}'(k) = \{i(k,j);\ j = 1, 2, \ldots, l_k\} \tag{A.7.25a}$$

if the kth node is a B–Tr unit, or

$$\mathrm{l}'(k) = \{l_i(k);\ k = 1, 2, \ldots, K\} \tag{A.7.25b}$$

if the kth node is an S-unit and

$$\mathbf{l}' = \{\mathbf{l}(k),\ k = 1, 2, \ldots, K\} \tag{A.7.26}$$

We call $l'(k)$ the state of the kth node and l' the state of the network. Notice that in the case of the B–Tr unit, the detailed state is dependent on the sequence of arrivals of packets, whereas in the case of the storage unit, only on the number of packets of various classes. We denote the set of all admissible states of the network by L.

We shall now derive the equations relating the intensities of leaving and entering the states of the network. Our reasoning will be a straightforward extension of our considerations in section 6.1.2.

Let us consider first a node which is a B–Tr unit. This can be equivalently stated that we consider a node $k_1 \in K_B$ where K_B denotes the set of nodes which are B–Tr units. By $\mathbf{l} + \mathbf{s}_{k_1}(i^*)$ we denote symbolically a detailed network state such that all components $\mathbf{l}'(k)$, $k \neq k_1$ are the same as the corresponding components of state $\mathbf{l}$, while the k_1th component, i.e. the state of the k_1th node is $l_1(k_1), \ldots, i_{k_1}(l_k), i^*$, where $i_1(k_1), \ldots, i_{k_1}(l_{k_1})$ are the components of the component $\mathbf{l}(k_1)$ of $\mathbf{l}$. In other words, $\mathbf{l} + \mathbf{s}_{i^*}(k_1)$ is a state into which the state $\mathbf{l}$ passes if the only change is the arrival at the kth B–Tr unit of a new i^*-class packet.

Next, we consider a node $k_1 \in K_S$, where K_S denotes the set of all nodes which are S-units. Similarly, $\mathbf{l} + \mathbf{s}_i(k_1)$ denotes a detailed network state which for all $k \neq k_1$ has the same components as state $\mathbf{l}$, while the k_1th component is $l_1(k_1)$, $l_2(k_1), \ldots, l_{i^*}(k_1) + 1, \ldots, l_I(k_1)$, whereas $l_1(k_1), l_{k_1}(2), \ldots, l_{k_1}(I)$ is the kth component of state $\mathbf{l}$. Notice that the definition of the state $\mathbf{l} + \mathbf{s}_{k_1}(i^*)$ is a generalisation of the definition of the state $\mathbf{l} + \mathbf{s}(k)$ introduced on page 000. The one difference is that in general the + sign now has only a purely symbolic meaning and does not imply a summation of vectors or matrices.

As with $\mathbf{l} + \mathbf{s}_{i^*}(k_1)$, we define by $\mathbf{l} - \mathbf{s}_{i^*}(k_1)$ the state of the network from which we pass to the state $\mathbf{l}$ if the longest-waiting packet, i.e. the l_{k_1}st packet is removed from the k_1th $(\text{B–Tr})_{k_1}$ unit. To make this definition reasonable, we must obviously take $i^* = i_{k_1}(l_{k_1})$. If k_1 is an S-unit, the state $\mathbf{l} - \mathbf{s}_{k_1}(i^*)$ is the one into which the network passes after removing a packet of class i^* from the storage. Obviously, we require that $l_k(i^*) \geqslant 1$. Further, as with $\mathbf{l} + \mathbf{s}_{k_1}(i^*)$, we define the states $\mathbf{l} + \mathbf{s}_{k_1}(i^*) \pm \mathbf{s}_{k_2}(i^*)^*$; the + and − signs are symbolic. Finally, we introduce the auxiliary function of integers defined by the formula

$$\epsilon_1(l) = \begin{cases} 1 & \text{if } l = 0 \\ 0 & \text{if } l = 1, 2, \ldots \end{cases} \tag{A.7.27}$$

Obviously, $\epsilon_1(l) = 1 - \epsilon(l)$, where $\epsilon(l)$ is defined by (A.7.3). Generalising the reasoning which led us to Table A.7.1 we get Table A.7.3. The rows of this table are obviously generalisations of the corresponding rows of Table A.7.2.

Table A.7.3

m	State $\mathbf{l}_m$	Event E_m in the time interval $\langle t, t+\Delta t\rangle$	Probability of passage $P[\mathbf{L}(t+\Delta t) = l, E_m \mid \mathbf{L}(t) = \mathbf{l}_m]$
1	$\mathbf{l}$	A new external packet neither arrives, nor is the transmission of a packet being processed at a B–Tr unit completed (except for the case when all packets in the B–Tr unit are of the same class and a packet is returned after processing to the same B–Tr unit) nor is the processing at an S-unit completed (except when the packet is processed into the same class and is returned to the same S-unit)	$1 - \Big\{\lambda(0) + \sum_{k\in K_B} \epsilon[l(k)]\mu(k) - \sum_{k\in K_{B_I}} \epsilon[l(k)] \sum_{i=1}^{I} \epsilon_1[l(k) - l_i(k)]\mu(k) P_{i\mid i}(k\mid k) + \sum_{k\in K_S}\sum_{i=1} \epsilon[l_i(k)]\mu(k)[1 - P_{i\mid i}(k\mid k)]\Big\}\Delta t + o(\Delta t)$
2	$\mathbf{l} - \mathbf{s}_i(k)$	A new external packet passes into the state $\pi_i(k)$	$\epsilon(l_i)\lambda(0)P_{i\mid 0}(k\mid 0)\Delta t + o(\Delta t)$
3a	$\mathbf{l} + \mathbf{s}_{i'}(k') - \mathbf{s}_i(k)$ $k \in K_B$	An internal packet passes into the state $\pi_k(i)$ (node k being a B–Tr unit) from the state $\pi_{i'}(k')$	$\epsilon[l(k)]\mu(k)P_{i\mid i'}(k\mid k')\Delta t + o(\Delta t)$
3b	$\mathbf{l} + \mathbf{s}_{i'}(k') - \mathbf{s}_i(k)$ $k \in K_S$	An internal packet passes into the state $\pi_i(k)$ (the node k being an S-unit) from the state $\pi_{i'}(k')$	$\epsilon[l(k)](l_{i'}(k') + 1)\mu(k), P_{i\mid i'}(k\mid k')\Delta t + o(\Delta t)$
4a	$\mathbf{l} + \mathbf{s}_i(k)$ $k \in K_B$	An internal packet which was in the state $\pi_k(i)$ (node k being a B–Tr unit) leaves the network	$\mu(k)P_{I+1\mid i}(K+1\mid k)\Delta t + o(\Delta t)$
4b	$\mathbf{l} + \mathbf{s}_i(k)$ $k \in K_S$	An internal packet which was in the state $\pi_i(k)$ (node k being an S-unit) leaves the network	$(l_i(k) + 1)\mu(k)P_{I+1\mid i}(K+1\mid k)\Delta t + o(\Delta t)$

On the basis of Table A.7.3 we proceed as in the case of the simple chain of B–Tr units considered in the previous subsection. As a generalisation of (A.7.4) we use the marginal probability equation

$$P(\mathbf{L}(t+\Delta t)=\mathbf{l}) = \sum_m P(\mathbf{L}(t+\Delta t) = \mathbf{l}$$
$$E_m \mid \mathbf{L}(t) = \mathbf{l}_m) P(\mathbf{L}(t)=\mathbf{l}_m) + o(\Delta t) \tag{A.7.28}$$

where E_m, l_m are states and events listed in Table A.7.3. Taking $\Delta t \to 0$, we obtain from (A.7.28) a differential equation which is a generalisation of (A.7.6). For the stationary probabilities, we are interested in, we take $\mathrm{d}/\mathrm{d}t\, P(\mathbf{L}(t)=\mathbf{l})=0$ and we ultimately obtain the algebraic equation, which is a generalisation of (A.7.8). This is the equation:

$$\sum_{k=1}^{K}\sum_{i=1}^{I} \epsilon[l(k)]\lambda(0)P_{i|0}(k|0)\,P[\mathbf{l}-\mathrm{s}_i(k)] +$$
$$+\sum_{k=1}^{K}\sum_{k'\in K_B}\sum_{i=1}^{I}\sum_{i'=1}^{I} \epsilon[l(k)]\mu(k), P_{i|i'}(k|k')P[\mathbf{l}+\mathrm{s}_{i'}(k')-\mathrm{s}_i(k)] +$$
$$+\sum_{k=1}^{K}\sum_{k'\in K_S}\sum_{i=1}^{I}\sum_{i'=1}^{I} \epsilon[l(k)]\,(l_{i'}(k')+1)\mu(k), P_{i|i'}(k|k')P[\mathbf{l}+\mathrm{s}_{i'}(k)-$$
$$-\mathrm{s}_i(k)] + \sum_{k\in K_B}\sum_{i=1}^{I}\mu(k)P_{I+1|i}(K+1|k)\,P[\mathbf{l}+\mathrm{s}_i(k)] +$$
$$+\sum_{k\in K_S}\sum_{i=1}^{I}(l_i(k)+1)\mu(k)\,P_{K+1|i}(K+1|k)\,P[\mathbf{l}+\mathrm{s}_i(k)] +$$
$$=\left\{\lambda(0)+\sum_{k\in K_{B\text{-}Tr}}\epsilon[l_k(k)]\mu(k)+\sum_{k\in K_S}\sum_{i=1}^{I}l_i(k)\mu(k)\;P(l)\right\} \tag{A.7.29}$$

Comparing this formula with Table A.7.3, we see that the terms of the LHS correspond to events E_1, the first term on the RHS to E_2, the second and third to E_{3a} and E_{3b}, while the last two correspond to E_{4a} and E_{4b}. Some terms occurring in Table A.7.3 do not appear in equation (A.7.29) since they cancel each other out (for details, see Reiser and Kobayashi [A.4]).

As with (A.7.8), equation (A.7.28) can be interpreted as a global equilibrium equation, stating that:

$$\text{(intensity of entering state } \mathbf{l}) = \text{(intensity of leaving state } \mathbf{l}) \tag{A.7.30}$$

We shall now show that the global equilibrium equalities can be satisfied if we satisfy suitably defined local equilibrium equations. The set of local equilibrium equations can be grouped into the following three categories:

$$\begin{pmatrix}\text{intensity of flow into } \mathbf{l} \text{ due to a} \\ \text{packet entering the same unit}\end{pmatrix} = \begin{pmatrix}\text{intensity of flow out of a state } \mathbf{l} \text{ due} \\ \text{to a packet leaving B--Tr unit}\end{pmatrix} \qquad \text{(A.7.31a}')$$

which has the form:

$$\sum_{i=1}^{I} \epsilon[l(k)]\lambda(0)\, P_{i|0}(k\,|\,0) P[\mathbf{l}-\mathrm{s}_i(k)] +$$

$$+ \sum_{k' \in K_B} \sum_{i=1}^{I} \sum_{i'=1}^{I} \epsilon[l(k)]\,\mu_{k'} P_{i|i'}(k\,|\,k')\, P[\mathbf{l}+\mathrm{s}_{k'}(i') - \mathrm{s}_k(i)]$$

$$+ \sum_{k' \in K_S} \sum_{i=1}^{I} \sum_{i'=1}^{I} \epsilon[l(k)]\,(l_{i'}(k')+1)\mu_{k'}\, P_{i|i'}(k\,|\,k')\, P[\mathbf{l}+\mathrm{s}_{i'}(k)]$$

$$= \epsilon[l(k)]\,\mu_k\, P(\mathbf{l}) \qquad \text{(A.7.31a}'')$$

$$\begin{pmatrix}\text{intensity of flow into } \mathbf{l} \\ \text{due to a class } j \text{ packet} \\ \text{entering the same unit}\end{pmatrix} = \begin{pmatrix}\text{intensity of flow out of} \\ \text{a state } \mathbf{l} \text{ due to a class } i \\ \text{packet leaving S-unit}\end{pmatrix} \qquad \text{(A.7.31b}')$$

which has the form:

$$\epsilon[l(k)]\lambda(0) P_{i|0}(k\,|\,0) P[l - \mathrm{s}_b(k)] +$$

$$+ \sum_{k' \in K_B} \sum_{i'=1}^{I} \epsilon[l(k)]\,\mu(k), P_{i|i'}(k\,|\,k')\, P[\mathbf{l}+\mathrm{s}_{i'}(k') - \mathrm{s}_i(k)] +$$

$$+ \sum_{k' \in K_S} \sum_{i'=1}^{I} \epsilon[l(k)]\,(l_{i'}(k') + 1)\mu(k), P_{i|i'}\,(k\,|\,k')\, P[\mathbf{l}+\mathrm{s}_{i'}(k')-\mathrm{s}_i(k)]$$

$$= l_i(k)\mu_k P(\mathbf{l}) \qquad \text{(A.7.31b}'')$$

$$\begin{pmatrix}\text{intensity of flow into state } \mathbf{l} \\ \text{due to a packet leaving the} \\ \text{network in a packet state} \\ \pi_k(i) \in G_{pi'}\end{pmatrix} = \begin{pmatrix}\text{intensity of flow out of a state } \mathbf{l} \\ \text{due to the arrival of an external} \\ \text{packet into packet state} \\ \pi_k(i) \in G_{pi'}\end{pmatrix} \qquad \text{(A.7.31c}')$$

which has the form:

$$\sum_{k\in K_B}\sum_{i'=1}^{I}\mu(k)P_{I+1|i}(K+1|k')\,P[\mathbf{l}+\mathbf{s}_k(i')]$$

$$+\sum_{k\in K_S}\sum_{i'=1}^{I}[l_i(k)+1]\,\mu(k)P_{I+1\,|i}(K+1|i')P[\mathbf{l}+\mathbf{s}_i(i')]$$

$$=\lambda(0)P(l) \qquad \text{(A.7.31c}'')$$

As in the case of the chain of B–Tr units, the local equilibrium equations are a heuristic tool for finding the solution of the global equilibrium conditions. It can be proved easily that

> if the local equilibrium conditions are satisfied for all admissible packet states, i.e. for $\pi_i(k)$, $k,i\in(I\times K)$, then the global equilibrium conditions are satisfied too.

From this theorem, it follows that if we succeed in finding the solution of the local equilibrium conditions, we then obtain the solution of the global equilibrium conditions, we then obtain the solution of the global equilibrium conditions. We will show in the next section that in an important case this is possible.

A.7.4 Stationary probabilities of detailed network states

We now consider the general case when the extended packet state graph can be decomposed into the set $G_{p1},\ldots,G_{pI}$ of non-decomposable subgraphs. The following theorem can be proved (see Reiser and Kobayashi [A.4]).

> If the model of the process of state transitions inside each of the subgraphs is an ergodic Markovian chain, there is a unique stationary probability distribution in the set L of all network states and the stationary probability $P(\mathbf{l})$, $\mathbf{l}\in L$, is given by the formula

$$P(\mathbf{l}) = \frac{1}{C}\prod_{k=1}^{K} f[\mathbf{l}'(k),k] \qquad \text{(A.7.32a)}$$

where C is the normalisation constant chosen such that:

$$\sum_{\mathbf{l}\in L} P(\mathbf{l}) = 1 \qquad \text{(A.7.32b)}$$

and $\mathbf{l}_k$ and $\mathbf{l}$ were defined by (A.7.25).

The function $f_k(\mathbf{l}_k)$ is defined as follows:

$$f[\mathbf{l}(k),k] = \begin{cases} \prod_{i=1}^{I} \left(\dfrac{\lambda_i(k)}{\mu(k)}\right)^{l_i(k)} & \text{for a B–Tr unit} \\ \prod_{i=1}^{I} \dfrac{1}{l_i(k)!}\left(\dfrac{\lambda_i(k)}{\mu(k)}\right)^{l_i(k)} & \text{for an S-unit} \end{cases} \tag{A.7.33}$$

The intensities $\lambda'_i(k)$ occurring here are determined from the set of equations (A.7.18).

The theorem discussed here is a special case of a theorem formulated by Baskett *et al.* [A.3]. The general theorem holds for networks which can have other types of nodes than the buffer and storage units assumed here. It also holds for the general case when the Laplacian transformation of distrubution of packet processing time is a rational function.

The general idea of the proof of the theorem is based on the three remarks: (1) it is known from the general theory of Markovian processes that when a stationary probability distribution exists, it is unique; (2) the probability distribution given by (A.7.29) satisfies the local equilibrium conditions; (3) if the local equilibrium conditions are satisfied, the global equilibrium conditions are also satisfied. To illustrate the theorem, we take the chain considered in Example (A.7.1), (see Fig. A.7). For that network we have:

$$k = 1,\ldots,K \quad \lambda_i(k) = \lambda_i^{(0)}(k) \quad i = 1,2,\ldots, \tag{A.7.34}$$

For the network considered, formula (A.7.32) takes the form:

$$P(\mathbf{l}) = \frac{1}{C}\prod_{k=1}^{K} [\nu_1(k)]^{l_1(k)}[\nu_2(k)]^{l_2(k)} \tag{A.7.35}$$

where

$$\nu_i(k) = \frac{\lambda_i(k)}{\mu(k)} \tag{A.7.36}$$

A.7.5 Stationary probabilities of locally aggregated network states

In many applications, we are not interested in the detailed network state introduced in the previous subsection, we are only interested in the total numbers of packets of a given class at a given node, irrespective of their arrival sequence. Let

$$\mathbf{l} = \{\mathbf{l}(1), \mathbf{l}(2), \ldots, \mathbf{l}(K)\} \tag{A.7.37a}$$

where

$$l(k) = \{l_i(k),\ i = 1,2,\ldots,I\} \tag{A.7.37b}$$

and $l_i(k)$ the number of packets of ith class at kth node. Comparing (A.7.37b) with (A.7.25a), (A.7.25b) we see that for an S-unit $\mathbf{l}(k) = \mathbf{l}'(k)$ but for a B–Tr unit $\mathbf{l}(k)$ and $\mathbf{l}(k)$ have a different meaning and it is possible to determine $\mathbf{l}'(k)$ knowing $\mathbf{l}(k)$ but not vice versa.

We call $\mathbf{l}(k)$ and $\mathbf{l}'$ the locally aggregated states of the node, resp. of the network. We introduce the term **locally aggregated** to emphasise that we distinguish between the nodes but we disregard the arrival sequence of packets.

Let $L(\mathbf{l}')$, be the set of detailed network states such that at the kth node, we have $l_i(k)$, $i = 1, 2, \ldots, I$, packets of the ith class, whereby $l_i(k)$ are components of the set $\mathbf{l}'(k)$. The network is in the detailed state $\mathbf{l} \in L(\mathbf{l}')$ only when it is in the locally aggregated state $\mathbf{l}'$. Denoting† by $P_{ag}(\mathbf{l}')$ the probability of the locally aggregated state $\mathbf{l}'$, we thus have:

$$P_{ag}(\mathbf{l}') = \sum_{\mathbf{l} \in L(\mathbf{l}')} P(\mathbf{l}) \tag{A.7.38}$$

where $P(\mathbf{l})$ is the stationary probability of the detailed state given by (A.7.31).

Let us assume now that we have only B–Tr units in the network, i.e. $K_S = \phi$. The set $L(\mathbf{l}')$ consists of all such detailed states $\mathbf{l}$ for which the numbers $l_{k_i}(k)$, $i = 1, 2, \ldots, I$, are fixed, and equal to the components of $\mathbf{l}'$ their sequence in the B–Tr unit being arbitrary. The set $L(\mathbf{l}')$ therefore contains

$$\prod_{k \in K_B} \frac{\left[\sum_{i=1}^{I} l_i(k)\right]!}{[l_1(k)]! \ldots [l_I(k)]!}$$

detailed states.

From formulae (A.7.37)–(A.7.38) it follows that the probability $P(\mathbf{l})$ of the detailed state $\mathbf{l}$ depends only on the numbers $l_i(k)$, not on the arrival sequence of the packets stored in the buffer. Thus from (A.7.31) and (A.7.38) it follows that:

$$P_{ag}(\mathbf{l}') = \frac{1}{C} \prod_{k=1}^{K} \left[\sum_{i=1}^{I} l_i(k)\right]! \prod_{i=1}^{I} \frac{1}{[l_i(k)]!} f[\mathbf{l}'(k); k] \tag{A.7.39}$$

where $f[\mathbf{l}(k); k]$ is given by (A.7.33).‡

† Subscript ag reminds us that we are considering an aggregated state.

‡ We write here $f[l(k); k]$, while in (A.7.33) we wrote $f[l'(k); k]$. However, from (A.7.33) it follows that f_k depends on $l(k)$, but not directly.

Let $\mathbf{l}'(k)$ be the locally aggregated state of kth node which is a component of $\mathbf{l}'$. The formula for marginal probabilities gives us

$$P_{ag}[\mathbf{l}'(k)] = \sum_{\mathrm{U}_{k';k' \neq k}} P_{ag}(\mathbf{l}') =$$

$$= \frac{1}{C'} \sum_{i=1}^{I} [l_i'(k)]\,! \prod_{i=1}^{I} \frac{1}{l_i'(k)!}\, f[l'(k);k] \tag{A.7.40}$$

Thus we can put (A.7.39) in the form

$$P_{ag}(l') = \frac{1}{C''} \prod_{k=1}^{K} P_{ag}[\mathbf{l}'(k)] \tag{A.7.41}$$

We can say that the stationary probability of the locally aggregated state l' is such if the stationary component states $\mathbf{l}'(k)$ were statistically independent.

We will now illustrate formula (A.7.39) by three examples.

Example A.7.2

We take the network assumed in Example A.6.1. Since in this network we have only B–Tr units, the locally aggregated state

$$\mathbf{l}(k) = (l_l(k), l_2(k)) \quad k = 1,2,\ldots,K \;.$$

Therefore from (A.7.39) we have:

$$P_{ag}(\mathbf{l}) = \frac{1}{C} \prod_{k=1}^{K} \frac{[l_1(k) + l_2(k)]\,!}{l_1(k)!\, l_2(k)!} [\nu_1(k)]^{l_1(k)} [\nu_2(k)]^{l_2(k)} \tag{A.7.42}$$

Example A.7.3

We assume that: (1) the network consists only of B–Tr units; (2) the mth source generates packets which are directed to the mth destination: the intensity of packets is λ_m, their length has an exponential distribution of mean $\bar{T}_m$, therefore we here call m 'the class'; (3) we take i to be the packet class; (4) the packets cannot change their class.

From (A.7.39) (A.7.33) we have

$$P_{ag}(\mathbf{l}') = \frac{1}{C} \prod_{k=1}^{K} \left[\sum_{m=1}^{M} l_m(k) \right]! \prod_{m=1}^{M} \frac{1}{[l_m(k)]\,!} \nu_m(k)^{l_m(k)} \tag{A.7.43}$$

where $\mathbf{l}' = \{l_m(k), m = 1, 2, \ldots, M, k = 1, 2, \ldots, K\}$, is the state of the network, $l_m(k)$ is the number of class m packets at node k,

$$\nu(m) = \frac{\lambda_m(k)}{\mu(k)} \tag{A.7.44}$$

C is the normalisation constant. From the above formulae we see, that to evaluate the probabilities $P_{\text{ag}}(\mathbf{l}')$ we must calculate intensities $\lambda_m(k)$. They are determined by the intensities of the external packets and the probabilities determining the packet handling rule. Since we have assumed that packets cannot change classes these are the probabilities

$$P_{m|m}(k) = P_{m|m}(k\,|\,k), \quad m = 1, 2, \ldots, M\ . \tag{A.7.45}$$

The relative intensity $\lambda'_m(k)$ of reaching the state $\pi_m(k)$ is found as the solution of the set of equations (A.7.18) which takes the form

$$\lambda'_m(k) = P_{m|0}(k\,|\,0) + \sum_{k'=1}^{K} \lambda'_m(k)\, P_{m|m}(k) \tag{A.7.46}$$

$$k = 1, 2, \ldots, K, \quad m = 1, 2, \ldots, M.$$

From (A.7.46) we obtain the intensities $\lambda_m(k)$. Knowing them we can evaluate $P_{\text{ag}}(\mathbf{l}')$ from (A.7.43).

Example A.7.4

We take the network considered in Example A.7.3. However, we introduce another definition. To distinguish the concept of class from the concept used previously, we call the classes which we consider here the secondary classes and we denote parameters characterising them by asterisks. To define the secondary class, we divide that set of integers $\mathbb{M} = \{1, \ldots, M\}$ into disjointed subsets $M(1), \ldots, M(\mathrm{I})$ covering the set $\mathbb{M}$. We say that a packet is of the ith secondary class if the number m of the source which generated the packet belongs to the subset $M(i)$. We can again use formula (A.7.39) which gives us

$$P_{\text{ag}}(\mathbf{l}') = \frac{1}{C} \prod_{k=1}^{K} \sum_{i=1}^{I} [l'_i(k)]!\, \prod_{i=1}^{I} \frac{1}{[l'_i(k)]!} [\nu'_i(k)]^{l'_i(k)} \tag{A.7.47}$$

where $\mathbf{l}' = \{\{l'_i(k), i = 1, \ldots, I\}; k = 1, 2, \ldots, K\}$ is the locally aggregated state of the network, $l'_i(k)$ is the number of packets of ith class of kth node and

$$\nu_i(k) = \frac{\lambda_i(k)}{\mu(k)} \tag{A.7.48}$$

where $\lambda_i(k)$ is the intensity of packets of ith class put into kth node. From the assumptions it follows that

$$l_i(k) = \sum_{m \in M(i)} l_m(k) \tag{A.7.49}$$

$$\lambda_i(k) = \sum_{m \in M(i)} \lambda_m^{(p)}(k) \tag{A.7.50}$$

where $l_m(k)$ is the number of packets directed from mth source to mth destination and $\lambda_m^{(p)}(k)$ is the intensity of packets put into kth node.†

We obtained formula (A.7.47) directly from the general formula (A.7.39). We will now show that it can be derived from formula (A.7.38), based on the probability of the locally aggregated states considered in the previous section. Let us note that in view of formula (A.7.49) we can consider the states $l_i(k)$ as an effect of two levels of aggregation. We first aggregate the detailed states into the states $l'_m(k)$ introduced in the previous example and next we aggregate states $\mathbf{l}'_m(k)$ into the states $l''_i(k)$. Taking such a point of view we have

$$P_{ag}(\mathbf{l}'') = \sum_{\mathbf{l}' \in L'(\mathbf{l}'')} P_{ag}(\mathbf{l}') \tag{A.7.51}$$

where $L'(\mathbf{l}'')$ is the set of first level aggregated states considered in the previous example, such that every $\mathbf{l}' \in L'(\mathbf{l}'')$ yields the second level aggregate state $\mathbf{l}''$, and $P_{ag}(\mathbf{l}'')$ is given by (A.7.39).

In view of A.7.49 we have

$$\sum_{\mathbf{l}' \in L'(\mathbf{l}'')} = \sum_{\mathbf{l}'_1 \in L'_1(\mathbf{l}''_1)} \sum_{\mathbf{l}'_2 \in L'_2(\mathbf{l}''_2)} \cdots \sum_{\mathbf{l}'_K \in L'_K(\mathbf{l}''_K)} \cdots \tag{A.7.52}$$

where $\mathbf{l}'_k$ is the first level aggregate state of kth node, while $L'_k(\mathbf{l}''_k)$ is the set of these states, such that (A.7.49) holds for all $l = 1, 2, \ldots, I$. Next we have

$$\sum_{\mathbf{l}'(k) \in L'_k[l''(k)]} = \prod_{i=1}^{I} \sum_{l'_m(k)} ; \sum_{m \in M(i)} l'_m(k) = l''_i(k) \tag{A.7.53}$$

† We have denoted it in the previous example briefly by $\lambda_m(k)$. We introduce now the index 'p' to remind that $\lambda_m^{(p)}(k)$ are intensities of primary classes, numbered by m.

Thus from (A.7.52), (A.7.53) we obtain

$$\sum_{\mathbf{l}' \in L'(\mathbf{l}'')} = \prod_{k=1}^{K} \sum_{l=1}^{I} \sum_{l'_m(k),\ \sum_{m \in M(i)} l'_m(k) = l''(k)} \tag{A.7.54}$$

From this and from (A.7.44) we obtain

$$P''_{\text{ag}}(\mathbf{l}'') = \frac{1}{C} \prod_{k=1}^{K} \left[\sum_{m=1}^{M} l'_m(k) \right]! \prod_{i=1}^{I} \sum_{l'_m(k),\ \sum_{m \in M(i)} l'_m(k) = l''_i(k)}$$

$$\prod_{m \in M(i)} \frac{1}{[l'_m(k)]!} [\nu'_m(k)]^{l_m(k)} \tag{A.7.55}$$

Let us next notice that (A.7.50) is equivalent to

$$\sum_{m \in M(i)} \nu'(m) = \nu''_i(k) \tag{A.7.56}$$

and following algebraic identity holds

$$\left[\sum_{m \in M(i)} \nu'_m(k) \right]^{l''_i(k)} = [l''_i(k)] \sum_{l'_m(k),\ \sum_{m \in M(i)} l'_m(k) = l''_i(k)} \frac{\nu'_m(k)}{[l'_m(k)]!} \tag{A.7.57}$$

From (A.7.55) and (A.7.57) we have immediately

$$P''_{\text{ag}}(\mathbf{l}'') = \frac{1}{C} \prod_{k=1}^{K} \left[\sum_{i=1}^{I} l''_i(k) \right]! \prod_{i=1}^{I} \frac{1}{[l''_i(k)]!} [\nu_i(k)]^{l''_i(k)} \tag{A.7.58}$$

But this is formula (A.7.47). We can thus state, that it would not apply for the general formula (A.7.42); but were we to use formula (A.7.44) for the first level aggregated states probability, we could derive the formula for the second level aggregated states probabilities. We have this derivation since it is similar to the derivation of the general formula (A.7.33), starting with the formula of the detailed state probability (A.7.28).

APPENDIX A.8 – DERIVATION OF THE NORMALISATION CONSTANT FOR A PROBABILITY DISTRIBUTION OF DETAILED SYSTEM STATES

The network shown in Fig. 7.3 is taken as the model of the system analysed in section 7.2.1. Let:

$$\mathbf{L}(i) \equiv (L_1(i), \ldots, L_K(i)), \; i = 1,2 \; .$$

As we have shown in Appendix A.7.5, the joint probability of $\mathbf{L}(1)$, $\mathbf{L}(2)$ is given by the formula

$$P[\mathbf{L}(1), \mathbf{L}(2)] = \frac{1}{C} \prod_{k=1}^{K} \frac{[L_1(k) + L_2(k)]!}{L_1(k)! \, L_2(k)!} [\nu_1(k)]^{L_1(k)} [\nu_2(k)]^{L_2(k)} \quad \text{(A.8.1)}$$

where

$$\nu_i(k) \equiv \frac{\lambda_i(k)}{\mu_i(k)} \; . \quad \text{(A.8.2)}$$

The set of admissible sets $(\mathbf{L}(1), \mathbf{L}(2))$ is the set

$$A[\hat{L}(1)] \equiv A[1; \hat{L}(1)] \times A(2, \infty) \quad \text{(A.8.3)}$$

where

$$A[1, \hat{L}(1)] \equiv \{\mathbf{L}(1) \in I_0^K : L_K(1) \leqslant \hat{L}(1), \; k = 1, \ldots, K\} \quad \text{(A.8.4a)}$$

$$A(2, \infty) \equiv \{\mathbf{L}(2) \in I_0^K\} \quad \text{(A.8.4b)}$$

The symbol I_0^K indicates the K-fold cartesian product set

$$I_0 \equiv \{0, 1, 2, \ldots\}$$

We take the constant C so as to satisfy the normalisation constraint:

$$\sum_{\mathbf{L}(1) \in A[1, \hat{L}(1)]} \; \sum_{\mathbf{L}(2) \in A(2, \infty)} P[\mathbf{L}(1), \mathbf{L}(2)] = 1 \quad \text{(A.8.5)}$$

that is,

$$C = \sum_{\mathbf{L}(1) \in A[1, \hat{L}(1)]} \; \sum_{\mathbf{L}(2) \in A(2, \infty)} r[\mathbf{L}(1), \mathbf{L}(2)] \quad \text{(A.8.6)}$$

where

$$r[\mathbf{L}(1), \mathbf{L}(2)] \equiv \prod_{k=1}^{K} \frac{[L_1(k) + L_2(k)]!}{L_1(k)! \, L_2(k)!} [\nu_1(k)]^{L_1(k)} [\nu_1(k)]^{L_2(k)} \quad \text{(A.8.7)}$$

After some simple algebra, we can rewrite the constant C in the form:

$$C = \sum_{\mathrm{L}(1)\in \mathrm{A}[1,\hat{L}(1)]} \prod_{k=1}^{K} \frac{1}{L_1(k)!}[\nu_1(k)]^{L_1(k)} \sum_{L_2(k)=0}^{+\infty} \frac{[L_1(k)+L_2(k)]!}{L_2(k)!}[\nu_2(k)]^{L_2(k)} \quad \text{(A.8.8)}$$

Notice that:

$$\sum_{L_2(k)=0}^{+\infty} \frac{[L_1(k)+L_2(k)]!}{L_2(k)!}[\nu_2(k)]^{L_2(k)} =$$

$$= \left[\sum_{L_2(k)=0}^{+\infty} \frac{\mathrm{d}^{L_1(k)}}{\mathrm{d}x^{L_2(k)}} x^{L_1(k)+L_2(k)}\right]_{x=\nu_2(k)} =$$

$$= \left[\frac{\mathrm{d}^{L_1(k)}}{\mathrm{d}x^{L_1(k)}} \sum_{L_2(k)=0}^{+\infty} x^{L_1(k)+L_2(k)}\right]_{x=\nu_2(k)} =$$

$$= \left[\frac{\mathrm{d}^{L_1(k)}}{\mathrm{d}x^{L_1(k)}} \frac{x^{L_1(k)}}{1-x}\right]_{x=\nu_2(k)} = \frac{[L_1(k)]!}{[1-\nu_2(k)]^{L_1(k)+1}} \quad \text{(A.8.9)}$$

After substituting in equation (A.8.8), we get

$$C = \sum_{\mathrm{L}(1)\in \mathrm{A}[1,\hat{L}(1)]} \prod_{k=1}^{K} \frac{z_k^{L_1(k)}}{1-\nu_2(k)} \quad \text{(A.8.10)}$$

where

$$z_k \equiv \frac{\nu_1(k)}{1-\nu_2(k)} \quad \text{(A.8.11)}$$

We now introduce an auxiliary function defined by the formula:

$$\psi[\hat{L}(1)] \equiv \sum_{\mathrm{L}(1)\in \mathrm{A}[1,\hat{L}(1)]} \prod_{k=1}^{K} z_k^{L_1(k)} \quad \text{(A.8.12)}$$

From equation (A.8.10) we get:

$$C = \psi[\hat{L}(1)] \prod_{k=1}^{K} \frac{1}{1-\nu_2(k)} \quad . \quad \text{(A.8.13)}$$

Finally, substituting the constant C in equation (A.8.1), we obtain:

$$P[\mathbf{L}(1),\mathbf{L}(2)] = \frac{1}{\psi[\hat{L}(1)]}\prod_{k=1}^{K}\frac{[L_1(k)+L_2(k)]!}{L_1(k)!\,L_2(k)!}[1-\nu_2(k)]$$
$$[\nu_1(k)]^{L_1(k)}[\nu_2(k)]^{L_2(k)} \quad . \tag{A.8.14}$$

In Chapter 7 we are interested in the non-admission probability

$$P^-(1) \equiv P\{\mathbf{L}(1)\in \mathcal{B}[1,\hat{L}(1)]\} \tag{A.8.15}$$

where

$$\mathcal{B}[1,\hat{L}(1)] \equiv A[1,\hat{L}(1)] - A[1,\hat{L}(1)-1] \tag{A.8.16}$$

We have:

$$P^-(1) = \sum_{\mathbf{L}(1)\in\mathcal{B}[1,\hat{L}(1)]}\;\sum_{L(2)\in A(2,\infty)} P[\mathbf{L}(1),\mathbf{L}(2)] =$$
$$= \sum_{\mathbf{L}(1)\in A[1,\hat{L}(1)-1]}\;\sum_{\mathbf{L}(2)\in A(2,\infty)} P[\mathbf{L}(1),\mathbf{L}(2)] -$$
$$- \sum_{\mathbf{L}(1)\in A[1,\hat{L}(1)-1]}\;\sum_{\mathbf{L}(2)\in A(2,\infty)} p[\mathbf{L}(1),\mathbf{L}(2)] \tag{A.8.17}$$

Taking into consideration equations (A.8.5)–(A.8.7), we obtain:

$$P^-(1) = 1-\frac{1}{C}\sum_{\mathbf{L}(1)\in A[1,\hat{L}(1)-1]}\;\sum_{\mathbf{L}(2)\in A(2,\infty)} r[\mathbf{L}(1),\mathbf{L}(2)] \tag{A.8.18}$$

Comparing equations (A.8.6) and (A.8.13) we notice that:

$$\sum_{\mathbf{L}(1)\in A[1,\hat{L}(1)]}\;\sum_{\mathbf{L}(2)\in A(2,\infty)} r[\mathbf{L}(1),\mathbf{L}(2)] =$$
$$= \psi[\hat{L}(1)-1]\prod_{k=1}^{K}\frac{1}{1-\nu_k(2)} \quad . \tag{A.8.19}$$

Now, if we take into account equations (A.8.13) and (A.8.19), we finally obtain from equation (A.8.18):

$$P^{-}(1) = 1 - \frac{\psi[\hat{L}(1)-1]}{\psi[\hat{L}(1)]} \quad . \tag{A.8.20}$$

REFERENCES

[A.1] Parzen, E., (1962), *Stochastic Processes*, Holden Day, San Francisco.

[A.2] Rosen, J. B., (1960), The gradient projection method for non-linear programming, Pt. Linear constraints, *SIAM Journ.*, **8**, 181–217.

[A.3] Baskett, F., Chandy, K. M., Muntz, R. R., and Palatios, F. G., (1975), Open, closed and mixed networks of queues with different classes of customers, *J.ACM*, **22**, 248–260.

[A.4] Reiser, M., and Kobayashi, H., (1975), Queueing networks with multiple closed chains: Theory and computational algorithms, *IBM J.Res.Develop*, 283–294.

Index